EUGENE L. GRANT received his B.S. and C.E. degrees from the University of Wisconsin and an M.A. in economics from Columbia University. He has taught at Montana State University and, since 1930, at Stanford University where he is now Professor of Economics of Engineering, Emeritus. During the past forty years, Professor Grant has written a great number of articles for professional and technical journals, as well as books on quality control, depreciation, and industrial cost accounting. Recognized as a pioneer in the field of engineering economy studies, Professor Grant is a registered Professional Engineer, State of California.

W. GRANT IRESON received his B.S. and M.S. degrees from Virginia Polytechnic Institute. He has taught there, at Illinois Institute of Technology and, since 1951, at Stanford University where he is currently Executive Head of the Department of Industrial Engineering. Author and editor of several books in the area of industrial engineering, Professor Ireson has acted as consultant to the Departments of the Navy and of the Air Force as well as to several foreign governments and the UNESCO Committee on Engineering Economy. He is a registered Professional Engineer in the States of California and Illinois.

EUGENE L. GRANT
STANFORD UNIVERSITY

W. GRANT IRESON
STANFORD UNIVERSITY

PRINCIPLES OF
ENGINEERING
ECONOMY

FIFTH EDITION

THE RONALD PRESS COMPANY · NEW YORK

Library of Congress Catalog Card Number: 74–110548

PRINTED IN THE UNITED STATES OF AMERICA

Preface

This is a book about a particular type of decision making. It explains the principles and techniques needed for making decisions about the acquisition and retirement of capital goods by industry and government. Normally, such decisions should be made on grounds of long-run economy. Because engineers make many such decisions and make recommendations for many others, the body of principles and techniques relating to them has been called "engineering economy."

The same concepts and methods that are helpful in guiding decisions about investments in capital goods are useful in certain kinds of decisions between alternative types of financing (for example, ownership versus leasing) and in many personal decisions. Applications to these other areas of decision making are also discussed in this book.

As in the past, our book may be used in two ways. First, it can serve as a college textbook. The material covered is appropriate not only for engineering students but also for students of economics, accounting, finance, and management. Second, it can serve as a working manual for engineers, management personnel, government officials, and others whose duties require them to make decisions about investments in capital goods.

The underlying philosophy regarding comparisons of alternatives is the same as in previous editions. As before, continued emphasis throughout the book is placed on the following two important points:

1. It is prospective *differences* between alternatives that are relevant in their comparison.

2. The fundamental question regarding a proposed investment in capital goods is whether the investment is likely to be recovered plus a return commensurate with the risk and with the return obtainable from other opportunities for the use of limited resources. The purpose of calculations that involve the time value of money should be to answer this question.

Although our underlying philosophy remains the same, we have rewritten much of the content of the book for this Fifth Edition. As in the nearly complete rewritings for the last three editions, our changes have been aimed in part at the introduction of new material and in part at improved presentation of fundamental principles. Some changes that will be of interest to users of the previous editions are as follows:

1. The first two chapters are now devoted to explicit introduction of the basic concepts that are developed and applied throughout the remainder of the book.

2. Comparisons that involve estimates of how a choice among alternatives will influence income taxes are introduced fairly early in the book using certain simple assumptions. This makes it possible to use realistic after-tax minimum attractive rates of return in early examples and problems. A more sophisticated look at how to estimate the income tax consequences of decisions is still deferred until the later chapters of the book.

3. The benefit–cost ratio, now so common as a technique for the evaluation of public works projects, is introduced fairly early in the book in a short new chapter.

4. In general, we have adopted the compound interest symbols suggested by the ad hoc standardization committee of the Engineering Economy Division of the American Society for Engineering Education. (However, we have continued the long-established practice of using the lower case n to represent number of compounding periods.) Functional symbols rather than mnemonic symbols have been selected to represent the various factors.

5. The former chapter on dealing with uncertainties in forecasts has been divided into two chapters, one dealing with sensitivity analysis and the other dealing with analysis that uses the mathematics of probability.

6. A new chapter has been added dealing with economy studies for regulated public utilities.

7. An appendix contains an expanded treatment of the analysis of proposals that, because cash flow series have two or more reversals of sign, combine investment at one time with borrowing or financing at another time.

8. In rewriting the problem material, we have tried to increase the complexity and sophistication of a number of problems. Our chief aim in writing certain new problems has been to provide a frame of reference for useful class discussion—in some cases discussion to illuminate basic concepts and in other cases to permit examination of controversial issues. Certain specialized topics are now introduced in problems rather than in examples in the text.

In the choice of interest rates and minimum attractive rates of return for the examples and problems in this new edition, we have tried to avoid being unduly influenced by the actual interest rates in effect at the time of writing. Our aim has been to illustrate a range of rates that may be reasonable in various settings and over a period of years.

Our arrangement of chapters recognizes the fact that some introductory courses are too short to permit a full coverage of the subject. Most of the material in Chapters 1 to 17 is fundamental and should be included in any presentation of basic principles. The subject matter of Chapters 18 to 21 is appropriate for an elementary course if time permits but might also be deferred until an advanced course. Appendixes A to D cover topics that might be omitted in elementary college courses but should be included in advanced courses and in any presentation to persons in industry.

The authors wish to thank many of the users of the Fourth Edition for helpful suggestions for changes and improvements. In this connection we want to make special mention of help from Professors Gerald Fleischer, Robert Hemmes, Donald Newnan, Robert Oakford, Henry Steiner, and Ralph Swalm, and from Messrs. Lawrence Bell, Carter Harrison, and Robley Winfrey.

We are indeed grateful for the widespread acceptance of this book over a period of four decades, and we appreciate the obligation that this acceptance places on us. In preparing this Fifth Edition, we have been mindful of our responsibility and have made every effort to provide the reader with a body of knowledge that he can carry well into the 1970's.

EUGENE L. GRANT
W. GRANT IRESON

Palo Alto, California
February, 1970

Contents

PART I
Some Basic Concepts in Engineering Economy

PART II
Judging the Attractiveness of Proposed Investments

PART III
Techniques for Economy Studies

APPENDIXES

I

SOME BASIC CONCEPTS IN ENGINEERING ECONOMY

1

Defining Alternatives and Predicting Their Consequences

> As the correct solution of any problem depends primarily on a true understanding of what the problem really is, and wherein lies its difficulty, we may profitably pause upon the threshold of our subject to consider first, in a more general way, its real nature; the causes which impede sound practice; the conditions on which success or failure depends; the directions in which error is most to be feared.—A. M. WELLINGTON [1]

Engineering involves many choices among alternatives. The question "Will it pay?" is nearly always present. This question may be broken down into subsidiary questions.

For example, there are the often-quoted three questions that were asked by General John J. Carty when he was chief engineer of the New York Telephone Company in the early years of the present century. He applied these questions to the many engineering proposals that came before him for review:

1. Why do this at all?
2. Why do it now?
3. Why do it this way?

Why do this at all? Shall a proposed new activity be undertaken? Shall an existing activity be expanded, contracted, or abandoned? Shall existing standards or operating procedures be modified?

Why do it now? Shall we build now with excess capacity in advance of demand, or with only sufficient capacity to satisfy the demand immediately in prospect? Are the costs of capital and other business conditions favorable to a present development?

Why do it this way? This choice among alternative ways of doing the same thing is common to all types of engineering activity.

This book deals with certain principles and techniques that are useful

[1] A. M. Wellington, *The Economic Theory of Railway Location*, 2d ed. (New York: John Wiley & Sons, Inc., 1887), p. 1.

in securing rational answers to questions of this type. The central problem discussed in the book is how we may judge whether any proposed course of action will prove to be economical in the long run, as compared to other possible alternatives. Such judgment should not be based on an unsupported "hunch"; it calls for an economy study. An economy study may be defined as a comparison between alternatives in which the differences between the alternatives are expressed so far as practicable in money terms. Where technical considerations are somehow involved, such a comparison may be called an engineering economy study. In most cases, the engineering economy studies discussed in this book deal with the evaluation of proposed investments.

Management's Responsibility for Decisions on Plant Investment. The earliest book on engineering economy was Wellington's *The Economic Theory of Railway Location.* Wellington wrote in a missionary spirit in a day when investments in railway plant in the United States were greater than the aggregate of all other investments in industrial assets. Railway location obviously is a field in which many alternatives are likely to be available. Nevertheless, Wellington observed what seemed to him to be an almost complete disregard by many locating engineers of the influence of their decisions on the prospective costs and revenues of the railways. In his first edition (1877) he said of railway location, "And yet there is no field of professional labor in which a limited amount of modest incompetency at $150 per month can set so many picks and shovels and locomotives at work to no purpose whatever."

Although salary rates and many other things have changed since Wellington's time, the type of problem that he recognized is an ever-present one in an industrialized civilization. If, in a business enterprise or in government, many important decisions that in the aggregate can have a major influence on the success (and sometimes on the survival) of the enterprise are badly made by persons of "modest incompetence," these bad decisions are not primarily the fault of those persons; they are the fault of management.

A Conceptual Framework for the Presentation of Engineering Economy. The first two chapters of this book introduce a number of concepts that the authors believe are important in decision making—particularly so with reference to decisions about proposed investments in physical assets. The reader will doubtless observe that these concepts are not mutually exclusive; some of them overlap a bit. Throughout the remainder of the book, the application of these concepts is discussed and illustrated in various ways, often with reference to specific examples that involve numerical solutions in the comparison of alternatives.

In these two initial chapters, each concept is first stated in italics and then expanded by means of a short discussion. Some of the discussions contain descriptions of cases chosen to illustrate specific points. These early examples are intentionally brief; the desired points in this initial presentation can be made without giving all the details needed for a formal analysis and a numerical solution.

Recognizing and Defining Alternatives. *Decisions are among alternatives; it is desirable that alternatives be clearly defined and that the merits of all appropriate alternatives be evaluated.*

There is no need for a *decision* unless there are two or more courses of action possible. However, many decisions are, in effect, made by default; although many alternatives exist, the decision maker fails to recognize them and considers only one possible course of action.

In many other instances, formal consideration is given to several alternatives. Nevertheless, an unwise decision is finally made (or recommended) because of an analyst's failure to examine an alternative that is superior to any of the ones selected. It is obvious that a poor alternative will appear to be attractive if it is compared with alternatives that are even worse.

A Case of a Failure to Recognize the Existence of Any Alternatives. An industrial concern owned a "total energy system" which had been operated for many years to furnish steam for heating, for operation of steam-driven pumps, steam-driven air compressors, and for generation of the electricity needed in the plant for lighting and for the operation of small motors. An increase in the concern's volume of business finally increased the demands for compressed air and for electric energy above the capacity of the existing plant.

Without any engineering survey of the situation, the general manager of the plant contracted to purchase from the local electric light and power company the excess of his needs for electric energy above the amount that could be generated in his existing plant. To meet the increased needs for compressed air, he bought a large electrically driven air compressor.

His decision proved to be a costly one. The air compressor purchased was a large single unit; it turned out that it was operated most of the time at a very small fraction of its capacity and at a correspondingly very low efficiency. The amount of energy purchased was too low to bring the unit rate into the lower blocks of the power company's rate schedule. No reduction was possible in labor cost for operation of boilers, prime movers, compressors, and pumps, or in the fuel and maintenance costs of the old and inefficient prime movers.

Finally, after a long period of uneconomical operation, an engineering economy study was made to discover and evaluate the possible alternatives. This study made it clear that there were a number of plans that would have been more economical than the one that had been adopted. Steam capacity might have been increased by the addition of new boilers and the old inefficient prime movers might have been replaced by modern efficient ones of greater capacity. Or the old prime movers might have been shut down with all electric energy requirements purchased from the power company, permitting all the steam generated to be used for operation of steam-driven compressors and pumps and for heating. Or the compressors and pumps might have been electrified and all electric energy requirements then purchased, with boilers operated for steam heat only in cold weather.

Some Cases of Failure to Consider Appropriate Alternatives. In a certain study of alternate highway locations, Proposal A required a major improvement of an existing through highway. Proposal B called for an entirely new location that would relegate the existing road chiefly to the service of local traffic. A prospective favorable consequence of the new location was to make possible the development of new economic activity in a certain area not now served by an adequate highway. This consequence, included in the economic analysis as a "benefit" for B but not for A, was a major factor in the analyst's recommendation favorable to proposal B. The analyst failed to recognize that the same benefit could be obtained by making a relatively small additional investment to add to Proposal A a low cost secondary road that would serve the new area.

In another case, an irrigation district was having great difficulty with the maintenance of a number of flumes in its main canal. The district's consulting engineer estimated a cost of $1,200,000 for his proposed plan of flume replacement. When the district's commissioners tried to sell the district's bonds for this amount, the bond house that they approached sent its engineer to investigate. This engineer suggested that the investment might be reduced and a more permanent ditch obtained by substituting earth fills for many of the low flumes that needed replacement. This plan was later carried out under his direction at a cost of about $400,000.

Improved Analytical Procedures as a Possible Alternative to Investments. Sometimes when an unsatisfactory condition is under review and an investment in fixed assets is proposed to correct this condition, no thought is given to possible methods of improving the condition without a substantial investment.

For example, new machinery may be proposed to reduce high labor costs on a certain operation. Work simplification methods based on motion study may provide an alternative way to reduce these costs. As another example, new machinery may be proposed to reduce the percentage of spoilage of a manufactured product that must meet close tolerances. Possibly the same result might be obtained through the use of the techniques of statistical quality control.

A number of organizations have reported that the analysis of procedural problems preparatory to the purchase or lease of a large, high-speed computer has resulted in the improvement of existing procedures to the point that the computer could not be justified. The introduction of a computer always requires the careful analysis of the problems to be solved on it in order to translate each problem into language the computer can understand. Such analysis frequently reveals flaws in the current procedures that could have been eliminated without waiting until the lease or purchase of a computer was proposed.

In the public works field, also, proposed investments may have alternatives that are not obvious at first glance. For instance, the cost of flood damage may be reduced by investment in flood protection reservoirs, levees, and channel improvement. This cost may also be reduced by a system of flood zoning that prevents certain types of land use where there is a likelihood of flooding. Moreover, the cost of flood damages often may be reduced by an improved system of flood forecasting accompanied by an effective system of transmitting the forecasts to people in the area subject to flood.

Imperfect Alternatives Are Sometimes the Most Economical. The satisfaction of the engineer's sense of perfection is not a necessary prerequisite for the most economical alternative. Sometimes it happens that a careful study will show that an alternative that at first was summarily rejected affords the most economical solution of a given problem.

An illustration is the case of a geographically diversified group of public utility companies that needed to buy a great many poles. Poles came in a number of classes, AA, A, B, C, D, E, F, and G, depending upon the top diameter and the butt diameter. The past practice of these companies in pole selection had been based on their experience of what had proved to be satisfactory rather than on any considerations of theoretical design, and usually had involved purchasing no poles below class B.

It was then decided to analyze pole requirements on the basis of such factors as the expected storm loads in different areas and the importance of each pole line to the entire system. This analysis showed that many of the lighter grades of poles that had not previously been purchased were satisfactory for certain conditions. Savings were effected because cheaper poles were used in many cases. Additional savings resulted because the distribution of pole requirements among all of the classes made it possible to use a "wood's run" of poles, so that lumber companies were able to set a lower price on poles A and B than was possible when they had trouble in selling their lower classes.

The Common Condition of the Existence of Major Alternatives and Subsidiary Alternatives. Earlier in this chapter, we cited a "hunch" decision by the manager of a factory that had a total energy system. When it was finally recognized that this was an uneconomical decision, an engineer was called in to survey the situation and make recommendations.

He examined the factory's past requirements for the relevant services— heat, pumping, compressed air, and electricity. After consideration of the trend of growth of production and of some changes in production methods that seemed to be in prospect, he made a forecast of the needs for these services for several years to come. With this forecast as a basis, he then made preliminary designs for meeting the expected needs by each of the possible alternatives that he had recognized. For each alternative, he then made approximate estimates of the immediate investment required and of the annual expenditures necessary in the future. With these estimates, he was able to make a preliminary comparison of the long-run economy of the several alternative plans (including as one plan a continuance of the existing scheme), and to select those that seemed to justify detailed study.

Of all the alternatives given preliminary study, two appeared to be much more economical than any of the others. One was a plan to modernize the power plant by the purchase of one or more steam turbines; the other was a plan for the electrification of the compressors and pumps and the purchase of all power. Each of these plans was given detailed study with complete designs, and with careful estimates of investment costs and operation and maintenance costs.

As is characteristic of all economy studies to determine general policy, each of these designs involved numerous subsidiary alternatives, and each selection between subsidiary alternatives required a subsidiary economy study. For example, in the first alternative what type and size of turbines should be selected? How many should there be? What boiler pressures should be used? Should the power generation be combined with other steam requirements by selecting turbines that exhaust at pressures that permit the use of their exhaust steam for other purposes? In the second alternative, several different possible rates were offered by the power company. "Primary" power could be taken at 23,000 volts, requiring the customer to install his own transformers for stepping down the voltage, and of course, to take the transformer losses involved; a variation of this was an off-peak rate that restricted the power that could be used in certain specified hours of certain months. Two other different rates were available under which the power company supplied electricity at the voltages at which it was ultimately to be used. The electrification of compressors and pumps involved several possible alternative designs.

What Alternatives Are "Appropriate" for Evaluation? Costs for design, estimating, and analysis are involved whenever an additional alternative is to be reviewed. Clearly a balance is required between the possible advantages to be gained from evaluating more alternatives in any given case and the expenses (including sometimes the adverse consequences of time delays) incident to the evaluation. It is reasonable to try to avoid the costs of examining alternatives that have no merit.

The statement (on page 5) that the merits of all appropriate alternatives should be evaluated obviously leaves room for interpretation of the word *appropriate*. In most instances, as in the case cited of the engineer's study of the total energy system, preliminary economic evaluation will serve to eliminate many alternatives that are physically possible. Detailed study can then be limited to those alternatives that have appeared to be best in the preliminary comparison.

The Need to Consider Consequences. *Decisions should be based on the expected consequences of the various alternatives.*

If there were no basis for estimating the results of choosing one proposed alternative rather than another, it would not matter which alternative was chosen. But in most proposals that involve investments in physical assets by business enterprises or by governmental bodies, it is possible to make estimates of differences in consequences. Clearly, rational decisions among alternatives should depend on prospective consequences to the extent that consequences can be anticipated. Because the consequences of a decision are necessarily *after* the moment of decision, this estimation always applies to the future.

As will be brought out by a variety of examples throughout this book, some types of consequences of investment decisions can be forecast with a fair amount of justifiable confidence, particularly if adequate effort is devoted to the job of estimation. In contrast, other consequences are inherently difficult to forecast. For example, other things being equal, consequences that are expected in the fairly distant future are harder to forecast than those in the near future. Moreover, some types of prospective consequences are fairly easy to quantify in a way that makes them commensurable with one another. But there may also be prospective consequences that are difficult or impossible to quantify in this way.

A Personal Investment Made Without Any Evaluation of Its Consequences. Although the following example deals with one particular case, the circumstances described are fairly common. Many of our readers doubtless will have observed similar cases.

A schoolteacher invested her small savings in a down payment on a rental property. She made this investment without any estimate of the future cash flow (receipts and disbursements) associated with ownership of the property. As a mater of fact, the particular property was greatly overpriced in relation to its prospective earnings and expenses. She finally sold the property several years later at a substantial loss. If she had substituted for her guess that all rental properties are profitable, specific estimates of receipts and disbursements for this particular property, and if she had given consideration to alternative possible investments, she would doubtless have reached the correct conclusion that this rental property was an unwise investment.

The Critical Issue of Consequences to Whom. *Before establishing procedures for project formulation and project evaluation, it is essential to decide whose viewpoint is to be adopted.*

The majority of the examples and problems in this book deal with economy studies for competitive business enterprise. In these studies we shall assume that the analysis is to be made primarily from the point of view of the owners of the enterprise.

The matter is a bit more complicated in economy studies for privately owned public utility companies that operate under the rules of rate regulation that have developed in the United States. We explain in Chapter 20 that the common practice of trying to minimize "revenue requirements" when choosing among design alternatives is, in effect, taking the viewpoint of the customers of a utility company. We also note certain circumstances in which such a customers' viewpoint may be insufficient or inappropriate.

The choice of viewpoint is much more complicated in economy studies made for governmental bodies. In many types of economy study for public works, it clearly is undesirable to restrict the viewpoint to the financial position of the particular governmental unit that is involved. We shall see first in Chapter 9 and later in Chapter 19 that, in principle, many such economy studies ought to be made considering prospective consequences "to whomsoever they may accrue." We shall also see that, because of their diffused nature, consequences are often much harder to estimate and evaluate in government projects than in private enterprise.

Commensurability. *In comparing alternatives, it is desirable to make consequences commensurable with one another insofar as practicable. That is, consequences should be expressed in numbers and the same units should apply to all the numbers. In economic decisions, money units are the only units that meet the foregoing specification.*

Words versus Monetary Figures as a Basis for Economic Decisions. Often a good way to start an economy study is to use words to itemize the expected differences among the alternatives being compared. But it is easy to reach unsound conclusions if differences expressed in words are not later converted into units that make the differences comparable.

To illustrate this point, consider a proposal that incandescent lamps be replaced by fluorescent fixtures in a certain industrial plant. The engineer who made this proposal listed the advantages and disadvantages as follows:

Advantages:
 1. More light for the same amount of power
 2. Smaller number of fixtures
 3. Less frequent lamp replacement
 4. Lower maintenance costs
 5. Better light
 6. Less heat to be dissipated
 7. Improvement of lighting without having to install new, larger conductors
 8. Improved working conditions
 9. Less eye fatigue for employees
 10. Better quality product
 11. Better employee morale

Disadvantages:
 1. Higher investment in fixtures
 2. Higher unit lamp cost
 3. Labor cost of installation
 4. Interruption of work during installation
 5. "Flicker" may occur and be very annoying

A common characteristic of such a tabulation is that the listed differences are not mutually exclusive; the same thing may be listed more than once with different words. Moreover, because the stated differences are not commensurable with one another, trivial differences between the alternatives tend to be given the same weight as important differences. A hazard of this verbal technique of comparing alternatives is that the decision will be unduly influenced by sheer weight of words.

Cash Flow and the Time Value of Money. Two steps generally are required before differences stated in words can be made commensurable with one another. First, the differences must be expressed in their appropriate physical units. Then the physical units must be converted to money units. For example, wire and conduit of various lengths and diameters, lamps and lamp fixtures of various types and sizes, hours of installation and maintenance labor, and kilowatt hours of electric energy are not commensurable with one another until they are converted to a common unit, namely, money.

But it is not sufficient to estimate the *amounts* of money receipts and disbursements influenced by a decision; it is also necessary to estimate the *times* of the cash flows. Because money has a time value, a monetary unit (e.g., dollar, peso, pound, yen, etc.) at one date is not directly comparable with the same monetary unit at another date. The relevance of the timing of cash flow is discussed at the start of Chapter 2 and developed throughout the remainder of this book.

The Issue of the Validity of Market Prices as a Basis for Decisions Among Investment Alternatives. In the long run, a competitive enterprise cannot survive without money receipts that more than offset its money disbursements. The case for evaluating proposals in terms of their influence on prospective cash flow to and from the enterprise is therefore quite clear and straightforward in competitive business. Market prices, in the sense used here, are simply the prices that the enterprise expects to pay for its various inputs and expects to receive for its various outputs.

It is explained in Chapters 9 and 19 that the matter is not so simple in economy studies for governments. Part of the difficulty is that no market may exist to establish prices for certain types of desired outputs from government projects. (Representative examples of such desired outputs are reduction of air pollution, reduction of deaths from aircraft and motor vehicle accidents, savings of time to operators of noncommercial motor vehicles.) Also, in certain cases where market valuations are available, some persons may deem such valuations to be unsuitable for assigning monetary figures to project outputs. At this point in our exposition, we shall merely note that we favor the use of market prices, where available, in the initial formulation and evaluation of the economic aspects of proposed government projects. However, final decisions may reasonably give weight to relevant matters that were omitted by such use of market prices. Some aspects of the pricing of the inputs and outputs from proposed public works projects are discussed in Chapter 19.

Irrelevance of Matters Common to All Alternatives. *Only the differences among alternatives are relevant in their comparison.*

This generally useful concept needs to be recognized in a number of ways that will be developed throughout this book. For example, the past is common to all alternatives for the future; there can be no consequences of a decision before the moment of decision. Also, it is easy to draw incorrect conclusions by basing estimates on average costs or allocated costs rather than on cost differences. Although this concept is illustrated by many examples throughout this entire book, it is given particular attention in Chapters 15, 16, and 17.

Separation of Decisions. *Insofar as practicable, separable decisions should be made separately.*

In most instances (although not all), decisions on the financing of physical plant are independent of decisions on the specific assets to be selected. The combining of a particular plant investment with a particular scheme of financing in a single analysis may lead to unsound decisions. This point is developed particularly in Chapter 18.

Many proposed engineering projects have a number of different possible levels of investment that are physically possible. Each separable increment of investment that might either be included or left out ought to be evaluated on its own merits. Otherwise, the fact that certain proposed separable increments are economically unproductive may be concealed by the evaluation of the project only as a whole. This point is developed in various places in Part II of this book but is particularly emphasized in Chapter 12 at the start of Part III.

Summary. The six concepts given in this chapter are here repeated for emphasis:

1. Decisions are among alternatives; it is desirable that alternatives be clearly defined and that the merits of all appropriate alternatives be evaluated.
2. Decisions should be based on the expected consequences of the various alternatives.
3. Before establishing procedures for project formulation and project evaluation, it is essential to decide whose viewpoint is to be adopted.
4. In comparing alternatives, it is desirable to make consequences commensurable with one another insofar as practicable. That is, consequences should be expressed in numbers and the same

units should apply to all the numbers. In economic decisions, money units are the only units that meet the foregoing specification.

5. Only the differences among alternatives are relevant in their comparison.

6. Insofar as practicable, separable decisions should be made separately.

The Need for Criteria and Analytical Procedures in Making Decisions about Proposed Investments

The most serious result of accepting or rejecting proposals primarily on the basis of how urgent they seem to be is that the capital budgeting program is likely to degenerate into a contest of personalities. The biggest share of the capital-expenditure money will go to the division heads who are the most eloquent or most persistent in presenting their requests, rather than to those who have taken the time and effort necessary to make an objective appraisal of the project's economic worth. The result is that all projects come up for review in an atmosphere of haste and emergency, with full scope allowed for the arts of persuasion and exhortation. Not only will projects whose economic desirability is dubious be pushed through to acceptance, but also a large proportion of investments that would yield big savings and high profits may be put off almost indefinitely.—JOEL DEAN [1]

Although investments in physical assets were involved in the actual cases that were described briefly in Chapter 1, the *concepts* presented were widely applicable to many types of decision making. In the present chapter, we look more specifically at concepts relevant to the investment-type decisions that so often are needed when engineering alternatives are present.

Need for Decision Criteria. *It is desirable to have a criterion for decision making, or possibly several criteria.*

Clearly, the criteria should be applied to the differences in conse-

[1] Joel Dean, "Measuring the Productivity of Capital," *Harvard Business Review*, January–February 1954.

quences that are anticipated from the choice among the different alternatives.

With reference to proposals for alternative investments in physical assets, it has been pointed out that the consequences of a choice should be expressed as far as practicable in terms of cash flows (or other monetary figures) at stated points in time. It is suggested in this chapter that there should always be a primary criterion applied to such monetary figures. In dealing with certain types of proposals, it may also be desirable to have one or more supplementary or secondary criteria applied to the monetary figures.

It was pointed out in Chapter 1 that not all prospective consequences of decisions about investments in physical assets are reducible to monetary terms. Weight often needs to be given to such irreducible data. It follows that there may also be secondary criteria for decision making that are related to differences in estimated consequences that have not been expressed as monetary figures.

Choice of a Primary Criterion. *The primary criterion to be applied in a choice among alternative proposed investments in physical assets should be selected with the objective of making the best use of limited resources.*

Whether one thinks of an individual, a family, a business enterprise, or a governmental unit such as a city, state, or nation, it is generally true that at any given time there is a limitation on the available resources that can be devoted to investment in physical assets. The resources that are limited may be of many types, such as land, labor, or materials. But because the market gives us money valuations on most resources, it usually is reasonable to express the overall limitation in terms of money.

In evaluating proposed investments, the question should be asked whether the investment will be productive enough, all things considered. "Productive enough" can be interpreted as yielding a sufficient rate of return as compared with one or more stated alternatives. Throughout this book, we shall assume that a decision can and has been made on the minimum rate of return that is attractive in any given setting and that this decision is the basis for the primary criterion to be used for investment decisions. Chapter 11 introduces some of the "all-things-considered" issues that may arise in selecting a minimum attractive rate of return. These issues are examined further in the remaining chapters of this book, particularly Chapters 13, 18, 19, 20, and 21.

We shall see in Chapters 3 to 10 that it is necessary to use the mathematics of compound interest to apply a primary criterion based on a stipulated minimum attractive rate of return. Four different ways to implement this criterion are explained in Chapters 6, 7, 8, and 9. It is pointed out in these chapters that with the same input data, all four methods lead to the same conclusion as to whether or not the primary criterion has been met.

Wherever income taxes are levied, such taxes tend to reduce the rate of return from investments in physical assets. However, income tax laws and regulations often favor certain types of investment as compared to other types; for various reasons related to the technicalities of income taxation, the after-tax rate of return is not a fixed percentage of the before-tax rate. It follows that, in principle, the income tax consequences of proposed investments ought to be estimated, and that a stipulated minimum attractive rate of return in private industry should be an after-tax rate rather than a before-tax rate.

The use of the after-tax minimum attractive rate of return is illustrated in examples starting with Chapter 6 using certain simplified assumptions about the relationship between before-tax and after-tax cash flow. A critical look at the complexities of the ways in which income taxes influence the relative merits of proposed investments is deferred until Chapters 16, 17, 18, and 20.

Secondary Criteria Applied to Consequences Expressed in Monetary Terms. *Even the most careful estimates of the monetary consequences of choosing different alternatives may turn out to be incorrect. It often is helpful to a decision maker to make use of secondary criteria that reflect in some way the lack of certainty associated with all estimates of the future.*

Such secondary criteria are illustrated in a number of examples and problems in Part III of this book. They are given particular attention in Chapters 13, 14, and 21.

"Irreducible Data of the Problem of Investment." *Decisions among investment alternatives should give weight to any expected differences in consequences that have not been reduced to money terms as well as to the consequences that have been expressed in terms of money.*

In the second edition of his *Engineering Economics*, published in 1923, Professor J. C. L. Fish coined the phrase "irreducible data of the problem of investment" to apply to prospective differences between alternatives that are not reduced to estimated receipts and disbursements for purposes of analysis. Some other words or phrases that have been applied to such nonmonetized differences are "judgment factors," "imponderables," and "intangibles."

There is no word or short phrase that by itself conveys the precise idea of something that is relevant in a particular decision but has not been expressed in terms of money for one reason or another. Often it is not so much that an analyst believes that the difference in question will not eventually influence receipts and disbursements as that he has no satisfactory basis for estimating how much the influence on cash flow will be and when this influence will occur.

In this book we have elected to use *irreducibles* or *irreducible data* in the special technical sense of relevant differences in the expected consequences of a decision that have not been reduced to money terms. There are two reasons for this election. One reason is historical, namely, that this usage dates back to 1923. The other reason is that the word or phrase is not generally used in everyday speech and therefore does not have a different popular meaning that might be a cause of its misinterpretation.

Irreducibles may play a particularly large part in personal investment decisions. For example, consider a choice between home ownership and renting. It is obvious that many aspects of the matter should be estimated in terms of money as a guide to intelligent decision making. Nevertheless, matters of personal taste that cannot be expressed in money terms should reasonably be given weight in such a decision. Thus the pride of home ownership may be of great importance to one family and a matter of complete indifference to another.

For reasons discussed in Chapter 19, irreducibles may also be given considerable weight in many governmental decisions.

The Need for a "System Viewpoint." *Often there are side-effects that tend to be disregarded when individual decisions are made. To consider such side-effects adequately, it may be necessary to examine the interrelationships among a number of decisions before any of the individual decisions can be made.*

The basic question here is whether too narrow a view is being taken of the alternatives that are being compared. If the side-effects of a particular decision are sufficiently trivial, presumably a study of them would not change the decision. However, a study of the interrelationships among a group of decisions may be needed to provide a basis for judgment on whether the side-effects are trivial or important. Comments on this topic are made in Chapters 12 and 21.

An Example of the Application of Certain Concepts. Near the start of Chapter 1 and again in the middle of that chapter, there was reference to the case of a company that owned a total energy system that had become inadequate. This story is now continued to its conclusion.

The reader may recall that when management finally recognized that a number of alternatives needed to be evaluated, a preliminary economy study narrowed the comparison to two alternatives, which were then studied in detail. One of these alternatives called for continuing the concept of a total energy system by the purchase and installation of a modern power plant. This plant would have greater thermal efficiency and greater capacity than the old inadequate plant. The other alternative involved the purchase of electric energy, the electrification of certain equipment, and the continued generation of steam only during the colder months of the year for purposes of space heating.

When the cash flow estimates for these two alternatives were assembled, it was evident that the total disbursements over a 20-year analysis period would be somewhat lower with the new power plant. However, the initial disbursement was of course much greater with the power plant. The question at issue (in relation to our primary criterion for investment decisions) was whether the annual operating savings over a 20-year period would be sufficient to recover the extra investment required for the new power plant and its related facilities plus a rate of return that was high enough to be attractive, all things considered.

In this company, experience had shown that there always seemed to be plenty of proposals for internal investment that promised an after-tax rate of return of 10% or more. Such projects absorbed all the funds that could be made available for internal investment. The consequence of accepting a proposal that had a prospective after-tax yield of less than 10% was the turning down of some other proposal that had a prospective yield of more than 10%. In effect, 10% after taxes was the minimum attractive rate of return in this company even though this particular phrase was not used.

An analysis was made of the difference in year-by-year estimated cash flow between the alternative with the new power plant and the alternative calling for the purchase of electricity. The prospective after-tax rate of return on the extra investment in the power plant alternative was about 6%. Because 6% was less than the stipulated 10%, the application of our primary criterion for decision making favored the alternative involving purchased electricity.

Secondary criteria based on certain modifications of the original cash flow estimates also favored the purchase of electricity. If one or more business recessions should occur during the analysis period, expenses for purchased electricity could be decreased more readily than expenses for the operation of a power plant; in the past, with power generated in the factory's own plant, it had been necessary to keep the power plant operating with a full labor force even when the factory was operating at only a small fraction of its full capacity. Moreover, if there should be an unanticipated rapid growth in the plant's demand for total energy, the need could be met more rapidly by purchasing more electricity than by expanding the power plant.

On the other hand, there was an irreducible factor adverse to the alternative involving purchased electricity. The change in policy would create certain personnel problems. An engine-room force would no longer be needed and a boiler-room force would not be required during the summer months. However, a survey of personnel requirements elsewhere in the plant indicated that these men could be retrained and transferred to other jobs.

In all decision making, it finally becomes necessary for some person (or possibly a group of persons) to make a choice. Other things being equal, a choice between investment alternatives should be based on the chosen primary criterion. In the frequent case where other things are not entirely equal, weight should be given to secondary criteria including irreducibles. In this example, the analysis clearly favored the alternative involving the purchase of electricity and this was the one actually chosen.

Some general points may be illustrated by this example. One point is that this was an *engineering* economy study because so many technical matters were involved that only an engineer could be expected to recognize the appropriate alternatives and make a competent analysis of them. (In this case the engineer who made the study *recommended* the decision and someone else made the decision following his recommendation.) Another point is that the setting of this decision was unique; no other plant would have exactly the same existing physical facilities, present and prospective needs for various forms of energy, personnel, financial circumstances, and so on. (Many economic comparisons that superficially seem to be similar actually turn out to be quite different because of differences in the surrounding circumstances.)

Still another point that we shall emphasize throughout this book is that only the *differences* between the two best alternatives are relevant in their comparison. Either of these two alternatives as well as several others that were discarded would have shown an after-tax rate of return of more than 10% as compared to the uneconomic alternative of continuing the present condition. It would not have been sufficient for an analyst to show that the proposed new power plant would yield, say, an 18% rate of return as compared to the present way of doing things. The proposed new power plant was not a sound investment unless it could sustain its challenge against the best of the other possible alternatives as well as against a continuation of the present condition.

Summary. The five concepts given in this chapter are here repeated for emphasis:

1. It is desirable to have a criterion for decision making, or possibly several criteria.

2. The primary criterion to be applied in a choice among alternative proposed investments in physical assets should be selected with the objective of making the best use of limited resources.

3. Even the most careful estimates of the monetary consequences of choosing different alternatives may turn out to be incorrect. It often is helpful to a decision maker to make use of secondary criteria that reflect in some way the lack of certainty associated with all estimates of the future.

4. Decisions among investment alternatives should give weight to any expected differences in consequences that have not been reduced to money terms as well as to the consequences that have been expressed in terms of money.

5. Often there are side-effects that tend to be disregarded when individual decisions are made. To consider such side-effects adequately, it may be necessary to examine the interrelationships among a number of decisions before any of the individual decisions can be made.

PROBLEMS

2–1. The owner of a party fishing boat has lost a number of days of operation because the engine of his boat has broken down several times, requiring a day of overhaul each time. He is afraid that too frequent breakdowns will give him a reputation for unreliable operation. What alternatives do you see that might be available to him? How would you expect future cash receipts and disbursements to be influenced by his choice among these alternatives? What irreducible data might reasonably be given weight in his decision among these alternatives?

2–2. In a growing city decisions must be made from time to time whether various physical means of traffic control are to be used at specific street intersections to control motor vehicle traffic and pedestrian traffic. The various possibilities at an intersection may include:
1. No control devices
2. Arterial stop sign on one street but not on the other
3. Arterial stop signs on both streets
4. Traffic lights with duration of signals in each direction controlled by preset timing devices
5. Traffic lights in which the frequency and duration of the traffic signals are determined by traffic activated devices on one of the intersecting streets
6. Traffic lights in which the frequency and duration of the traffic signals are determined by traffic activated devices on both of the intersecting streets

Decisions by city officials among such alternatives often are made largely by intuition, although weight may be given to such matters as traffic counts of motor vehicles, the current state of the city budget, the occurrence of recent accidents at a particular intersection, and pressures from residents living near the various intersections. It has been suggested that decision making might be improved by the practice of using formal economy studies requiring an evaluation (in money terms as far as practicable) of the various benefits and costs associated with each alternative.

Consider some street intersection in your vicinity that is now in condition (2) above. If possible, select an intersection for which some residents have proposed a change to (3), (4), (5), or (6).

Discuss the problems of making the decision between continuing condition (2) and changing to one of the other conditions. Tie your discussion to the eleven concepts stated in Chapters 1 and 2. Which of these concepts, if any, seem to you to be of particular importance in a decision of this type?

2–3. What are some alternative methods that a college might consider for the provision of janitorial service for the college buildings? Discuss the problem of choice among these alternatives with reference to the concepts stated in Chapters 1 and 2.

2–4. What are some alternatives that a married student might consider for the provision of family housing while he is in college? Discuss the problem of choice among these alternatives with reference to the concepts stated in Chapters 1 and 2.

2–5. A ranch owner who is 5 miles from the nearest public utility power line wishes to consider providing electric power for his ranch. What alternatives do you see that might be available to him? Discuss the problem of choice among these alternatives with reference to the concepts stated in Chapters 1 and 2.

II

JUDGING THE ATTRACTIVENESS OF PROPOSED INVESTMENTS

Equivalence

3

(The) growth of money in time must be taken into account in all combinations and comparisons of payments.—J. C. L. Fish [1]

Most problems in economy involve determining what is economical in the long run, that is, over a considerable period of time. In such problems it is necessary to recognize the time value of money; because of the existence of interest, a dollar now is worth more than the prospect of a dollar next year or at some later date.

Definition of Interest. Interest may be defined as money paid for the use of borrowed money. Or, broadly speaking, interest may be thought of as the return obtainable by the productive investment of capital. While the point of view required in dealing with problems in engineering economy is the one implied in the latter broader definition, it is, nevertheless, desirable to start the discussion of interest by considering situations in which money is actually borrowed. The broader viewpoint is developed in Chapter 6 and thereafter.

Interest Rate. The rate of interest is the ratio between the interest chargeable or payable at the end of a period of time, usually a year or less, and the money owed at the beginning of that period. Thus if $6 of interest is payable annually on a debt of $100, the interest rate is $6/$100 = 0.06 per annum. This is customarily described as an interest rate of 6%, the "per annum" being understood unless some other period of time is definitely stated.

Even though interest is frequently payable oftener than once a year, the interest rate per annum is usually what is meant when an interest rate is stated. Thus rates of 0.005 payable monthly, 0.015 payable quarterly, or 0.03 payable semiannually are all described as 6%. The difference between the payment of interest annually and its payment more frequently is discussed briefly in the next chapter under the heading "Nominal and Effective Interest Rates."

[1] J. C. L. Fish, *Engineering Economics,* 2d ed. (New York: McGraw-Hill Book Co., Inc., 1923), p. 20.

TABLE 3–1

Four Plans for Repayment of $10,000 in 10 Years with Interest at 6%

	End of Year	Interest Due (6% of money owed at start of year)	Total Money Owed Before Year-End Payment	Year-end Payment	Money Owed After Year-End Payment
	0				$10,000
	1	$600	$10,600	$ 600	10,000
	2	600	10,600	600	10,000
	3	600	10,600	600	10,000
	4	600	10,600	600	10,000
Plan I	5	600	10,600	600	10,000
	6	600	10,600	600	10,000
	7	600	10,600	600	10,000
	8	600	10,600	600	10,000
	9	600	10,600	600	10,000
	10	600	10,600	10,600	0
	0				$10,000
	1	$600	$10,600	$1,600	9,000
	2	540	9,540	1,540	8,000
	3	480	8,480	1,480	7,000
	4	420	7,420	1,420	6,000
Plan II	5	360	6,360	1,360	5,000
	6	300	5,300	1,300	4,000
	7	240	4,240	1,240	3,000
	8	180	3,180	1,180	2,000
	9	120	2,120	1,120	1,000
	10	60	1,060	1,060	0
	0				$10,000.00
	1	$600.00	$10,600.00	$1,358.68	9,241.32
	2	554.48	9,795.80	1,358.68	8,437.12
	3	506.23	8,943.35	1,358.68	7,584.67
	4	455.08	8,039.75	1,358.68	6,681.07
Plan III	5	400.86	7,081.93	1,358.68	5,723.25
	6	343.40	6,066.65	1,358.68	4,707.98
	7	282.48	4,990.45	1,358.68	3,631.77
	8	217.91	3,849.68	1,358.68	2,491.00
	9	149.46	2,640.46	1,358.68	1,281.78
	10	76.90	1,358.68	1,358.68	0.00
	0				$10,000.00
	1	$ 600.00	$10,600.00	$ 0.00	10,600.00
	2	636.00	11,236.00	0.00	11,236.00
	3	674.16	11,910.16	0.00	11,910.16
	4	714.61	12,624.77	0.00	12,624.77
Plan IV	5	757.49	13,382.26	0.00	13,382.26
	6	802.94	14,185.20	0.00	14,185.20
	7	851.11	15,036.31	0.00	15,036.31
	8	902.18	15,938.49	0.00	15,938.49
	9	956.31	16,894.80	0.00	16,894.80
	10	1,013.69	17,908.49	17,908.49	0.00

Plans for Repayment of Borrowed Money. Consider the plans shown in Table 3–1 by which a loan of $10,000 might be repaid in 10 years with interest at 6% payable annually. In the tables showing these plans, the date of the loan is designated as 0 years and time is measured in years from that date. The $10,000 is called the *principal* of the loan.

Characteristics of Repayment Plans. The student of engineering economy should carefully examine these four plans because they are representative of various schemes in common use for the repayment of money borrowed for a term of years. Plan I involves no partial payment of principal; only interest is paid each year, and the principal is paid in a lump sum at the end of the period. A cash flow diagram to represent the borrower's receipts and payments for Plan I is shown in Figure 3–1a.

Plans II and III involve systematic reduction of the principal of the debt by uniform repayment of principal with diminishing interest in Plan II and by a scheme that makes the sum of the interest payments and the principal payment uniform in Plan III. The cash flow diagram for Plan II is shown in Figure 3–1b. The cash flow diagram for Plan III is shown in Figure 3–1c.

Plan IV, on the other hand, involves no payment of either principal or interest until the single payment of both at the end of the tenth year. Its diagram is shown in Figure 3–1d.

The advantages and disadvantages of the various plans from the standpoint of different classes of borrowers will be discussed in a later chapter. The point for immediate consideration is their relation to compound interest and to the time value of money.

Compound Interest. In Plan IV, interest is *compounded;* that is, the interest each year is based on the total amount owed at the end of the previous year, a total amount that included the original principal plus the accumulated interest that had not been paid when due. The formulas and tables explained in the next chapter are all based upon the compounding of interest.

The distinction is made, both in the literature of the mathematics of investment and in the law, between *compound interest* and *simple interest.* If in Plan IV a lump-sum payment of principal and interest had been called for at simple rather than compound interest, the only interest payable would have been that charged on the original principal of $10,000. The total payment required under simple interest would thus have been $16,000 instead of the $17,908 that is required under compound interest.

Where money is borrowed for a period of years, the usual business practice is for interest to be due—and nearly always actually paid—annually or oftener. This practice, in effect, involves compound interest,

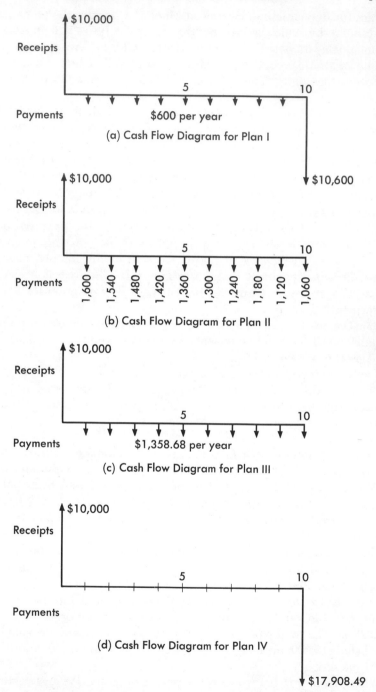

FIGURE 3–1. Cash Flow Diagram for Repayment of $10,000 in 10 Years

whether considered from the viewpoint of the lender or the borrower. Where interest is paid each year, the lender receives a payment that he can use immediately. Also, the borrower, in paying his interest annually, is foregoing the opportunity to use the money that he pays to the lender.

Thus compound interest is the general practice of the business world, and Plans I, II, and III involve what is, in effect, compound interest, because interest is paid annually in each plan. It will be shown in the following chapters how compound interest formulas may be used in dealing with all these various types of repayment situations. Problems in engineering economy generally require consideration of compound interest; simple interest (chiefly of importance in connection with loans for periods of a year or less) will not be discussed further in these pages. Wherever the term "interest" is used, compound interest (i.e., interest due annually or oftener) is implied.

Equivalence. The concept that payments that differ in total magnitude but that are made at different dates may be equivalent to one another is an important one in engineering economy. In developing this concept, we may place side by side for comparison, as in Table 3–2, the $10,000 borrowed and the four series of money payments that we have seen would repay it with interest at 6%. (Payments are shown to four significant figures only.)

TABLE 3–2

Five Equivalent Series of Payments

Year	Investment	I	II	III	IV
0	$10,000				
1		$ 600	$1,600	$1,359	
2		600	1,540	1,359	
3		600	1,480	1,359	
4		600	1,420	1,359	
5		600	1,360	1,359	
6		600	1,300	1,359	
7		600	1,240	1,359	
8		600	1,180	1,359	
9		600	1,120	1,359	
10		$10,600	1,060	1,359	$17,910

If interest is at 6%, these five sets of payments are equivalent to one another. They are equivalent from the standpoint of a prospective lender (investor) with $10,000, because with that sum he can get any one of the four future series of payments (or more precisely, someone's promise to make the payments) in exchange for the present $10,000. Similarly, from the standpoint of the prospective borrower who needs $10,000 (perhaps to invest productively in his business), the four future series are equivalent to each other and to $10,000 now; because, by agreeing to pay any one of these future series, he may secure the needed present sum.

Obviously, we might think of any number of series of payments that would serve to just repay $10,000 with interest at 6%. All of these would be equivalent to $10,000 now, and to each other.

The meaning of equivalence may be explained by using an analogy from algebra: If a number of things are equal to one thing, then they are equal to each other. Given an interest rate, we may say that any payment or series of payments that will repay a present sum of money with interest at that rate is equivalent to that present sum. Therefore, *all future payments or series of payments that would repay the present sum with interest at the stated rate are equivalent to each other.*

Present [2] Worth. From the foregoing we found that a loan of $10,000 can be repaid with interest in four different ways, involving different amounts of money and at different times over a period of 10 years. To the lender (investor) the loan (investment) is the amount necessary to secure the promise of the future payment or series of payments, with interest at the given rate. The investment necessary to secure the promise of the future payment or payments is the present worth of the future payments. To the borrower, the present worth may be thought of as the present sum that may be secured in exchange for the promise to make specified future payments or series of payments. To both the lender and the borrower the repayment series of payments is equivalent to the present worth. Also, since the four different series of payments are equivalent to the same present worth, the series of payments are equivalent to each other.

Significance of Equivalence in Engineering Economy Studies. The five columns in Table 3–2 show equivalent series of payments; however, the total payments called for are quite different, totaling $10,000, $16,000, $13,300, $13,590, and $17,910, respectively. The longer the repayment period the greater this apparent difference. Thus, if the repayment period were 20 years, the corresponding total payments for similar equivalent series would be $10,000, $22,000, $16,300, $17,436, and $32,070.

---

[2] Of course the "present" may be moved in the imagination of the analyst to any convenient date. Thus we may speak in 1970 of the present worth in 1978 of a payment to be made in 1985.

Engineering economy studies usually involve making a choice of several alternative plans for accomplishing some objective of providing a given service. If a given service could be provided by five alternative methods requiring payments as shown in the five columns of Table 3–2, all of the alternative plans would be equally economical with interest at 6%; that is, they could each be financed by a present sum of $10,000. This fact would not be evident from a comparison of the total payments called for in the various plans; it would be clear only if the different money series were converted either to equivalent single payments (e.g., present worth) or to equivalent uniform series.

Engineering economy studies usually require some conversion as a basis for intelligent decision. A comparison of total payments involved in alternative plans, without the use of interest factors to convert the two series to make them comparable, is nearly always misleading.

Equivalence Depends on the Interest Rate. It was shown that the five payment series in the columns of Table 3–2 were equivalent because each series would repay an original loan of $10,000 with interest at 6%. These series payments would not be equivalent if the stated interest rate had been anything other than 6%. If the rate is less than 6%, the series of payments in the four plans will repay a greater amount than the present worth of $10,000; if the rate is greater than 6%, they will all repay a lesser amount. Table 3–3 shows the present worths of the four series of payments at various interest rates.

TABLE 3–3

Present Worths at Various Interest Rates of Payment Series Shown in Table 3–2

Interest Rate	Plan I	Plan II	Plan III	Plan IV
0%	$16,000	$13,300	$13,590	$17,910
2%	13,590	12,030	12,210	14,690
4%	11,620	10,940	11,020	12,100
6%	10,000	10,000	10,000	10,000
8%	8,660	9,180	9,120	8,300
10%	7,540	8,460	8,350	6,900

A present sum is always equivalent at some interest rate to a larger future sum of payments. In many engineering economy problems the answer desired is the interest rate that will make two series equivalent to each other; this is often described as the rate of return obtainable on a proposed extra investment. This viewpoint is developed in Chapter 8.

Summary. The main points of this chapter may be stated as follows:

One definition of interest is money paid for the use of borrowed money. The rate of interest may be defined as the ratio between the interest chargeable or payable at the end of a stipulated period of time and the money owed at the beginning of that period. The general practice of the business world is for interest to be chargeable or payable annually or oftener.

Any future payment or series of payments that will exactly repay a present sum with interest at a given rate is *equivalent* to that present sum; all such future payments or series of payments that will repay the given present sum are equivalent to one another. The present sum is the *present worth* of any future payment or series of payments that will exactly repay it with interest at a given rate.

Equivalence calculations are necessary for a meaningful comparison of different money time series; they are thus usually required in engineering economy studies. Economy studies, however, generally imply a broader definition of interest as the return obtainable by the productive investment of capital.

PROBLEMS

3–1. Prepare a table similar to Table 3–1, showing four plans for the repayment of $1,000 in 4 years with interest at 10%. The uniform annual payment in the plan corresponding to Plan III is $315.47.

3–2. Prepare a table similar to Table 3–1, showing four plans for the repayment of $5,000 in 5 years with interest at 4%. The uniform annual payment in the plan corresponding to Plan III is $1,123.14.

3–3. Prepare a table similar to Plan III of Table 3–1, showing the interest due each year and the money owed after each year-end payment when a debt of $1,000 is repaid in 7 years with interest at 8%. The uniform annual payment is $192.07.

3–4. Prepare a table similar to Plans II and III of Table 3–1, showing the annual repayment (principal and interest) of a loan of $2,000 in 5 years with interest at 8%. The annual payment for Plan III is $500.91.

3–5. Prepare a table similar to Plan III of Table 3–1, showing the interest due and the money owed after each year-end payment when a debt of $1,000 is repaid in 4 years with interest at 7%. The uniform annual payment is $295.23.

4

Interest Formulas

Some engineers may be discouraged when they find that financial analysis generally involves compound interest concepts and terms. To most, compound interest would seem to be something for the banker rather than the engineer. The mastery of the use of compound interest in cost studies is not in itself really difficult. Perhaps more difficult is the process of becoming convinced that it is needed at all.—AMERICAN TELEPHONE AND TELEGRAPH COMPANY, ENGINEERING DEPARTMENT [1]

Symbols. These symbols are used in the following explanation of interest formulas:

i represents an interest rate per interest period.
n represents a number of interest periods.
P represents a present sum of money.
F represents a sum of money at the end of n periods from the present date that is equivalent to P with interest i.
A represents the end-of-period payment or receipt in a uniform series continuing for the coming n periods, the entire series equivalent to P at interest rate i.

Although a one-year interest period is used in most of the illustrations in this book, the formulas presented apply to interest periods of any length.

The various symbols are chosen so that each is an initial letter of a key word associated with the most common meaning of the symbol. Thus i applies to *interest*, n applies to *number* of periods, P applies to *present* worth, F applies to *future* worth, and A applies to *annual* payment or *annuity*.

Formulas. The fundamental interest formulas that express the relationship between P, F, and A in terms of i and n are as follows.

---

[1] *Engineering Economy,* 2d ed., p. 74, copyright American Telephone and Telegraph Company, 1963. While this text was written basically for internal Bell System use, it has been made available outside the System through the Graybar Electric Company.

Given P, to find F. $F = P(1 + i)^n$ (1)

Given F, to find P. $P = F\left[\dfrac{1}{(1 + i)^n}\right]$ (2)

Given F, to find A. $A = F\left[\dfrac{i}{(1 + i)^n - 1}\right]$ (3)

Given P, to find A. $A = P\left[\dfrac{i(1 + i)^n}{(1 + i)^n - 1}\right]$ (4)

or $A = P\left[\dfrac{i}{(1 + i)^n - 1} + i\right]$ (4)

Given A, to find F. $F = A\left[\dfrac{(1 + i)^n - 1}{i}\right]$ (5)

Given A, to find P. $P = A\left[\dfrac{(1 + i)^n - 1}{i(1 + i)^n}\right]$ (6)

or $P = A\left[\dfrac{1}{\dfrac{i}{(1 + i)^n - 1} + i}\right]$ (6)

The following explanation of the formulas assumes the interest period as one year; the explanation can be made general by substituting "period" for "year."

Development of Formulas for Single Payments. If P is invested at interest rate i, the interest for the first year is iP and the total amount at the end of the first year is $P + iP = P(1 + i)$.

The second year the interest on this is $iP(1 + i)$, and the amount at the end of this year is $P(1 + i) + iP(1 + i) = P(1 + i)^2$. Similarly, at the end of the third year the amount is $P(1 + i)^3$; at the end of n years it is $P(1 + i)^n$.

This is the formula for the compound amount, F, obtainable in n years from a principal, P,

$$F = P(1 + i)^n \qquad (1)$$

If we express P in terms of F, i, and n,

$$P = F\left[\dfrac{1}{(1 + i)^n}\right] \qquad (2)$$

P may then be thought of as the principal that will give a required amount F in n years; in other words, P is the present worth of a payment of F, n years hence.

The expression $(1 + i)^n$ is called the *single payment compound amount factor*. Its reciprocal $1/(1 + i)^n$ is called the *single payment present worth factor.* Throughout this book, we shall occasionally abbreviate these terms to caf and pwf, respectively.

Development of Formulas for Uniform Annual Series of End-of-Year Payments. If A is invested at the end of each year for n years, the total amount at the end of n years will obviously be the sum of the compound amounts of the individual investments. The money invested at the end of the first year will earn interest for $(n-1)$ years; its amount will thus be $A(1+i)^{n-1}$. The second year's payment will amount to $A(1+i)^{n-2}$; the third year's to $A(1+i)^{n-3}$; and so on until the last payment, made at the end of n years, which has earned no interest. The total amount F is $A[1+(1+i)+(1+i)^2+(1+i)^3 \ldots +(1+i)^{n-1}]$.

This expression for F in terms of A may be simplified to its customary form by the following algebraic manipulations:

$$F = A[1 + (1+i) + (1+i)^2 \ldots + (1+i)^{n-2} + (1+i)^{n-1}]$$

Multiplying both sides of the equation by $(1+i)$,

$$(1+i)F = A[(1+i) + (1+i)^2 + (1+i)^3 \ldots + (1+i)^{n-1} + (1+i)^n]$$

Subtracting the original equation from this second equation

$$iF = A[(1+i)^n - 1]$$

Then

$$A = F\left[\frac{i}{(1+i)^n - 1}\right] \tag{3}$$

A fund established to produce a desired amount at the end of a given period of time by means of a series of payments throughout the period is called a *sinking fund*. The expression

$$\frac{i}{(1+i)^n - 1}$$

is called the *sinking fund factor.* Throughout this book, we shall occasionally abbreviate this to sff.

To find the uniform end-of-year payment, A, which can be secured for n years from a present investment, P (as in Plan III of Table 3–1), substitute in equation (3) the value given for F in equation (1):

$$A = F\left[\frac{i}{(1+i)^n - 1}\right] = P(1+i)^n\left[\frac{i}{(1+i)^n - 1}\right]$$

$$= P\left[\frac{i(1+i)^n}{(1+i)^n - 1}\right] \tag{4}$$

This may also be expressed as

$$A = P\left[\frac{i}{(1+i)^n - 1} + i\right] \tag{4}$$

This expression

$$\frac{i(1+i)^n}{(1+i)^n - 1}$$

is called the *capital recovery factor*. As shown by its identity with

$$\left[\frac{i}{(1+i)^n - 1} + i\right]$$

it is always equal to the sinking fund factor plus the interest rate. When multiplied by a present debt (which, from the point of view of the lender, is a present investment), it gives the uniform end-of-year payment necessary to repay the debt (the lender's investment) in n years with interest rate i. This factor, or an approximation to it, is used in the solution of many problems in engineering economy. We shall frequently abbreviate *capital recovery factor* to crf.

Formulas (3) and (4) may be reversed to show F and P in terms of A as follows:

$$F = A\left[\frac{(1+i)^n - 1}{i}\right] \tag{5}$$

$$P = A\left[\frac{(1+i)^n - 1}{i(1+i)^n}\right] \tag{6}$$

The expression

$$\left[\frac{(1+i)^n - 1}{i}\right]$$

is called the *uniform series compound amount factor*. This is usually abbreviated to *series compound amount factor*.

The expression

$$\left[\frac{(1+i)^n - 1}{i(1+i)^n}\right]$$

is called the *uniform series present worth factor*. Similarly, this is usually abbreviated to *series present worth factor*.

Functional Symbols. Throughout the later chapters of this book, many equations will be written using symbols that show the conversion to be made rather than the corresponding mathematical expressions involving i and n. These functional symbols are:

$(F/P,i\%,n)$ is the single payment compound amount factor

$$(1+i)^n$$

$(P/F,i\%,n)$ is the single payment present worth factor

$$\frac{1}{(1+i)^n}$$

$(A/F,i\%,n)$ is the sinking fund factor

$$\frac{i}{(1+i)^n - 1}$$

$(A/P,i\%,n)$ is the capital recovery factor

$$\frac{i(1+i)^n}{(1+i)^n - 1}$$

$(F/A,i\%,n)$ is the uniform series compound amount factor

$$\frac{(1+i)^n - 1}{i}$$

$(P/A,i\%,n)$ is the uniform series present worth factor

$$\frac{(1+i)^n - 1}{i(1+i)^n}$$

Interest Tables. The solution of problems in equivalence is greatly facilitated by the use of interest tables. Tables F–1 to F–25 in Appendix E give values of the single payment compound amount factor, single payment present worth factor, the sinking fund deposit factor, the capital recovery factor, the uniform series compound amount factor, and the uniform series present worth factor for each value of n from 1 to 35, and for values of n that are multiples of 5 from 40 to 100. Each interest rate has a separate table; the interest rates given are 1%, 1¼%, 1½%, 1¾%, 2%, 2½%, 3%, 3½%, 4%, 4½%, 5%, 5½%, 6%, 7%, 8%, 10%, 12%, 15%, 20%, 25%, 30%, 35%, 40%, 45%, and 50%.

If the payment given $(P, F, \text{ or } A)$ is unity (in any units desired, dollars, pounds, pesos, francs, etc.), the factor from the interest tables gives directly the payment to be found. Thus, the respective columns in each table might have been headed:

Compound amount of 1
Present worth of 1
Uniform series that amounts to 1
Uniform series that 1 will purchase
Compound amount of 1 per period
Present worth of 1 per period

Interest tables in books on the mathematics of investment commonly use these headings or some variations of them.

Relationship Between Interest Factors. In using the interest tables, it is desirable that the student be familiar with the simple relationships that exist between the different factors for a given value of i and n. The illustrations given all apply to $i = 0.06$ and $n = 5$. The factors have been rounded off to agree with the number of places in Table E–13, Appendix E.

Single payment compound amount factor and single payment present worth factor are reciprocals. Thus

$$\frac{1}{(F/P,6\%,5)} = (P/F,6\%,5) = \frac{1}{1.3382} = 0.7473$$

Sinking fund factor and uniform series compound amount factor are reciprocals. Thus

$$\frac{1}{(A/F,6\%,5)} = (F/A,6\%,5) = \frac{1}{0.17740} = 5.637$$

Capital recovery factor and series present worth factor are reciprocals. Thus

$$\frac{1}{(A/P,6\%,5)} = (P/A,6\%,5) = \frac{1}{0.23740} = 4.212$$

Series compound amount factor equals 1.000 plus sum of first $(n-1)$ terms in column of single payment compound amount factors. Thus

$$(F/A,6\%,5) = 1.000 + (F/P,6\%,1) + (F/P,6\%,2) + (F/P,6\%,3) + (F/P,6\%,4)$$

$$= 1.0000 + 1.0600 + 1.1236 + 1.1910 + 1.2625 = 5.6371$$

Series present worth factor equals sum of first n terms of single payment present worth factors. Thus

$$(P/A,6\%,5) = (P/F,6\%,1) + (P/F,6\%,2) + (P/F,6\%,3) + (P/F,6\%,4) + (P/F,6\%,5)$$

$$4.212 = 0.9434 + 0.8900 + 0.8396 + 0.7921 + 0.7473$$

Capital recovery factor equals sinking fund factor plus interest rate. Thus

$$(A/P,6\%,5) = (A/F,6\%,5) + i$$

$$0.23740 = 0.17740 + 0.06$$

Nominal and Effective Interest Rates. Many loan transactions stipulate that interest is computed and charged more often than once a year.

For example, interest on deposits in savings banks may be computed and added to the deposit balance four times a year; this is referred to as interest "compounded quarterly." Interest on corporate bond issues usually is payable every 6 months. Building and loan associations, automobile finance companies, and other organizations making personal loans often require that interest be computed monthly.

Consider a loan transaction in which interest is charged at 1% per month. Sometimes such a transaction is described as having an interest rate of 12% per annum. More precisely, this rate should be described as a *nominal* 12% per annum compounded monthly.

It is desirable to recognize that there is a real difference between 1% per month compounded monthly and 12% per annum compounded annually. Assume that $1,000 is borrowed with interest at 1% per month. Using Table E–1, the amount owed at the end of 12 months may be calculated as follows:

$$F = \$1,000(1.01)^{12}$$
$$= \$1,000(F/P,1\%,12)$$
$$= \$1,000(1.1268) = \$1,126.8$$

If the same $1,000 had been borrowed at 12% per annum compounded annually, the amount owed at the end of the year would have been only $1,120, $6.80 less than $1,126.8. The monthly compounding at 1% has the same effect on the year-end compound amount as the charging of a rate of 12.68% compounded annually. In the language of financial mathematics, the *effective* interest rate is 12.68%.

The phrases *nominal interest rate* and *effective interest rate* may be defined more precisely as follows:

Let interest be compounded m times a year at an interest rate $\dfrac{r}{m}$ per compounding period.

The nominal interest rate per annum $= m \left(\dfrac{r}{m} \right) = r.$

The effective interest rate per annum $= \left(1 + \dfrac{r}{m} \right)^{m} - 1.$

Nominal rates of interest for different numbers of annual compoundings are not comparable with one another until they have been converted into the corresponding effective rate. The more frequent the number of compoundings at a given nominal rate, the greater the difference between the effective and nominal rates. (For example, a nominal rate of 12% compounded semiannually yields an effective rate of 12.36% in contrast to the 12.68% for a nominal 12% compounded monthly.) The higher the nominal rate for a given m, the greater both the absolute and the relative difference between effective and nominal rates. (For example, a nominal rate of 24% compounded monthly yields an effective rate of 26.82%, 2.82% more than the nominal rate. In contrast, the effective rate is only 0.68% above the nominal rate with interest at a nominal 12% compounded monthly.)

In engineering economy studies it usually is preferable to deal with effective interest rates rather than nominal rates.

Continuous Compounding of Interest. The mathematical symbol e (the base of natural or "Napierian" logarithms) may be defined as the limit approached by the quantity $\left(1 + \dfrac{1}{k}\right)^k$ as k increases indefinitely. It is shown in textbooks on calculus that $e = 2.71828+$. The common logarithm of e is 0.43429.

If a sum P is invested for n years with a nominal interest rate r and with m compounding periods a year, the compound amount F may be expressed as follows:

$$F = P\left(1 + \frac{r}{m}\right)^{mn}$$

If we designate $\dfrac{m}{r}$ by the symbol k, $m = rk$, and

$$F = P\left(1 + \frac{1}{k}\right)^{rkn} = P\left[\left(1 + \frac{1}{k}\right)^k\right]^{rn}$$

As the number of compounding periods per year, m, increases without limit, so also must k. It follows that the bracketed quantity in the foregoing formula approaches the limit e. Therefore, the limiting value of F is Pe^{rn}.

With continuous compounding, the single payment compound amount factor is e^{rn}. The single payment present worth factor is, of course, e^{-rn}.

Although continuous compounding formulas assume that interest is computed and added to principal at every moment throughout the year, the results obtained using continuous compounding are very close to the results obtained using monthly compounding with a nominal rate r.

Application of Continuous Compounding in Engineering Economy. Although continuous compounding is rarely used in actual loan transactions, the topic is of importance in connection with certain problems of decision making. Two types of application are important.

In some economy studies it may be desired to recognize that certain receipts or disbursements will be spread throughout a year rather than concentrated at a particular date. Continuous compounding is well adapted to the assumption of a continuous flow of funds at a uniform rate throughout a stated period of time. Formulas and tables that may be used for this purpose are explained in Appendix A.

In the development of certain mathematical models intended as aids to decision making, the mathematical treatment is facilitated by the use of continuous compounding rather than periodic compounding.

Interest Tables for Uniform Gradient. Engineering economy problems frequently involve disbursements or receipts that increase or decrease each year by varying amounts. For example, the maintenance expense for a piece of mechanical equipment may tend to increase somewhat each year. If the increase or decrease is the same every year the yearly increase or decrease is known as a *uniform arithmetic gradient*. Even when it is reasonable to believe that the annual expenses or receipts will increase or decrease somewhat irregularly, a uniform gradient may be the best and most convenient way to estimate the changing condition.

Since the amount of money is different each year, the uniform series interest factors previously discussed cannot be used and each year's disbursement or receipt must be handled by means of the single payment factors. This time-consuming computation can be avoided by deriving simple formulas for the equivalent cost of a gradient and for the present worth of a gradient for n years.

Figure 4–1 gives the cash flow diagram for a uniform gradient. Using end-of-year payments, the payment the second year is greater than the first year by G, the third is G greater than the second year, and so on. Thus, the payments by years are as follows:

End of Year	Payment
1	0
2	G
3	$2G$
4	$3G$
. . . .	
$(n-1)$	$(n-2)G$
n	$(n-1)G$

These payments may be thought of as a set of payments that will accumulate to an amount F at the end of the nth year, and that amount can be converted to a uniform series of payments by multiplying F by the sinking fund factor. For convenience, it can be assumed that a series of annual payments of G is started at the end of the second year, another series of G is started at the end of the third year, and so on. Each of these series terminate at the same time, the end of the nth year. The

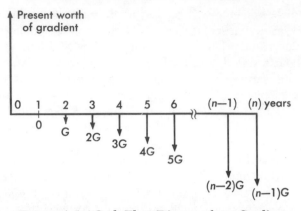

FIGURE 4–1. Cash Flow Diagram for a Gradient

series compound amount factor can be applied to each series of G per year to determine its compound amount on this terminal date:

Sum of compound amounts

$$= G\left[\frac{(1+i)^{n-1}-1}{i}+\frac{(1+i)^{n-2}-1}{i} \cdots +\frac{(1+i)^2-1}{i}+\frac{(1+i)-1}{i}\right]$$

$$= \frac{G}{i}\left[(1+i)^{n-1}+(1+i)^{n-2} \cdots +(1+i)^2+(1+i)-(n-1)\right]$$

$$= \frac{G}{i}\left[(1+i)^{n-1}+(1+i)^{n-2} \cdots +(1+i)^2+(1+i)+1\right]-\frac{nG}{i}$$

The expression in brackets is the compound amount of a sinking fund of 1 for n years. Hence

$$\text{Sum of compound amounts} = \frac{G}{i}\left[\frac{(1+i)^n-1}{i}\right]-\frac{nG}{i}$$

The equivalent uniform annual figure for n years may be found by multiplying this sum of the compound amounts by the sinking fund factor for n years. Hence

$$A = \frac{G}{i}\left[\frac{(1+i)^n-1}{i}\right]\left[\frac{i}{(1+i)^n-1}\right]-\frac{nG}{i}\left[\frac{i}{(1+i)^n-1}\right]$$

$$= \frac{G}{i}-\frac{nG}{i}\left[\frac{i}{(1+i)^n-1}\right]$$

This is a general expression applicable to any value of n. Values for the equivalent uniform annual cost of a uniform gradient of unity for interest rates of 1%, 2%, 3%, 4%, 5%, 6%, 7%, 8%, 10%, 12%, 15%, 20%, 25%, 30%,

35%, 40%, 45%, and 50%, and for n from 2 to 100 years are given in Table E–26, Appendix E. The use of these gradient factors will be illustrated in Chapter 5.

The factor to convert a gradient series to a present worth may be obtained by multiplying the factor to convert a gradient series to an equivalent uniform annual series by the series present worth factor for n years at interest i. The values of the gradient present worth factors are given in Table E–27 for the same interest rates as Table E–26 and for values of n from 1 to 50 years.

The functional symbols for the factors used in dealing with arithmetic gradients are:

$(A/G,i\%,n)$ = factor to convert a gradient series to an equivalent uniform annual series.

$(P/G,i\%,n)$ = factor to convert a gradient series to a present worth.

The relationship between these two factors can be shown as:

$$(P/G,i\%,n) = (A/G,i\%,n)(P/A,i\%,n)$$

Finding Unknown Interest Rates. Frequently, the sum to be invested (or loaned) is known, and the prospective future series of money receipts (or plan of repayment) is known, and it is desired to find the interest rate that will be earned on the investment.

When a single payment and a single receipt are involved, when n is known and i is wanted, the problem is quite simple. Formula (1) becomes

$$i = \sqrt[n]{\frac{F}{P}} - 1 \tag{7}$$

This may be solved by logarithms.

When a single payment and a uniform series are involved, the problem becomes more complicated to solve directly. When nonuniform payments or receipts are involved, the only reasonable method of solution is by interpolation. The use of the interest tables in Appendix E makes the solution of unknown interest problems relatively simple by the interpolation method. Approximate methods using interpolation are recommended for engineering economy studies and are illustrated and explained in Chapters 5 and 8.

Interest Formulas and Tables in Relation to Engineering Economy. "Will it pay?" (which is the central question of engineering economy) usually means "Will an investment pay?" An investment will not pay unless it can ultimately be repaid with interest. Thus interest enters into most problems in engineering economy.

But the engineer's decision as to whether a proposed investment will pay must be based on estimates rather than on a certain knowledge of the future. Even the most careful estimates are likely to go wrong; frequently, also, engineers' decisions regarding economy must be based on preliminary estimates made in advance of design that necessarily have a considerable danger of large errors.

For this reason great precision is not usually required in interest calculations made for economy studies. For instance, where cost estimates are subject to errors of 5% or 10%, there is no justification for carrying out interest calculations to seven significant figures, as is sometimes done. Interest tables giving three significant figures are adequate for purposes of most economy studies; in many cases slide-rule calculations are entirely satisfactory. Similarly, the difference between paying interest once a year and paying it more often (i.e., the difference between compounding annually and compounding semiannually, quarterly, or monthly—a difference of considerable importance to the financier) is usually neglected in economy studies; the interest rate used in economy studies will frequently be considerably higher than the cost of borrowed money for a number of reasons that are explained in Chapter 11.

PROBLEMS

4–1. Develop a formula for the *beginning-of-period* payment, T, into a sinking fund to amount to F at the end of n periods with interest at i per cent per period.

4–2. How could you determine a desired *uniform series compound amount factor*, if you had only

(a) a table of *single payment compound amount factors?*
(b) a table of *sinking fund deposit factors?*
(c) a table of *capital recovery factors?*
(d) a table of *uniform series present worth factors?*

Illustrate your solution using the 8% table, Table E–15, to obtain the factor for 12 years.

4–3. How would you determine a desired *capital recovery factor*, if you had only

(a) a table of *single payment compound amount factors?*
(b) a table of *single payment present worth factors?*
(c) a table of *sinking fund factors?*
(d) a table of *uniform series compound amount factors?*
(e) a table of *uniform series present worth factors?*

Illustrate from the 5% table, Table E–11, showing how you would obtain the desired factor for 10 years.

4-4. What effective interest rate per annum corresponds to a nominal rate of 18% compounded semiannually? Compounded quarterly? Compounded monthly?

4-5. What effective interest rate per annum corresponds to a nominal rate of 15% compounded monthly?

4-6. The interest rate charged by various banks that operate credit card systems is 1½% per month. What nominal and effective rates per annum correspond to this?

5

Solving Interest Problems

> The mere accumulation of savings . . . does not necessarily lead to
> technological progress. There must also be investment of savings
> in capital facilities, either directly by purchase of capital facilities,
> or through purchase of the securities of business representing capi-
> tal facilities. But the investment of savings under the private enter-
> prise system will occur in adequate volume only when there is
> adequate prospect of profit therefrom.
> —MACHINERY AND ALLIED PRODUCTS INSTITUTE [1]

This chapter illustrates the use of interest tables and formulas in the
solution of practical problems related to economy. Each illustrative
example is numbered for convenient reference.

Many of the illustrative examples are stated in several different ways.
It is desirable that the student of engineering economy recognize the
variety of questions that may be answered by the same equivalence
calculation.

In solving any interest problem, it is necessary to note which of the
various elements of such problems (i, n, P, F, and A) are known and
which are wanted. This is the first step in any solution and follows
immediately after the problem statement in each illustrative example.

Unless otherwise stated, it is to be assumed in the following examples
that interest is payable (or compounded) annually.

**Examples Illustrating the Use of the Interest Factors Relative to
Time.** The concept of equivalence was introduced in Chapter 3, and
Table 3–1 gave four plans for the repayment of a loan with interest. All
these plans were equivalent to each other. Examples 5–1 through 5–7
illustrate the use of the interest factors to compute equivalence in terms
of both single payments and series of payments over different periods of
time. An initial amount of $1,000 is assumed on January 1, 1971, and is
converted to equivalent amounts at different times, and finally, the
original $1,000 is obtained by converting a series to a single amount as

[1] *Capital Goods and the American Enterprise System,* Machinery and Allied Products Institute, 1939, p. 42.

of January 1, 1971. These examples show that "now" or zero time can be assumed at any date, and an equivalent amount or a series of amounts can be obtained for dates either preceding or following the assumed zero time. The cash flow diagrams for Examples 5–1 through 5–7 are shown in Figure 5–1.

EXAMPLE 5–1

If $1,000 is invested at 6% compounded interest on January 1, 1971, how much will be accumulated by January 1, 1981?   (Figure 5–1a.)

Solution:

$$i = 0.06; n = 10; P = \$1,000; F =?$$
$$F = P(F/P,6\%,10)$$
$$= \$1,000(1.7908) = \$1,791$$

EXAMPLE 5–2

How much would you have to invest at 6% interest on January 1, 1975, in order to accumulate $1,791 on January 1, 1981?   (Figure 5–1b.)

Solution:

$$i - 0.06; n = 6; F = \$1,791; P = ?$$

In this case zero time is assumed to be January 1, 1975.

$$P = F(P/F,6\%,6) = \$1,791(0.7050)$$
$$- \$1,263$$

EXAMPLE 5–3

What is the present worth on January 1, 1968, of $1,263 on January 1, 1975, if interest is at 6%?   (Figure 5–1c.)

Solution:

$$i = 0.06; n = 7; F = \$1,263; P = ?$$
$$P = F(P/F,6\%,7) = \$1,263(0.6651)$$
$$= \$840.0$$

EXAMPLE 5–4

If $840.0 is invested at 6% on January 1, 1968, what equal year-end withdrawals can be made each year for 10 years, leaving nothing in the fund after the tenth withdrawal?   (Figure 5–1d.)

Solution:

$$i = 0.06; n = 10; P = \$840.0; A = ?$$

Now zero time is January 1, 1968.

$$A = P(A/P,6\%,10) = \$840.0(0.13587)$$
$$= \$114.1$$

EXAMPLE 5–5

How much will be accumulated in a fund, earning 6% interest, at the end of 10 years if $114.1 is deposited at the end of each year for 10 years, beginning in 1968? (Figure 5–1e.)

Solution:

$$i = 0.06; n = 10; A = \$114.1; F = ?$$
$$F = A(F/A,6\%,10) = \$114.1(13.181)$$
$$= \$1,504$$

EXAMPLE 5–6

How much must be deposited at 6% each year for 7 years beginning on January 1, 1972 in order to accumulate $1,504 on the date of the last deposit, January 1, 1978? (Figure 5–1f.)

Solution:

$$i = 0.06; n = 7; F = \$1,504; A = ?$$
$$A = F(A/F,6\%,7) = \$1,504(0.11914)$$
$$= \$179.2$$

EXAMPLE 5–7

How much would you need to deposit at 6% on January 1, 1971 in order to draw out $179.2 at the end of each year for 7 years, leaving nothing in the fund at the end? (Figure 5–1g.)

Solution:

$$i = 0.06; n = 7; A = \$179.2; P = ?$$
$$P = A(P/A,6\%,7) = \$179.2(5.582)$$
$$= \$1,000$$

Note that the final date of January 1, 1971, is the same as zero date for this series of seven examples. The final figure of $1,000 is the same as the initial figure. All multiplications have been carried to only four significant figures because some of the interest factors used in the series of examples have only this number of significant figures.

Comments on Examples 5–1 Through 5–7. These examples illustrate several important points. First, in each simple problem four of the five elements i, n, P, F, and A are present and three of the four elements must be known. In these examples i, n, and one other element were always known. In solving the problem, the known elements are first identified and the unknown or desired element is specified. Then the unknown element is equated to the proper interest factor times the known monetary amount. (If i or n is unknown, then the value of the interest

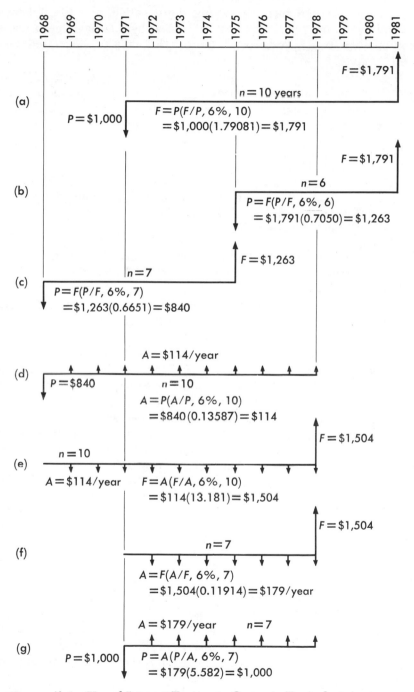

FIGURE 5–1. Use of Interest Factors to Compute Equivalent Amounts and Equivalent Series

factor must be determined by solving the equation, and the unknown is found by referring to the interest tables and by interpolating, if necessary, between two factors found there. This will be illustrated later in this chapter.)

Next, these examples demonstrate that, with a given interest rate, equivalent single amounts or series of amounts can be found at many different relative times. Thus, all of the following are equivalent to $1,000 now, assuming that "now" is January 1, 1971:

$1,791 10 years hence
$1,263 4 years hence
$840.0 3 years previously
$114.1 a year (year-end payments) for 10 years beginning 3 years ago
$1,504 7 years hence
$179.2 a year for the next 7 years

Since these amounts or series of amounts are all equivalent to $1,000 now, they must be equivalent to each other. The difference in the timing of the payments or receipts is the significant element in these computations, and it is very important to determine precisely the n for each problem. Dates have been used for these examples, but the n was determined in the solution of each example. Normally it is more convenient to select the starting point in time, calling it date zero or year zero, and to determine the number of years from that selected time. Thus, in Example 5–2, the desired quantity was that necessary investment in 1975 to obtain $1,791 in 1981, and 1975 became a convenient starting point for the example. Year zero is 1975 and 1981 is 6.

Another point that is emphasized in Examples 5–4 through 5–7 is that conventional interest tables and formulas are based upon uniform payments made at the *end* of each period (not at the beginning of the period). The only time this convention may become confusing occurs when one is converting from the compound amount, F, to uniform periodic payments or vice versa. The confusion arises from the fact that the date of the compound amount is the same date as the last of the uniform series of payments or receipts. Practice in using the interest tables will soon eliminate this source of possible confusion.

Examples Involving Conversion of Single Payments at One Date to Equivalent Single Payments at Another Date. Examples of this type involve i, n, P, and F, and any one of these four elements may be unknown. Examples 5–1, 5–2, and 5–3 were of this type, with either P or F unknown. The following examples illustrate other aspects of such problems.

EXAMPLE 5–8

If $2,000 is invested now, $1,500 2 years hence, and $1,000 4 years hence, all at 4%, what will the total amount be 10 years hence?

or

What is the compound amount of $2,000 for 10 years plus $1,500 for 8 years plus $1,000 for 6 years with interest at 4%?

or

What must be the prospective saving 10 years hence in order to justify spending $2,000 now, $1,500 in 2 years, and $1,000 in 4 years, if money is worth 4%?

Solution: It is evident from the cash flow diagram (Figure 5–2a) that this requires three separate calculations: in the first the "present" is now; in the second it is two years hence; in the third it is 4 years hence:

$$i = 0.04; \begin{cases} n_1 = 10; \ P_1 = \$2,000 \\ n_2 = \ \ 8; \ P_2 = \$1,500 \\ n_3 = \ \ 6; \ P_3 = \$1,000 \end{cases}; \ \Sigma F = F_1 + F_2 + F_3 = ?$$

$$F_1 = P_1(F/P,4\%,10) = \$2,000(1.4802) = \$2,960$$
$$F_2 = P_2(F/P,4\%,8) \ = \$1,500(1.3686) = \$2,053$$
$$F_3 = P_3(F/P,4\%,6) \ = \$1,000(1.2653) = \underline{\$1,265}$$
$$\Sigma F = \qquad\qquad\qquad\qquad\qquad\qquad \$6,278$$

EXAMPLE 5–9

What is the compound amount of $3,500 for 18 years with interest at 4.25%?

Solution:

$$i = 0.0425; \ n = 18; \ P = \$3,500; \ F = ?$$
$$F = P(F/P,4.25\%,18) = \$3,500(1.0425)^{18}$$

As the tables do not give compound amount factors for 4.25%, the problem must be solved by logarithms:

Log 1.0425 = 0.018076	18 Log 1.0425 = 0.32537
	Log 3,500 = 3.54407
	Log F = 3.86944
	F = \$7,404

An approximate solution may be obtained by linear interpolation between the compound amount factors for 4% and 4½% as follows:

$$(1.04)^{18} = 2.0258; \ (1.045)^{18} = 2.2085$$

Approximate value of

$$(1.0425)^{18} = 2.0258 + \frac{25}{50}(2.2085 - 2.0258) = 2.1172$$

$$\text{Approximate } F = \$3,500(2.1172) = \$7,410$$

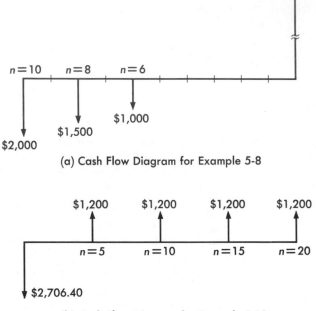

(a) Cash Flow Diagram for Example 5-8

(b) Cash Flow Diagram for Example 5-12

FIGURE 5–2.   Cash Flow Diagrams for Examples 5–8 and 5–12

This particular approximation involves an error of less than one-tenth of 1%. The per cent of error involved in such interpolations increases with an increase in n, and is greater with higher interest rates.

EXAMPLE 5–10

What is the compound amount of $400 for 8 years with interest at 6% compounded semiannually?

Solution: Here the rate per interest period is 6% ÷ 2 = 3%; the number of periods is $8(2) = 16$:

$$i = 0.03; \; n = 16; \; P = \$400; \; F = ?$$
$$F = P(F/P,3\%,16)$$
$$= \$400(1.6047) = \$641.9$$

EXAMPLE 5–11

What is the compound amount of $1,000 for 64 years with interest at 4%?

Solution:

$$i = 0.04; \; n = 64; \; P = \$1,000; \; F = ?$$

By noting that the compound amount factor for 64 years, which is not given in our tables, is the product of the respective factors for 60 years and 4 years, this can be solved without recourse to logarithms:

$$F = P(F/P,4\%,60)(F/P,4\%,4)$$
$$= \$1,000(10.5196)(1.1699) = \$12,307$$

EXAMPLE 5–12

How much invested now at 5% would be just sufficient to provide $1,200 5 years hence, $1,200 10 years hence, $1,200 15 years hence, and $1,200 20 years hence?

or

What is the present worth of $1,200 at the end of each 5 years for the next 20 years if interest is at 5%?

or

What present loan at 5% would be completely paid back by payments of $1,200 at the end of 5, 10, 15, and 20 years?

or

What payment now is acceptable in place of prospective payments of $1,200 at the end of 5, 10, 15, and 20 years, if interest is at 5%?

or

How much is it justifiable to spend now in order to save prospective expenditures of $1,200 at the end of 5, 10, 15, and 20 years if money is worth 5%?

Solution: This cash flow series is shown in Figure 5–2b.

$$i = 0.05; \begin{cases} n_1 = 5; F_1 = \$1,200 \\ n_2 = 10; F_2 = 1,200 \\ n_3 = 15; F_3 = 1,200 \\ n_4 = 20; F_4 = 1,200 \end{cases} ; \Sigma P = P_1 + P_2 + P_3 + P_4 = ?$$

$$P_1 = F_1(P/F,5\%,5) \ \ = \$1,200(0.7835) = \$ \ \ 940.20$$
$$P_2 = F_2(P/F,5\%,10) = \ \ 1,200(0.6139) = \ \ \ \ 736.70$$
$$P_3 = F_3(P/F,5\%,15) = \ \ 1,200(0.4810) = \ \ \ \ 577.20$$
$$P_4 = F_4(P/F,5\%,20) = \ \ 1,200(0.3769) = \ \ \ \ 452.30$$
$$\Sigma P = \$2,706.40$$

EXAMPLE 5–13

In how many years will an investment of $1,000 now, increase to $2,000 with interest at 3%?

or

How long will it take for money to double itself with interest at 3%?

or

Within how many years must a prospective expenditure of $2,000 be required in order to justify spending $1,000 now to prevent it, if money is worth 3%?

Solution:

$$i = 0.03; \ P = \$1{,}000; \ F = \$2{,}000; \ n = ?$$

$$(F/P,3\%,n) = \frac{F}{P} = \frac{\$2{,}000}{\$1{,}000} = 2.000$$

The value of n can be determined by examining the compound amount factors, single payment, in the 3% table, and interpolating between the next higher and next lower values:

$$n = 23, \ (F/P,3\%,23) = 1.9736$$

$$n = 24, \ (F/P,3\%,24) = 2.0328$$

Therefore

$$n = \text{approximately } 23\tfrac{1}{2} \text{ years}$$

EXAMPLE 5–14

A savings certificate costing $80 now will pay $100 in 5 years. What is the interest rate?

or

At what interest rate will $80 accumulate to $100 in 5 years?

or

Spending $80 now to avoid spending $100 5 years hence is, in effect, securing what interest rate?

Solution:

$$n = 5; \ P = \$80; \ F = \$100; \ i = ?$$

$$(F/P,i\%,5) = \frac{F}{P} = \frac{\$100}{\$80} = 1.2500$$

By interpolation between the next higher and the next lower single payment compound amount factor for 5 years in the interest tables, the approximate interest rate can be determined:

$$i = 0.045, \ (F/P,4.5\%,5) = 1.2462$$

$$i = 0.050, \ (F/P,5\%,5) \quad = 1.2763$$

$$i = 0.045 + 0.005 \ \frac{1.2500 - 1.2462}{1.2763 - 1.2462}$$

$$= 0.0456 \text{ or } 4.56\%$$

A more exact solution may be obtained by using logarithms to solve for the value of i in formula (7), of Chapter 4.

$$i = \sqrt[n]{\frac{F}{P}} - 1 = \sqrt[5]{\frac{100}{80}} - 1 = \sqrt[5]{1.25} - 1$$

$$\text{Log } \sqrt[5]{1.25} = \frac{\text{Log } 1.25}{5} = \frac{0.096910}{5} = 0.019382$$

$$\sqrt[5]{1.25} = 1.04564$$

$$i = 1.04564 - 1.0 = 0.04564 \text{ or } 4.564\%$$

Examples Involving Conversions to or from Uniform Series of Payments. The general technique for solving a problem involving a uniform series is similar to the technique used in the previous examples. The four elements of such problems are either i, n, A, and P or i, n, A, and F. Note whether it is P or F that enters into the given problem; note which three elements are known and their values. If the unknown, the value of which is desired, is A, P, or F, and the given values of i and n are values for which factors are available in the tables, use the interest tables. Otherwise, solve by interpolation. If i or n is the unknown, an exact solution is seldom possible, and interpolation is employed to obtain an approximate solution. For engineering economy purposes, the errors introduced by straight-line interpolation are usually acceptable, and the solutions obtained thereby are adequate for the decision-making function.

EXAMPLE 5–15

How much must be invested at the end of each year for 30 years in a sinking fund which is to amount to $200,000 at the end of 30 years, if interest is at 4%?

or

What annual investment must be made at 4% to replace a $200,000 structure 30 years hence?

or

What uniform annual expenditure for 30 years is justifiable in order to avoid having to spend $200,000 30 years hence, if money is worth 4%?

Solution:

$$i = 0.04; \; n = 30; \; F = \$200,000; \; A = ?$$
$$A = F(A/F, 4\%, 30)$$
$$= \$200,000(0.01783) = \$3,566$$

EXAMPLE 5–16

How much would be accumulated in the sinking fund of Example 5–15 at the end of 18 years?

or

If $3,566 is invested at the end of each year for 18 years with interest at 4%, how much will have accumulated at the end of that time?

or

What must be the prospective saving 18 years hence in order to justify spending $3,566 a year for 18 years, if money is worth 4%?

Solution:

$$i = 0.04; \; n = 18; \; A = \$3,566; \; F = ?$$
$$F = A(F/A, 4\%, 18)$$
$$= \$3,566(25.645) = \$91,450$$

EXAMPLE 5–17 [2]

What annual year-end payment for 10 years is necessary to repay a present loan of $10,000 if interest is at 6%?

or

With interest at 6%, what uniform annual end-of-year payment for 10 years is equivalent to $10,000 now?

or

What 10-year annuity can be purchased for $10,000 if interest is at 6%?

or

If $10,000 is deposited now with interest at 6%, what uniform amount A could be withdrawn at the end of each year for 10 years and have nothing left at the end of the 10th year?

or

What is the annual cost of capital recovery of $10,000 in 10 years with interest at 6%?

or

What is the annual payment for 10 years the present worth of which is $10,000 if interest is at 6%?

or

What annual saving for 10 years must be anticipated to justify an additional present expenditure of $10,000 if money is worth 6%?

Solution:

$$i = 0.06; \ n = 10; \ P = \$10,000; \ A = ?$$
$$A = P(A/P,6\%,10)$$
$$= \$10,000(0.13587) = \$1,358.70$$

(The reader will recognize this as the annual repayment used—without explanation of where the figure came from—in Plan III of Table 3–1 in Chapter 3.)

EXAMPLE 5–18

In the loan described in Example 5–17, how much would be owed after the fourth payment had been made?

or

What is the present worth of $1,358.70 a year for 6 years with interest at 6%?

or

What present investment must be made at 6% to secure $1,358.70 a year for 6 years?

or

[2] The type of calculation called for in this illustrative example is the most common one used in dealing with the time value of money in economy studies. The reader should examine carefully the different ways in which questions requiring this calculation are phrased.

What present investment is justified in order to make a prospective saving of $1,358.70 a year for 6 years if money is worth 6%?

Solution:

$$i = 0.06; \ n = 6; \ A = \$1,358.70; \ P = ?$$
$$P = A(P/A,6\%,6)$$
$$= \$1,358.70(4.917) = \$6,681$$

(The answer to this problem as phrased in the first of the four statements of the question may also be calculated more exactly and more laboriously by the method of Table 3–1. The answer obtained by a calculation from the interest table should not be expressed to more than the four significant figures given in the table. Thus the $6,681 calculated above corresponds to the figure of $6,681.07 given in Table 3–1.)

EXAMPLE 5–19

A present investment of $50,000 is expected to yield receipts of $7,000 a year for 15 years. What is the approximate rate of return that will be obtained on this investment?

Solution:

$$n = 15; \ P = \$50,000; \ A = \$7,000; \ i = ?$$
$$A = P(A/P,i\%, 15)$$
$$(A/P,i\%,15) = \frac{A}{P} = \frac{\$7,000}{\$50,000} = 0.1400$$

This can be solved approximately by interpolation in the interest tables for capital recovery factors:

$$\text{For } i = 10\%, \ (A/P,10\%,15) = 0.13147$$
$$i = 12\%, \ (A/P,12\%,15) = 0.14682$$

By interpolation,

$$i = 0.10 + \left[\frac{0.1400 - 0.13147}{0.14682 - 0.13147} \right] 0.02$$
$$= 0.111 \text{ or } 11.1\%$$

EXAMPLE 5–20

On the day a baby boy was born, his father decided to establish a fund for his college education by depositing a certain amount in a fund on each of his birthdays from the first through the 18th, so that the son can withdraw $2,000 on his 18th, 19th, 20th, and 21st birthdays. If the fund earns 4% per year, how much must the annual deposit be?

Solution: This example will be used to show how the same problem can be solved several different ways. The answers will be the same in all cases except for the slight errors that result from using the five-digit interest tables. Figure 5–3 shows the cash flow diagram for this example. Note that the last deposit is made on the date of the first withdrawal.

$$i = 0.04; \ n_1 = 18; \ A_1 = ?$$
$$n_2 = 4; \ A_2 = \$2,000$$

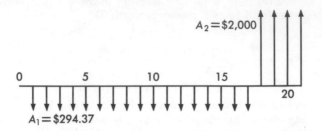

FIGURE 5–3. Cash Flow Diagram for Example 5–20

Method 1: Find the present worth of four single withdrawals at zero date. Multiply that sum by the capital recovery factor for $n = 18$ to obtain the annual deposit, A_1.

$$A_1 = \$2,000[(P/F,4\%,21) + (P/F,4\%,20) + (P/F,4\%,19) \\ + (P/F,4\%,18)](A/P,4\%,18)$$
$$= \$2,000(0.4388 + 0.4564 + 0.4746 + 0.4936)(0.07899)$$
$$= \$294.38$$

Method 2: Find the present worth at year 18 of the four withdrawals. Find the annual deposit for 18 years to accumulate that sum.

$$A_1 = [\$2,000 + \$2,000(P/A,4\%,3)](A/F,4\%,18)$$
$$= [\$2,000 + \$2,000(2.775)](0.03899) = \$294.37$$

Method 3: Find the compound amount of the uniform series of $2,000 for four years at date 21, and then convert to the present worth at date zero. Multiply by the capital recovery factor.

$$A_1 = \$2,000(F/A,4\%,4)(P/F,4\%,21)(A/P,4\%,18)$$
$$= \$2,000(4.246)(0.4388)(0.07899) = \$294.37$$

EXAMPLE 5–21

How much can one afford to spend each year for 15 years to avoid spending $1,000 at zero date, $1,500 after 5 years, and $2,000 after 10 years, if money is worth 8%?

or

What is the equivalent uniform annual cost for 15 years of disbursements of $1,000 at once, $1,500 5 years hence, and $2,000 10 years hence if interest is at 8%?

Solution: The first step in solving problems of this type is to convert all disbursements either to present worth at zero date or compound amount at the final date. Then the present worth or compound amount can be converted into an equivalent uniform annual series A.

$$i = 8\%; \begin{cases} n_1 = \ 0; P_1 = \$1,000; \\ n_2 = \ 5; P_2 = \$1,500; \\ n_3 = 10; P_3 = \$2,000; \\ n_4 = 15; \end{cases} A = ?$$

Method 1:

$A = [\$1,000 + \$1,500(P/F,8\%,5) + \$2,000(P/F,8\%,10)](A/P,8\%,15)$

$= [\$1,000 + \$1,500(0.6806) + \$2,000(0.4632)](0.11683) = \$344.33$

Method 2:

$A = [\$1,000(F/P,8\%,15) + \$1,500(F/P,8\%,10) + \$2,000(F/P,8\%,5)](A/F,8\%,15)$

$= [\$1,000(3.1722) + \$1,500(2.1589) + \$2,000(1.4693)](0.03683)$

$= \$344.33$

Illustration of the Use of Gradient Factors. Just as in other compound interest problems, a first step in solving problems involving arithmetic gradients is to identify what is known and what is wanted. Usually *i*, *n*, and *G* are known. The unknown element in the problem may be either *A* or *P* depending on whether it is desired to find an equivalent uniform annual series or the present worth of the gradient series. The appropriate factor from Table E–26 or Table E–27 for the given *i* and *n* is multiplied by the gradient *G*.

EXAMPLE 5–22

A piece of construction equipment will cost $6,000 new and will have an expected life of 6 years, with no salvage value at the end of its life. The disbursements for taxes, insurance, maintenance, fuels, and lubricants are estimated to be $1,500 the first year, $1,700 the second, $1,900 the third, and to continue to increase by $200 each year thereafter.

What is the equivalent uniform annual cost of this piece of equipment if the rate of interest is 12%?

Solution: This example is representative of many engineering economy problems because it involves several different patterns of disbursement. All disbursements should be converted to their respective equivalent uniform annual amounts and added together.

$$i = 0.12; n = 6; \begin{cases} P = \$6,000; A_1 = ? \\ \quad\quad\quad A_2 = \$1,500 \\ G = \quad \$200; A_3 = ? \end{cases}$$

$\Sigma A = A_1 + A_2 + A_3$

$A_1 = \$6,000(A/P,12\%,6) = \$6,000(0.24323) = \$1,459$

$A_2 = \$1,500$

(The problem stated that the annual disbursements would be $1,500 plus a gradient of $200 per year. The $1,500 portion requires no conversion because it is already a uniform annual figure.)

$A_3 = G(A/G,12\%,6) = \$200(2.17) = \$434$

$\Sigma A = \$1,459 + \$1,500 + \$434 = \$3,393$

EXAMPLE 5–23

What is the present worth at 12% of the disbursements described in Example 5–22?

Solution: The initial cost of the equipment is already at zero date. However, the annual outlays must be reduced to their present worths.

$$i = 0.12; n = 6; \begin{cases} P_1 = \$6,000 \\ A_2 = \$1,500; P_2 = ? \\ G = \quad \$200; P_3 = ? \end{cases}$$

$$\Sigma P = P_1 + P_2 + P_3$$

$$P_2 = A(P/A,12\%,6) = \$1,500(4.111) = \$6,166$$

$$P_3 = G(P/G,12\%,6) = \$200(8.9302) = \$1,786$$

$$\Sigma P = \$6,000 + \$6,166 + \$1,786 = \$13,952$$

Comments on Examples 5–22 and 5–23. Having obtained the equivalent annual cost in Example 5–22, the present worth could have been found by multiplying that amount by the series present worth factor, or, having found the present worth in Example 5–23, the equivalent annual cost could have been found by multiplying the present worth by the capital recovery factor. Thus,

$$A = P(A/P,12\%,6) = \$13,952(0.24323) = \$3,394$$

The slight difference in the final results is due to the rounding off of the factors in both the gradient and regular interest tables.

EXAMPLE 5–24

A bank offers the following personal loan plan called "The Seven Per Cent Plan."

The bank adds 7% to the amount borrowed; the borrower pays back one-twelfth of this total at the end of each month for a year. On a loan of $1,000, the monthly payment is $1,070/12 = $89.17.

What is the true interest rate per month? What are the nominal and effective rates per annum?

Solution:

$$n = 12; P = \$1,000; A = \$89.17; i = ?$$

$$A = P(A/P,i\%,n)$$

Solve by interpolation.

$$(A/P,i\%,12) = \frac{A}{P} = \frac{\$89.17}{\$1,000} = 0.08917$$

Try $i = 0.01$

$$(A/P,1\%,12) = 0.08885$$

Try $i = 0.0125$

$$(A/P,1.25\%,12) = 0.09026$$

Interpolating,

$$i = 0.01 + \left(\frac{0.08917 - 0.08885}{0.09026 - 0.08885}\right)(0.0025)$$

$$= 0.01 + \left(\frac{0.00032}{0.00141}\right)(0.0025)$$

$$= 0.01 + 0.00057 = 0.01057 \text{ or } 1.057\%$$

The *nominal interest rate per annum* corresponding to this monthly rate is:
$$12(0.01057) = 0.1268 \text{ or } 12.68\%$$
The *effective interest rate per annum* corresponding to this monthly rate is:
$$(1.01057)^{12} - 1 = 0.1345 \text{ or } 13.45\%$$

Deferred Annuities. Frequently it is necessary to deal with a series of uniform annual payments or receipts that begin sometime in the future and continue for some number of years. Such a deferred series of uniform annual payments or receipts is known as a *deferred annuity*. It may be desired to convert a deferred annuity to a present worth, to an equivalent annual series over some different period of years, or to a compound amount at some future time. Two methods of solving such a problem are illustrated in Example 5–25.

EXAMPLE 5–25

How much could you afford to spend each year for the next 6 years to avoid spending $500 a year for 10 years, beginning 5 years hence, if money is worth 8%?

or

What is the equivalent annual cost over the period of the next 6 years of spending $500 a year for 10 years beginning 5 years hence, if interest is at 8% per annum?

Solution:

$$i = 0.08; \ n_1 = 6; \ A_1 = ?$$
$$n_2 = 10; \ A_2 = \$500$$
$$n_3 = 5;$$

Method 1: Subtract uniform series present worth factor for 4 years from uniform series present worth factor for 14 years and multiply by the capital recovery factor for 6 years.

$$A_1 = \$500[(P/A,8\%,14) - (P/A,8\%,4)](A/P,8\%,6)$$
$$= 500(8.244 - 3.312)(0.21632)$$
$$= 500(4.932)(0.21632) = \$533.40$$

Method 2: Multiply the uniform series present worth factor for 10 years by the single payment present worth factor for 4 years and multiply that by the capital recovery factor for 6 years.

$$R_1 = \$500(P/A,8\%,10)(P/F,8\%,4)(A/P,8\%,6)$$
$$= 500(6.710)(0.7350)(0.21632)$$
$$= \$533.40$$

Summary. The general technique for solving a problem in compound interest equivalence is to determine first which elements of the problem are known and which element is unknown. If the problem is one to which available interest tables apply, it will usually be most convenient to use them in its solution. Otherwise, it is necessary to substitute the known elements of the problem in the appropriate interest formula, and to solve for the unknown one.

PROBLEMS

5–1. Solve the following, assuming interest at 4% compounded annually:

(a) $100 at the end of each year for 13 years will repay a present debt of how much? (*Ans.* = $998.60.)

(b) A payment of how much now is acceptable in place of a payment of $1,500 18 years hence? (*Ans.* = $740.)

(c) A present investment of $10,000 will secure a perpetual income of how much a year? (*Ans.* = $400.)

(d) An annual end-of-year investment of how much is required to provide $22,000 at the end of 30 years? (*Ans.* = $392.30.)

(e) The present worth of $5,000 37 years hence is how much? (*Ans.* = $1,171.)

5–2. Solve the following with interest at 6% compounded annually:

(a) If $2,500 is deposited now, what uniform amount could be withdrawn at the end of each year for 15 years and have nothing left at the end of the 15th year? (*Ans.* = $257.40.)

(b) What present investment is necessary to secure a perpetual income of $1,000 a year? (*Ans.* = $16,667.)

(c) How much will be accumulated in a fund at the end of 25 years if $2,000 is invested now? (*Ans.* = $8,583.8.)

(d) What annual saving for 20 years must be expected to justify a present expenditure of $5,000? (*Ans.* = $435.90.)

5–3. On January 1, 1970, $100 is deposited in a fund drawing 4% interest compounded annually. Another $100 is to be deposited on each January 1 up to and including January 1, 1980. The purpose of the fund is to provide a series of uniform annual withdrawals starting January 1, 1985. The final withdrawal on January 1, 1990, will exhaust the fund. How much can be withdrawn each year during the period 1985–90? (*Ans.* = $301.)

5–4. (a) A man is to receive an annuity of $1,000 a year for 15 years, the first payment being made on March 1, 1981. He offers to sell the annuity on March 1, 1978. With interest at 3½% compounded annually, what is a fair price? (*Ans.* = $10,751.)

(b) Black borrows $10,000 at 6% compounded semiannually, agreeing to repay it in 30 equal semiannual payments. How much of the principal of the loan is still unpaid immediately after he has made the 8th payment? (*Ans.* = $8,131.)

5–5. (a) A proposed product modification to avoid production difficulties will require an immediate expenditure of $14,000 to modify certain dies. What annual savings must be realized to recover this expenditure in 4 years with interest at 10% (*Ans.* = $4,416.)

(b) What must be the prospective saving in money 6 years hence to justify a present investment of $2,250? Use interest at 7% compounded annually. (*Ans.* = $3,377.)

(c) What extra semiannual expenditure for 5 years would be justified for the maintenance of a machine in order to avoid an overhaul costing $3,000 at the end of that period? Assume interest at 8% compounded semiannually. (*Ans.* = $250.)

(d) What present expenditure would be justified by the prospect of an annual saving of $500 a year for 12 years? Assume interest at 15%. (*Ans.* = $2,710.)

5–6. Using interest tables and interpolation as far as possible, determine the approximate rates of interest indicated by the following valuations for prospective series of future payments:

    (a) $2,000 for $160 a year for 15 years (*Ans.* = 2.4%.)
    (b) $4,000 for $700 a year for 10 years (*Ans.* = 11.7%.)
    (c) $5,000 for $250 a year for 20 years (*Ans.* = 0.0%.)
    (d) $50,000 for $2,700 a year forever (*Ans.* = 5.4%.)
    (e) $1,050 for $40 a year for 15 years and $1,000 at the end of the 15th year (*Ans.* = 3.6%.)

5–7. Maintenance expenditures for a structure with a 20-year life will come as periodic outlays for overhaul of $1,000 at the end of the 5th year, $2,000 at the end of the 10th year, and $3,500 at the end of the 15th year. With interest at 10%, what is the equivalent uniform annual cost for the 20-year period? (*Ans.* = $262.)

5–8. Solve the following, using interest at 7% compounded annually:

(a) What is the amount that will be accumulated in a sinking fund at the end of 15 years if $200 is deposited in the fund at the *beginning* of each of the 15 years? (*Ans.* = $5,378.)

(b) Uniform deposits are to be made on January 1 of 1971, 1972, 1973, and 1974 into a fund that is intended to provide $1,000 on January 1 of 1985, 1986, and 1987. What must be the size of these deposits? (*Ans.* = $300.)

5–9. A company leased a storage yard from a city and prepaid the rent for 6 years; the terms of the lease permit the company to continue to rent the site for 6 years more by payment of $1,500 at the beginning of each year of the second 6-year period.

Two years of the prepaid period have expired and the city is in need of funds; it proposed to the company that it now prepay the rental that was to have been paid year by year in the second 6-year period. If interest is figured at 3½%, what is a fair payment to be made now in lieu of these six annual payments? (*Ans.* = $7,207.)

5–10. An investor paid $1,000 for 10 shares of stock 12 years ago. He received dividends of $6 a share at the end of each year for the first 7 years and $3 a share at the end of each of the next 5 years. He has just sold the stock for $860. What rate of return did he make on his investment? (*Ans.* = 4.0%.)

5–11. Using interest tables and interpolation as far as possible, determine the approximate rates of interest indicated by the following valuations of prospective series of future cash receipts:

    (a) $8,000 now for $1,300 at the end of each year for 12 years
    (b) $6,000 now for $680 at the end of each year for 15 years
    (c) $6,000 now for $400 at the end of each year for 15 years
    (d) $10,000 now for $300 at the end of the first year, $350 at the end of the second year, and receipts increasing by $50 at the end of each year to a final receipt of $1,250 at the end of the 20th year.
    (e) $5,000 now for $225 at the end of each year forever

5–12. A company can either buy certain land for outdoor storage of equipment or lease it on a 15-year lease. The purchase price is $80,000. The annual rental is $5,000 payable at the *start* of each year. In either case, the company must pay property taxes, assessments, and upkeep. It is estimated that the land will be needed for only 15 years and will be saleable for $100,000 at the end of the 15-year period. What rate of return before income taxes will the company receive by buying the land instead of leasing it?

5–13. The landowner in Problem 5–12 also offers a 15-year lease for a prepaid rental of $55,000. If the company has decided to lease rather than to buy, what interest rate makes the prepaid rental equivalent to the annual rental? How should this rate be interpreted as a basis for the company's choice between prepaid and annual rental?

5–14. A person engaged in making small loans offers to lend $200 with the borrower required to pay $14.44 at the end of each week for 16 weeks to extinguish the debt. By appropriate use of your interest tables, find the approximate interest rate per week. What is the nominal interest rate per annum? What is the effective interest rate per annum?

5–15. The purchase of certain unimproved city lots is under consideration. The price is $20,000. The owner of this property will pay annual property taxes of $400 the first year; it is estimated that these taxes will increase by $40 each year thereafter. It is believed that if this property is purchased, it will be necessary for the investor to wait for 10 years before he can sell it at a favorable price. What must be the selling price in 10 years for the investment to yield 12% before income taxes?

5–16. It is desired to invest a lump sum of money on a boy's 4th birthday to provide him $2,000 on each birthday from the 18th to the 22nd, both inclusive. If interest of 4% can be obtained from a tax-exempt investment, what lump sum must be invested?

5–17. Assume that in the circumstances described in Problem 5–16, it is not practicable to invest the entire lump sum indicated by your calculations. $1,500 will be invested on the 4th birthday and a uniform annual deposit in the fund will be made on the 5th to 12th birthdays, both inclusive. Assuming 4% interest, what must be the annual deposit from the 5th to 12th birthdays?

5–18. What uniform annual payment for 30 years is equivalent to spending $10,000 immediately, $10,000 at the end of 10 years, $10,000 at the end of 20 years, and $2,000 a year for 30 years? Assume an interest rate of 7%.

5–19. A purchaser of furniture on a time-payment plan agrees to pay $47 at the end of each month for 26 months. The same furniture could be purchased for cash for $1,000. By appropriate use of your interest tables, find the approximate interest rate per month. What is the nominal interest rate per annum? What is the effective interest rate per annum?

5–20. Xavier Jones was born on July 1, 1967. On July 1, 1968, an uncle started a fund that was intended to help the boy in two ways. The fund was established by a payment of $1,000 on July 1, 1968; another $1,000 was to be deposited on each July 1 thereafter up to and including July 1, 1979—a total outlay of $12,000 by the uncle. One purpose of the fund was to help the boy finance his college education; it was provided that $2,500 should be withdrawn for this purpose each year for 4 years starting with the boy's 18th birthday, July 1, 1985—a total withdrawal of $10,000. The remainder of the fund was to accumulate until Xavier is 30 years old on July 1, 1997 to be paid to him on

that date to help him finance the purchase of a home. If the fund earns 4½%
compounded annually after taxes, how much will be paid to Xavier on his 30th
birthday?

5–21. A self-employed person invests $2,000 each year in special United
States Retirement Plan Bonds yielding 4.15% if held until retirement. Purchases of the bonds are to be made each year on his birthday from age 40 to
64. He plans to withdraw $5,000 on each birthday starting at age 65. By
interpolation in available interest tables find the approximate amount that will
remain in the fund if he dies just after he has made the withdrawal on his
75th birthday.

5–22. It is desired to make an initial lump sum investment that will provide for a withdrawal of $500 at the end of year 1, $600 at the end of year 2,
and amounts increasing $100 per year to a final $2,400 at the end of year 20.
How great an initial investment will be required if it earns 5% compounded
annually?

5–23. Solve Problem 5–22 assuming that the $2,400 withdrawal will be
at the end of year 1 and that withdrawals will decrease by $100 a year to a
final $500 at the end of year 20.

5–24. $100,000 is borrowed at a nominal 7% compounded semiannually,
to be repaid by a uniform series of payments, partly principal and partly interest, to be made at the end of each 6-month period for 30 years. How much
of the principal of the loan will have been repaid at the end of 10 years, just
after the 20th payment has been made?

5–25. How much must be deposited on January 1, 1971 and every 6
months thereafter until July 1, 1979, in order to withdraw $1,000 every 6
months for 5 years starting January 1, 1980? Interest is at a nominal 5% compounded semiannually.

5–26. At 10% interest, what uniform annual payment for 10 years is equivalent to the following irregular series of disbursements: $10,000 at zero date,
$5,000 at date 5, $1,000 at the end of year 1, $1,500 at the end of year 2, and
year-end payments increasing by $500 a year to $5,500 at the end of year 10?

5–27. A loan of $600 is to be repaid in 15 equal end-of-month payments
computed as follows:

Principal of loan	$600
Interest for 15 months at "1% per month"	90
Loan fee of 5%	30
	$720

Monthly payment = $720 ÷ 15 = $48

What nominal and effective interest rates per annum are actually paid?

6

Equivalent Uniform
Annual Cash Flow

> Every engineering structure, with few exceptions, is first suggested
> by economic requirements; and the design of every part, excepting
> few, and of the whole is finally judged from the economic stand-
> point.
>
> It is therefore apparent that the so-called principles of design
> are subordinate to the principles which underlie economic judg-
> ment.—J. C. L. FISH [1]

Proposed investments in industrial assets are unattractive unless it
seems likely they will be recovered with interest; the rate of interest
should be at least the minimum rate of return that is attractive in the
particular circumstances. This rate is designated throughout the remainder of this book as i^* (this might be pronounced "eye-star").

The introduction of the time value of money into economy studies
reflects this requirement that capital be recovered with a return. This
chapter and the three following chapters explain four possible ways to
compare proposed alternatives that involve different series of prospective
receipts and disbursements. These ways are:

1. Equivalent uniform annual cash flow, with a stipulated minimum
   attractive rate of return i^* used as an interest rate.
2. Present worth, with a stipulated minimum attractive rate of return
   i^* used as an interest rate.
3. Prospective rate of return, with the calculated rate of return
   compared with the stipulated minimum attractive rate i^*.
4. Benefit-cost ratio (applicable chiefly to governmental projects),
   with a stipulated minimum attractive rate of return i^* used as an
   interest rate.

In our initial explanation of these four methods in Chapters 6 through
9, we shall consider alternatives in pairs and shall limit our examples and

[1] J. C. L. Fish, *Engineering Economics,* 1st ed. (New York: McGraw-Hill Book
Co., Inc., 1915), first two paragraphs of preface, p. v.

problems to cases where there are no more than three proposals. In Chapter 12, we shall examine certain special aspects of analysis where many alternatives are being compared. The discussion in Chapter 12 will be related to all the four methods of analysis introduced in Chapters 6 through 9.

As we develop the subject, it will become evident to the reader that, correctly applied with the same minimum attractive rate of return, the four methods will lead to the same decision among alternative designs in the common type of case where it is physically possible to choose only one of the alternatives. However, we shall also see that each method has certain advantages and disadvantages as a guide to judgment. Because it often is necessary for a decision maker to give weight to matters that have not been expressed in money terms, it is not necessarily a matter of indifference which method is to be used.

It also will become evident that a critical matter is the choice of the minimum attractive rate of return. Proposals that look good at values of i^* of, say, 4% or 5%, will be decidedly unattractive at rates of, say, 12% or 15%. In Chapters 6 through 9, the value of i^* will be stipulated in all examples and problems without discussion of why a particular i^* was chosen. Chapter 11 examines a number of aspects of the selection of i^*. It stresses the point, already mentioned in Chapter 2, that an important element in selecting a minimum attractive rate of return is to make the best possible use of the limited resources that can be devoted to capital investment.

Cash Flow. This chapter introduces the equivalent uniform annual cash flow method as applied to relatively simple circumstances. The method is illustrated by a series of simple examples. Applications of equivalent uniform annual cash flow to more complex situations are developed in later chapters.

The data for all of the examples and problems in Chapters 6, 7, and 8 are given in terms of prospective cash flow (i.e., receipts and disbursements) associated with the stated alternatives. In the examples and problems in the present chapter, the differences between the alternatives are almost entirely in disbursements; the only differences in receipts entering into the comparisons are in receipts from salvage values.

Many of the problems in economy that confront the engineer are of this type; the prospective receipts from the sale of a product or service are unaffected by the engineer's choice among the various alternatives available to him. Economy studies in such cases must start with estimates of the amounts and dates of the disbursements for each alternative. It also is necessary either to estimate the full period of service from each alternative or to concentrate attention in the economy study on some shorter period that might be described as the study period or analysis period.

Once such estimates have been made, a mere inspection of the figures may settle the question of relative economy; one alternative may involve less disbursements both initially and subsequently. But in the many cases where this is not true, the common situation is for one alternative to involve a higher first cost that leads to some future advantages, such as lower annual disbursements or longer life or higher salvage value. The question at issue in such cases is whether these future advantages are sufficient to justify the greater initial investment.

"Annual Cost" Means Equivalent Uniform Annual Net Disbursements. To compare nonuniform series of money disbursements where money has a time value, it is necessary somehow to make them comparable. One way to do this is by reducing each to an equivalent uniform annual series of payments. In general, the phrase *annual cost* when used in connection with economy studies is simply a short way of saying *equivalent uniform annual net disbursements*. As a practical matter, however, it sometimes is expedient to use various approximations to the desired equivalent uniform annual figure. These approximations may also be described as *annual cost*. A brief description of some common types of approximation and an evaluation of their merits is given in Chapter 10.

Income Tax Considerations in Investment Evaluation. In private enterprise in most industrialized countries and in many developing countries, prospective income taxes may be influenced by decisions regarding investments in physical assets. If decisions are to be made from the viewpoint of the owners of an enterprise, the expected income tax effects of each decision need to be recognized.

Most of the examples and problems in this book are based on analysis of differences in estimated cash flows associated with alternatives that are being compared. Prospective differences in disbursements for income taxes constitute one of the elements of cash flow. In principle, therefore, differences in cash flow for income taxes ought to be included in any analysis based on cash flow.

In general, there is no entirely satisfactory answer to the question: "At what point and in what way should income tax matters be introduced in the study of engineering economy?" The difficulty is that, although under certain circumstances the estimation of the income tax effects of decisions is fairly simple, under other circumstances this estimation is a complex matter requiring an understanding of accounting and a familiarity with income tax laws and regulations. Doubtless, the best that can be done is to give the student of engineering economy a basis for identifying the numerous routine types of economy studies in which it is a fairly simple matter for an analyst to consider income taxes in a way that is good enough for practical purposes; also he should have a basis for recognizing the cases where an analyst may need advice from a tax specialist.

The more complex aspects of estimating the income tax aspects of decisions are presented in Chapter 16. However, starting with the examples and problems in the present chapter, we shall include in many cash flow series, the estimated difference between alternatives in cash flow for income taxes. Usually this income tax difference will be a separately identified item, although occasionally it may be combined with other cash flow differences. Where the income tax difference is separately identified for cases in competitive industry, it is computed under fairly simple assumptions that are explained in Chapter 10.

There are two main reasons for using the *after-tax* minimum attractive rate of return. One reason is that its use in examples and problems is correct in principle; prospective differences between alternatives in the more distant future are discounted too greatly when the higher *before-tax* values of i^* are used. The other reason is that the important subject of the impact of income tax considerations on business decisions receives its appropriate emphasis when specific figures are given for differences in income tax disbursements.

As pointed out in Chapter 20, economy studies for regulated public utilities in the United States generally are different in principle from economy studies for competitive industry in relation to the way prospective income tax differences ought to be estimated. Under certain assumptions explained in Chapter 20, it is appropriate to estimate the portion of public utility income taxes affected by a choice among proposed alternatives as a percentage of the first costs of the respective proposed assets.

Income taxes as such are not a factor in the usual economy studies for governments. However, it is pointed out in Chapter 19 that income taxes (and other taxes) foregone ought to be considered as one element in any governmental decision on the question of whether certain activities should be carried out by government or by private industry.

EXAMPLE 6–1. A PROPOSED INVESTMENT
TO REDUCE LABOR COSTS

Statement of Alternatives. At present a certain materials handling operation in the warehouse of a manufacturing company is being done by hand labor. Annual disbursements for this labor and for certain closely related expenses (such "labor extras" as social security taxes, industrial accident insurance, paid vacations, and various employees' fringe benefits) are $9,200. The proposal to continue materials handling by the present method is called Plan A.

An alternative proposal, Plan B, is to build certain equipment that will reduce this labor cost. The first cost of this equipment will be $15,000. It is estimated that the equipment will reduce annual disbursements for labor and labor extras to $3,300. Annual payments for power, maintenance, and property taxes and insurance are estimated to be $400, $1,100, and $300 respectively. Extra annual disbursements for income taxes over those required with Plan A are estimated to be $1,300.

It is expected that the need for this particular operation will continue for 10 years and that because the equipment in Plan B is specially designed for the particular purpose, it will have no salvage value at the end of that time. It is assumed that the various annual disbursements will be uniform throughout the 10 years. The minimum attractive rate of return after income taxes is 8%.

Annual Cost Comparison. Everything but the initial $15,000 is already assumed to be a uniform annual disbursement. The only compound interest calculation needed is a conversion of this $15,000 to its equivalent uniform annual cost of capital recovery. The equivalent uniform annual disbursements may then be tabulated for each plan and their totals may be compared.

Plan A		*Plan B*	
Labor and labor extras	$9,200	CR = $15,000($A/P$,8%,10)	
		= $15,000(0.14903)	= $2,235
		Labor and labor extras	3,300
		Power	400
		Maintenance	1,100
		Property taxes, insurance	300
		Extra income taxes	1,300
Comparative equivalent uniform annual disbursements	$9,200	Comparative equivalent uniform annual disbursements	$8,635

Plan B is therefore more economical than Plan A.

Simplicity of a Uniform Annual Series of Disbursements. Experience indicates that it is almost inevitable that certain disbursements will vary from year to year. Maintenance costs fluctuate and tend to increase with age; wage rates change; property tax rates and assessed valuations change; and so forth. Nevertheless, it often happens that there is no rational basis for making different estimates for each year. Even where there is some basis for making separate year-by-year estimates, the prospective differences in year-by-year totals may be so small that it is good enough for practical purposes merely to estimate average annual disbursements and to treat the average figures as if they were uniform.

Whatever may be the reason for estimates of uniform annual disbursements, it is evident that such estimates simplify the comparison of equivalent uniform annual costs; only the capital costs require conversion by appropriate compound interest factors.

Tabulation of Cash Flow. A useful tool in many economy studies is a year-by-year tabulation of estimated disbursements and receipts associated with each of two alternatives, followed by a tabulation of the differences in cash flow between the alternatives. Table 6–1 shows such a tabulation for Example 6–1.

Many such tabulations appear throughout this book. In all of them a net disbursement is preceded by a minus sign and a net receipt is preceded by a plus sign. The final column of Table 6–1 recognizes that a reduction of disbursements is, in effect, an increase in receipts. That is, spending $2,800 less has the same effect on the company's cash as receiving $2,800 more.

The figures for totals at the bottom of cash flow tables provide a check on the arithmetic in the table. Although this check seems unnecessary in Table 6–1, it will prove useful in more complicated types of circumstances such as are discussed later in this book. It should be noted by the reader that the totals from any such cash flow tables disregard the time value of money; therefore, these totals do not by themselves provide a satisfactory basis for choosing between the alternatives being compared. Such totals may be thought of as giving the present worth of the cash flow using an interest rate of 0%.

TABLE 6–1

Tabulation of Comparative Cash Flow, Example 6–1

Year	Plan A	Plan B	B − A
0		−$15,000	−$15,000
1	−$9,200	−6,400	+2,800
2	−9,200	−6,400	+2,800
3	−9,200	−6,400	+2,800
4	−9,200	−6,400	+2,800
5	−9,200	−6,400	+2,800
6	−9,200	−6,400	+2,800
7	−9,200	−6,400	+2,800
8	−9,200	−6,400	+2,800
9	−9,200	−6,400	+2,800
10	−9,200	−6,400	+2,800
Totals	−$92,000	−$79,000	+$13,000

In a tabulation such as Table 6–1 that is intended to show how receipts and disbursements will be influenced by a particular decision, the source of an estimated receipt or disbursement is immaterial. For example, a dollar spent for one purpose in a particular year has the same effect on cash flow as a dollar paid out for some other purpose; in a cash flow analysis, it is a matter of indifference whether the dollar is spent for labor, for power, for property taxes, for income taxes, or for anything else. Although this point seems obvious in Example 6–1, it is not always so evident; we shall have need to mention it again when we discuss increment costs and sunk costs in Chapter 15 and when we take a more critical look at the income tax effects of decisions in Chapter 16.

Moreover, in a tabulation such as Table 6–1 showing expected cash flow for two alternatives, it is the right-hand column—the column of differences in cash flow—that is significant. This column of differences serves to clarify the question at issue in the choice between the alternatives. In Example 6–1, the question—quite obviously—is whether it will pay to spend $15,000 at once in order to save $2,800 a year (after income taxes) for the next 10 years.

Interpretation of Annual Cost Comparison in Example 6–1. Our annual cost comparison has answered the foregoing question in the affirmative. The smaller equivalent annual cost computed for Plan B means "Yes, it will pay to spend the proposed $15,000."

This answer should properly be viewed as a qualified "Yes," subject to the appropriateness of the 8% i^* used in the equivalence conversion and to the weight, if any, to be given to irreducible data. If an 8% return after income taxes is high enough to be attractive, all things considered, and if other matters not reflected in the cash flow estimates do not favor Plan A, it is clear that Plan B is better.

It should also be recognized that the answer "Yes, it will pay" refers only to the relative merits of Plans A and B. Conceivably there may be some other possible plan that, if considered, would prove to be superior to both A and B.

The Borrowed Money Point of View. Assume that all the $15,000 to be invested in the new equipment is to be borrowed at 8% interest. Assume also that this borrowing will be repaid by uniform annual end-of-year payments over the 10-year life of the equipment in the manner illustrated in Plan III, Table 3–1. These annual payments would then be $2,235, the computed capital recovery cost for Plan B in our solution of Example 6–1.

Although this point of view is helpful in understanding the calculation of equivalent uniform annual costs, it is only rarely that borrowing takes place in this manner. Moreover, for reasons that are explained in Chapter 11, the appropriate minimum attractive rate of return for use in an economy study is nearly always higher than the bare cost of borrowed money. In addition, as explained in Chapter 18, borrowed money and equity funds are treated differently for income tax purposes. But regardless of whether the first cost is to be borrowed 100%, or to be financed 100% out of the funds of the prospective owner, or to be financed by some combination of borrowed funds and of owner's funds, and regardless of the plans for the repayment of any borrowed funds, the calculated equivalent uniform annual costs provide an entirely valid method of comparing the long-run economy of the two alternatives, once a particular interest rate is accepted as a standard.

Nevertheless, questions of financing, separate from those of long-run economy, arise whenever proposed assets are to be financed by borrowing that must be paid back rapidly. Here a separate question is always whether the repayment obligation can be met. This topic is discussed in Chapter 18.

The End-of-Year Convention in Economy Studies. In Plan B the $2,235 capital recovery cost was an end-of-year series for 10 years. If the date of the $15,000 investment is designated as zero (0) date, the ten $2,235 figures apply to dates 1 to 10 respectively.

When we add this $2,235 year-end figure to the $6,400 that we expect will actually be paid out each year, we are, in effect, assuming that the $6,400 is also a year-end figure. As a matter of fact the disbursements included in the $6,400 are expected to occur throughout each year. Some of the disbursements (such as wages of labor) will doubtless take place at a fairly uniform rate during the year; others (such as property taxes and income taxes) will occur at regular intervals; still others (such as maintenance) will occur irregularly.

It is convenient in economy studies to treat receipts and disbursements that occur throughout a year as if they took place at year end. This end-of-year convention is used in nearly all of the examples and problems in this book; unless otherwise stated, it is implied in cash flow tables and in calculations of annual costs, present worths, and rates of return. The convention greatly simplifies the required compound interest conversions. In most cases the assumption is good enough for practical purposes in the sense that it will not lead to errors in decisions between alternatives.

If continuous compounding of interest is assumed, a different convention may be adopted—namely, that all receipts and disbursements occur uniformly throughout each year. This latter convention is discussed and illustrated in Appendix A. Its chief advantages occur where the study period is short and the prospective rate of return is high.

EXAMPLE 6–2. A PROPOSED INVESTMENT THAT HAS A SALVAGE VALUE

Statement of Alternatives. Plan C, an alternative to Plan B in Example 6–1, calls for the purchase of certain general-purpose materials handling equipment. The first cost of this equipment will be $25,000, a considerable increase over the $15,000 first cost in Plan B. However, it is estimated that this general-purpose equipment will have a $5,000 net salvage value at the end of the 10-year period of service. (The net salvage value may be defined as the gross receipts from the sale of the equipment minus any disbursements required by its removal and sale.) This equipment, which has more automatic features than the equipment in Plan B, is expected to reduce annual disbursements for labor and labor extras to $1,700. Estimated annual disbursements for power, maintenance, and property taxes and insurance are $600, $1,500, and $500 respectively.

The extra annual disbursement for income taxes in Plan C as compared to Plan A is estimated as $1,450. (The reader will recall that Plan A was used as the base of comparison in computing the extra income tax payments to be made under Plan B.) It is now desired to compare Plan C with Plan B using an i^* of 8%.

Annual Cost of Plan C. Using Plan A as a base, the annual cost of Plan B has already been calculated as $8,635. With the same base, equivalent annual net disbursements for Plan C are as follows:

CR = ($25,000 − $5,000)($A/P$,8%,10) + $5,000(0.08)	
= $20,000(0.14903) + $5,000(0.08) = $2,981 + $400	= $3,381
Labor and labor extras	1,700
Power	600
Maintenance	1,500
Property taxes, insurance	500
Extra income taxes	1,450
Comparative equivalent uniform annual net disbursements	$9,131

It is evident that although Plan C is slightly more economical than Plan A, it is less economical than Plan B. The savings of $650 in annual disbursements promised by Plan C are not enough to offset its higher capital recovery cost.

The Influence of Salvage Value on the Annual Cost of Capital Recovery. Let P = first cost of a machine or structure, n = the life, study period, or analysis period in years, L = prospective net salvage value or net terminal value at the end of n years, and i^* = minimum attractive rate of return. The equivalent uniform annual cost of capital recovery may then be expressed as follows:

$$CR = (P - L)\left[\frac{i^*(1 + i^*)^n}{(1 + i^*)^n - 1}\right] + Li^*$$

or

$$CR = (P - L)(A/P,i^*,n) + Li^*$$

This formula, considered algebraically, is also applicable with a zero salvage value or a negative salvage value.

The borrowed money viewpoint may be helpful in examining the rational basis of this formula. Let us apply this viewpoint to the $25,000 initial disbursement, the prospective $5,000 receipt from salvage value at the end of 10 years, and the 8% i^* in Plan C. Assume that the $25,000 is borrowed at 8% interest and that it is anticipated that $5,000 of the debt will be repaid from the proceeds of the salvage value. In effect, the $25,000 debt may be divided into two parts. One part of the debt, $20,000 (i.e., $P - L$ or $25,000 - $5,000), must be repaid by uniform annual payments of $2,981 for 10 years (obtained as the product of $20,000 and the 10-year crf, 0.14903). On the other part of the debt, $5,000, it is necessary merely to pay interest of $400 each year because the investment itself will generate the $5,000 salvage necessary to repay the principal. The total annual payment on the debt is therefore $2,981 + $400 = $3,381.

In general, where there is a prospective salvage value after n years, the annual cost of capital recovery may be computed as the sum of two figures. One figure is the product of first cost minus estimated salvage, $(P - L)$, and the capital recovery factor $(A/P,i^*,n)$. The other is the product of salvage, (L), and interest rate i^*. The foregoing method of calculation is the one used in examples throughout this book.

Three other correct methods of computing capital recovery cost where salvage values exist are described and illustrated in the following paragraphs.

In one method the capital recovery cost is calculated as the sum of the product of first cost and interest rate, and the product of the difference between first cost and salvage value and the sinking fund factor. This may be expressed algebraically as

$$CR = Pi^* + (P - L)\left[\frac{i^*}{(1 + i^*)^n - 1}\right]$$

or

$$CR = Pi^* + (P - L)(A/F,i^*,n)$$

As applied to the data of Plan C

$$CR = \$25,000(0.08) + (\$25,000 - \$5,000)(0.06903)$$
$$= \$2,000 + \$1,381 = \$3,381$$

Another method converts the salvage value to its present worth at zero date by multiplying salvage by the single payment present worth factor. The difference between the first cost and the present worth of the salvage is then multiplied by the capital recovery factor. This may be expressed algebraically as

$$CR = \left[P - \frac{L}{(1 + i^*)^n}\right]\left[\frac{i^*(1 + i^*)^n}{(1 + i^*)^n - 1}\right]$$

or

$$CR = [P - L(P/F,i^*,n)](A/P,i^*,n)$$

As applied to the data of Plan C, the present worth of the salvage is $5,000(0.4632) = $2,316.

$$CR = (\$25,000 - \$2,316)(0.14903) = \$3,381$$

A third method converts the first cost to a uniform annual series over the life by multiplying it by the capital recovery factor. From this product there is subtracted a uniform annual figure obtained by multiplying the salvage value by the sinking fund factor. This may be expressed algebraically as

$$CR = P\left[\frac{i^*(1 + i^*)^n}{(1 + i^*)^n - 1}\right] - L\left[\frac{i^*}{(1 + i^*)^n - 1}\right]$$

or

$$CR = P(A/P,i^*,n) - L(A/F,i^*,n)$$

As applied to the data of Plan C

$$CR = \$25,000(0.14903) - \$5,000(0.06903)$$
$$= \$3,726 - \$345 = \$3,381$$

Cash Flow for Example 6–2. Table 6–2 compares cash flow in Plans B and C. The tabulation makes it evident that the question at issue is whether it is desirable to pay out $10,000 at once in order to receive $5,000 at the end of 10 years and to avoid disbursements of $650 a year throughout the 10-year period. Although the extra $10,000 investment will ultimately be recovered with $1,500 to spare by the combination of reduced annual disbursements and receipts from salvage, our annual cost analysis has told us that this recovery will not be rapid enough to yield the stipulated 8%.

TABLE 6–2

Tabulation of Comparative Cash Flow, Example 6–2

Year	Plan B	Plan C	C – B
0	−$15,000	−$25,000	−$10,000
1	−6,400	−5,750	+650
2	−6,400	−5,750	+650
3	−6,400	−5,750	+650
4	−6,400	−5,750	+650
5	−6,400	−5,750	+650
6	−6,400	−5,750	+650
7	−6,400	−5,750	+650
8	−6,400	−5,750	+650
9	−6,400	−5,750	+650
10	{ −6,400	{ −5,750 { +5,000	{ +650 { +5,000
Totals	−$79,000	−$77,500	+$1,500

EXAMPLE 6–3. COMPARING ALTERNATIVES
THAT HAVE DIFFERENT LIVES

Statement of Alternatives. In the design of certain industrial facilities, two alternate structures are under consideration. We shall call them Plans D and E. The receipts from the sale of goods and services will not be affected by the choice between the two plans. Estimates for the plans are:

	Plan D	Plan E
First cost	$50,000	$120,000
Life	20 years	40 years
Salvage value	$10,000	$20,000
Annual O & M disbursements	$9,000	$6,000

The estimated annual O & M disbursements include operation, maintenance, property taxes, and insurance. Extra annual disbursements for income taxes with Plan E are estimated as $1,250.

It is desired to compare these alternatives using a minimum attractive rate of return of 8% after income taxes.

Annual Cost Comparison. The comparative equivalent uniform annual disbursements are as follows:

Plan D

CR = ($50,000 − $10,000)(A/P,8%,20) + $10,000(0.08)
    = $40,000(0.10185) + $10,000(0.08) − $4,074 + $800   = $ 4,874
Annual O & M disbursements   9,000
Comparative equivalent uniform annual disbursements $13,874

Plan E

CR = ($120,000 − $20,000)(A/P,8%,40) + $20,000(0.08)
    = $100,000(0.08386) + $20,000(0.08) = $8,386 + $1,600   = $9,986
Annual O & M disbursements   6,000
Extra annual income taxes   1,250
Comparative equivalent uniform annual disbursements $17,236

Plan D has the lower annual cost.

Some Considerations in Annual Cost Comparisons When Two Alternatives Have Different Lives. When annual cost comparisons such as the preceding one are made, an objection along the following lines is sometimes raised: "Plan E has an important advantage over Plan D in that it has a much longer prospective life. How is this advantage reflected in your annual cost comparison? Doesn't your $13,874 a year give you service for only 20 years, whereas your $17,236 a year gives you service for 40 years?"

Such an objector doubtless missed a fundamental point in the mathematics of compound interest. Nevertheless, he has introduced an interesting and important topic. We shall discuss various facets of this topic in different places throughout this book.

A direct answer to our objector may be made by pointing out that the 20-year estimated life in Plan D was reflected by the use of the 20-year capital recovery factor, 0.10185, in obtaining the $4,874 CR cost, and the 40-year estimated life in Plan E was reflected by the use of the 40-year crf, 0.08386, in obtaining the CR cost of $9,986. The answer may be amplified by pointing out that the estimate of a 40-year life in Plan E implied that a service of at least this long would be required. Although the $13,874 a year for Plan D is for 20 years only, the service must be continued after the 20-year structure is retired. Presumably, although not necessarily, the annual costs of continuing the service will be of the same order of magnitude. If it is assumed that as good an estimate as any is that the replacement structure will have the same first cost, life, salvage value, and annual disbursements as the initial structure, the $13,874 annual cost in Plan D will be repeated during the second 20 years.

A somewhat more sophisticated view of the matter recognizes that the present decision between a long-lived and a short-lived alternative is simply a decision as to what to do *now*. In aiming to have the decision now turn out to be the best decision in the long run, it is appropriate to consider what may happen after the end of the life of the shorter-lived alternative. In Example 6–3, a forecast that the replacement structure in the second 20 years will have much higher annual costs than the initial structure is favorable to Plan E. Similarly, the prospect that a replacement structure with much lower annual costs will be available should be given weight in the present choice as a factor favoring Plan D. In general, prospects for price increases and for extra costs incident to replacement are favorable to the selection of longer-lived alternatives; prospects for technological improvements, changes in service requirements, and price reductions are favorable to the selection of shorter-lived alternatives. The extent to which such prospects may be evaluated numerically in the cost comparison and the extent to which they must be considered only as irreducible data will naturally depend on circumstances. This topic is explored further in Chapter 13 and thereafter. In this chapter and in the three that follow, wherever some specific assumption is necessary for the cost comparison, it will be assumed that replacement assets will repeat the costs that have been forecast for the initial asset.

Cash Flow Tabulations When Alternatives Have Different Lives. If cash flow for Plans D and E is to be compared for a 40-year period, some assumptions must be made regarding disbursements in the final 20 years of Plan D. In Table 6–3 it is assumed that the final 20 years will repeat the costs of the first 20. The table has been shortened by using a single line for each series of years in which cash flow is uniform.

TABLE 6–3

Tabulation of Comparative Cash Flow, Example 6–3

Years	Plan D	Plan E	E − D
0	−$50,000	−$120,000	−$70,000
1–19	−9,000 per year	−7,250 per year	+1,750 per year
20	{ −9,000 / +10,000 / −50,000	{ −7,250	{ +1,750 / +40,000
21–39	−9,000 per year	−7,250 per year	+1,750 per year
40	{ −9,000 / +10,000	{ −7,250 / +20,000	{ +1,750 / +10,000
Totals	−$440,000	−$390,000	+$50,000

The final column of the table shows that the initial extra outlay of $70,000 will ultimately be recovered plus an additional $50,000. Nevertheless, our annual cost comparison has indicated that this recovery of capital is too slow to yield 8% after income taxes and that, by the standard we have set, this extra $70,000 outlay for Plan E is undesirable.

Because 20 years is evenly divisible into 40 years, it was a simple matter to tabulate prospective cash flow for a period that would give the same number of years of service for the two plans. All that was required was our assumption regarding the disbursements during the second 20 years. In most comparisons of alternatives with different lives, the matter is more complicated than in Example 6–3; the total years tabulated must be the least common multiple of the estimated lives of the two alternatives. For example, if one alternative had a 10-year life and the other a 25-year life, it would be necessary to consider a 50-year period, with 5 life cycles for one alternative and 2 for the other. If lives were, say, 13 and 20 years, a 260-year period would have to be tabulated before reaching the point where the alternatives gave equal years of service.

We shall see that a disparity in lives of alternatives creates the same difficulty in present worth comparisons and in calculation of rates of return that we now observe in the tabulations of comparative cash flow. Various methods of dealing with this difficulty are developed in subsequent chapters. Because no one method is completely satisfactory, the method selected is properly influenced by the circumstances of the economy study.

EXAMPLE 6–4. COMPARING ALTERNATIVES THAT HAVE PERPETUAL LIVES

Statement of Alternatives. In the design of an aqueduct that is assumed to have a perpetual period of service, two alternative locations are proposed for a certain section.

Location J involves a tunnel and flume. The tunnel is estimated to have a first cost of $200,000 and is assumed to be permanent. Its annual upkeep costs are estimated as $500. The flume will cost $90,000, has an estimated life of 20 years, and is expected to have annual maintenance costs of $2,000.

Location K involves a steel pipe line and several miles of concrete-lined earth canal. The pipe line has an estimated first cost of $70,000, an estimated life of 50 years, and an estimated annual maintenance cost of $700. The earth canal will cost $80,000 and is assumed to be permanent. During the first 5 years it is estimated that maintenance on the earth canal will be $5,000 a year; thereafter, it is estimated as $1,000 a year. The concrete lining will cost $40,000; it has an estimated life of 25 years with annual maintenance cost of $300.

All salvage values are assumed to be negligible. The stipulated i^* is 5%. Because this is a government project, no income tax differences are involved.

Annual Cost Comparison. Annual costs may be compared as follows:

Location J

Tunnel

Interest = $200,000(0.05)	= $10,000
Maintenance	500

Flume

CR = $90,000($A/P$,5%,20) = $90,000(0.08024)	= 7,222
Maintenance	2,000
Total equivalent uniform annual disbursements	$19,722

Location K

Pipe line

CR = $70,000($A/P$,5%,50) = $70,000(0.05478)	= $ 3,835
Maintenance	700

Earth canal

Interest on first cost = $80,000(0.05)	= 4,000
Interest on PW of extra early maintenance	
= $4,000($P/A$,5%,5)(0.05) = $4,000(4.329)(0.05)	= 866
Maintenance	1,000

Concrete lining

CR = $40,000($A/P$,5%,25) = $40,000(0.07095)	= 2,838
Maintenance	300
Total equivalent uniform annual disbursements	$13,539

Selection of Location K will result in a saving of nearly $6,200 in annual costs.

Two new points arise in this solution. One deals with the annual cost associated with a perpetual life for a structure. Here interest (or return) on investment takes the place of capital recovery; as n approaches infinity, the capital recovery factor approaches the interest rate. If one adopts the borrowed money point of view, it is as if the $200,000 for the tunnel, for example, were borrowed under terms that permitted a perpetual debt with $10,000 interest paid every year.[2]

The extra maintenance of $4,000 a year for the first 5 years for the earth canal is a nonrecurring expenditure somewhat comparable to first cost. To translate this into an equivalent perpetual annual cost, it first must be converted into its present worth of $17,316 on zero date. Then, like the $80,000 investment in the canal itself, it is converted into an equivalent perpetual series by multiplying by the interest rate.

The Small Difference in Annual Cost Between Very Long Life and Perpetual Life. Forever is a long time! Past experience suggests that even the projects that appear likely to be longest-lived will eventually reach the end of their usefulness, despite the difficulty of estimating the specific cause and date of termination of life. The estimator whose economy studies imply permanence of certain constructions does not really have the illusion that his projects will last forever; he merely expects that they will last a very long time, possibly 100 years or more.

In an economy study the difference between 100 years and forever is very small indeed. For example, at 5% interest the capital recovery factor for 100 years is 0.05038. That is, an increase of the interest rate from 5% to 5.04% would have the same effect on annual cost as reducing the estimated life of a structure from forever to 100 years. Even with interest at 3%, the difference between 100 years and forever has the same influence on annual cost as a difference of ⅛ of 1% in the interest rate.

In many long-lived projects, economy studies are made and costs are computed as if the expected life were 50 years. This is common both in public works projects, such as federal river basin projects in the United States (see Chapter 19) and in private projects.

EXAMPLE 6–5. COMPARING ALTERNATIVES IN WHICH ANNUAL DISBURSEMENTS HAVE A UNIFORM GRADIENT

Statement of Alternatives. Many tractors of a particular type but of different ages are being used by a company engaged in large-scale farming operations. Although there have been no formal rules on replacement policy, the usual practice has been to replace tractors when they were about 10 years old. The first cost of a tractor is $12,000. Records have been kept of maintenance

---

[2] Because of the common practice of bond refunding in the public utility industry, many business debts are, in effect, perpetual. This matter is discussed in Chapter 18. But if this were an aqueduct for a municipal water supply or for an irrigation district, there would nearly always be a public requirement that the debt be paid off within a specified number of years, possibly 40 or less. Such a requirement would not affect the validity of the annual cost calculations based on perpetual life. However, as brought out in Chapter 18, it would create an additional question of the actual total disbursements for debt service and other purposes with each of the proposed alternative locations.

costs under conditions of fairly uniform use from year to year. There is clearly a marked upward tendency in maintenance costs as tractors get older, even though the maintenance costs at a given age differ from tractor to tractor. An analysis indicates that, on the average, maintenance costs will be $1,600 the first year, $1,930 the second, $2,260 the third, and will increase by $330 a year for each year of age.

It is desired to compare the equivalent annual costs for an average tractor assuming a 7-year life with such costs for an average tractor assuming a 10-year life. Estimated salvage value will be $4,000 for a 7-year-old tractor and $2,800 for a 10-year-old one. It is believed that costs other than maintenance and capital recovery costs can be disregarded in this comparison as these costs will be practically the same whether tractors are retired after 7 years or after 10 years. The stipulated i^* is 8%. Long-run differences in income taxes are assumed to be so small that they can be neglected in the analysis.

Annual Cost Comparison. The year-by-year maintenance costs may be treated as if they are made up of two parts. The first part is a uniform series of $1,600 a year. The second part is $0 the first year, $330 the second, $660 the third, and so on, increasing $330 each year. The second part constitutes a gradient series, which may be converted to an equivalent uniform annual series by the use of the appropriate gradient factor from Table E–26.

Tractor Retired After 7 Years

CR = ($12,000 − $4,000)(A/P,8%,7) + $4,000(0.08)
= $8,000(0.19207) + $4,000(0.08) = $1,537 + $320   = $1,857

Equivalent uniform annual maintenance cost
= $1,600 + $330(A/G,8%,7)
= $1,600 + $330(2.69) = $1,600 + $888   = 2,488

Total of equivalent annual net disbursements compared $4,345

Tractor Retired After 10 Years

CR = ($12,000 − $2,800)(A/P,8%,10) + $2,800(0.08)
= $9,200(0.14903) + $2,800(0.08) = $1,371 + $224   = $1,595

Equivalent annual maintenance cost
= $1,600 + $330(A/G,8%,10)
= $1,600 + $330(3.87) = $1,600 + $1,277   = 2,877

Total of equivalent annual net disbursements compared $4,472

The equivalent annual costs over the life of the 7-year tractor will be somewhat lower than those over the life of the 10-year one.

Comments on Example 6–5. Where it seems reasonable to estimate that disbursements (or receipts) will increase or decrease by a uniform amount each year, the gradient factor is helpful in computing an equivalent uniform annual figure. It often happens that the estimate of a uniform gradient is as good an estimate as it is practicable to make in cases where upward or downward trends are expected.

Where disbursements are expected to vary irregularly from year to year and the figures for each year are predicted for use in the economy study, the gradient approach is not suitable; it is necessary first to convert all disbursements to present worth before converting to equivalent uniform annual cost. This type of calculation is illustrated in the next chapter.

Although Example 6–5 introduces the subject of the time at which it is economical to replace an asset that is physically capable of being continued in service, this example omits consideration of a number of matters that are important in replacement economy. A more adequate consideration of this interesting and important subject is deferred until Chapter 17 and thereafter.

The Usefulness of Calculations of Equivalent Uniform Annual Cash Flow Is Not Limited to Comparisons of Alternatives Involving Different Series of Disbursements. Although the examples given in this chapter have all dealt with comparisons of alternatives of the "Why this way?" type, a number of other uses of equivalent uniform annual figures are illustrated in later chapters. Where proposals involve differences in estimated annual receipts, comparisons may be made of equivalent uniform annual net positive cash flow (rather than of equivalent annual net negative cash flow as in the examples in this chapter). Where for some reason, such as public regulation of certain prices or agreement between the parties concerned, the pricing of a product or service is to be based on an equivalent uniform figure, the purpose of such a calculation may be to find a justified selling price. In economy studies for public works, as introduced in Chapter 9 and discussed at greater length in Chapter 19, equivalent uniform annual costs may be computed for comparison with equivalent uniform annual benefits.

Omission of Discussion of Irreducibles in This Chapter. Economy studies are generally undertaken to arrive at a decision on action or at a recommendation for action. Insofar as possible, it is helpful to reduce alternative courses of action to money terms in order to have a common unit to measure the differences between alternatives. Nevertheless, as pointed out in Part I, it often happens that important matters for consideration simply cannot be reduced to terms of money in any satisfactory way. Such irreducibles should be considered along with the money figures in arriving at any decision among alternatives. In those borderline cases where the money comparisons are close, the irreducibles are likely to control the decision.

In this chapter and the three that follow, we deal chiefly with the calculations necessary to reflect the time value of money in comparing alternatives that involve different estimated cash flows. It is desirable that persons responsible for decisions on matters of economy understand the principles involved in such interest conversions. These are definite principles that exist regardless of the irreducibles entering into any particular situation. Experience shows that they frequently are not clearly understood by engineers and other persons who need to understand them. In order to permit concentration of attention on these principles, the subject matter has been deliberately de-emotionalized in these chapters by references to Plans A and B, Locations J and K, and so forth, and by the omission of irreducibles as far as possible. A more complete discussion of economy studies in a realistic setting involving irreducibles is deferred until Part III of this book.

Summary. One way of reflecting in economy studies the desirability of recovering invested capital with a return is to compare alternatives on the basis of equivalent uniform annual net disbursements, using as an interest rate the minimum attractive rate of return. Because many of the estimated disbursements are the same year after year, such annual cost comparisons are likely to be convenient. The basic data for such comparisons consist of estimated cash flows associated with the alternatives being compared. Conversions into equivalent uniform annual figures require the use of appropriate factors obtained from compound interest tables or formulas.

PROBLEMS

6–1. Compare the equivalent uniform annual costs of grinding mills M and N for a 12-year service in a chemical plant. Use an i^* (minimum attractive rate of return) of 10% after income taxes.

	Mill M	Mill N
First cost	$7,800	$14,400
Salvage value after 12 years	0	2,700
Annual operating cost	1,745	1,200
Annual repair cost	960	540
Extra annual income taxes		320

(*Ans.* = Mill M, $3,850; Mill N, $4,047.)

6–2. For a certain service in a manufacturing plant, a centerless grinder must be purchased. A secondhand machine that will be satisfactory will cost $5,000; a new machine of more up-to-date design will cost $12,800. Annual disbursements for labor and labor extras are estimated as $9,200 with the secondhand machine and $8,300 with the new one. Annual maintenance costs are estimated to be $600 the first year and to increase $150 each year with the secondhand machine and to be $400 the first year and to increase $100 each year with the new machine. The expected period of service is 10 years. At the end of this period, it is estimated that the secondhand machine will have a negligible salvage value and that the new one will have a $4,000 salvage value. Estimated disbursements for income taxes will be $360 higher with the new machine in the first year, $385 in the second, and the difference in income taxes will increase by $25 each year thereafter. Prepare a tabulation of cash flow for each machine. Compare the equivalent uniform annual costs of the two machines assuming an after-tax i^* of 12%. (*Ans.* Secondhand machine has lower annual cost by $323.)

6–3. A certain service can be performed satisfactorily either by Machine V or W. Machine V has a first cost of $6,000, an estimated life of 12 years with zero salvage value, and annual disbursements (for all purposes except income taxes) of $5,100. The corresponding figures for Machine W are $14,000, 18 years, $3,200 salvage value, and $3,500. Extra annual disbursements for income taxes with Machine W are estimated to be $750. Compare the annual costs assuming an i^* of 8% after income taxes. (*Ans.* = Machine V, $4,796; Machine W, $4,558.)

6–4. Compare the annual costs of the following two types of power plant to be used for an isolated mine. The expected period of service is 10 years and the after-tax i^* is 15%.

	Steam Plant	Diesel Plant
First cost	$20,000	$30,000
Salvage value after 10 years	1,000	5,000
Annual operation and repair cost	9,200	6,000
Extra annual income tax		1,300

(*Ans.* = Steam, $13,136; Diesel, $13,031.)

6–5. Two different methods are being considered for elevating rock into a crusher. It is expected that the rock crusher will be in place for 6 years. Cost estimates for the two methods are as follows:

	Method A	Method B
First cost	$4,200	$2,800
Salvage value after 6 years	600	1,000
Annual fuel cost	200	450
Annual maintenance cost	130	300
Extra annual income tax	60	

Compare the annual costs of the two conveyors using an after-tax i^* of 12%. (*Ans.* = A, $1,338; B, $1,308.)

6–6. Compare the two methods of Problem 6–5 making your comparison before income taxes and using an i^* of 20%.

6–7. Compare the two methods of Problem 6–5 after income taxes using an i^* of 10%. The change in the minimum attractive rate of return does not change the $60 extra annual payment for income taxes for Method A.

6–8. To produce a new product, a manufacturer needs a special machine for a certain operation. The machine may be either hand-operated or semi-automatic. To compare the two, the following estimates are made:

	Hand-operated	Semi-automatic
First cost, including installation	$6,000	$14,000
Life in years	10	6
Annual disbursements for labor, labor extras, repairs, property taxes, and insurance	$7,000	$4,000
Net terminal salvage value	zero	$2,000
Extra annual income taxes		$800

(a) Compare annual costs of the two machines after income taxes using an i^* of 10%.

(b) Make the same comparison before income taxes using an i^* of 20%.

6–9. Compare the equivalent annual costs of perpetual service for the following two plans for a government project using an i^* of 6%:

Plan I involves an initial investment of $150,000. Of this, $75,000 is for land (assumed to be permanent) and $75,000 is for a structure that will require renewal, without salvage value, at an estimated cost of $75,000 every 30 years. Annual disbursements will be $10,000 for the first 10 years and $7,000 thereafter.

Plan II involves an initial investment of $250,000. Of this, $100,000 is for land and $150,000 is for a structure that will require renewal, with a $30,000 salvage value, every 50 years. Assume that the net outlay for each renewal is $120,000. Annual disbursements will be $4,000.

6–10. A university has pumped its water supply from wells located on the campus. The falling water table has caused pumping costs to increase greatly, the quantity of available water to decrease, and the quality of the water to deteriorate. A public water company has now built a large main carrying water of a satisfactory quality to a point within 3 miles of the university's present pumping station. The decision has been made to build a pipe line connecting to the water company's main and to purchase water. Two alternative types of pipe are considered to supply the needs for a 60-year period, with estimates as follows:

	Type A	Type B
Initial investment in pipe	$120,000	$80,000
Estimated life of pipe	60 years	30 years
Initial investment in pumping equipment	$15,000	$20,000
Estimated life of pumping equipment.	20 years	20 years
Annual energy cost for pumping in first year	$3,000	$4,000
Yearly increase in energy cost for pumping	$60	$80

Using a 60-year study period, compare the equivalent uniform annual costs that will be influenced by the choice of the type of pipe. Use an i^* of 6%. (Because the university is a nonprofit organization, no income taxes are involved.) Assume zero net terminal salvage values for pipe and pumping equipment and assume that renewal costs during the 60-year period will be the same as the initial investment.

6–11. A school district considers two alternative plans for an athletic stadium. An engineer makes the following cost estimates for each:

Concrete Bleachers. First cost, $350,000. Life, 90 years. Annual upkeep cost, $2,500.

Wooden Bleachers on Earth Fill. First cost of entire project, $200,000. Painting cost every 3 years, $10,000. New seats every 15 years, $40,000. New bleachers every 30 years, $100,000. Earth fill will last for the entire 90-year period.

Compare equivalent uniform annual costs for a 90-year period using an i^* of 7%.

6–12. Two types of heat exchanger are to be compared for service in a chemical plant. Type Y has a first cost of $8,400, an estimated life of 6 years with zero salvage value, and annual operating costs of $1,700. Type Z has a first cost of $10,800, an estimated life of 9 years with zero salvage value, and annual operating costs of $1,500. Estimated extra annual income taxes with Type Z are $200.

Compare equivalent uniform annual costs using an after-tax i° of 15%.

6-13. Annual disbursements (other than driver's wages) for operation and maintenance of certain trucks under particular operating conditions tend to increase by $300 a year for the first 5 years of operation; first-year disbursements are $2,400. The first cost of a truck is $5,400. The estimated salvage value after 4 years is $1,400; after 5 years it is $900. In the long run, it is estimated income taxes will be about the same with a 4-year or 5-year life. Using an i° of 10%, compare the equivalent uniform annual costs of a truck held for 4 years with one held for 5 years.

6-14. Machine J has a first cost of $50,000, an estimated service period of 12 years, and an estimated salvage value of $20,000 at the end of the 12 years. Estimated annual disbursements for operation and maintenance are $6,000 for the first year, $6,300 the 2nd year, and will increase $300 each year thereafter. An alternate is Machine K, which has a first cost of $30,000 and an estimated zero salvage value at the end of the 12-year service period. Estimated annual disbursements for operation and maintenance are $8,000 for the first year, $8,500 the 2nd year, and will increase $500 each year thereafter. Estimated extra income taxes with Machine J are $1,000 the first year, $1,100 the 2nd, and will increase $100 each year thereafter. Using an after-tax i° of 10%, compare the equivalent uniform annual costs of a 12-year service from Machines J and K.

6-15. A manufacturer proposes to build a new warehouse. A reinforced concrete building will cost $116,000, whereas the same amount of space can be secured in a frame and galvanized metal building for $60,000. The life of the concrete building is estimated as 50 years; average annual maintenance cost is estimated as $1,000. The life of the frame building is estimated to be 25 years; average annual maintenance cost is estimated as $1,800. Fire insurance will be carried on the building and its contents in either case; the annual rate will be $1.50 per $1,000 of insurance for the concrete building and $4.00 per $1,000 of insurance for the frame building. Assume that the average amount of insurance will be on contents of $400,000 plus 75% of first cost of the building. Average annual property taxes are estimated at 1.5% of the first cost. The deductible expenses for income taxes for the frame building will exceed those for the concrete building, resulting in the payment of extra income taxes of $545 per year if the concrete building is chosen. Find the comparative equivalent uniform annual costs for the two types of warehouse using an after-tax i° of 8%. Neglect any possible salvage values at the ends of the lives of the buildings.

6-16. Make a comparison of annual costs before income taxes for the two proposed warehouses in Problem 6-15, using a before-tax i° of 15%.

7

Present Worth

> Because today's capital expenditures make the bed that the company must lie in tomorrow, today's decisions must be based on definite assumptions as to what tomorrow will be like.—JOEL DEAN [1]

Two uses of present worth calculations in engineering economy are explained and illustrated in this chapter, namely:

1. Comparison of alternative series of estimated money receipts and disbursements.
2. Placing a valuation on prospective net money receipts.

A third important use of present worth, discussed in Chapter 8, is for trial-and-error calculations to determine unknown rates of interest or rates of return.

Because calculation of present worth is often called *discounting*, writers on economics often refer to an interest rate used in present worth calculations as a *discount rate*.

Use of Present Worth To Compare Plans A, B, and C of Examples 6–1 and 6–2. It will be recalled that Plans A, B, and C involved, respectively, annual disbursements of $9,200, $6,400, and $5,750 for a 10-year period. Plan A had no first cost; Plan B had $15,000 first cost and zero salvage value; Plan C had $25,000 first cost and $5,000 salvage value. The stipulated i^* was 8%. The data for the following calculations consist of these estimates of cash flow for the three plans; no use is made of the annual costs that were calculated in Chapter 6.

Plan A

PW of annual disbursements
= $9,200(P/A,8%,10) = $9,200(6.710)   = $61,730

Plan B

PW of annual disbursements
= $6,400(P/A,8%,10) = $6,400(6.710)   = $42,940
First cost   15,000
PW of all disbursements for 10 years $57,940

[1] Joel Dean, "Measuring the Productivity of Capital," Harvard Business Review, XXXII, No. 1, (January–February, 1954), p. 122.

Plan C

PW of annual disbursements = \$5,750(P/A,8%,10) = \$5,750(6.710)	= \$38,580
First cost	25,000
PW of all moneys paid out for 10 years	\$63,580

Less

PW of salvage value = \$5,000(P/F,8%,10) = \$5,000(0.4632)	= 2,320
PW of net disbursements for 10 years	\$61,260

Present worths are calculated as of the zero date of the series of payments being compared. Because first costs are already at zero date, no interest factors need to be applied to first cost. Where an estimated salvage value occurs, as in Plan C, the present worths of the salvage value must be subtracted to obtain the present worth of the net disbursements.

Simplicity of Conversion from Present Worth to Annual Cost and Vice Versa. In Chapter 6 the equivalent uniform annual costs for these three plans were calculated directly from the estimated cash flows. An alternate way to find annual costs would be to calculate them from the present worths. Each present worth can be converted into an equivalent uniform annual series by multiplying it by 0.14903, the capital recovery factor for 8% and 10 years.

Annual cost, Plan A = \$61,730(0.14903) = \$9,200
Annual cost, Plan B = \$57,940(0.14903) = \$8,635
Annual cost, Plan C = \$61,260(0.14903) = \$9,130

These figures, of course, are substantially identical with the annual cost figures obtained in Chapter 6. (There is a \$1 difference in Plan C due to loss of significant figures by rounding.) In a similar manner an alternate way to have computed the present worths for the three plans would have been to multiply each annual cost calculated in Chapter 6 by 6.710, the series present worth factor for 8% and 10 years.

The general statement may be made that annual cost can be calculated from present worth by multiplying present worth by the appropriate capital recovery factor; present worth can be calculated from annual cost by multiplying annual cost by the appropriate series present worth factor (or dividing by the capital recovery factor). The alternative that is favored in an annual cost comparison is also favored in a present worth comparison, and by the same proportion. For example, the annual cost of Plan B is 5.4% below the annual cost of Plan C; the present worth of B is also 5.4% below C. Of course this convertibility between annual cost and present worth depends on the use of the same interest rate in both calculations and on the use of identical cash flow estimates for the same period of years.

Where alternatives involve irregular series of payments, the first step in computing annual costs should be to find the present worths.

EXAMPLE 7–1. COMPARISON OF ALTERNATIVES INVOLVING IRREGULAR SERIES OF DISBURSEMENTS

Statement of Alternatives. Engineers for a public utility company have proposed two alternate plans to provide a certain service for the next 15 years. Each plan includes sufficient facilities to take care of the expected growth of the demand for the particular utility service during this period.

Plan F calls for a three-stage program of investment in facilities; $60,000 will be invested at once, $50,000 more after 5 years, and $40,000 more after 10 years. Plan G, a two-stage program, calls for a $90,000 immediate investment followed by a $30,000 investment at the end of 8 years. In both plans estimated annual income taxes are 3% of the investment that has been made up to date and estimated annual property taxes are 2% of the investment to date. Annual maintenance costs in Plan F are estimated as $1,500 for the first 5 years, $2,500 for the second 5 years, and $3,500 for the final 5 years. For Plan G, annual maintenance costs are estimated as $2,000 for the first 8 years and $3,000 for the final 7 years. Salvage value at the end of 15 years is estimated to be $45,000 for Plan F and $35,000 for Plan G.

Table 7–1 presents the foregoing estimates as a tabulation of cash flows. For purposes of the economy study, a minimum attractive rate of return of 7% is to be used.

Comparison of Present Worths. The present worths of the respective net disbursements for 15 years may be computed as follows:

Plan F

Initial investment		$ 60,000
PW of investment made after 5 years		
$= \$50,000(P/F,7\%,5) = \$50,000(0.7130)$	=	35,650
PW of investment made after 10 years		
$= \$40,000(P/F,7\%,10) = \$40,000(0.5083)$	=	20,330
PW of annual disbursements, years 1 to 5		
$= \$4,500(P/A,7\%,5) = \$4,500(4.100)$	=	18,450
PW of annual disbursements, years 6 to 10		
$= \$8,000(P/A,7\%,10 \text{ minus } P/A,7\%,5)$		
$= \$8,000(7.024 - 4.100) = \$8,000(2.924)$	=	23,390
PW of annual disbursements, years 11 to 15		
$= \$11,000(P/A,7\%,15 \text{ minus } P/A,7\%,10)$		
$= \$11,000(9.108 - 7.024) = \$11,000(2.084)$	=	22,920
PW of all moneys paid out for 15 years		$180,740

Less

PW of salvage value		
$= \$45,000(P/F,7\%,15)$		
$= \$45,000(0.3624)$	=	16,310
PW of net disbursements for 15 years		$164,430

Plan G

Initial investment	$90,000
PW of investment made after 8 years	
$= \$30,000(P/F,7\%,8) = \$30,000(0.5820)$	$=$ 17,460
PW of annual disbursements, years 1 to 8	
$= \$6,500(P/A,7\%,8) = \$6,500(5.971)$	$=$ 38,810
PW of annual disbursements, years 9 to 15	
$= \$9,000(P/A,7\%,15 \text{ minus } P/A,7\%,8)$	
$= \$9,000(9.108 - 5.971) = \$9,000(3.137)$	$=$ 28,230
PW of all moneys paid out for 15 years	$\$174,500$

Less

PW of salvage value	
$= \$35,000(P/F,7\%,15) = \$35,000(0.3624)$	$=$ 12,680
PW of net disbursements for 15 years	$\$161,820$

TABLE 7–1

Tabulation of Cash Flow, Example 7–1

Year	Plan F	Plan G	G − F
0	−$60,000	−$90,000	−$30,000
1	−4,500	−6,500	−2,000
2	−4,500	−6,500	−2,000
3	−4,500	−6,500	−2,000
4	−4,500	−6,500	−2,000
5	{ −4,500 { −50,000	{ −6,500 {	{ −2,000 { +50,000
6	−8,000	−6,500	+1,500
7	−8,000	−6,500	+1,500
8	{ −8,000 {	{ −6,500 { −30,000	{ +1,500 { −30,000
9	−8,000	−9,000	−1,000
10	{ −8,000 { −40,000	{ −9,000 {	{ −1,000 { +40,000
11	−11,000	−9,000	+2,000
12	−11,000	−9,000	+2,000
13	−11,000	−9,000	+2,000
14	−11,000	−9,000	+2,000
15	{ −11,000 { +45,000	{ −9,000 { +35,000	{ +2,000 { −10,000
Totals	−$222,500	−$200,000	+$22,500

Comparison of Annual Costs. To compute equivalent uniform annual costs for the 15-year period, the respective present worths must be multiplied by the crf for 7% and 15 years.

Plan F

$$\text{Annual cost} = \$164,430(0.10979) = \$18,050$$

Plan G

$$\text{Annual cost} = \$161,820(0.10979) = \$17,770$$

Which Plan Should Be Selected? The present worth (and annual cost) of Plan G is only slightly less than that of Plan F. Here is a case where a small change in the basic estimates for the two plans (either in amount or timing of cash flows) could have altered the present worths enough to shift the balance in favor of Plan F. Generally speaking, when a comparison is as close as this one, the decision should be made on the basis of any differences between the plans that have not been reduced to money estimates—on the so-called irreducible data entering into the problem of choice. Further comment is made in Appendix B regarding certain other aspects of this example.

Present Worth Comparisons When Alternatives Have Different Lives. There is no point in converting two or more alternative cash flow series into present worth and then comparing the present worths unless the cash flow series relate to a provision of a needed service for the same number of years.

Some of the difficulties arising in comparing alternatives with different lives were discussed in Chapter 6. In our discussion there it was pointed out that a convenient simple assumption is that replacement assets will repeat the costs that have been forecast for the initial asset. In the present chapter we shall continue to make this assumption; a more critical look at the matter will be deferred until Chapter 13 and thereafter. Sometimes it is desirable to choose an arbitrary analysis period that is shorter than the expected service period, with valuations assigned to all assets at the end of the analysis period; this technique is illustrated in Example 9–1 and discussed further in Chapter 13.

If the assumption is made that costs will be repeated for replacement assets, a study period can be selected that is the least common multiple of the lives of the various assets involved. Or, in some cases a present worth study may be for a perpetual period. Usually present worths for an assumed perpetual period of service are referred to as *capitalized costs*.

Illustration of a Comparison of Present Worths for a Least Common Multiple of the Lives of the Alternatives. It will be recalled that in Example 6–3, Plan D had $50,000 first cost, 20-year life, $10,000 salvage value, and $9,000 annual disbursements; Plan E had $120,000 first cost, 40-year life, $20,000 salvage value, and $7,250 annual disbursements. Table 6–3, page 79, shows estimated cash flow for a 40-year period. The interest rate was 8%. A comparison of the present worths of a 40-year service, computed directly from the cash flow data, is as follows:

Plan D

First cost	$ 50,000
PW of net disbursement for renewal in 20 years	
$= (\$50,000 - \$10,000)(P/F,8\%,20)$	
$= \$40,000(0.2145)$	$=$ 8,580
PW of annual disbursements	
$= \$9,000(P/A,8\%,40) = \$9,000(11.925)$	$=$ 107,320
Total PW of disbursements	$165,900

Less

PW of receipt from final salvage value after 40 years
  $= \$10,000(P/F,8\%,40)$
  $= \$10,000(0.0460)$ = $\underline{\hspace{1cm} 460}$

PW of net disbursements for 40 years = $\$165,440$

Plan E

First cost	$\$120,000$
PW of annual disbursements	
$= \$7,250(P/A,8\%,40) = \$7,250(11.925)$	$\underline{\hspace{1cm} 86,460}$
Total PW of disbursements	$\$206,460$

Less

PW of receipt from salvage value after 40 years
  $= \$20,000(P/F,8\%,40)$
  $= \$20,000(0.0460)$ = $\underline{\hspace{1cm} 920}$

PW of net disbursements for 40 years = $\$205,540$

It will be noted that in Plan D, the $10,000 receipt from salvage of the first asset was subtracted from the $50,000 investment in the renewal asset in order to find the net disbursement required after 20 years; the $40,000 figure thus obtained was then multiplied by the 20-year present worth factor. However, it was necessary to make a separate calculation of the present worth of the receipt from the final salvage value after 40 years and to subtract this present worth from the present worth of all disbursements.

In Chapter 13, we shall discuss the subject of the sensitivity of the conclusions of an economy study to moderate changes in the estimates. It is evident from the present worth comparison of Plans D and E that the estimates of salvage values after 40 years have very little influence on the choice between the plans; a dollar 40 years hence is equivalent to only 4.6 cents today when interest is at 8%. In general, it may be stated that comparisons of economy are not sensitive to changes in estimated distant salvage values unless the interest rate used is very low.

Moreover, in comparing Plans D and E, the choice is relatively insensitive to the estimated cost of the renewal asset in Plan D. For example, if the estimated net disbursement for the renewal asset 20 years hence should be doubled, the total present worth for Plan D would be increased by only $8,580; Plan D would still be considerably more economical than Plan E.

The present worths for Plans D and E may be converted into annual costs by multiplying them by the crf for 8% and 40 years:

Annual cost, Plan D $= \$165,440(0.08386) = \$13,874$
Annual cost, Plan E $= \$205,540(0.08386) = \$17,236$

Of course, these annual cost figures agree with the ones that were computed directly from the cash flow series in Example 6–3 (page 77).

Capitalized Cost. The calculation of the present worth of perpetual service may be illustrated by comparing Plans D and E, as follows:

Plan D

First cost	$ 50,000
PW of infinite series of renewals	
$= (\$50,000 - \$10,000)(A/F,8\%,20) \div 0.08$	
$= \$40,000(0.02185) \div 0.08 = \$874 \div 0.08$	$=$ 10,925
PW of perpetual annual disbursements	
$= \$9,000 \div 0.08$	$=$ 112,500
Total capitalized cost	$173,425

Plan E

First cost	$120,000
PW of infinite series of renewals	
$= (\$120,000 - \$20,000)(A/F,8\%,40) \div 0.08$	
$= \$100,000(0.00386) \div 0.08$	$=$ 4,825
PW of perpetual annual disbursements	
$= \$7,250 \div 0.08$	$=$ 90,625
Total capitalized cost	$215,450

The calculation of the present worth of an infinite series of renewals starts with the conversion of the periodic renewal cost into an equivalent perpetual uniform annual series. Thus $40,000 at the end of any 20-year period is multiplied by the 20-year sinking factor to convert it to $874, a uniform annual figure throughout the 20-year period. Therefore, $40,000 at the end of every 20th year is equivalent to $874 a year forever. The present worth of this infinite series in Plan D is then $874 ÷ 0.08 = $10,925.

It will be noted that the figures for the present worths of perpetual service in Plans D and E are only slightly greater than the previous figures for the present worths of 40 years' service. The $42,025 advantage for Plan D in capitalized cost is not much more than the $40,100 advantage in present worth of 40 years' service. Considered from the viewpoint of present worth at 8%, the difference between 40 years and forever is small.

Capitalized costs are simply annual costs divided by the interest rate. The annual cost in Plan D was $13,874; the capitalized cost is $13,874 ÷ 0.08 = $173,425.

Effects of Anticipated Growth of Demand on the Choice Between an Immediate and a Deferred Investment. An engineer is often concerned with trying to get something done that must be completed tomorrow at two o'clock or that has some similar urgency concerned with it. In such circumstances it is sometimes better to make a second-rate decision immediately than to make a first-rate one at some later time. Nevertheless, decisions made only with a view to meeting immediate emergencies are likely to prove costly in the long run.

Piecemeal construction, in which each piece of apparatus is installed to meet a present emergency without regard to its adequacy under prospective future conditions, will ordinarily be less economical than development of a long-range planned expansion. Where planning is neglected, mistakes are likely to be made that will cost a great deal more to correct than they would have cost to avoid. A forecast of growth is an essential part of engineering designs.

In a program of planned development the installation of extra capacity as part of the original construction is likely to require less money outlay than will be required to add this capacity when needed in the future. This saving in money outlay may be due to the inherently lower costs per unit of capacity that are often associated with larger units. It may be due to the fact that future changes involve expenses that are avoidable when excess capacity is provided initially. As an example, each addition to the capacity of any underground conduit in a city's streets requires a ditch that must be refilled and repaved.

This necessity of providing excess capacity against an expected growth of demand exists whenever that growth is reasonably certain to occur and where its rate may be predicted with some degree of confidence in the forecast. This is usually the situation in the engineering of most public utility equipment. Example 7–2 deals with the calculations that are appropriate once forecasts of growth have been made.

EXAMPLE 7–2. COMPARING AN IMMEDIATE WITH A DEFERRED INVESTMENT

A Preliminary Solution Considering Investments Only. Cost comparisons to determine whether a proposed investment in capacity that is in excess of present needs is economically justifiable are usually made on a present worth basis. The degree of complexity of the calculations will depend on the assumptions made by the estimator. An example of an economy study in which these assumptions are very simple is as follows:

In the design of an aqueduct for municipal water supply, a tunnel is necessary. It is estimated that a tunnel built to half the ultimate capacity of the aqueduct will be adequate for 20 years. However, because of certain fixed elements in the cost of tunnel construction, it is estimated that a full-capacity tunnel can be built now for $300,000 as compared with $200,000 for a half-capacity tunnel. The problem is whether to build the full-capacity tunnel now, or to build a half-capacity tunnel now—supplementing it by a parallel half-capacity tunnel when needed.

At first glance it appears as if the disbursements to be compared are as follows:

Full Capacity Now	*Half Capacity Now*
$300,000 now	$200,000 now
	$200,000 20 years hence

Since the $200,000 present investment necessary in either case can be canceled out as irrelevant, this appears to be the question of whether it is better to spend $100,000 now or $200,000 in 20 years. If interest is taken at 5%, the present worth of $200,000 20 years hence is $200,000(0.3769) = $75,400. This indicates an advantage of $24,600 in present worth for the half-capacity plan.

This solution to the problem implies "all other things being equal." Two matters that might not be equal are the expected service lives with the two plans, and their respective operation and maintenance costs.

A Solution Considering Capitalized Operation and Maintenance Costs. In these circumstances it might be reasonable to assume the expected service lives as perpetual for both plans; if this assumption is made, the two plans do not differ in expected service life. However, there does appear to be a prospective difference in operation and maintenance costs. (In studies of this character there is sometimes a tendency to neglect the possibility of such differences; this tendency should be resisted by an examination of the circumstances to see if differences are likely to occur.)

Let us assume that in this situation the estimator notes that the two half-capacity tunnels will involve a larger area of tunnel lining with correspondingly greater periodic costs of lining repairs. Lining repair costs for the full-capacity tunnel is estimated as $10,000 every 10 years; for each half-capacity tunnel it is estimated as $8,000 every 10 years. The estimator also notes that friction losses will be somewhat greater in the half-capacity tunnel; it is estimated that this will increase pumping costs in the aqueduct line by $1,000 a year so long as a single tunnel is in use, and by $2,000 a year after the second tunnel has come into use. It now appears as if the disbursements to be compared for perpetual service with the two plans are as follows:

Full Capacity Now	*Half Capacity Now*
$300,000 now	$200,000 now
10,000 10 years hence and every 10th year thereafter	8,000 10 years hence and every 10th year thereafter
	1,000 a year forever
	200,000 in 20 years
	8,000 30 years hence and every 10th year thereafter
	1,000 a year, starting 20 years hence

With interest at 5%, a capitalized cost comparison of these alternatives is as follows:

Full Capacity Now

Investment	$300,000
Lining repairs $10,000 $\left(\dfrac{0.07950}{0.05}\right)$	15,900
Total capitalized cost	$315,900

Half Capacity Now

First tunnel:

Investment	$200,000
Lining repairs $8,000 $\left(\dfrac{0.07950}{0.05}\right)$	12,720
Extra pumping costs $\left(\dfrac{\$1,000}{0.05}\right)$	20,000

Second tunnel:

Investment $200,000(0.3769) .... $ 75,380
Lining repairs $12,720(0.3769)   4,790
Extra pumping costs $20,000(0.3769)   7,540
                                                              $320,430

The recognition of the higher operation and maintenance costs associated with the half-capacity plan therefore shifts the advantage to the full-capacity plan. The rate of return on the extra $100,000 investment is evidently slightly greater than the 5% interest rate assumed in this calculation; that is, a slightly higher interest rate would result in the two plans having the same capitalized cost.

Annual Cost vs. Present Worth for Comparing Alternative Series of Disbursements. Historically, present worth methods have been advocated by a number of writers on engineering economy.[2] Capitalized costs were widely used for many years, particularly by civil engineers. The widespread use of capitalized costs probably had its origin in Wellington's classic work *The Economic Theory of Railway Location* (1887). This— in a day in which most engineers worked for railways during at least part of their careers—influenced the thinking of the entire engineering profession. Wellington—considering that many elements of the railway had perpetual life—would divide an expected saving by the interest rate to determine the justifiable increase in first cost to bring about that estimated saving.

For most economy studies comparing mutually exclusive design alternatives, the authors of this book prefer comparisons of equivalent uniform annual costs to comparisons of present worths. The most important advantage is that, generally speaking, people seem to understand annual costs better than they understand present worths. A relatively minor advantage is that annual costs are usually somewhat easier to compute except in circumstances such as Examples 7–1 and 7–2 where irregular series of disbursements are involved.

Nevertheless, when present investments are large in proportion to other disbursements, it seems natural to make comparisons on a present worth basis. This often is the case in a comparison of immediate and deferred investments such as was illustrated in Example 7–2.

It already has been emphasized that, given the same interest rate and the same estimated series of disbursements, comparisons by annual cost lead to the same conclusions as comparisons by present worth.

[2] Goldman's *Financial Engineering* (New York: John Wiley & Sons, Inc., 1921) developed the subject of engineering economy through capitalized cost comparisons; the term coined for capitalized cost in this book was "vestance." Johannesson in his *Highway Economics* (New York: McGraw-Hill Book Co., Inc., 1931) based nearly all his comparisons on capitalized cost, assuming perpetual life for most highway improvements.

Nevertheless, certain serious errors in the basic data of economy studies seem to have been more common when analysts have used present worth methods.

Some Common Errors When Present Worth Comparisons Are Used. Three errors that the authors have often observed in present worth studies are as follows:

1. Perpetual lives are assumed, particularly in capitalized cost comparisons, even though the observed facts indicate that the lives of the proposed machines and structures are likely to be fairly short.

2. The dates when accounting charges are to be made are substituted for the dates of expected disbursements before the present worths are computed. As an example, assume a proposed structure with a first cost of $100,000 and an estimated life of 50 years with zero salvage value. If straight-line depreciation accounting (explained in Chapter 10) is used, the annual depreciation charge in the accounts will be $2,000 (i.e., $100,000 ÷ 50) for 50 years. An uncritical analyst might add this $2,000 a year to the expected disbursements during each year and then convert his annual total to present worth at zero date at, say, 5% interest. As the present worth of $2,000 a year for 50 years at 5% is $36,500, he has, in effect, converted $100,000 at zero date to $36,500 at zero date. This peculiar result comes from the use of two interest rates in a series of conversions, one forward through 50 years at 0%, the other backward through the same years at 5%. By such confused conversions using two interest rates, it is possible to appear to prove that three is equal to one— or to any other figure!

3. Interest rates used in present worth comparisons are frequently too low.

The pointing out of these common errors is an indictment of analysts using present worth methods rather than of the methods themselves. But the evidence obtained from examination of many economy studies is that many of the cost comparisons that have been made by present worth methods have, in fact, led to incorrect conclusions for the reasons that have been outlined.

What Is a "Conservative" Interest Rate To Use in a Present Worth Comparison? The purpose of the interest calculations in economy studies is to determine whether proposed investments are justified— whether it seems likely that they will be recovered with at least a stipulated minimum attractive rate of return. For reasons that are explained in Chapter 11, this rate often should be considerably higher than the bare cost of borrowed money.

If the question were asked, "How large an endowment fund is required to endow a scholarship of $1,000 a year?" it is obvious that the answer should be obtained by capitalizing $1,000 a year at an interest rate that can be obtained on securities involving a minimum risk of loss. This will be a low interest rate, perhaps 4% or 5%.

The present worth of the disbursements required for a given service may be described as the sum of money necessary to endow that service. This description of present worth sometimes leads analysts to the selection of an interest rate appropriate to an endowment fund; such a rate is viewed as a "conservative" one. Such analysts fail to recognize that the economy-study calculations are made to guide a decision between alternatives and that no actual endowment is contemplated.

The use in economy studies of a low interest rate appropriate to endowment funds has the effect of making alternatives requiring higher investments appear to be desirable even though they show the prospect of yielding a relatively small return. The interest rate used for present worth conversions in economy studies usually should be considerably higher than an endowment-type rate; it should be the rate of return required to justify an added investment considering all of the circumstances of the case.

An Estimate of the Value of an Income-Producing Property to a Present or Prospective Owner Implies a Present Worth Calculation. Many different kinds of property are acquired for the purpose of securing prospective future money receipts in excess of the future disbursements, if any, associated with the ownership of the property.

To determine the maximum amount that it is reasonable to pay for any such income-producing property, the following are required:

1. An estimate of the amounts and dates of prospective money receipts resulting from ownership of the property
2. An estimate of the amounts and dates of prospective money disbursements resulting from ownership of the property
3. A decision on the minimum attractive rate of return required to justify this investment in the light of its risk and in the light of returns available from other prospective investments
4. A calculation to determine the net present worth, that is, the excess of the present worth of the prospective receipts over the present worth of the prospective disbursements

If the purchase price of the income-producing property is greater than this computed net present worth, the estimates indicate that the property will fall short of earning its minimum attractive rate of return. Hence if reliance is to be placed on these estimates, the purchase of the property is not attractive.

The same set of estimates and calculations is appropriate in judging the value of a property to its present owner. Generally speaking, a property is worth to its owner at least the net amount for which he can sell it (i.e., the amount to be received from the sale minus the disbursements incident to the sale). In other words, market value in the sense of the net price for which a property could actually be sold tends to place a *lower* limit on the value of a property to its owner. If the sole service of a property to its owner is to produce future net money receipts, an *upper* limit on the value of a property to its owner is generally placed by the excess of present worth of prospective receipts over prospective disbursements. If this present worth is less than the net price for which the property can be sold, it will ordinarily pay to sell the property.

Other factors entering into the estimate of the value of a property to its owner are discussed in later chapters. One important factor is the cost of replacement with an equally desirable substitute.

The remainder of this chapter gives examples of the calculation of net present worth for three different types of income-producing property, as follows:

1. A series of uniform annual payments for a limited number of years
2. A perpetual series of uniform annual payments
3. A government bond

The general subject of the present worth aspects of valuation is explored further by a number of problems and examples throughout the remainder of this book.

Valuation of Uniform Annual Series. It was shown in Plan III of Table 3–1 that the present worth of $1,358.68 a year for 10 years was $10,000 with interest at 6%. The influence of interest rate on value may be observed if we consider the question of how much an investor would be willing to pay for the prospect of these payments if he required a 7% return on his investment. Here $P = \$1,358.68(P/A,7\%,10) = \$1,358.68-(7.024) = \$9,543$. If he were satisfied with a 5% return, he would pay $\$1,358.68(P/A,5\%,10) = \$1,358.68(7.722) = \$10,492$.

Valuation of Perpetual Annual Series. As has already been pointed out in Chapter 5, the present worth of a perpetual uniform annual series is the annual payment divided by the interest rate; this stretches the definition of present worth to mean the investment that will provide—as interest on it—a desired annual payment forever.

Whenever an investment is made where the termination of the income series at a definite time is not contemplated, valuation calculations are likely to be made on this basis. Thus, a stock paying an annual dividend of $6 would be valued at $120 on a 5% basis. The implications of such valuations should be recognized by those who make them; it is unlikely that the corporation will continue its existence forever—or that dividends will always be paid at exactly the present rate—or that a given investor's ownership of the stock will continue indefinitely. Consideration should be given to the question of whether or not the assumption of perpetuity is a fairly close approximation to what is anticipated, before using calculation methods that assume perpetuity.

This comment is also pertinent with respect to comparisons of economy on the basis of capitalized cost, such as are described in this chapter. This limitation particularly applies to the determination of the investment that may be justified by a prospective annual saving.

EXAMPLE 7–3. VALUATION OF A BOND

Expected Cash Flow. Most corporation bonds and many bonds issued by governments are promises to pay interest, usually semiannually, at a given rate, and to pay the principal of the bond at a definite future date. Consider a 3.5%, $10,000 government bond due after 25 years. This calls for a payment of $175 every six months during the 25-year period and a payment of $10,000 at the end of the 25 years. Assume that this bond is to be valued to yield a nominal 5% compounded semiannually.

Calculation of Present Worth. Because this is a nominal rate and the interest period is half a year, present worths should be computed using an i of 2.5%, i.e., half of 5%. The value of the bond is the sum of the present worths of the interest payments and the principal payment, as follows:

PW of 50 interest payments
$$= \$175(P/A,50,2.5\%) - \$175(28.362) \qquad = \$4,963$$
PW of principal payment
$$= \$10,000(P/F,50,2.5\%) = \$10,000(0.2909) = \underline{\ 2,909}$$
Value of bond to yield a nominal 5%,
  compounded semiannually $\qquad\qquad\qquad$ $7,872

This 5% is, of course, the *before-tax* yield to a buyer at this price; we have not considered the effect of the bond ownership on his payments of income taxes.

There are published bond value tables that give the relation between price and yield to the investor for bonds with various coupon rates and years to maturity. In the common case where such tables are available, calculations of the type illustrated in this example are unnecessary.

Compound Amount Comparisons in Economy Studies. Money time series may be compared by converting them to equivalent single payments at some specified date; the present usually is the most convenient date. With respect to economy studies regarding proposed investments, the "present" is usually the beginning of the period of time under consideration. An alternative possible date is the end of this period; this requires compound amount conversions rather than present worth conversions.

Although such compound amount comparisons are occasionally used in economy studies, the use of compound amount would seem to have no merit not possessed by present worth. On the other hand, small changes in the interest rate have a deceptively large effect on the differences in compound amount. Hence the chances of misinterpretation of a compound amount study would seem much greater than the chances of misinterpretation of a study based on present worth.

Summary. Valuation of prospective future series of net money receipts is a problem in present worth. In economy studies the comparison of estimated disbursements for alternative plans may be done by present worth conversions. If such comparisons are for a limited number of years of service, the present worth of the cost of the same number of years of service should be calculated for each alternative. When such comparisons are of the present worth of the cost of perpetual service, they are termed capitalized cost comparisons.

The interest rate used in conversions for economy studies should be the rate of return required to justify an investment; this applies to present worth conversions as well as to annual cost conversions. For various reasons, present worth comparisons in economy studies seem more difficult to interpret than annual cost comparisons. Except in certain special situations to which present worth comparisons seem particularly adapted, it is recommended that annual cost comparisons be preferred.

PROBLEMS

7–1. For a given pumping service for a regulated public utility, it is proposed to use either a 10-in. or a 12-in. pipe. The 10-in. pipe has a first cost of $4,500 and the annual pumping cost is estimated as $900. The 12-in. pipe has a first cost of $6,000 and the annual pumping cost is estimated as $550. The service will be required for 15 years; no salvage value is expected for either pipe at the end of this period. Annual property taxes are estimated as 2% of first cost and annual income taxes as 3% of first cost. Compare the present worths of the cost of 15 years' service, using an interest rate of 6%. ($Ans. =$ $15,426 for 10-in.; $14,256 for 12-in.)

7–2. The following alternatives are being considered for a governmental service. Compare the present worths of the cost of 24 years' service, using an i^* of 6%.

	Structure Y	Structure Z
First cost	$9,000	$20,000
Estimated life	12 years	24 years
Estimated salvage value	none	$4,000
Annual disbursements	$2,200	$1,400

($Ans. =$ Structure Y, $41,080; Structure Z, $36,580.)

7-3. Two alternate plans are being considered in a growth situation for a regulated public utility. Compare the present worths of the costs of 20 years' service, using an i^* of 7% after income taxes.

Plan I requires an immediate investment of $30,000. The life of this plant is 20 years with a $3,000 salvage value at the end of the life. Annual maintenance cost is $2,000. Annual property taxes are 2.5% of first cost and annual income taxes are 4.5% of first cost.

Plan II requires an immediate investment of $20,000 which has a life of 20 years, a $2,000 salvage value at the end of the life, and annual maintenance cost of $1,600. Tax rates are the same as in Plan I. This will be supplemented by an additional investment of $12,000 in 10 years. This latter plant will have a life of 10 years, a $3,000 salvage value, annual maintenance cost of $1,200, property taxes of 2.5% of first cost, and income taxes of 5.0% of first cost. (*Ans.* = Plan I, $72,600; Plan II, $64,090.)

7-4. Two possible types of road surface are being considered with cost estimates per mile as follows:

	Type A	Type B
First cost	$21,000	$32,000
Resurfacing period	10 years	15 years
Resurfacing cost	$11,000	$12,000
Average annual upkeep cost	$1,300	$900

The periodic resurfacings will involve replacement only of the wearing surface and not of the base or subsurface. Compare these on the basis of the present worth of the cost of 30 years service, assuming zero terminal salvage value for both types at the end of 30 years and using an i^* of 7%. (*Ans.* = Type A, $45,560; Type B, $47,520.)

7-5. A promissory note is offered for sale on which the yearly payments are $587. There are 11 annual payments still due, the first one of these due one year from now. How much should an investor pay for this note in order to get 8% interest, compounded annually, before income taxes? To get 7%? To get 6%? (*Ans.* = 8%, $4,191; 7%, $4,402; 6%, $4,630.)

7-6. Interest on a 4½%, $5,000 bond due in 20 years is payable semiannually with the first payment 6 months from now. What will be the price of this bond to have a before-tax yield of a nominal 6%, compounded semiannually? (*Ans.* = $4,133.)

7-7. A full program of development of a certain public water supply project is to be compared with a stepped program of development. The full program calls for a $700,000 investment now. The stepped program requires $400,000 now, $300,000 in 10 years, and $300,000 in 20 years. Estimated annual disbursements under the full program are $10,000 more during the first 10 years, equal during the second 10 years, and $5,000 less thereafter. Compare capitalized costs of the two programs using an i^* of 7%. For purposes of this economy study, assume the investments are in permanent construction and that the service is perpetual. (*Ans.* = full program now, $770,240; stepped program, $648,470.)

7-8. In the construction of an aqueduct to serve a city with water, a tunnel is necessary. In order to determine whether it will pay to build this tunnel to the ultimate capacity of the aqueduct, the engineers have forecast the growth of the demand for water in terms of tunnel capacity as follows.

A one-third capacity tunnel will be adequate for 10 years.
A one-half capacity tunnel will be adequate for 20 years.
A two-thirds capacity tunnel will be adequate for 35 years.

Estimated construction costs are as follows:

One-third capacity	$2,000,000
One-half capacity	2,400,000
Two-thirds capacity	2,700,000
Full capacity	3,400,000

Extra pumping costs for the smaller size tunnels above costs for the full capacity tunnel are estimated as follows:

One-third capacity tunnel, running full, $11,000 a year. Thus for an ultimate development of 3 such tunnels the extra pumping costs would be $33,000 a year.

One-half capacity tunnel, running full, $10,000 a year. Thus for an ultimate development of 2 such tunnels the extra pumping costs would be $20,000 a year.

Two-thirds capacity tunnel, running full, $8,000 a year. Thus for an ultimate development of 1 two-thirds and 1 one-third capacity the extra pumping costs would be $19,000 a year.

Set up the four plans of development suggested by these estimates. Compare them on the basis of the capitalized cost of perpetual service, using an i^* of 5% and assuming the continuance of present price levels. In calculating excess pumping costs, assume that the differences in costs given apply from the date a tunnel is put in service. What size tunnel would you recommend for present construction? (*Ans.* = two-thirds capacity now; capitalized cost is $3,263,000.)

7–9. Estimates for alternate plans in the design of certain industrial facilities are:

	Plan R	*Plan S*
First cost	$25,000	$45,000
Life	20 years	30 years
Salvage value	$5,000	none
Annual disbursements	$5,500	$2,800

Estimated extra annual income taxes with Plan S are $1,100. Using an after-tax i^* of 8%, compare the present worths of the net disbursements for 60 years with the two plans. Assume that the replacement facilities in both plans will have the same first costs, lives, salvage values, and annual disbursements as the initial facilities.

7–10. Compare Plans C and D for a proposed public works project on the basis of the capitalized cost of perpetual service using an i^* of 5½%. Plan C calls for an initial investment of $500,000, with disbursements of $20,000 a year for the first 20 years and $30,000 a year thereafter. It also calls for the expenditure of $200,000 at a date 20 years from the date of the initial investment and every 20th year thereafter. Plan D calls for an initial investment of $800,000 followed by a single investment of $300,000 30 years later. It also involves annual expenditures of $10,000.

7–11. Two earth moving machines are being considered for purchase by a construction company. Both machines have the capacity required, but the

Giant is considerably heavier and more rugged than the Trojan and it is believed it will have a longer life. Estimates of the matters that will be influenced by the choice are as follows:

	Trojan	Giant
First cost delivered	$20,000	$28,000
Cost for maintenance and lost time in first year of a machine's service	4,000	3,000
Annual increase in cost of maintenance and lost time during the life of a machine	800	400
Life	4 years	6 years
Terminal salvage value	$4,000	$4,000

The Trojan machine will require a major overhaul costing $5,000 at the end of its first 2 years; the Giant machine will require a major overhaul costing $3,600 at the end of its first 3 years.

Prepare a table comparing the relevant cash flows for a 12-year period assuming that replacement machines will have the same cash flows as the initial machines. Compare the present worths before income taxes using a before-tax i^* of 15%.

7–12. A construction company must set up a temporary office building at a construction site. Two alternate schemes are proposed for heating this building. "Bottled gas" can be used for floor type furnaces, or electric radiant panels can be installed in the walls and ceiling. It is estimated that the building will be used for 5 years before being dismantled.

The gas installation will require an investment of $3,200. It is believed its net realizable value will be zero at the end of the 5 years. The estimated annual fuel and maintenance cost is $800.

The electric radiant panel installation will require an investment of $4,600; it has an estimated salvage value of $1,000. Estimated annual energy and maintenance cost is $500. Choice of the electric installation will cause an estimated extra payment for income taxes of $110 a year.

Compare the present worths of the costs of these two alternatives using an after-tax i^* of 10%.

7–13. Two plans are under consideration to provide certain facilities for a publicly owned public utility. Each plan is designed to provide enough capacity during the next 18 years to take care of the expected growth of load during that period. Regardless of the plan chosen now, it is forecast that the facilities will be retired at the end of 18 years and replaced by a new plant of a different type.

Plan I requires an initial investment of $50,000. This will be followed by an investment of $25,000 at the end of 9 years. During the first 9 years, annual disbursements will be $11,000; during the final 9 years, they will be $18,000. There will be a $10,000 salvage value at the end of the 18th year.

Plan II requires an initial investment of $30,000. This will be followed by an investment of $30,000 at the end of 6 years and an investment of $20,000 at the end of 12 years. During the first 6 years annual disbursements will be $8,000; during the second 6 years they will be $16,000; during the final 6 years they will be $25,000. There will be no salvage value at the end of the 18th year.

Using an i^* of 7%, compare the present worths of the net disbursements for the two plans.

7–14. Interest on a 3%, $10,000 bond, due in 20 years, is payable semi-annually with the first payment 6 months from now. What should be the price of this bond to have a before-tax yield of a nominal 7% compounded semi-annually?

7–15. Interest on a 5¾%, $1,000 bond, due in 16 years, is payable semi-annually with the first payment 6 months from now. What should be the price of this bond to have a before-tax yield of a nominal 5% compounded semi-annually?

7–16. An investor is considering the purchase of a rental property. The excess of receipts over disbursements is estimated as $3,540 a year for 15 years. It is estimated that the property can be sold for $25,000 at the end of the 15 years. At what price for this property would an investor just recover his investment with a 10% rate of return before income taxes?

7–17. The owner of a patent has made a contract with a corporation that is given the exclusive right to use the patent. The corporation has agreed to pay him $1,000 a year at the end of each of the first 4 years during the period of developing a market for the invention, $5,000 at the end of each year for the next 8 years, and $2,000 at the end of each year for the final 5 years of the 17-year life of the patent. At what price would the purchaser receive exactly a 10% return before income taxes?

7–18. Two schemes of partial federal subsidy of public works projects have been used in the United States. In certain types of projects, outright grants have been made to local governmental units for a portion of the construction cost of approved projects, with the remainder of the cost to be repaid by the local units with interest over a period of years. For example, a grant of 30% might be made, with the remaining 70% to be paid at interest over a 20-year period. Another plan of subsidy has been to require the repayment of all the construction cost without any interest. This latter plan is suggested for a proposed college dormitory project. The government is asked to put up $2,000,000 for this project, with the college paying back this amount at $50,000 a year for 40 years.

Assume that, all things considered, an appropriate interest rate to charge on such a "loan" is 5½%. On this assumption, the plan to make the $2,000,000 repayment in 40 years without interest really amounts to a subsidy of how many dollars?

7–19. The XYZ Tile Co. secures its tile clay from property owned by John Doe, adjacent to the tile plant. Some years ago the company made a royalty contract with Doe on which it pays royalties of 50 cents per ton for all clay removed from his property. This contract has 5 years to run. It is estimated that Doe's holdings will supply the company's needs of 20,000 tons per year for the next 15 years before the clay is exhausted. The company owns a large deposit of clay at some distance from the plant; in relation to the company's needs, the deposit may be viewed as practically inexhaustible. Costs of removing the clay would be substantially the same as from Doe's holdings; however, the cost of transporting the clay to the plant would be greatly increased. Doe is aware of this fact; it is believed that a new royalty contract (5 years hence) for the final 10 years would need to provide a royalty rate of $1 per ton. At this royalty rate, it will continue to be advantageous to use Doe's clay rather than the company's more distant holdings.

The president of the XYZ Tile Co. has just learned that Doe would consider an outright sale of his land to the company. By purchasing this land, the company would no longer have to pay royalty for the clay removed. It is believed that at the end of 15 years, when the clay is exhausted, the land can be sold for $10,000.

At what price for this property would the XYZ Co. have an investment that would yield 12% before income taxes as compared to the alternative of continuing to pay royalties?

7–20. A company needs to add boring machine capacity in order to handle its increased business. Typically, the products are very intricate and precise and produced in small quantities. The choice lies between one fully automatic tape controlled machine or two manually controlled machines. The manual machines will cost $36,500 each. They have estimated lives of 20 years with estimated salvage values of $5,000 each. Annual maintenance and energy cost is estimated as $5,000 for each machine. A major overhaul will be required every 5 years at an estimated cost of $3,000 for each machine. Estimated costs of labor and labor extras are $8,000 a year for each machine.

The automatic tape controlled machine consists of the basic machine and the tape control unit. The basic machine will cost $90,000, have an estimated life of 20 years with a salvage value of $6,000. Estimated annual maintenance and energy costs are $3,500. A major overhaul will be required every 5 years at an estimated cost of $6,000. The tape control unit will cost $30,000, have an estimated life of 10 years and a salvage value of $2,500. Its annual maintenance and energy cost will be $1,000. Estimated costs of labor and labor extras are $12,000 a year.

If the automatic machine is selected, the estimated extra annual income tax payment is $2,850. Compare the alternatives on the basis of the present worth of the cost of 20 years service, using an after-tax i^* of 8%.

7–21. The construction cost of a certain federal reclamation project is to be repaid without interest over a period of years. Assume that costs are $250 an acre for a certain farm of 160 acres, a total of $40,000 to be repaid. No payments at all are to be made for the first 5 years. Then $1,000 is to be paid at the end of each year for 40 years to pay off the $40,000 without interest.

It is evident that the omission of interest by the government is, in effect, a subsidy to the farmer. It has been suggested that in this case a measure of the subsidy is the difference between the $40,000 construction cost paid by the government and the present worth of the deferred annuity paid by the farmer. Accepting this suggestion and computing interest at 4½%, what appears to be the amount of the subsidy in this case?

7–22. Compare the capitalized costs of perpetual service of the two plans in Problem 6–9 (page 86). Use the given i^* of 6%.

7–23. Compare the present worths of 60 years of service of the two alternatives in Problem 6–10 (page 86). Use the given i^* of 6%.

7–24. Compare the present worths of 90 years of service of the two types of stadium in Problem 6–11 (page 86). Use the given i^* of 7%.

7–25. Compare the present worths of 12 years of service of Machines J and K in Problem 6–14 (page 87). Use the given after-tax i^* of 10%.

7–26. A donor wishes to endow a scholarship at a certain university. The endowment must be by an addition to the university's "merged general fund." Based on past experience, it is estimated that this fund will have tax-exempt earnings of 4½% per annum.

The donor desires that the scholarship pay the tuition of one student each year. The first award is to be made for a date one year from the date of the gift to the university. The tuition charge for the first year of this scholarship will be $2,120. The university administration predicts that its annual tuition charge will increase by $80 each year and that this yearly increase will continue into the indefinite future.

(a) What gift is necessary to provide tuition scholarships for the next 12 years? Assume that it is possible to pay a part of the scholarship from current endowment income and the remainder by a reduction of the principal of the endowment fund. Assume the endowment fund for this scholarship is to be exhausted when the 12th tuition scholarship is paid.

(b) Assume that the donor wishes to provide a tuition scholarship for the next 12 years and a $3,000 annual scholarship thereafter. What is the amount of the endowment that will accomplish this objective?

8

Calculating an Unknown
Interest Rate

Discounted-cash-flow analysis makes three contributions to top management thinking:

1. An explicit recognition that *time* has economic values to the corporation; hence that near money is more valuable than distant money
2. A recognition that *cash flows* are what matter; hence capitalization accounting and the resulting book depreciation is irrelevant for capital decisions except as it affects taxes
3. A recognition that *income taxes* have such an important effect upon cash flow that their amount and timing must be explicitly figured into project worth—JOEL DEAN [1]

Our examples in Chapters 6 and 7 started with the assumption of an interest rate or minimum attractive rate of return. Calculations were then made to provide a basis for judgment as to whether proposed investments would meet this standard.

Often it is a good idea to compute the prospective rate of return on an investment rather than merely to find out whether the investment meets a given standard of attractiveness. Usually this calculation is carried out to best advantage by a trial-and-error method. Two or more interest rates are assumed, present worths or equivalent uniform annual cash flows are calculated, and the rate of return is found by interpolation.

Moreover, in a number of instances where money is borrowed, the circumstances are such that the cost of borrowed money (expressed as an interest rate) cannot be found without similar trial-and-error calculations. Often, it turns out that the true cost of borrowed money is considerably higher than it is believed to be by the prospective borrower.

Although economy studies necessarily deal with prospective invest-

[1] Joel Dean, Sec. 2, Managerial Economics, in *Handbook of Industrial Engineering and Management*, W. G. Ireson and E. L. Grant, eds. (Englewood Cliffs, N.J.: Prentice-Hall, Inc., 2d ed., copyright 1970).

ments, an example of the finding of the rate of return on a terminated investment may throw light on certain aspects of the subject that need to be understood. Our first example is of this type. It is followed by a number of examples dealing with prospective investments and prospective borrowings. Where disbursements for income taxes can be introduced in a relatively simple way (as in Examples 8–3, 8–5, 8–6, and 8–7), examples and problems involve calculation of rates of return *after* income taxes. However, in cases where the income tax aspects are fairly complicated (Examples 8–1, 8–2, and 8–4), the analysis is for rate of return *before* income taxes. The reasons for the complications in such cases are discussed in Chapter 16. All examples and problems involving the cost of borrowed money expressed as an interest rate deal with this cost *before* income taxes.

EXAMPLE 8–1. RATE OF RETURN ON A PAST INVESTMENT

Facts of the Case. This example relates to a completed 7-year period. Our assumed zero date is January of the first year when an investor purchased a residential rental property for $9,950. As the investor immediately spent $950 for various improvements to the property, his total initial outlay was $10,900. In late December at the end of the seventh year, the property was sold for a gross sales price of $22,000. From this was deducted a 5% broker's commission of $1,100, leaving a net receipt from the sale of $20,900. The second column of Table 8–1 shows the receipts that occurred during the period of ownership. The third column shows all disbursements (other than income taxes), including maintenance costs, property taxes, and insurance. The fourth column combines these figures to give the year-by-year net cash flow before income taxes. Two lines are devoted to the final year (year 7), one showing the receipts and disbursements in connection with rentals and the other showing receipts and disbursements in connection with the sale of the property.

TABLE 8–1

Cash Flow from a Terminated Investment in Rental Property

Year	Receipts	Disbursements	Net Cash Flow
0		−$10,900	−$10,900
1	+$1,500	−500	+1,000
2	+1,800	−550	+1,250
3	+1,800	−570	+1,230
4	+1,800	−450	+1,350
5	+1,800	−360	+1,440
6	+1,800	−430	+1,370
7	+1,700	−410	+1,290
7	+22,000	−1,100	+20,900
Totals	+$34,200	−$15,270	+$18,930

Calculation of Rate of Return. The rate of return is the interest rate at which the present worth of the net cash flow is zero. Here this is the interest rate at which the present worth of the net receipts that occurred in years 1 to 7 is just equal to the $10,900 disbursement that was made at zero date.

TABLE 8–2

Present Worth Calculations for Trial-and-Error Determination of Rate of Return on a Terminated Investment in Rental Property

Year	Net Cash Flow	$(P/F,15\%,n)$	PW at 15%	$(P/F,20\%,n)$	PW at 20%
0	−$10,900	1.0000	−$10,900	1.0000	−$10,900
1	+1,000	0.8696	+870	0.8333	+833
2	+1,250	0.7561	+945	0.6944	+868
3	+1,230	0.6575	+809	0.5787	+712
4	+1,350	0.5718	+772	0.4823	+651
5	+1,440	0.4972	+716	0.4019	+579
6	+1,370	0.4323	+592	0.3349	+459
7	+22,190	0.3759	+8,341	0.2791	+6,193
Totals	+$18,930		+$ 2,145		−$ 605

In the present worth calculations in Table 8–2, the end-of-year convention has been used. (It will be recalled that this convention has been used throughout Chapters 6 and 7.) The cash flow figures for each year have been multiplied by the respective present worth factors for interest rates of 15% and 20%. The sum of the present worths is +$2,145 at 15% and −$605 at 20%. The following linear interpolation between these values indicates that this investment yielded a return of a little less than 19% before income taxes.

$$\text{Rate of return} = 15\% + \frac{\$2,145}{\$2,750} (20\% - 15\%) = 18.9\%$$

EXAMPLE 8–2. RATE OF RETURN ON A PROSPECTIVE INVESTMENT IN A RENTAL MACHINE

Estimates Relative to a Proposed Investment. John Smith has received an inheritance of $12,000. A friend engaged in the business of rental of construction machinery suggests that Smith invest this $12,000 in a tractor of a certain type. The friend will serve as Smith's agent in the rental of this asset on a commission basis and will remit to Smith the net receipts from each year's rentals at the end of the year. He estimates that for rental purposes the machine will have a useful life of 8 years, with a 10% final salvage value. His estimates of year-by-year receipts from rentals and of disbursements for all purposes are shown in Table 8–3. Disbursements are chiefly for repairs and maintenance but also include storage, rental commissions, property taxes, and insurance.

Calculation of Rate of Return. Table 8–4 indicates that if the friend's estimates of cash flow turn out to be correct, Smith's return before income taxes will be 12%. In Table 8–4 and in subsequent tables of this type, the present

TABLE 8–3

Estimated Cash Flow from Purchase and Ownership of a Rental Machine

Year	Receipts	Disbursements	Net Cash Flow
0		−$12,000	−$12,000
1	+$4,200	−500	+3,700
2	+3,900	−900	+3,000
3	+3,600	−1,200	+2,400
4	+3,500	−1,400	+2,100
5	+3,100	−1,400	+1,700
6	+3,000	−1,500	+1,500
7	+2,800	−1,500	+1,300
8	+2,650	−1,500	+1,150
8 a	+1,200		+1,200
Totals	+$27,950	−$21,900	+$6,050

a Receipt from salvage value.

worth factors are omitted. In Table 8–2 these factors were shown for each year and for each interest rate.

In deciding whether or not to undertake this particular investment, Smith should compare the prospective return of 12% before income taxes with the prospective return before income taxes obtainable from alternative investments that he believes are of comparable risk. He must also decide whether he is willing to undertake the risks associated with this type of investment.

TABLE 8–4

Present Worth Calculations To Determine Prospective Rate of Return, Example 8–2

Year	Estimated Cash Flow	Present Worth		
		at 10%	at 12%	at 15 %
0	−$12,000	−$12,000	−$12,000	−$12,000
1	+3,700	+3,364	+3,304	+3,218
2	+3,000	+2,479	+2,392	+2,268
3	+2,400	+1,803	+1,708	+1,578
4	+2,100	+1,434	+1,335	+1,201
5	+1,700	+1,056	+965	+845
6	+1,500	+847	+760	+648
7	+1,300	+667	+588	+489
8	+2,350	+1,096	+949	+768
Totals	+$6,050	+$746	+$1	−$985

EXAMPLE 8–3. RATE OF RETURN WHEN THE INVESTMENT PERIOD EXTENDS OVER SEVERAL YEARS

Estimates Relative to a Proposed New Product Investment. A chemical company is considering a proposal to buy land and build a plant to manufacture a new product. The required investment of $300,000 in land must be made 2 years before the start of operation of the plant. Of the $1,500,000 estimated investment in plant and equipment, $800,000 will have been spent one year before the plant starts to operate, and the remaining $700,000 in the year just preceding the start of operations. For purpose of analysis, the date of starting operations will be adopted as zero date on the time scale.

It is estimated that the life of the plant will be 15 years from the date of the start of operation. (It is believed the life will be terminated by product obsolescence.) Throughout the period of operation, it is estimated that $200,000 will be invested in working capital, chiefly in the inventories of raw materials, work in process, and finished product, and in the excess of accounts receivable over accounts payable. (See Chapter 15 for a discussion of certain problems that arise in estimating such working capital requirements.) For purposes of the economy study, this investment will be assumed to be a negative cash flow of $200,000 at zero date, finally recoverable by a positive $200,000 cash flow at date 15. It will also be assumed that the land will be sold for its $300,000 original cost at date 15. The plant and equipment is assumed to have zero net salvage value at date 15.

Receipts from the sale of the chemical product and disbursements in connection with its production and sale are estimated for each of the 15 years. It is expected that there will be an initial 3-year period involving start-up costs and development of markets before the full earning power of the project is developed, and that there will be a period of declining earning power in the final 4 years. The specific estimates of net positive before-tax cash flow from operations year by year are: 1, $100,000; 2, $300,000; 3, $400,000; 4 through 11, $500,000; 12 and 13, $400,000; 14, $300,000; and 15, $200,000. These positive cash flows will be diminished by yearly disbursements for income taxes estimated to be 50% of the amount that each year's figure exceeds $100,000.

Calculation of Rate of Return. Table 8–5 tabulates the before-tax and after-tax cash flows from year minus 2 to year 15. The equivalent sum of money at zero date is computed at 8% and 10% interest. (Although this might loosely be described as a present worth calculation at zero date, it will be noted that compound amount calculations are required for the conversions from years minus 1 and minus 2.) Interpolation between the sums of the equivalent amounts at zero date indicates a prospective after-tax return of slightly over 9.1%.

This 9.1% interpolated figure is independent of the choice of reference date. That is, if present worths had been calculated at year minus 2, or if compound amounts had been calculated at year 15, the interpolated rate of return would still have turned out to be 9.1%. However, in systematic evaluation of a number of projects of this type, it seems reasonable that zero date should always be chosen as the date of start of operations. Chapter 21 illustrates industrial capital budgeting forms that are based on this assumption.

The $300,000 land investment at date minus 2 and the $200,000 working capital investment at date 0 have no effect on prospective taxable income or

TABLE 8-5

Present Worth Calculations To Determine Prospective Rate of Return, Example 8-3

(000 omitted)

Year	Estimated Before-tax Cash Flow	Estimated After-tax Cash Flow (and PW at 0%)	Equivalent Amount at Zero Date	
			at 8%	at 10%
−2	−$300	−$300	−$350	−$363
−1	−800	−800	−864	−880
0	−900	−900	−900	−900
1	+100	+100	+93	+91
2	+300	+200	+171	+165
3	+400	+250	+198	+188
4	+500	+300	+221	+205
5	+500	+300	+204	+186
6	+500	+300	+189	+169
7	+500	+300	+175	+154
8	+500	+300	+162	+140
9	+500	+300	+150	+127
10	+500	+300	+139	+116
11	+500	+300	+129	+105
12	+400	+250	+99	+80
13	+400	+250	+92	+72
14	+300	+200	+68	+53
15	+700	+650	+205	+156
Totals	+$4,600	+$2,300	+$181	−$136

on income taxes because it is assumed that they will be recovered at date 15 without either increase or decrease. The tabulated cash flow at date 15, both before and after taxes, includes the recovery of this total of $500,000.

If we had specified a minimum attractive after-tax rate of return of, say, 7%, this new-product proposal would clearly be acceptable. If we had specified, say, 15%, it would clearly be unacceptable. However, a common state of affairs in industry is for the available capital funds and other resources to be insufficient to permit accepting all the major investment proposals that seem likely to have fairly high rates of return. For this reason, decision making about such proposals is rarely quite as simple as reaching either a "Yes" or "No" decision by comparing a figure such as our 9.1% with a stipulated i°. Chapters 11, 13, 14, 18, and 21 include comments on various aspects of the problem of choice among major proposed investments in relation to the common need for capital rationing.

Some Comments on Examples 8-1, 8-2, and 8-3. Example 8-1 is an actual case with receipts and disbursements rounded off to multiples of $10. Examples 8-2 and 8-3 make use of assumed data with figures that were chosen to be useful in illustrating several different facets of engineering economy. From time to time throughout this book we shall refer to the data of these three examples to illustrate a number of matters.

It will be noted that the method used for finding rate of return is the same in all examples, even though one deals with a past investment and the others with proposed investments.

One aspect of these examples is that a single project constitutes a separate activity for which all receipts and disbursements are assumed to be identifiable. It is rarely true of the capital goods of modern industry that specific receipts can be identified with individual machines or structures. For example, the receipts from the sale of a manufactured product cannot be identified with, say, the factory building, or with a specific machine used in a sequence of operations, or with a specific item of materials handling equipment. In this particular respect these three examples are not typical of the usual rate-of-return analysis for purposes of decision making in industry. Subsequent examples throughout this book will continue to emphasize the point brought out in earlier chapters that it is the prospective differences in cash flow between alternatives that need to be forecast and analyzed as a basis for choosing between any given alternatives.

Different Names Applied to the Computation of Rate of Return by the Methods Illustrated in This Chapter. Rate of return calculations of the type illustrated in Examples 8–1, 8–2, and 8–3 are as old as writings on the mathematics of finance. Since the early 1950's, however, the use of such calculations by industrial companies in the United States has greatly increased. Various names have been applied to this method of calculation. One name is the *discounted cash flow method;* another is the *Investor's Method.* Rate of return calculated in this way has been called the *Profitability Index* (sometimes abbreviated to PI), *interest rate of return, solving rate of return,* and *internal rate of return.*[2]

Of the six phrases mentioned, "discounted cash flow" seems to be the one most widely used in industry. It describes the data required and the method of calculation illustrated in Tables 8–2, 8–4, and 8–5. *Cash flow* refers to the fact that the required data must be given as the amounts and dates of receipts and disbursements. *Discounted* applies to the calculation of present worth.

But the phrase "discounted cash flow" is properly applied to *any* calculation to find the present worth of cash flow whether or not the

[2] The phrase "discounted cash flow" is associated with the writings of Joel Dean. The phrase "Investor's Method" (usually capitalized) is associated with the writings of Horace G. Hill, Jr., and John C. Gregory. The phrase "Profitability Index" (also usually capitalized) is associated with the writings of Ray I. Reul. The phrase "interest rate of return" is associated with the writings of J. B. Weaver and R. J. Reilly.

calculation is to be used in computing a rate of return. Thus the phrase is applicable generally to present worth comparisons for economy studies; it also applies to annual cost comparisons for which a finding of present worth has been an intermediate computational step. Moreover, the calculation of rates of return by correct methods often may be done without employing present worths; frequently the use of equivalent uniform annual figures is equally satisfactory.

Therefore it is misleading either to assume that a discounted cash flow calculation yields a rate of return or that a correct calculation of rate of return necessarily requires an analyst to discount cash flow. In general, the phrase "rate of return" used in this book means a rate found by applying appropriate compound interest analysis to past or prospective cash flow.

There are a number of methods in common use in industry that give figures purporting to be rates of return. The most common of these methods are described in Chapter 10. Because these methods so often give figures that differ widely from one another as well as from the rate that would be computed by correct compound interest techniques, the rates computed by these methods are referred to in Chapter 10 as "so-called rates of return."

Calculations such as were illustrated in Tables 8–2, 8–4, and 8–5 require a fair amount of arithmetic; it is necessary to multiply each year's cash flow by the single payment present worth factor for two or more interest rates. Where uniform annual cash flows are involved, the arithmetic is somewhat simpler; capital recovery factors or series present worth factors may be used. In some problems, calculations may be simplified by the use of gradient factors or gradient present worth factors. Where frequent trial-and-error calculations must be made to find unknown interest rates, and where a digital computer is available, it is a common practice to program the computer to make the trial-and-error solutions.

The examples in the remainder of this chapter illustrate methods of computing unknown interest rates where the facts are simpler than in Examples 8–1, 8–2, and 8–3.

EXAMPLE 8–4. DETERMINING THE PROSPECTIVE RATE OF RETURN ON A BOND INVESTMENT

Facts of the Case. A $10,000 3.5% government bond due in 25 years was described in Example 7–3. This bond can be purchased for $8,140. On the assumption that a buyer at this price will hold the bond to maturity, it is desired to find his before-tax rate of return. In acccordance with the usual practice in stating bond yields, this rate is to be expressed as a nominal interest rate assuming semiannual compounding.

Calculation of Bond Yield. In Example 7–3, it was found that with a semi-annual i of 2.5%, the present worth of the payments was $7,872. A similar calculation using a semiannual i of 2% gives a present worth of $9,214. Linear interpolation between these figures gives an i of 2.4%. The nominal rate per annum compounded semiannually is therefore $2(2.4\%) = 4.8\%$.

As explained in Example 7–3, the foregoing type of approximate calculation is unnecessary in the common case where published tables of bond yields are available.

EXAMPLE 8–5. DETERMINING THE PROSPECTIVE RATE OF RETURN FROM A UNIFORM ANNUAL SERIES OF NET RECEIPTS

Data from Example 6–1. The final column of Table 6–1 (page 71) showed that the differences in cash flow between Plans B and A consisted of a negative cash flow of $15,000 at zero date and positive after-tax cash flow of $2,800 a year for 10 years.

Calculation of Rate of Return. The present worth of the net cash flow may be computed for various interest rates using the series present worth factors for 10 years.

$$\text{PW at } 12\% = -\$15,000 + \$2,800(P/A,12\%,10)$$
$$= -\$15,000 + \$2,800(5.650) = +\$820$$
$$\text{PW at } 15\% = -\$15,000 + \$2,800(5.019) = -\$947$$

Interpolation indicates a rate of return of about 13.4%.

In the special case where the prospective positive cash flow from an investment, P, constitutes a uniform annual series, A, an alternate solution is to compute P/A or A/P and to interpolate between the appropriate factors in the interest tables. In this instance, $P/A = \$15,000/\$2,800 = 5.357$. Interpolation between 5.650 and 5.019, the respective series present worth factors for 12% and 15%, also indicates an after-tax rate of return of about 13.4%.

A comment on the use of the capital recovery factor in this type of calculation is made later in this chapter in connection with the discussion of the errors introduced by linear interpolation.

EXAMPLE 8–6. PROSPECTIVE RATE OF RETURN IN EXAMPLE 6–2

Data from Example 6–2. Plan B in Example 6–2 had a first cost of $15,000, annual disbursements of $6,400, a 10-year life, and zero salvage value. Plan C had a first cost of $25,000, annual disbursements of $5,750, a 10-year life, and a $5,000 salvage value. (The foregoing disbursements included extra income taxes as compared to Plan A.) The difference in cash flow between C and B (shown in the final column of Table 6–2, page 76) was −$10,000 initially, +$650 a year for 10 years, and +$5,000 at the end of 10 years.

Calculation of Rate of Return. A calculation of present worth of the net difference in cash flow using 1¾% and 2% interest indicates that the extra $10,000 investment in Plan C will be recovered with an after-tax rate of return of about 1.9%.

$$\text{PW at } 1\tfrac{3}{4}\% = -\$10,000 + \$650(P/A,1\tfrac{3}{4}\%,10) + \$5,000(P/F,1\tfrac{3}{4}\%,10)$$
$$= -\$10,000 + \$650(9.101) + \$5,000(0.8407) = +\$120$$
$$\text{PW at } 2\% = -\$10,000 + \$650(8.983) + \$5,000(0.8203) = -\$59$$

In Example 8–5 and in the foregoing calculation, we dealt only with the differences in cash flow between the two alternatives that were being compared. Of course the same conclusion is reached when present worths of *all* disbursements are computed for both alternatives. The following tabulation shows that the two alternatives have the same present worth at about 1.9%.

	Plan B	Plan C	Difference (B − C)
PW at 1¾%	$73,250	$73,130	+$120
PW at 2%	$72,490	$72,550	−$60

The rate of return on extra investment must also be the interest rate at which the alternatives have the same equivalent uniform annual cost. The following tabulation shows that this occurs at about 1.9%.

	Plan B	Plan C	Difference (B − C)
Annual cost at 1¾%	$8,048	$8,035	+$13
Annual cost at 2%	$8,070	$8,077	−$7

It will be noted that although the elements of cash flow common to Plans B and C have been included in the foregoing present worth and annual cost figures, it is only the differences in cash flow that have any influence on the conclusion regarding rate of return. The common elements of cash flow will contribute equally to the present worths (or to the annual costs) of both alternatives regardless of the interest rate assumed.

A Possible Misinterpretation of Rate of Return When Three or More Alternatives Are Being Compared. It will be recalled that in Examples 6–1 and 6–2, Plan A was to continue the present method of carrying out a certain materials handling operation. Plan B required a $15,000 investment in equipment intended to reduce labor costs; Plan C required a $25,000 investment in such equipment. The minimum attractive rate of return after income taxes was 8%. Plan B was favored by the annual cost comparison in Chapter 6 and by the present worth comparison in Chapter 7.

Our calculations of rate of return should also lead us to the conclusion that Plan B is the best of the three plans. The $15,000 investment in Plan B promises a 13.4% rate of return after income taxes as compared to the present method, Plan A. Because 13.4% is higher than our 8% standard, B is superior to A. On the other hand, the extra $10,000 investment required for Plan C will yield only 1.9% after income taxes as compared to B. Since 1.9% is less than our 8% standard, the $10,000 investment is not justified and Plan C should be rejected.

Once a particular i^* is selected for the comparison of alternatives, a correct analysis of relevant rates of return will invariably lead to the same conclusion that will be obtained from a correct annual cost comparison or a correct present worth comparison.

Nevertheless, incorrect conclusions are sometimes reached by computing rates of return from the wrong pairs of alternatives. For example, if Plan C is compared with Plan A, the prospective rate of return on the $25,000 investment is 8.4% after income taxes. Someone favoring Plan C might argue that because it promises 8.4% as compared to the present method of doing things and because 8.4% exceeds the stipulated i^* of 8%, the full $25,000 investment is justified.

If Plan B were not available, it is true that the 8.4% rate of return would indicate the justification of Plan C. But because of the availability of B, C is unattractive. The $10,000 increment of investment in C over B will not pay its way, yielding only 1.9% after income taxes. In general, each separable increment of proposed investment ought to be considered separately in relation to its justification. Unsound proposals often appear to be justified because they are improperly combined with sound ones from which they may be separated.

The prospective return on Plan C as compared to Plan A has no useful meaning as a guide to decision making in this case. The viewpoint presented here is expanded in Chapter 12 which deals with comparisons of multiple alternatives.

Demonstrating the Validity of a Rate of Return Computed by Compound Interest Methods. In our introductory discussion of compound interest in Chapter 3, Table 3–1 illustrated four cases where an investment of $10,000 was recovered in 10 years with a return of 6%. The four cases involved four quite different series of year-end cash receipts by the investor of the original $10,000. The figures in Table 3–1 showed the year-by-year unrecovered balances in each case and demonstrated that the four cases were alike in providing complete capital recovery of the original $10,000 with interest at 6%.

Whenever correct compound interest methods are used to compute an unknown interest rate, a similar tabulation may be used to show the validity of the computed rate. For example, it will be recalled that in Example 8–2 our discounted cash flow calculations indicated capital recovery with a return of 12%. Table 8–6 demonstrates the correctness of this 12% figure by year-by-year calculations of unrecovered balances assuming an interest rate of 12%. All but 59 cents of the initial $12,000 investment turns out to be recovered with 12% interest.

Where someone questions the meaning of a computed rate of return, a tabulation such as Table 8–6 will sometimes help to clarify matters. Where persons are suspicious of compound interest methods and prefer some other "approximate" method of computing rate of return (such as one of those discussed later in Chapter 10), such a tabulation may be useful in demonstrating the correctness of the compound interest method and the incorrectness of the other methods.

TABLE 8–6

A Demonstration That the Flow of Cash Receipts in Example 8–2
Leads to a Recovery of Capital with a 12% Return

End of Year	Year's Interest, at 12% on Unrecovered Balance	Unrecovered Balance Plus Year's Interest	End-of-year Cash Receipts	End-of-year Unrecovered Balance Assuming 12% Interest
0				$12,000.00
1	$1,440.00	$13,440.00	$3,700	9,740.00
2	1,168.80	10,908.86	3,000	7,908.80
3	949.06	8,857.86	2,400	6,457.86
4	774.94	7,232.80	2,100	5,132.80
5	615.94	5,748.74	1,700	4,048.74
6	485.85	4,534.59	1,500	3,034.59
7	364.15	3,398.74	1,300	2,098.74
8	251.85	2,350.59	2,350	0.59

Rate of Return Calculations Assume the Termination of the Consequences of an Investment Decision.   Example 8–1 viewed an investment in retrospect: that is, it considered a past investment in income-producing property from the date of acquisition of the property until the date of its final disposal. With full information about the money receipts and disbursements that were associated with this investment, it was possible to compute the rate of return obtained. Although Examples 8–2 to 8–6 dealt with prospective investments rather than with past ones, the viewpoint was really the same as in Example 8–1; the transactions were viewed from the date of prospective acquisition to the prospective date of termination of ownership.

Although an economy study regarding the desirability of a proposed investment may properly take the point of view of a terminated transaction, this viewpoint is hardly possible with regard to a past investment not yet terminated. For this reason, all judgments regarding profits or losses in business enterprises not yet terminated should really be thought of as preliminary estimates that in the long run may turn out to be either too favorable or not favorable enough. For example, the relatively high return of 18.9% in Example 8–1 was caused by the sale of the rental property for approximately twice its cost; if there had been accounts for this enterprise, a conventional analysis of the accounts at any time before the property was sold would have indicated a return of much less than 18.9%.

Conclusions regarding the profitability of investments not yet terminated are usually drawn from the accounts of business enterprises. Some aspects of the difference in viewpoint between an economy study to determine whether or not to make a proposed investment and the accounting procedures relating to the same investment once it is actually made are explored in Chapter 10.

Chapters 6 and 7 explained that when alternatives deal with assets having different estimated lives, a convenient simple assumption is that replacement assets will repeat the cycle of disbursements and receipts that have been forecast for the initial asset. Example 8–7 illustrates the use of this assumption in computing rate of return.

EXAMPLE 8–7. RATE OF RETURN CALCULATIONS WHEN ALTERNATIVES HAVE DIFFERENT LIVES

Data from Example 6–3. It will be recalled that Plan D in Example 6–3 had a first cost of $50,000, a life of 20 years, a $10,000 terminal salvage value, and annual O & M disbursements of $9,000. Plan E had a first cost of $120,000, a life of 40 years, a $20,000 terminal salvage value, annual O & M disbursements of $6,000, and extra annual income tax disbursements of $1,250. These plans were compared in Chapters 6 and 7 by annual costs, present worths, and capitalized costs using an after-tax i^* of 8%.

Calculation of Rate of Return. To compute a prospective rate of return on the $70,000 extra investment in Plan E, it is necessary that the two plans apply to service for the same number of years. Assume that the first 20 years' estimated disbursements for Plan D will be repeated in the second 20 years as shown in the cash flow tabulation, Table 6–3 (page 79).

One way to find the rate of return on extra investment is to compute the present worths of the net disbursements for 40 years assuming different interest rates. Interpolation between the following differences in present worth shows that the two plans have the same present worth at about 2.7%.

	Plan D	Plan E	Difference (D – E)
PW at 2.5%	$296,620	$294,550	+$2,070
PW at 3%	$277,120	$281,450	−$4,330

The same 2.7% rate of return is found by interpolating between the differences in equivalent uniform annual net cash flow using different interest rates.

	Plan D	Plan E	Difference (D − E)
Equivalent annual cost at 2.5%	$11,816	$11,734	+$82
Equivalent annual cost at 3%	$11,989	$12,126	−$137

Still another method, not illustrated here, would be to compute the capitalized costs of perpetual service using interest rates of 2.5% and 3% and to interpolate between the differences.

Although any of the foregoing methods of solution will give the correct answer, the point that 2.7% is really the prospective rate of return on extra investment may be somewhat clearer if the problem is approached using only the differences in cash flow between the two plans. These differences were tabulated in the final column of Table 6–3 (page 79). Plan E requires an extra disbursement of $70,000 at zero date, offset by reduced after tax disbursements of $1,750 a year for 40 years and $40,000 at the end of the 20th year, and by an increased receipt of $10,000 from the larger salvage value at the end of the 40th year. Present worths of the differences in cash flow are as follows:

$$
\begin{aligned}
\text{PW at 2.5\%} &= -\$70,000 + \$1,750(P/A,2.5\%,40) + \$40,000(P/F,2.5\%,20) \\
&\quad + \$10,000(P/F,2.5\%,40) \\
&= -\$70,000 + \$1,750(25.103) + \$40,000(0.6103) \\
&\quad + \$10,000(0.3724) \\
&= +\$2,070 \\
\text{PW at 3\%} &= -\$70,000 + \$1,750(23.115) + \$40,000(0.5537) \\
&\quad + \$10,000(0.3066) \\
&= -\$4,330
\end{aligned}
$$

Again interpolation gives us the 2.7% figure. If a year-by-year calculation should be made similar to Table 8–6, it would show that if a person invested $70,000 and as a result of this investment received $1,750 a year for 40 years plus single payments of $40,000 and $10,000 at the end of 20 and 40 years respectively he would recover his $70,000 with interest at approximately 2.7%.

Guessing the Rate of Return Before a Trial-and-Error Calculation. In computing unknown rates of return by compound interest methods, it usually is necessary to compute present worths (or equivalent uniform annual costs) at two or more interest rates. The time needed for calculation will be minimized if the first interest rate tried is fairly close to the correct rate. Frequently a simple inspection of the cash flow series will tell whether to start by guessing a fairly low rate or a fairly high one.

Where the cash flow series is irregular, it sometimes saves time to make a preliminary calculation before deciding on the first guessed rate. In such a calculation the cash flow series being analyzed may be changed in a way that makes it possible to find the interest rate quickly with the help of interest tables. The following paragraphs illustrate how such preliminary calculations might have been made for the cash flow series of Examples 8–1 and 8–2.

In Example 8–1 most of the positive net cash flow is concentrated in the 7th or final year. A first guess might assume the entire amount, +$29,830, in the 7th year. In effect, the cash flow series is changed so that a P of $10,900 leads to an F of $29,830 at the end of 7 years. The corresponding single payment present worth factor is then $P \div F$ = $10,900 \div \$29,830 = 0.365$. For $n = 7$, P/F at 15% is 0.376 and P/F at 20% is 0.279. If *all* the net positive cash flow had actually been concentrated in the 7th year, it is evident that the return would have been slightly over 15%. Because some of the net positive cash flow occurred in years 1 to 6, the actual return must be higher than this figure. Good tactics in this case would be to make the first trial at 20%; the second trial could then be at either 15% or 25%, depending on the result of the first trial.

In Example 8–2 the net positive cash flow is not concentrated at the end of the period; it is well distributed throughout the 8 years. Substitute a cash flow series with the same net positive cash flow spread uniformly over the 8 years. In such a series, A is $18,050 \div 8 = $2,256$. The corresponding series present worth factor is then $P \div A = $12,000 \div $2,256 = 5.32$. For $n = 8$, P/A at 10% is 5.33 and P/A at 12% is 4.97. With uniform cash flow the return would have been about 10%. Because there is more positive cash flow in the early years than in the later years, the return must be more than 10%. Good tactics in this case would be to make the first trial at 12%; the second trial could then be at either 10% or 15%, depending on the result of the first trial.

Minor Errors Introduced by Linear Interpolation in Computing Rates of Return. Suppose that in Example 8–2 we had computed the present worth of net cash flow only at 10% and 15%. The respective present worths at these rates, as shown in Table 8–4, are +$746 and −$985. A linear interpolation between these figures is as follows:

$$\text{Estimated rate of return} = 10\% + \frac{746}{1,731}\,(15\% - 10\%) = 12.2\%$$

We already know from Example 8–2 that the return is 12%. It is evident that the foregoing interpolated value is a little too high. It is obvious that all such relationships between interest rate and present worth must be curvilinear. Where present worths have been computed for interest rates separated by 0.5% (such as the 2.5% and 3% rates in Example 8–7), the possible error from linear interpolation is relatively small. This error naturally can be larger where present worths are computed for rates separated by 5% (such as the 15% and 20% rates in Example 8–1). The possible error from linear interpolation is greatest when the rate of return is midway between the two interest rates used in the calculation.

Some analysts use graphical methods in finding unknown rates of return. In order to show the curvature of the present worth curve, graphical methods usually require calculation of present worths assuming three or more interest rates.

In this book the practice is to use linear interpolation and to state the interpolated rates of return to the nearest tenth of a per cent. Advantages of linear interpolation are that the calculation can be made quickly by slide rule and that present worths need be calculated at only two interest rates. Analysts should recognize that linear interpolation sometimes causes an error in the rate of return of one or two tenths of a per cent.

In general, the calculations of rates of return in economy studies are made to influence decisions among alternatives. The errors introduced by a linear interpolation in any compound interest method are usually so small as to have no appreciable influence on the decision making.

The errors, if any, introduced by linear interpolation, using present worth methods usually tend to give computed rates of return a little above the true rate. In contrast, the errors, if any, introduced by linear interpolation in annual cost methods usually tend to give computed rates of return slightly below the true rate. This point is illustrated by the following simple example. Consider a $10,000 investment that is expected to result in an end-of-year net positive cash flow of $1,259 a year for 12 years. P is $10,000; A is $1,259. Therefore the series present worth factor is $P \div A = 7.943$, and the capital recovery factor is $A \div P = 0.12590$. It can be seen from the 7% table that the return is exactly 7%. But assume that no 7% table is available and that it is necessary to interpolate between figures from 6% and 8% tables. In these tables the series present worth factors are 8.384 and 7.536 respectively; a linear interpolation to hundredths of a per cent indicates a return of 7.04%. The capital recovery factors are 0.11928 and 0.13270 respectively; a linear interpolation indicates a return of 6.99%. However, if interpolated values had been stated only to the nearest tenth of a per cent, both methods would have given 7.0%, the correct figure.

Use of Interest Tables Based on Continuous Compounding in Computing Unknown Rates of Return.

The end-of-year convention in economy studies was explained in Chapter 6. This convention has been employed in the calculations of rates of return in the present chapter and is used in such calculations throughout the main body of this book.

In some economy studies in industry, a different convention is used; it is assumed that all prospective receipts and disbursements during each year will occur uniformly throughout that year. To use this alternate convention, it is necessary to assume continuous compounding of interest (explained in Chapter 4) and to have interest tables based on continuous compounding and on the uniform flow of funds throughout each year.

Tables E–28 and E–29 (in Appendix E) are such tables. Their use in connection with rate of return calculations is explained in Appendix A. This appendix also discusses the circumstances under which the uniform-flow convention may be preferable to the end-of-year convention.

Rate of Return from a Combination of Two Separable Proposed Investments That Have Different Prospective Rates of Return.

A certain mining property is for sale for $1,500,000. The engineer for the prospective purchaser estimates the remaining life of the mine as 8 years.

For each of these years he estimates that the excess of receipts over disbursements will be $391,000. He desires to compute the prospective rate of return.

In mining enterprises there is a traditional method of determining rate of return known as Hoskold's method. In this method it is assumed that uniform annual deposits will be made into a conservatively invested sinking fund that will earn interest at a relatively low rate. The annual deposits are to be just sufficient to replace the original investment at the end of the life of the property. The rate of return is computed by dividing the investment into the annual amount remaining after setting aside the sinking fund deposit.

To illustrate Hoskold's method, assume 4% interest on the sinking fund. The annual deposit in the fund to recover $1,500,000 at the end of 8 years is $1,500,000 $(A/F,4\%,8)$ = $1,500,000(0.10853) = $162,800. The annual cash remaining for the owners of the property after they have made the sinking fund deposit will be $391,000 − $162,800 = $228,200. As $228,200 ÷ $1,500,000 = 0.152, this project is viewed as one promising a 15.2% return.

If the same proposal is analyzed by correct compound interest methods, the computed rate of return is 20%; $391,000 $(P/A,20\%,8)$ = $391,000(3.837) = $1,500,000. The difference between the viewpoints underlying these 15.2% and 20.0% figures deserves some comment here, particularly because the viewpoint leading to the 15.2% figure is by no means restricted to the mineral industries.

If the purchaser of the mining property actually makes the two investments contemplated in the 15.2% calculation and if receipts and disbursements turn out as forecast, it is true that his combined rate of return will be 15.2%. From the combination of the two investments he will have a cash flow of −$1,500,000 at zero date, +$228,200 a year for 8 years, and +$1,500,000 at the end of the 8th year.

The important point to recognize here is that this 15.2% return is the result of *two* separate investments, one yielding 20% and the other yielding only 4%. Presumably the decision to make the investment with the 20% yield does not require that there also be a decision to make the 4% investment. If not, the 4% investment has no relevance in making the decision about the proposed investment with the 20% yield. It is the 20% figure, not the 15.2% one, that should be used as the index of attractiveness of the proposed investment in the mining property.

This Hoskold-type viewpoint on computing rate of return is rarely, if ever, appropriate as a basis for decision making on proposed investments. It seems particularly indefensible in the common case where it is used when no actual sinking fund is contemplated. Further comment on this topic is made in Appendix C.

Determining the True Cost of Borrowed Money. In finding the true interest rate paid by a corporation that borrows money by the sale of bonds, the calculations are similar to those indicated for computing rate of return on a bond investment. However, it is necessary to recognize that borrowing causes the corporation to make certain disbursements that are not receipts to the bond investor.

For instance, a $10,000,000 bond issue of 4.5%, 20-year bonds that was sold by investment bankers to the ultimate investor at 95 (i.e., $950 per $1,000 bond) might have been sold by the issuing corporation to an investment banking syndicate at 91½. Thus the corporation would receive $9,150,000 for its promise to pay $450,000 a year for 20 years and $10,000,000 at the end of that time. These payments would repay the amount received with interest at about 5.2%.

If the initial expenses to the corporation in connection with the bond issue were $200,000 (for such items as engraving bonds, preparing a registration statement for the Securities and Exchange Commission, accounting and legal expenses in connection with the issue), and if the annual disbursements involved in fees for registrar and trustee, costs of making interest payments, and the like were $30,000, the true cost of this borrowed money would be even greater. The corporation is really receiving a net sum of $8,950,000 now in exchange for an obligation to pay $480,000 a year for 20 years and $10,000,000 2 years hence. Present worth calculations and interpolation indicate that the true cost of this borrowed money is about 5.7%.

Thus a given loan may appear to have different interest rates, depending on the point of view. In this illustration the coupon rate on the bonds was 4.5%; the yield to the bond investors was 4.9%; the bonds were sold by the corporation to the investment bankers at a price giving a yield of 5.2%; considering the cost incidental to the borrowing of money, the actual cost of money to the corporation was 5.7%.

The foregoing analysis disregards income tax considerations. The usual result of income taxation in the United States is—in effect—to reduce the cost of borrowing money to private borrowers below a figure obtained from the foregoing type of calculation. Certain aspects of the relationship between income taxes and borrowing are discussed in Chapter 18.

Interest Rates Are Not Always What They Seem. There are many situations in which a superficial examination of the facts may lead to an underestimate of the interest rate being paid by a borrower. One such situation has just been described. Another was described in Chapter 5 in which a "Seven Per Cent Plan" turned out to involve an interest rate of nearly 14% per annum.

Another such situation exists whenever, in a purchase of a property "on terms," there is a difference between the selling price to a cash buyer and one to a buyer who agrees to pay the purchase price in periodic installments with interest.

For instance, a residential property is for sale for $24,000 under the following arrangements: $4,000 cash and the balance of $20,000 to be repaid with interest at 7% in uniform installments for 15 years. Investigation discloses that a buyer on these terms must also pay $600 immediately for various expenses incidental to securing the loan. It also appears that the same property can be purchased for $21,000 cash.

For the sake of simplicity in our calculations, let us assume uniform *annual* payments rather than monthly payments as would customarily be required. The uniform payment, A, to repay a P of $20,000, with $i = 0.07$ and $n = 15$, is $20,000(0.10979) = $2,196.

It is evident that a buyer for cash will pay $21,000 at once and thus conclude the transaction. A buyer on borrowed money will pay out $4,600 at once and $2,196 a year for 15 years. This $2,196 a year is clearly an alternative to a $16,400 immediate cash payment; if the buyer had the $16,400 he could substitute it for the promise to pay $2,196 a year for 15 years. To find the real cost of borrowed money to him, it is necessary to find the interest rate at which his annual payments for 15 years would repay $16,400. As $A/P = $2,196/$16,400 = 0.1339$, interpolation between the capital recovery factors for 10% and 12% shows this interest rate to be approximately 10.3%.

The difference between the apparent 7% interest and the actual 10.3% interest paid by the buyer on credit was concealed in the difference between the cash price and credit price, and in the initial charges incident to the loan.

Certain Cases in Which Two or More Solutions Are Possible in Computing an Unknown Interest Rate. Some proposals involving estimated prospective cash flows combine one or more periods of time that are, in effect, investment periods with one or more periods of time that are, in effect, borrowing or financing periods. Proposals of this type occur from time to time in the production operations of the petroleum industry and occasionally in other industries. They may be identified by the fact that the series of estimated cash flows has two or more reversals of sign.

This chapter has illustrated conventional types of trial-and-error calculations to find an unknown interest rate. Such calculations are appropriate for the common types of proposals that are solely investment or solely borrowing/financing. In an investment-type proposal, an initial negative cash flow is succeeded by one or more prospective positive cash flows. In a borrowing/financing-type proposal, an initial positive cash flow is succeeded by one or more prospective negative cash flows. For mixed proposals, where the cash flow series has two or more reversals of sign, such conventional calculations may give two or more values for the "solving" interest rate or, sometimes, no values at all. In such mixed proposals, misleading conclusions often will be reached from *any* conventional type of compound interest analysis, whether the analysis is based on net present worth, equivalent uniform annual cash flow, or the calculation of an unknown interest rate or rate of return. This subject is explored in Appendix B.

In that appendix it is explained that the key to an analysis of a mixed proposal that is primarily an investment proposal is the use of an auxiliary interest rate during the borrowing or financing period. For a proposal that is primarily a borrowing or financing proposal, the key is using an auxiliary interest rate during the investment period. It also is explained that in many cases, the conclusions of an analysis are relatively insensitive to large changes in the value of the assumed auxiliary interest rate; in such cases it usually is good enough for practical purposes to make conventional compound interest analyses even though the prospective cash flow series being analyzed has two or more reversals of sign.

Another Meaning for "Rate of Return on Investment." Throughout this book, the phrase "rate of return on investment" is used in the meaning illustrated in this chapter, as the rate of "interest" at which an investment is repaid by an increase in net cash receipts. However, it should be pointed out that another meaning is sometimes given to this phrase. In this other use, "rate of return" is taken to mean the excess of the return over the current interest rate on borrowed capital, or the excess of the return over the going interest rate on conservative investments. A return described in this book as 9% would be described as a 3% return in a case where the going rate of interest was assumed to be 6%.

This other meaning for "rate of return" corresponds somewhat to the economic theorist's concept of "profit," just as the meaning adopted in this book corresponds more closely to the accountant's concept of profit. Either meaning is a possible one, but it is obvious that both cannot be used without confusion. The meaning used here has been chosen because it seems better adapted to practical business situations. Thus, wherever "rate of return" is used throughout these pages, it means a figure to be compared with the interest obtainable on investments elsewhere, rather than a figure in excess of such interest.

Summary. A comparison between alternatives involving money payments and receipts of different amounts at different dates may be expressed by an interest rate, the rate that makes the two alternatives equivalent. When one alternative involves a higher present investment and higher future net receipts (possibly as a result of lower future disbursements), this interest rate may be called the prospective rate of return on the extra investment. Its calculation provides one of the several methods of determining in an economy study whether a proposed investment will be recovered with a return commensurate with the risk—in other words, one of the methods of considering the time value of money in economy studies.

The actual rate of return realized by an investor from an investment cannot be determined until his association with the investment has terminated; it may differ substantially from the apparent rate of return at some intermediate period. The viewpoint of an engineering economy study for a proposed investment, involving, as it does, estimates for the full expected economic life of a machine or structure, implies calculations of rate of return of the same type as would be required to judge the actual return realized from terminated investments.

In a loan transaction the true cost of money to the borrower, which should be obtained by viewing the transaction as the difference between the net present cash provided by the borrowing and the future money outlays that the borrowing necessitates, will often be much greater than the apparent or contract rate of interest.

PROBLEMS

General Notes Regarding Problems for Chapter 8. Unless otherwise stated, the end-of-year convention is to be assumed for receipts and disbursements occurring during a year. Where alternative assets have different lives, it is to be assumed that replacement assets will have the same first costs, lives, salvage values, and annual disbursements as the assets they replace. Answers to Problems 8–1 to 8–12 are approximate, determined by interpolation to the nearest tenth of a per cent.

8–1. An unimproved city lot was purchased for $3,400 in January 1958. Property taxes on it were paid as follows:

1958	$40	1962	$60	1966	$ 80
1959	40	1963	60	1967	80
1960	40	1964	60	1968	100
1961	40	1965	80	1969	100

At the end of 1969 the lot was sold for $7,000, less a 5% commission to the real estate broker. What rate of return before income taxes was obtained on this investment? (*Ans.* = 4.4%.)

8–2. The purchase of an unimproved residential lot in a city is under consideration as a speculation. The purchase price of the lot is $4,000. It is believed that if this lot is held for 8 years it can be sold for $6,400. From this must be deducted a 6% sales commission of $384 and a $96 payment for title insurance, leaving a prospective net receipt of $5,920 on the date of the sale.

Throughout the 8 years there will be no receipts from the ownership of the lot. Annual disbursements for property taxes are estimated to be $120 throughout the period of ownership. What is the prospective rate of return on the investment? (*Ans.* = 2.5%.)

8–3. A project has a first cost of $120,000 and an estimated salvage value of $20,000 at the end of 25 years. Estimated average annual receipts are $27,900. Estimated average annual disbursements for everything except income taxes are $15,060. Estimated average annual disbursements for income taxes are $4,420. Assuming that annual receipts and disbursements will be uniform throughout the 25 years, compute the prospective after-tax rate of return. (*Ans.* = 5.4%.)

8–4. In Problem 8–3, assume that receipts will be $31,500 in the first year and that they will decline by $300 each year to $24,300 in the 25th year. Assume that disbursements for everything except income taxes will be $12,660 in the first year and will increase by $200 a year to $17,460 in the 25th year. Assume that disbursements for income taxes will be $7,420 in the first year and will decrease by $250 a year to $1,420 in the 25th year. Compute the prospective after-tax rate of return. (*Ans.* = 6.2%.)

8–5. In Problem 6–1 (page 84), what is the prospective after-tax rate of return on the extra investment required for Mill N? (*Ans.* = 6.4%.)

8–6. In Problem 6–3 (page 85), what is the prospective after-tax rate of return on the extra investment in Machine W? (*Ans.* = 11.3%.)

8–7. A promissory note calling for payments of $1,600 at the end of each year for the next 11 years is offered for sale for $11,470. What is the prospective before-tax rate of return to a purchaser at this price? (*Ans.* = 7.9%.)

8–8. Interest on a 4½%, $5,000 bond due in 15 years is payable semiannually with the first payment due 6 months from now. The bond is for sale for $4,250. If a buyer at this price holds the bond till maturity, find the nominal rate of interest compounded semiannually that he will receive. (*Ans.* = 6.0%.)

8–9. A subdivider offers lots for sale at $5,000, $1,000 to be paid down and $1,000 to be paid at the end of each year for the next 4 years with "no interest" to be charged. In discussing a possible purchase, you find that you can get the same lot for $4,500 cash. You also find that on a time purchase there will be a service charge of $100 at the date of the purchase to cover legal and handling expenses and the like. What rate of interest before income taxes will actually be paid if the lot is purchased on this time plan? (*Ans.* = 6.8%.)

8–10. A corporation receives a net $9,300,000 as a result of an issue of $10,000,000 of 5½%, 20-year bonds on which interest is payable semiannually. There will be estimated semiannual expenditures of $15,000 for trustee's and registrar's fees and clerical and other expenses in connection with interest payments. What nominal interest rate compounded semiannually expresses the true before-tax cost of this borrowed money to the corporation? (*Ans.* = 6.4%.)

8–11. It is proposed to purchase a machine to be used for rental purposes. The first cost is $20,000. For the first year of ownership, $5,400 is estimated as the excess of receipts over disbursements for everything except income taxes. Considering declining rental receipts with age and increased upkeep costs, it is believed that this figure will decline by $300 each year and will be $5,100 in the second year, $4,800 in the third, and so on. It is estimated that the machine will be retired after 15 years with a $2,000 salvage value. Estimated disbursements for income taxes are $2,100 the first year, $1,950 the second, and will decrease by $150 each year thereafter. What is the prospective after-tax rate of return? (*Ans.* = 9.6%.)

8–12. A new-product proposal in a manufacturing company will require a $400,000 investment in land which must be made 2 years before the date of the start of plant operation. Investment in depreciable plant of $1,200,000 must be made one year before the date of start of plant operation; a further investment of $1,050,000 in such plant must be made at the date of the start of operation. A $300,000 investment in working capital is required on the date of the start of operation. The excess of receipts over all disbursements except those for income taxes is estimated as $150,000 for the first year of operation; $300,000 the 2nd; $450,000 the 3rd; and $600,000 each year thereafter from the 4th year through the 13th. In the 14th year this figure is estimated as $400,000, and in the 15th, $200,000. Annual disbursements for income taxes are estimated as 50% of the excess of the foregoing figure over $150,000; for example, income taxes will be $225,000 in the 4th year.

Compute the prospective after-tax rate of return on the assumption that the depreciable plant will have zero net salvage value at the end of 15 years and that the investments in land and working capital will be fully recovered at that date. (*Ans.* = 7.3%.)

8–13. In Problem 8–12, assume that the before-tax excess of receipts over disbursements will be $300,000 in the first year, $600,000 for each year from the 2nd through the 14th, and $300,000 in the 15th year. With only this change in the data of the problem, what is the prospective after-tax rate of return on the investment?

8–14. In Problem 8–12, assume that the required investment in land is only $150,000 rather than $400,000. With only this change in the data of the problem, what is the prospective after-tax rate of return on the investment?

8–15. In Problem 8–12, what is the prospective before-tax rate of return on the investment?

8–16. In Problem 6–2 (page 84), what is the prospective after-tax rate of return on the extra investment required for the new centerless grinder?

8–17. In Problem 6–4 (page 85), what is the prospective after-tax rate of return on the extra investment required for the Diesel plant?

8–18. In Problem 6–5 (page 85), what is the prospective after-tax rate of return on the extra investment required for method A?

8–19. In Problem 6–12 (page 86), what is the prospective after-tax rate of return on the extra investment required for the type Z heat exchanger?

8–20. In Problem 6–10 (page 86), compute the prospective rate of return on the $35,000 extra investment that will be required if the decision is made to select pipe of type A.

8–21. Two alternate designs are to be evaluated for a certain new project that has been proposed. Design Y involves a present investment of $100,000. Estimated annual receipts for 20 years are $45,000; estimated annual disbursements for everything except income taxes are $20,000. Design Z involves a present investment of $150,000, estimated annual receipts for 20 years of $64,500, and annual disbursements for everything except income taxes of $36,000. It is expected that there will be no value remaining in the project after 20 years regardless of the choice between the two designs. Estimated annual income taxes will be $10,000 with design Y and $10,500 with Z. Compute the prospective after-tax rate of return on the project with design Y and with design Z. Compute the prospective after-tax rate of return on the extra investment required for design Z. If the after-tax $i°$ is 10%, would you recommend Y, Z, or neither?

8–22. In Problem 7–12 (page 105), what is the prospective after-tax rate of return on the extra investment required for the electric radiant panels?

8–23. The rental property described in Problem 7–16 (page 106) is for sale for $37,500. What is the prospective before-tax rate of return to a buyer at this price who expects to hold the property for 15 years and sell it for $25,000 at the end of the 15-year period?

8–24. The patent described in Problem 7–17 (page 106) is for sale for $30,000. What is the prospective before-tax rate of return to a buyer at this price?

8–25. In the circumstances described in Problem 7–19 (page 106), Doe has offered his property to the XYZ Co. for $120,000. What would be the before-tax yield to the company from an investment in the property at this price as compared to the alternative of continuing to pay royalties to Doe?

8–26. In Problem 7–20 (page 107), what is the prospective after-tax rate of return on the extra investment needed to purchase the fully automatic tape controlled boring machine rather than the two manually controlled machines?

8–27. The first cost of a piece of business property containing stores and offices is $120,000. A prospective investor estimates that annual receipts from rentals will be $14,800 and that annual disbursements other than income taxes will be $6,200. He also estimates that the property will be saleable for a net $90,000 at the end of 20 years. What is his prospective before-tax rate of return if he purchases the property at this price and holds it for 20 years?

8–28. An investor purchased a piece of vacant property in 1954 for $6,300. He paid taxes of $90 a year for 15 years and finally sold the property in 1969 for $11,800. What was his before-tax rate of return?

8–29. An investor purchased 100 shares of stock in the JKL Corporation for $4,500. He received no dividends for the first 2 years, $3 a share dividends each year for the next 4 years, and $4 a share dividends each year in the 7th, 8th, and 9th year. After holding the stock for these 9 years, he sold it for $9,300. What was his before-tax rate of return?

8–30. A promissory note calling for payments of $2,310 a year for the next 13 years is offered for sale for $19,500. What is the prospective before-tax rate of return?

8–31. Two pumps are being considered for a certain service of 25 years. The Toltec pump has a first cost of $3,000 and an estimated annual cost of $2,200 for electric energy used for pumping purposes. The Mandan pump has a first cost of $2,550. Because it is less efficient, its annual costs for pumping energy will be $60 higher than those of the Toltec pump. Estimated annual income taxes will be $21 higher with the Toltec pump. It is anticipated that there will be no other cost differences and no salvage values. What is the prospective after-tax rate of return on the extra investment required to purchase the Toltec pump?

8–32. A corporation sells an issue of $20,000,000 of 6%, 20-year bonds to an investment banking concern for $19,200,000. The corporation's initial disbursements for fees of lawyers, accountants, trustee, and other outlays in connection with the bond issue are $400,000. Each year the disbursements for fees to the trustee and registrar of the bonds and the clerical and other expenses in connection with interest payments are $150,000. What is the before-tax cost of this borrowed money expressed as an interest rate? To simplify calculations, assume that interest is payable annually.

8–33. A home is offered for sale for $37,000, the purchaser to make a $7,000 down payment and to pay the balance in uniform end-of-year payments for 18 years with interest at 6½%. Or the property may be purchased for cash for $34,500. A prospective purchaser is undecided whether to buy this home on the installment plan or to dispose of another investment in order to take advantage of the cash price. It is evident to him that because the cash price is lower than the installment price, he will, in effect, be paying more than the apparent 6½% interest for this loan. Compute for him the before-tax cost of this borrowed money expressed as an interest rate.

8–34. A magazine offers three types of subscription, payable in advance, as follows:

1 year	$ 7
2 years	10
Life	75

(a) In comparing the economy of a 1-year subscription with that of a 2-year subscription, what is the rate of return on the extra investment in the 2-year subscription?

(b) A subscriber to this magazine is convinced that he wants to subscribe to it for the rest of his life. He desires to compare the economy of a life subscription with that of continuing to renew a 2-year subscription. According to a standard mortality table his remaining life expectancy is 30 years. If he takes the life subscription and lives exactly 30 years more and if there is no increase in the price of the 2-year subscription, what will be his rate of return on the extra investment in the life subscription?

8–35. Two mutually exclusive proposals are Projects X and Y. Project X requires a present investment of $250,000. Estimated annual receipts for 25 years are $84,000; estimated annual disbursements other than income taxes are $32,000; estimated annual income taxes are $22,000. Project Y requires a present investment of $350,000. Estimated annual receipts for 25 years are $100,000; estimated annual disbursements other than income taxes are $40,000; estimated annual income taxes are $24,000. Each project is estimated to have a $50,000 salvage value at the end of 25 years. Assuming an after-tax i° of 8%, make the necessary calculations to determine whether to recommend Project X, Project Y, or neither. Make a specific recommendation and explain why you made it.

8–36. An investor purchased a piece of unimproved city property for $7,000 in 1954. He paid property taxes of $150 a year on this for 10 years. Then in 1964 he sold a part of this property for $5,000. He paid property taxes of $100 a year on the remainder for 6 more years and in 1970 sold it for $15,000. Using your interest tables, make the necessary calculations to find out as accurately as possible the before-income-tax rate of return that he made on this investment. For the sake of simplicity in your calculations, assume that the transactions occurred on January 1, 1954, 1964, and 1970, respectively, and assume that the property taxes were end-of-year payments.

8–37. An investor bought 10 shares of C & B Co. stock for $10,000. He held this stock for 15 years. For the first 5 years he received annual dividends of $500. For the next 4 years he received annual dividends of $400. For the final 6 years he received annual dividends of $300. At the end of the 15th year, he sold his stock for $7,500. What before-tax rate of return did he make on this investment?

8–38. It is proposed to purchase a machine to be used for rental purposes. The first cost is $50,000. It is estimated that in the first year of ownership, receipts will exceed disbursements for everything except income taxes by $10,000. Considering declining rental receipts with age and increased up-keep costs, it is believed this figure will decline by $500 each year and will be $9,500 in the second year, $9,000 in the third, and so on. Estimated income taxes for the first year are $3,375; these will decline by $250 each year thereafter. It is estimated that the machine will be retired after 12 years with an $11,000 salvage value. What is the prospective after-tax rate of return?

8–39. A certain rental property has a first cost of $50,000. If this property is purchased, it is believed that it will be held for 10 years and then sold. It is estimated that after 10 years the property will be saleable for $40,000. The estimated receipts from rentals are $10,000 a year throughout the 10 years. Estimated annual disbursements in connection with ownership and operation of the property (maintenance, property taxes, insurance, etc.) will be $3,000 the first year and will increase $200 each year thereafter to a figure of $4,800 in the 10th year. In addition, it is estimated that there will be a single non-recurrent outlay of $2,000 for a maintenance overhaul at the end of the 5th year. What is the prospective rate of return before income taxes?

9

Benefit-Cost Ratio

It is hereby recognized that destructive floods upon the rivers of the United States, upsetting orderly processes and causing loss of life and property, including the erosion of lands, and impairing and obstructing navigation, highways, railroads, and other channels of commerce between the States, constitute a menace to national welfare; that it is the sense of Congress that flood control on navigable waters or their tributaries is a proper activity of the Federal Government in cooperation with States, their political subdivisions, and localities thereof; that investigations and improvements of rivers and other waterways, including watersheds thereof, for flood-control purposes are in the interest of the general welfare; that the Federal Government should improve or participate in the improvement of navigable waters or their tributaries, including watersheds thereof, for flood-control purposes if the benefits to whomsoever they may accrue are in excess of the estimated costs, and if the lives and social security of people are otherwise adversely affected.
—FLOOD CONTROL ACT OF JUNE 22, 1936 [1]

We started this book with General Carty's questions "Why at all?" "Why now?" "Why this way?" These questions are just as relevant in government as in private enterprise. The basic procedures in decision making about proposed governmental outlays for fixed assets ought to be the same as in proposed outlays in private business, namely:

1. Define alternatives clearly and try to determine the differences in consequences of various alternatives.

2. Insofar as practicable, make these differences commensurable by expressing them in terms of money.

3. Apply some criterion to the monetary figures to provide a basis for judgment whether proposed investments are justified. The time value of money should be recognized in establishing this criterion.

4. Choose among alternatives applying the foregoing criterion but also giving consideration to tne differences among alternatives that were not reduced to money terms.

[1] *United States Code,* 1940 ed. (Washington, D.C.: Government Printing Office), p. 2964.

135

Economic Evaluation of Proposed Public Works in Terms of "Benefits" and "Costs." In the famous passage quoted at the start of this chapter, the United States Flood Control Act of 1936 stipulated that "benefits to whomsoever they may accrue" should exceed "estimated costs." Although this phrasing of a primary criterion for project evaluation applied officially only to flood control projects in the United States that were to be financed entirely or partially by the federal government, the phrasing gradually was adopted in the economic evaluation of various other types of federal public works projects. Then, as time went on, it was also applied to the evaluation of many proposed local public works projects within the United States. During the 1950's and 1960's, the same type of formulation of project evaluation standards was introduced in many other countries throughout the world.

Some Difficulties in Identifying and Measuring Relevant Consequences in Economy Studies for Proposed Government Projects. Conceptually, matters are more complicated in evaluating proposed public works projects than in evaluating similar projects in private enterprise. Also, the application of concepts is more difficult where governmental activity is involved. Certain differences between economy studies for private enterprise and economy studies for governments may be illustrated by contrasting the evaluation of a proposed relocation of a portion of a privately owned railway with the evaluation of a proposed relocation of a section of highway.

In both cases an economic evaluation calls for consideration of the required investment and of the influence of the project on roadway maintenance costs and on the costs associated with the movement of traffic. But there is an important point of difference. The railway company makes the investment and expects itself to recover the investment plus an adequate return through savings in costs of moving traffic and, in some cases, also through increased revenues and/or reduced maintenance costs. In contrast, although governmental agencies make the investment and pay highway maintenance costs, the savings in costs of moving traffic are made by the general public, not by any government agency. Therefore, the answer to the question "Whose viewpoint should be adopted?" is different for two projects that physically are similar. Clearly, the difficulty in estimating and valuing consequences is much less for the railway project than for the highway project.

Moreover, in looking at the railway decision from the viewpoint of the company's owners, an economy study can be based on cash flow, i.e., on receipts and disbursements by the railway company. In contrast, when one looks at the highway decision from the viewpoint of consequences "to whomsoever they may accrue," it is not practicable to look at *all* cash flows. If one considers the entire population, every positive cash flow (receipt) by someone is a negative cash flow (disbursement) by someone else. Therefore, the algebraic sum of the cash flows would be zero and there would be no basis for an economic evaluation.

For example, if a project is expected to reduce highway accidents, there will be reduced *disbursements* by highway users for automobile repairs, medical and hospital services, and legal services. But the reduction in these outlays by the highway users will be accompanied by an equal reduction in *receipts* by the automobile repair shops, physicians, hospitals, and lawyers.

The foregoing illustration brings out the point that it becomes necessary in the economic analysis of a public works project to make a judgment as to which consequences are to be counted and which are to be disregarded. In the case of a proposed reduction in highway accidents, this judgment is not a difficult one. From the public viewpoint, highway accidents are deemed to be undesirable; one of the purposes of a proposed highway improvement may be to reduce them. When we take a more critical look at the subject in Chapter 19, we shall see that it is difficult to get a fully satisfactory monetary evaluation of all their adverse consequences. Nevertheless, a way to start such an evaluation is to estimate the reduction in monetary outlays by accident victims associated with a prospective reduction in the number and severity of highway accidents. Such a monetary saving is reasonably counted as a project *benefit*. The prospective reduction in receipts by repair shops, physicians, hospitals, and lawyers is disregarded in a project analysis; such consequences should not be included as "negative benefits" or "disbenefits" or "costs" of a proposed highway project.

Purpose of This Chapter. Although most persons would doubtless agree that the foregoing reasoning is acceptable in the evaluation of highway accident reduction, decisions separating consequences considered to be relevant in an economy study from consequences considered to be irrelevant are not always so clear and noncontroversial. Chapter 19 deals with economy studies for governmental activities. We shall put off until that chapter our discussion of a number of conceptual issues and practical difficulties involved in identifying relevant benefits and costs and placing money values on them. In examples and problems before Chapter 19 we shall assume that suitable year-by-year money figures have been obtained to measure the relevant benefits and costs.

The objective of the present chapter is to show the relationship between the various benefit-cost techniques and the methods of analysis that have already been explained. We shall see that with the same input data (including of course a stipulated minimum attractive rate of return), the *decision* reached by comparing benefits with costs is the same decision that will be reached by the methods explained in Chapters 6, 7, and 8. However, we shall also see that the same proposed project may have several different values of the benefit-cost *ratio* depending on whether certain adverse items are subtracted from benefits or added to costs.

Both of the examples in this chapter involve three alternatives, one of which is a continuation of a present condition. Examples and problems involving more than three alternatives are introduced in Chapter 12.

Importance of the Interest Rate Selected in Economy Studies for Governments. Various names have been applied to the value of i^* used in the economic analysis of proposed public works. Whether this is called an imputed interest rate, a discount rate, a vestcharge, or given some other name, it is, in effect, the chosen minimum attractive rate of return. Moreover, even though the primary criterion for decision making may be phrased in terms of benefits and costs, it is the chosen value of i^* that really sets the standard for the investment decision. A discussion of the issues involved in selecting i^* in governmental economy studies is deferred until Chapter 19. The two examples in this chapter assume values of 7% and 6%, respectively.

EXAMPLE 9–1. APPLICATION OF SEVERAL METHODS OF ANALYSIS TO A SIMPLE HIGHWAY ECONOMY STUDY

Facts and Estimates. A certain stretch of rural highway is in such bad condition that its resurfacing or relocation is required. The present location is designated as H; two possible new locations that will shorten the distance between the terminal points are designated as J and K. Location K is somewhat shorter than J but involves a considerably higher investment for grading and structures. An economy study comparing the proposals for the three locations is to use a study period of 20 years and an i^* of 7%.

The estimated initial investment to be made by government highway agencies would be $110,000 at location H, $700,000 at J, and $1,300,000 at K. If location H is abandoned now, it will have no net salvage value; also it is assumed to have no residual value at the end of 20 years if this location is kept in service. However, because the estimated useful lives of the works that would be constructed at J or K are longer than the 20-year analysis period, residual values are estimated at the end of 20 years. These are $300,000 for J and $550,000 for K. Estimated annual maintenance costs, also to be paid by the government, are $35,000 for location H, $21,000 for J, and $17,000 for K.

It is forecast that the traffic on this section of highway will increase by a uniform amount each year until year 10 and will then continue at a constant level until year 20. It is not expected that the volume of traffic will be influenced by this decision on the location of the highway. For location H, annual road user costs deemed to be relevant in the economic analysis are estimated as $210,000 in year 1, $220,000 in year 2, and increasing by $10,000 each year until they reach $300,000 in the 10th year; thereafter they will continue at $300,000. For location J, which is shorter, the corresponding estimates are $157,500 for year 1, an increase of $7,500 a year until year 10, and a constant annual figure of $225,000 thereafter. For the even shorter location K, the corresponding figures are $136,500, $6,500, and $195,000. There are no differences in nonuser consequences that need to be considered.

Comparison of Present Worths of Relevant Costs. A tabulation of the present worths of the foregoing costs using an i^* of 7% is given in Table 9–1. This tabulation does not separate the capital and maintenance costs paid by the government from the road user costs paid by the general public. It is evident that location J has the lowest total present worth.

TABLE 9–1

Tabulation of Present Worths, Example 9–1

	Location H	Location J	Location K
Investment less PW of residual value ...	$ 110,000	$ 622,000	$1,158,000
PW of maintenance costs	371,000	223,000	180,000
PW of road user costs	2,823,000	2,117,000	1,835,000
Total	$3,304,000	$2,962,000	$3,173,000

Comparison of Equivalent Uniform Annual Costs. Table 9–2 shows a comparison of the equivalent uniform annual figures using an i^* of 7%. Of course the three totals are in the same proportions to one another as the present worths totals in Table 9–1; in fact, each total annual cost figure is the product of total present worth and 0.09439, the crf for 7% and 20 years.

TABLE 9–2

Tabulation of Equivalent Uniform Annual Costs, Example 9–1

	Location H	Location J	Location K
Capital recovery cost	$ 10,400	$ 58,800	$109,300
Annual maintenance cost	35,000	21,000	17,000
Equivalent uniform annual road user cost..	266,500	199,900	173,200
Total	$311,900	$279,700	$299,500

Calculation of Prospective Rates of Return on Extra Investments. Trial and error calculations of the type illustrated in Chapter 8 will show that, as compared to location H, the extra investment in location J will yield a prospective rate of return of approximately 12.8%. That is, the prospective savings in maintenance costs and road user costs plus the greater residual value are just sufficient to recover the extra $590,000 initial outlay with an interest rate of 12.8%. Because 12.8% exceeds the stipulated i^* of 7%, location J is economically superior to location H.

Similar calculations comparing K with J will show that the extra investment in K over J has a prospective rate of return of approximately 3%. Because 3% is less than the stipulated i^* of 7%, the extra investment of $600,000 needed for K is not economically justified. Of course, the rate-of-return analysis reaches the same conclusion as the present worth analysis and the annual cost analysis; it favors J as compared to H or K.

Calculation of the Excess of Benefits over Costs. In the solutions given in this example, it will be assumed that a prospective saving in road user costs (a favorable consequence to road users) is classified as a "benefit" and that the initial investment and the annual outlay for maintenance (both paid by the government) are classified as "costs." An analysis comparing benefits with costs can be made using either present worths or equivalent uniform annual figures.

Using present worths and designating benefits by **B** and costs by **C**:

To compare location J with location H,

$$
\begin{aligned}
\mathbf{B} &= \$2,823,000 - \$2,117,000 & &= \quad\$706,000 \\
\mathbf{C} &= (\$622,000 + \$223,000) - (\$110,000 + \$371,000) &&= \quad\underline{364,000} \\
\mathbf{B} - \mathbf{C} & & &= +\$342,000
\end{aligned}
$$

To compare location K with location J,

$$
\begin{aligned}
\mathbf{B} &= \$2,117,000 - \$1,835,000 & &= \quad\$282,000 \\
\mathbf{C} &= (\$1,158,000 + \$180,000) - (\$622,000 + \$223,000) &&= \quad\underline{493,000} \\
\mathbf{B} - \mathbf{C} & & &= -\$211,000
\end{aligned}
$$

The foregoing differences of course are the same differences in total present worths that could have been calculated from Table 9–1. Naturally, the conclusion is favorable to location J just as in Table 9–1.

Using equivalent annual figures:

To compare J with H,

$$
\begin{aligned}
\mathbf{B} &= \$266,500 - \$199,900 & &= \quad\$66,600 \\
\mathbf{C} &= (\$58,800 + \$21,000) - (\$10,400 + \$35,000) &&= \quad\underline{34,400} \\
\mathbf{B} - \mathbf{C} & & &= +\$32,200
\end{aligned}
$$

To compare K with J,

$$
\begin{aligned}
\mathbf{B} &= \$199,900 - \$173,200 & &= \quad\$26,700 \\
\mathbf{C} &= (\$109,300 + \$17,000) - (\$58,800 + \$21,000) &&= \quad\underline{46,500} \\
\mathbf{B} - \mathbf{C} & & &= -\$19,800
\end{aligned}
$$

Here we have the same differences that could have been computed from the three totals in Table 9–2.

Calculation of Benefit-Cost Ratios. The reader will recall that the 1936 flood control act quoted at the start of this chapter merely stated that benefits should exceed costs. Nevertheless, analysts who compare benefits with costs nearly always compute a ratio of benefits to costs. The stipulation $\mathbf{B} - \mathbf{C} > 0$ can also be expressed as $\mathbf{B/C} > 1$. The **B/C** ratios in this example will of course be the same whether they are computed from present worths or from equivalent uniform annual figures.

To compare J with H,

$$
\mathbf{B/C} = \frac{\$706,000}{\$364,000} \text{ or } \frac{\$66,600}{\$34,400} = 1.94
$$

To compare K with J,

$$B/C = \frac{\$282,000}{\$493,000} \text{ or } \frac{\$26,700}{\$46,500} = 0.57$$

Like all the other types of analysis that have been illustrated, the analysis using the B/C ratios favors location J. However, later in this chapter we shall see that the same input data can give different values of the B/C ratio depending on whether certain items are viewed as affecting the numerator or the denominator of the B/C fraction.

EXAMPLE 9-2. BENEFIT-COST ANALYSIS OF FLOOD CONTROL ALTERNATIVES

Facts and Estimates. Just before Willow Creek has its outlet into a salt water bay, it goes through an urban area. Because there have been occasional floods that have caused damage to property in this area, a flood control project has been proposed. Estimates have been made for two alternative designs, one involving channel improvement (CI) and the other involving a dam and reservoir (D & R). Economic analysis is to be based on an estimated 50-year project life assuming zero terminal salvage value and using an i^* of 6%.

The "expected value" of the annual cost due to flood damages is $480,000 with a continuation of the present condition of no flood control (NFC). The alternative CI will reduce this figure to $105,000; the alternative D & R will reduce it to $55,000. (Obviously, some years will have no flood damage; other years may have considerable damage. It is not possible to predict the specific dates of the years that will have the severe floods; the best that can be done is to predict the long-run relative frequencies of flood magnitudes and their related damages. The "expected value" is obtained from such estimates by the use of the mathematics of probability; methods of computation are illustrated in Chapter 14. In that chapter we shall see why it is reasonable in this type of economic analysis to treat the respective figures of $480,000, $105,000, and $55,000 as if they were uniform annual figures.)

The CI alternative has an estimated first cost of $2,900,000 and estimated annual maintenance costs of $35,000. Both of these require disbursements by the government.

The D & R alternative has an estimated first cost of $5,300,000, and estimated annual operation and maintenance costs of $40,000, both requiring disbursements by the government. This alternative also has two types of adverse consequences related to the conservation of natural resources. These are to be treated in the economic analysis as disbenefits (sometimes called "negative benefits" or "malefits"). The dam will cause a damage to anadromous fisheries; this is priced at $28,000 a year. The reservoir will cause a loss of land for agricultural purposes including grazing and crop raising; this is priced at $10,000 a year.

Benefit-Cost Analysis. Example 9-1 made the point that it was possible to use equivalent uniform annual figures in a benefit-cost analysis. Because most of the estimates in the present example consist of annual figures, our analysis will be based on annual benefits and annual costs.

In comparing the alternative of channel improvement (CI) with a continuation of the present condition of no flood control (NFC), the annual benefits are due to the reduction in the expected value of flood damages. The annual costs are the annual capital recovery costs and maintenance costs of CI.

$$\text{B (CI} - \text{NFC)} = \$480,000 - \$105,000 \qquad\qquad = \quad \$375,000$$
$$\text{C (CI} - \text{NFC)} = \$2,900,000(A/P,6\%,50) + \$35,000 \ = \quad \underline{219,000}$$
$$\text{B} - \text{C} \qquad\qquad\qquad\qquad\qquad\qquad\qquad\qquad = +\$156,000$$
$$\text{B/C} = \frac{\$375,000}{\$219,000} = 1.71$$

In comparing the dam and reservoir (D & R) with channel improvement, the extra annual benefit is the further reduction in the expected value of flood damages minus the disbenefits associated with the loss of fisheries and agricultural resources. The extra annual cost is the extra capital recovery cost due to the greater investment plus the extra annual operation and maintenance cost.

$$\text{B (D \& R} - \text{CI)} = (\$105,000 - \$55,000)$$
$$\qquad\qquad\qquad - (\$28,000 + \$10,000) \qquad = \quad \$\ 12,000$$
$$\text{C (D \& R} - \text{CI)} = [\$5,300,000(A/P,6\%,50) + \$40,000]$$
$$\qquad\qquad\qquad - [\$2,900(A/P,6\%,50) + \$35,000]$$
$$\qquad\qquad\qquad\qquad\qquad\qquad\qquad\qquad = \quad \underline{157,000}$$
$$\text{B} - \text{C} \qquad\qquad\qquad\qquad\qquad\qquad\qquad\qquad = -\$145,000$$
$$\text{B/C} = \frac{\$12,000}{\$157,000} = 0.08$$

With the given input data associated with a criterion stated either as **B − C > 0** or **B/C > 1**, it is evident that channel improvement is economically justified whereas the proposed dam and reservoir are not economically justified.

The Fallacy of Merely Comparing All Proposals for Change with a Continuation of a Present Condition. In both of the foregoing examples, one alternative was to continue a present condition (location H in 9–1 and no flood control in 9–2).

In Example 9–1, Location J was economically superior to both locations H and K. Similarly in Example 9–2, channel improvement was economically superior both to no flood control and to the proposed dam and reservoir. Nevertheless, the higher investments required for location K and for the dam and reservoir would have appeared to be justified if comparison had been made only with a continuation of the present condition. If K should be compared to H, the **B/C** ratio would be 1.15. If D & R should be compared with NFC, the **B/C** ratio would be 1.03.

It should be clear to the reader that where there are more than two alternatives, it is *never* sufficient to compare a proposed alternative only with the least attractive of the remaining alternatives. This is elaborated in Chapter 12 and discussed further in some of the later chapters.

The Arbitrary Aspects of the Classification of Certain Items in a Benefit-Cost Analysis. The present-worth and annual-cost solutions in Example 9–1 treated all input data as affecting costs; road user costs were included as one of the components of all the relevant costs. Subsequently, in the solutions using benefits and costs, reductions in road user costs were classified as *benefits*. The capital recovery cost of the highway investment and the highway maintenance cost were classified as *costs*. In the D & R alternative in Example 9–2, the adverse consequences associated with the loss of certain natural resources were classified as *disbenefits*.

Our practice in the benefit-cost analyses in these two examples was consistent with a rule that relevant consequences to the general public should be classified as benefits or disbenefits and that consequences involving disbursements by governmental units should be classified as costs. However, such a rule of classification is entirely arbitrary; different rules are used by different analysts. For example, annual maintenance costs are sometimes deducted from benefits rather than added to costs. Certain adverse consequences to the general public (such as the loss of natural resources in Example 9–2) are sometimes added to costs rather than treated as disbenefits.

The Influence on the Benefit-Cost Ratio of the Decision on Whether Certain Items Are Classified as Costs or as Disbenefits. It is a deficiency of the benefit-cost *ratio* as a scheme of project evaluation that legislators, administrative officials, and concerned members of the general public often have the view that the higher the ratio the better the project and vice versa. Actually, although $(B - C)$ is unaffected by the decision as to whether an item is classified as a cost or as a disbenefit, the ratio B/C can be considerably influenced by this arbitrary decision.

For example, consider a project that has $300,000 of benefits, $100,000 of costs, and a $90,000 adverse item that some analysts would classify as a cost and others would classify as a disbenefit. If this $90,000 item should be classified as a cost:

$$B/C = \frac{\$300,000}{\$100,000 + \$90,000} = \frac{\$300,000}{\$190,000} = 1.58$$

However, if it should be classified as a disbenefit:

$$B/C = \frac{\$300,000 - \$90,000}{\$100,000} = \frac{\$210,000}{\$100,000} = 2.10$$

With either classification, $(B - C) = \$110,000$. The real merits of the project are unrelated to the classification of the $90,000 adverse item. However, to an uncritical observer the apparent merits of the project may be greatly influenced by this classification.

Some General Comments on the Subject Matter of This Chapter. In public works, just as in private enterprise, valid economy studies can be made without using the word "benefits." In fact, we illustrated such studies in Chapters 6 and 7 (Examples 6–4 and 7–2). Moreover, even in Example 9–1 we noted that present worth, annual cost and rate of return analyses gave the same conclusion yielded by the benefit-cost analysis. It is not necessary or desirable to phrase decision criteria in terms of benefits and costs in the economic evaluation of all proposed governmental investments.

The authors of this book have observed that the attempt sometimes made to formulate the economic analysis of *all* government projects in terms of so-called benefits and costs has occasionally been an obstacle to sound thinking. In cases where all the relevant differences expressed in monetary terms can be described as estimated cash flows by a governmental body, as was the case in Examples 6–4 and 7–2, there is no good reason for a benefit-cost type of formulation. The special useful concept emphasized by a formulation using the word *benefits* is that it is desirable to examine prospective consequences "to whomsoever they may accrue."

It was pointed out near the start of this chapter that we are putting off until Chapter 19 our discussion of certain troublesome and controversial matters that often arise in the evaluation of public works proposals. Among these matters are the choice of a minimum attractive rate of return, the selection of a method for placing a money valuation on consequences to the general public, and the decision as to *which* prospective consequences to the public are deemed to be relevant in any given economic evaluation. In that chapter, also, we shall take a brief look at certain institutional factors that sometimes create obstacles to sound decision making in the public sector of the economy.

PROBLEMS

9–1. Example 9–1 followed the practice, which has been fairly common in highway economy studies, of classifying highway maintenance expenditures as "costs" in computing **B/C** ratios. The respective **B/C** ratios for locations J over H, K over J, and K over H, were 1.94, 0.57, and 1.15.

It has been suggested that outlays for maintenance ought to be classed as disbenefits. Compute the three **B/C** ratios making this change in classification. (*Ans.* = 1.67; 0.61; 1.13.)

9–2. In Example 9–2, the $38,000 a year figure for the prospective loss of natural resources that would be caused by the D & R project was classed as a disbenefit. The respective **B/C** ratios for D & R as compared to CI and NFC were 0.08 and 1.03. What would these **B/C** ratios have been if the loss of natural resources had been classified as a cost rather than as a disbenefit? (*Ans.* = 0.26; 1.03.)

9–3. Make the necessary calculations to check the present worth figures given in Table 9–1.

9–4. Make the necessary calculations to check the annual cost figures given in Table 9–2. (Do not use the present worth figures from Table 9–1.)

9–5. Example 9–1 states that location J shows a prospective rate of return of approximately 12.8% as compared to location H, and location K shows a prospective rate of return of approximately 3% as compared to location J. Make the necessary calculations to check these stated rates of return.

9–6. In Example 9–2, what is the prospective rate of return on the extra investment in CI as compared to NFC? What is the prospective rate of return on the extra investment in D & R as compared to CI?

9–7. A study is made to determine the most economical traffic control method for an isolated intersection of two city streets, Doe Street and Roe Avenue. Three types of control are considered for analysis:

R. A continuation of the present condition in which stop signs require all traffic from Roe Avenue to stop before entering Doe Street

S. The installation of stop signs on Doe Street to convert the intersection into a 4-way stop

T. The installation of 2-phase fixed time signals

The new investment required by the city would be $100 for S and $9,450 for T. All investments are considered to have a 10-year life with negligible net salvage value when retired. Annual operation and maintenance costs by the city are estimated as $25 for R, $50 for S, and $1,270 for T. There is no evidence that there will be any difference in police department costs or other municipal disbursements.

Differences in costs of road user consequences that the analyst deems to be relevant in an economic analysis are:

1. Extra costs of motor vehicle operation due to required motor vehicle stops at the intersection

2. Extra costs of the time of commercial vehicle traffic due to vehicles stopping or slowing down at the intersection

3. Costs associated with accidents

For the expected volume of traffic at this intersection and for actual vehicle speeds, and considering the hourly traffic distribution throughout the day, the division of the traffic among passenger vehicles, single-unit trucks, and combination trucks, the division of traffic between commercial and noncommercial vehicles, the division of traffic between Doe Street and Roe Avenue and the proportion of the various types of turning movements, the following estimates are made:

1. Average daily extra motor vehicle operating costs due to stops will be $28.50 for R, $53.20 for S, and $26.10 for T.

2. Average daily costs of time delays will be $37.20 for R, $61.90 for S, and $34.30 for T. These estimates consider only time delays for commercial vehicles and disregard time delays for noncommercial vehicles.

3. Average daily accident costs will be $7.20 for R, $3.80 for S, and $6.60 for T. These figures are based on the average accident records for the past 5 years at approximately 100 similar installations of these three types in this city and neighboring cities.

Assuming a 365-day year and a 10-year study period, and using an i^* of 7%, make an economic analysis of the benefits and costs of the three types of traffic control. What is the **B/C** ratio of S as compared to R? Of T as compared to R? Of T as compared to S? If a **B/C** ratio greater than unity is sufficient to justify a proposed investment, which alternative would you recommend?

9–8. In Problem 9–7, matters treated as irreducible data included the time loss to users of noncommercial vehicles, the time loss by pedestrians, the differences in the contributions to regional air pollution due to the differences in the numbers of stops and starts of motor vehicles, and the adverse consequences of accidents that were not reflected by the monetary evaluation. Discuss these irreducibles in relation to the problem of choice among R, S, and T.

9–9. For a certain proposed government project, annual capital costs to the government are $200,000 and annual operation and maintenance costs to the government are $100,000. Annual favorable consequences to the general public of $1,000,000 are offset by certain annual adverse consequences of $400,000 to a portion of the general public. What is the **B/C** ratio if all consequences to any of the general public are counted in the numerator of the ratio and all consequences to the government are counted in the denominator? What will it be if the classification of the $400,000 adverse consequences to the general public is changed from a disbenefit to a cost? If the $100,000 operation and maintenance cost to the government is changed from a cost to a disbenefit? If both changes are made? Regardless of the classification of these items, what is the excess of benefits over costs?

9–10. For a certain proposed government project, annual capital costs to the government are $300,000 and annual operation and maintenance costs to the government are $700,000. Annual favorable consequences to the general public of $1,000,000 are partially offset by certain annual adverse consequences of $200,000 to a portion of the general public. What is the **B/C** ratio if all consequences to any of the general public are counted in the numerator of the ratio and all consequences to the government are counted in the denominator? What will it be if the classification of the $200,000 adverse consequences to the general public is changed from a disbenefit to a cost? If the $700,000 operation and maintenance cost to the government is changed from a cost to a disbenefit? If both changes are made?

Regardless of the classification of these two items, the benefits are $200,000 less than the costs. However, this is a project that will be of great advantage to certain persons in the general public who are promoting it enthusiastically. These persons have argued that irreducibles favorable to the project are so important that the project should be undertaken even though the estimated benefits are somewhat less than the estimated costs. Which classification of these two items will make the project appear to be the most favorable by giving it a **B/C** ratio nearest to unity? Which classification will be least favorable to the project?

9–11. Two alternate storage flood control projects are proposed for the Crow River. A low dam (LD) project has an estimated first cost of $1,500,000 and annual operation and maintenance costs of $28,000. A high dam (HD) project has an estimated first cost of $4,000,000 and annual operation and maintenance costs of $47,000. The "expected value" of the annual cost of flood damages is $310,000 with a continuation of the present condition of no flood control, $145,000 with LD, and $60,000 with HD. The HD project has annual disbenefits of $23,000 due to a loss of land for agricultural purposes in the reservoir site. Find the relevant **B/C** ratios to evaluate the merits of these projects using an i^* of 7%, a 50-year life for the projects, and zero terminal salvage values.

9–12. Solve Problem 9–11 changing the i^* to 4½%.

9–13. Solve Problem 9–11 changing the estimated terminal salvage values to 100% of the first costs.

9–14. A relocation of a stretch of rural highway is to be made. Alternate new route locations are designated as M and N. The initial investment by government highway agencies will be $3,000,000 for M and $5,000,000 for N. Annual highway maintenance costs will be $120,000 for M and $90,000 for the shorter location N. Relevant annual road user costs are estimated as $880,000 for M and $660,000 for N. Compute the **B/C** ratio or ratios that you believe to be relevant for an economy study comparing the two locations. Use an i^* of 7%, a 20-year study period, and assume residual values equal to 60% of first cost.

9–15. Solve Problem 9–14 assuming that the stated road user costs are for the first year of service, and that these costs will increase by $20,000 each year at M and $15,000 each year at N throughout the 20-year analysis period.

10

Some Relationships Between Depreciation Accounting and Engineering Economy

A word is not a crystal, transparent and unchanged; it is the skin of a living thought, and may vary greatly in color and content according to the circumstances and the time in which it is used.
—JUSTICE OLIVER WENDELL HOLMES [1]

The examples of economy studies in Chapters 6, 7, and 8 started with estimates of the effect on cash flow of proposed decisions between alternatives. No mention was made of the effect on the accounts of an enterprise. The topic of the relationship between accounting and economy studies is introduced in the present chapter. This chapter deals primarily with one facet of accounting, namely, accounting for depreciable fixed assets (such as buildings, structures, machinery, and equipment).

Why Should Students of Engineering Economy Learn About Depreciation Accounting? Persons responsible for decisions on the acquisition and retirement of fixed assets need a general understanding of depreciation accounting for a variety of reasons. Four of these reasons are developed in the present chapter:

1. Often it is necessary to reconcile economy studies with the accounts of an enterprise. This need arises in various ways. Some data for economy studies come from the accounts and must be modified by conversion to cash flow before they are suitable for use in the economy studies. Frequently it is necessary that economy studies be related to the accounts for presentation to colleagues, to management personnel, or to the general public. The follow-up (if any) of decisions based on economy studies must be based in part on figures from the accounts.

[1] In a 1918 United States Supreme Court decision, *Towne v. Eisner*, 245 U.S. 418.

2. Economy studies for private enterprise require estimates of the amounts and dates of the outlays for income taxes that will be affected by a choice among proposed alternatives. In most cases, such estimates involve consideration of the depreciation methods that will be used for tax purposes. Although depreciation deductions from taxable income in any given year are not always equal to depreciation deductions from accounting income, it is necessary to understand depreciation accounting if one is to understand the income tax treatment of depreciation. In fact, the authors believe that this relationship between depreciation accounting and income taxes makes it essential that persons responsible for economy studies have some understanding of depreciation accounting.

3. Several approximate methods used by some analysts for computing the annual cost of capital recovery are related to two methods of depreciation accounting, namely, the straight-line method and the sinking-fund method.

4. There are in common use several methods of making so-called rate of return studies that depend on the depreciation accounts. The student of engineering economy needs to understand these methods in order to be aware of their deficiencies.

This book deals with depreciation accounting primarily in relation to engineering economy; there are many aspects of the subject that are not presented at all or that are discussed only briefly and superficially. Some other aspects of depreciation accounting referred to later in the book are as follows:

1. Chapters 15 and 17 point out certain common errors made in economy studies for retirements and replacements—errors that are related in part to a misunderstanding of depreciation accounting.

2. Chapter 18 shows the relationship between depreciation accounting and one source of funds for investment in fixed assets. It also discusses the relationship between depreciation accounting and the provision of funds for the replacement of assets.

3. Chapter 21 discusses a common misuse of depreciation accounting in computing so-called payoff periods.

A Classification of Reasons for Retirement. Property units are generally retired for one or more of the following reasons:

1. *The availability of improved machines or structures for performing the same service.* Research and development work by scientists and engineers is continually leading to new and more economical ways of doing existing jobs. If the prospective economies from new methods are sufficient, it will pay to replace old assets with new ones or to relegate the old assets to stand-by purposes or other inferior uses.

2. *Changes in the amount and type of service requirements.* This includes such changes as increase or decrease in the amount of service required from the old asset, due to an increase or decrease in the demand for its product or service. It also includes changes in the product or service required. These changes frequently arise from competitive situations, either from competition among producers in a single industry or from competition with substitute products or services. They may also be caused by acts of public authority.

3. *Changes in the existing machines or structures themselves.* Machines and structures wear out, corrode, and decay as the result of age and use. Often this increases maintenance costs and decreases the quality and reliability of performance to the extent that it pays to replace assets that are still capable of continuing to render service. In some circumstances wearing out, corrosion, and decay may make retirement imperative rather than merely economical.

4. *Changes in public requirements regarding the machine or structure.*

5. *Casualties.*

These reasons for retirement are not mutually exclusive, but in most cases operate in combination with one another. Thus an old machine might be replaced by a new one that (1) incorporated new automatic features that reduced unit labor costs, (2) provided increased capacity to meet an increased demand for the product, and (3) had the prospect of initial maintenance costs considerably lower than the current high maintenance costs of the old machine.

Obsolescence (1), inadequacy (2), wearing out (3), etc., also are responsible for reductions in value of old assets long before the assets reach the point where immediate retirement is economical.

Mortality Dispersion for Physical Property Units. Not all human beings die at the same age. Some die young and others live to a ripe old age. Nevertheless, it is possible to analyze human mortality experience to determine curves and tables that give satisfactory estimates of average life and of the percentage of survivors at any age. Thus a life insurance company can predict with confidence what percentage of 100,000 healthy white native males 20 years old will survive to the ages of 27 or 49 or 65, even though it is not possible to say with respect to any individual whether he will survive any given number of years.

Physical property units are like human beings in having a mortality dispersion. Of a number of property units that seem identical, some will be retired at an early age and others will serve many years before retirement. This fact of mortality dispersion is illustrated in Figure 10–1.

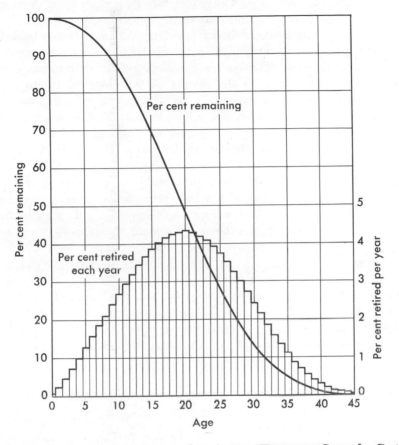

FIGURE 10–1.   Survivor Curve and Retirement-Frequency Curve for Certain Telephone Underground Cable

This figure shows two curves that have been derived in the analysis of the retirement experience of telephone exchange underground cable.

The reversed curve starting in the upper left-hand corner of the diagram is called a *survivor curve*. It shows the percentage of this type of plant that, in the particular group of cable studied, may be expected to be in service at any given number of years after its installation. For instance, 70% will be in service after 15 years of life. The lower stepped curve is a *retirement frequency curve*. It shows the annual retirements expressed as a percentage of the original amount installed. Although the maximum number of retirements is at age 20, retirements are taking place from the 1st year of life to the 44th year.

These curves are mathematically fitted ideal curves derived from a certain group of actual data involving several million dollars' worth of exchange underground cable. Curves of this type have been developed in connection with the requirements of depreciation accounting.

Such curves may be developed from statistical analysis that uses data involving exposures to the risk of retirement and actual retirements of units of various ages. The curves therefore reflect retirements for all causes; they give weight to the results of technological progress and environmental changes as well as to the tendency of industrial assets to deteriorate as they get older. As might be expected, a series of such statistical analyses made over a period of years often indicates that average service lives are shortening for some classes of assets and lengthening for other classes.

Statistical analysis of the type used in obtaining curves such as Figure 10–1 can only reflect the ages at which retirements actually have been *made*. For various reasons mentioned in Chapter 17, it often happens that assets are kept in service beyond the date at which it would have paid to retire them. It follows that economic service lives often are shorter than the average service lives that will be determined from a statistical analysis of retirements.[2]

The statistical approach to industrial property mortality obviously requires that there have been a fair number of retirements of the type of assets being studied. For this reason, difficulties arise in applying the statistical approach to new types of assets or to very long-lived types of assets.

The Various Meanings of "Depreciation." The meanings of words develop out of their use. Many words are used in a number of different meanings. Depreciation is such a word. In any use of the word, there needs to be a clear differentiation among these various meanings.

In his outstanding book, *Valuation of Property*, Professor J. C. Bonbright[3] points out that substantially all the different technical meanings attached to the word *depreciation* are variants of four basic concepts. These are:

1. DECREASE IN VALUE. This concept implies that the value of one asset is in some way computed at two different dates. The value at the later date subtracted from the value at the earlier date is the *depreciation* regardless of what combination of causes may have been responsible for the value change. When depreciation is used in everyday speech, this

---

[2] For a concise explanation of the various statistical methods of finding average service life, see E. L. Grant and P. T. Norton, Jr., *Depreciation* (New York: The Ronald Press Co., 1955), chap. v. See also Robley Winfrey, *Statistical Analysis of Industrial Property Retirements*, (Ames, Iowa: Bulletin 125, Iowa Engineering Experiment Station, 1935).

[3] J. C. Bonbright, *Valuation of Property* (New York: McGraw-Hill Book Co., Inc., 1937), chap. x.

is the meaning generally implied; it is also implied by most dictionary definitions.

Like depreciation, *value* is a word with many meanings. As pointed out by Professor Bonbright, the two most important and useful of these meanings in the economic sense of the word are *market value* and *value to the owner*. Depreciation in the sense of decrease in value may apply to either of these two concepts of value. Values may be determined by actual market price, by appraisal, or in any other appropriate way.

2. AMORTIZED COST. This is the accounting concept of depreciation, which is being discussed in the present chapter. From the viewpoint of accounting, the cost of an asset is a prepaid operating expense to be apportioned among the years of its life by some more or less systematic procedure. It should be emphasized that it is cost, not value, that is apportioned in orthodox accounting.

The accounting concept of depreciation is well described in a report of the Committe on Terminology of the American Institute of Certified Public Accountants as follows: [4]

Depreciation accounting is a system of accounting which aims to distribute the cost or other basic value of tangible capital assets, less salvage (if any), over the estimated useful life of the unit (which may be a group of assets) in a systematic and rational manner. It is a process of allocation, not of valuation. Depreciation for the year is the portion of the total charge under such a system that is allocated to the year. Although the allocation may properly take into account occurrences during the year, it is not intended to be a measurement of the effect of all such occurrences.

Although we shall use the common phrase *book value* to describe the difference between the cost of an asset and the total of the depreciation charges made to date against the asset, this difference is more accurately described as *unamortized cost*.

3. DIFFERENCE IN VALUE BETWEEN AN EXISTING OLD ASSET AND A HYPOTHETICAL NEW ASSET TAKEN AS A STANDARD OF COMPARISON. This is the appraisal concept of depreciation. Many appraisals of old assets are based on replacement cost. A replacement cost appraisal should answer the question "What could one afford to pay for this asset in comparison with the most economical new one?"

An upper limit on the value to its owner of an old asset may be determined by considering the cost of reproducing its service with the most economical new asset available for performing the same service. This most economical new substitute asset may have many advantages over an existing old asset, such as longer life expectancy, lower annual dis-

[4] *Accounting Terminology Bulletin No. 1: Review and Resume* (para. 56), American Institute of Certified Public Accountants, 1953.

bursements for operation and maintenance, increased receipts from sale of product or service. The deduction from the cost of the hypothetical new substitute asset should be a measure in money terms of all of these disadvantages of the existing old asset.

In the language of appraisal, this deduction is called *depreciation*. Appraisal depreciation, therefore, should mean the value inferiority at some particular date (the date of the appraisal) of one asset, the existing old one being appraised, to another asset, a hypothetical new one used as the basis of valuation. This concept implies two assets and the measurement of their values at one date.

4. IMPAIRED SERVICEABLENESS. As machines become older they are often unable to hold as close tolerances as when they were new. Similarly, the strength of structures may be impaired by the decay of timber members or the corrosion of metal members. Engineers have sometimes used the word *depreciation* to refer to such impaired functional efficiency.

It should be emphasized that this is not a value concept at all. Impaired serviceableness may result in decrease in value, but there are many other common reasons for decrease in value. Assets that are physically as good as new are not necessarily as valuable as when they were new. They may have higher operation and maintenance costs; they will nearly always have shorter life expectancy; service conditions may have changed; more economical alternative methods may have become available. As the use of depreciation in the sense of impaired serviceableness has generally led to confusion in valuation matters, the word is not used in this sense elsewhere in this book.

Concepts of Value.[5] As previously stated, the most useful economic concepts of value are *market value* and *value to the owner*.

Market value properly refers to the price at which a property could actually be sold. For certain types of valuation this is not an appropriate concept to use. Often only one owner is in a position to make effective use of a given item of property; although continued possession of this property may be of great monetary importance to its owner, the property might bring only a negligible price if sold to someone else.

Hence the concept of value to a specific owner is of great importance in the valuation of property. Value to the owner may be defined as the money amount that would be just sufficient to compensate the owner if he were to be deprived of the property. Generally speaking, this value will not be greater than the money amount for which the owner could soon replace the property with the best available substitute, with due allowance for the superiority or inferiority of that substitute. And, gen-

[5] For an authoritative and thorough discussion of value concepts, see Bonbright, *op. cit.*, chaps. 3, 4, and 5.

erally speaking, value to the owner will not be less than the market price for which the property could be sold. The concept of value to the owner may properly be applied to a prospective owner as well as to a present owner.

The word *value* is also sometimes used in what might be called a neutral sense as any money amount that is associated with specific items of property for some given purpose. An example of this is the use of the phrase *book value* to describe the unamortized cost of property as shown by the books of account.

The Balance Sheet and Profit and Loss Statement. Any presentation of the elements of accounting must focus attention on two important types of statements obtained from the accounts.

One of these, the *balance sheet*, describes the condition of an enterprise at a particular moment, for example, at the close of business on the final day of a fiscal year. The balance sheet shows what the enterprise owns (its assets), what it owes (its liabilities), and shows the "value" of the owners' equity in the enterprise as the excess of assets over liabilities. All balance sheet valuations are arrived at using the formal and systematic rules of accounting and sometimes differ greatly from market value of the same properties.

The other statement, the *profit and loss statement*, also called the *income statement*, gives the incomes and expenses of an enterprise as shown by the books of account for a period of time and states whether the enterprise has made a profit or loss and how much. The longest period of time covered by the usual profit and loss statement is a fiscal year. (A business fiscal year does not always coincide with the calendar year, as it may start on some date other than January 1.) The figures in the profit and loss statement, like those in the balance sheet, are determined using the formal and systematic rules of accounting.

Example 10–1 illustrates the relationship between depreciation accounting and the balance sheet and profit and loss statement in an extremely simple case. This example describes an actual investment from which certain complicating factors have been omitted. Example 10–2 deals with another actual case that is relatively simple, illustrating a common method of estimating year-by-year return on investment from the accounts. Both examples deal with terminated business enterprises. It will be noted that in Example 10–1 the enterprise finally turned out to be unsuccessful even though the initial indication from the accounts was that the enterprise was extremely profitable. In contrast, Example 10–2 deals with an enterprise that finally turned out to be much more profitable than it first seemed to be from an analysis of the accounts.

EXAMPLE 10–1. DEPRECIATION IN THE ACCOUNTS OF A MINIATURE GOLF COURSE

Facts of the Case. During the early days of so-called miniature golf courses during the depression years in the United States, an individual whom we shall call George Spelvin built the first such course in his home city. He rented a vacant lot in a strategic central location and spent $4,500 to construct his golf course. When he shut down for the winter at the end of his first year, he had taken in $5,000 in admission fees and had paid out $1,500 for various operating expenses. At this time he refused an offer of $8,500 from an amusement syndicate for his golf course and lease. When he commenced operations again in the spring of his second year, the local interest in miniature golf had declined to the point where his receipts barely covered his operating disbursements. He continued operations for a few months on this unsatisfactory basis and then abandoned his venture.

Financial Statements for the First Year and Their Relationship to Depreciation Accounting. At the time of completion of the construction of the golf course, the balance sheet for this enterprise (if one had been prepared) would have been as follows:

Assets		Liabilities and Owner's Equity	
Golf Course	$4,500	G. Spelvin, Invested Capital	$4,500

At the close of his first season, if Spelvin had not recognized that part of the service life of his golf course had expired, he would have believed that his profit was $3,500, the excess of his receipts over his disbursements. Under this unrealistic assumption, his balance sheet before his withdrawal of any of this "profit" would have been:

Assets		Liabilities and Owner's Equity	
Cash	$3,500	G. Spelvin, Invested Capital	$4,500
Golf Course	4,500	G. Spelvin, Retained Earnings	3,500
	$8,000		$8,000

Actually he estimated a 5-year life for his golf course and decided to allocate $900, one-fifth of his $4,500 outlay, as the depreciation expense of the first year's operations. (We shall see that this is the straight-line method of depreciation accounting.) The book value of his golf course was reduced by $900 as a result of his accounting entry for this depreciation, and the figure for profit shown by his accounts was $900 less than it would have been if no depreciation had been recognized. His year-end balance sheet after giving recognition to this depreciation write-off was:

Assets			Liabilities and Owner's Equity	
Cash		$3,500	G. Spelvin, Invested Capital	$4,500
Golf Course	$4,500		G. Spelvin, Retained Earnings	2,600
Less				
Allowance for Depreciation	900	3,600		
		$7,100		$7,100

His profit and loss statement for the year was:

Receipts from admissions		$5,000
Less		
Operating Expenses:		
Disbursements for rent, taxes, attendance, upkeep	$1,500	
Depreciation on golf course	900	2,400
Profit from first year's operations		$2,600

This profit shown by the books was 58% of Spelvin's original $4,500 investment.

Comment on the Foregoing Financial Statements. This simple example illustrates several important points regarding depreciation accounting, as follows:

1. The operation of making the $900 depreciation charge on the books of account involved no cash flow. In effect, the $900 depreciation entry was an allocation to the first year of operation of a portion of a previous $4,500 cash flow that the accounts had viewed as causing the acquisition of an asset rather than as the incurring of an expense.

(Later in this chapter, we shall see that even though the act of making a depreciation entry on the books does not in itself change the cash on hand, a depreciation entry in an income tax return influences the cash flow for income taxes. If Spelvin had paid income taxes and if the depreciation figure in his tax return had been based on his books of account, his tax payments would have been influenced by the depreciation charge entered in his books.)

2. The profit as shown by the books of account depends on the depreciation charge and therefore is influenced by the estimated life and salvage value and by the depreciation accounting method selected. Thus Spelvin's use of straight-line depreciation accounting and his assumption of a 5-year life and no salvage value gave him a profit figure of $2,600. If he had assumed a 2-year life and charged half of the $4,500 cost of the golf course as depreciation, his profit figure would have been only $1,250. If he had assumed that the golf course would always have 100% salvage value, his profit figure would have been $3,500. Although, as the quoted definition said, depreciation accounting requires the writing off of cost "in a systematic and rational manner," there are many different systematic and rational ways to write off cost, and these different ways give different figures for profit.

3. The valuation of assets on the balance sheet is similarly influenced by the depreciation charge. The so-called book value of an asset is merely that portion of the cost of the asset that has not yet been charged off as depreciation expense. The book value of the golf course was

$3,600 at the end of the first year because $900 of depreciation had been charged against the year's operations and deducted from the $4,500 cost of the course. If the depreciation charge had been less than $900, the book value would have been higher; if the depreciation charge had been more than $900, the book value would have been lower.

The quoted definition of depreciation accounting pointed out that "it is a process of allocation and not of valuation." The valuation shown for a depreciable asset on the books of account is not influenced by unpredicted fluctuations in market value. Thus the $3,600 book value for the golf course was not influenced by the fact that the syndicate's offer, turned down by Spelvin, indicated that the course had a market value of $8,500 on the year-end date when the balance sheet was prepared.

EXAMPLE 10–2. YEAR-BY-YEAR ESTIMATES OF RATES OF RETURN FROM AN INVESTMENT IN RENTAL PROPERTY

Facts of the Case. Example 8–1 (page 110) described an investment in rental property. The cash flow series from this investment was shown in Table 8–1. The rate of return on the investment was 18.9% before income taxes, as computed in Table 8–2 by appropriate compound interest methods. Because a property costing $10,900 was sold for a net $20,900 after 7 years of ownership, the actual rate of return from the terminated investment was considerably higher than the rate of return had appeared to be during the period of ownership.

Table 10–1 shows the figures for annual profits as shown by the accounts of this enterprise for its first 6 years of operation. For purposes of accounting, the $10,900 investment was broken down as follows:

Land $1,500
Buildings 8,000
Furniture 1,400

TABLE 10–1

Accounting Figures for Annual Profits and Current Estimates of Rate of Return for Data of Example 8–1

Year	Book Value at Start of Year	Receipts for Year	Expenses for Year		Profits for Year	Apparent Rate of Return on Investment
			Repairs Taxes, etc.	Depre- ciation		
1	$10,900	$1,500	$500	$340	$ 660	6.1%
2	10,560	1,800	550	340	910	8.6
3	10,220	1,800	570	340	890	8.7
4	9,880	1,800	450	340	1,010	10.2
5	9,540	1,800	360	340	1,100	11.5
6	9,200	1,800	430	340	1,030	11.2

In accordance with the conventions of accounting, no prospective decrease (or increase) in the value of land was considered in the accounts. For purposes of depreciation accounting, the buildings were assumed to have a 40-year life with no salvage value, and the furniture was assumed to have a 10-year life with no salvage value. Straight-line depreciation was charged in the accounts at $200 a year for the buildings and at $140 a year for furniture, a total of $340 a year. The profit figures for each year shown in the next-to-last column of Table 10–1 are the years' positive cash flows diminished by the $340 depreciation charge.

The table also shows the book value of the property at the start of each year. In the first year this was the investment of $10,900; each year it was diminished by the $340 depreciation charge made in the books of account. The final column of the table shows the profit for each year expressed as a percentage of the start-of-year book value. This latter figure may be thought of as a current estimate of rate of return on investment computed by a method that often is used in relation to the accounts of an enterprise.[6]

Tentative Character of Accounting Figures for Profit and for Rate of Return. An incidental aspect of Examples 10–1 and 10–2 is that both examples illustrate the point that intermediate judgments about profitability and about rates of return may be considerably in error. In fact, the two actual cases used in these examples are extreme cases deliberately selected to emphasize this point. In Example 10–1 the rate of return appeared to be 58% at the end of the first year even though when the investment was terminated it turned out that there was not even a 0% return. In Example 10–2, the rates of return for the first three years appeared to be less than 9% even though the over-all rate of return on the terminated investment turned out to be approximately 19%.

Of course the true over-all rate of return obtained over the life of an investment cannot be known until ownership has been terminated. Nevertheless, year-by-year figures for profit are essential in the conduct of a business (and in the collection of income taxes); it is not practicable to wait until the termination of a business enterprise to draw conclusions regarding its profitability. It is natural to compute year-by-year rates of return by relating the profit figures taken from the accounts to some investment figure also taken from the accounts.

At this point in our discussion a clear distinction needs to be made between the problem of computing a single figure for rate of return on an investment based on the full period of consequences of the investment and the problem of estimating year-by-year figures for rate of return. As explained in Chapter 8 (and demonstrated in Table 8–6), compound interest methods are required to find the correct figure for rate of return

---

[6] An alternate method, also frequently used, is to express the year's profit as a percentage of the average of the book values at the start and the finish of the year. For example, the 5th year's profit, $1,100, would be divided by $9,370 (the average of $9,540 and $9,200) to obtain an apparent return of 11.7%.

over the life of an investment. The foregoing statement applies both to the calculation of rate of return from a terminated past investment and to the calculation of estimated rate of return from estimates of cash flow for the entire period of service of a proposed investment.

It is rarely, if ever, of much importance to find the rate of return on a terminated past investment (such as the one in Example 10–2). Although the rate of return may be of historical interest, nothing can be done about terminated investments.

In contrast, the estimation of rate of return on a proposed investment is a matter of great practical importance. An important criterion of attractiveness of a proposed investment is the single figure that expresses the prospective rate of return over the life of the investment. It needs to be emphasized that it is this over-all rate of return that is significant for proposed investments, not year-by-year estimates of rates of return of the type illustrated in Table 10–1.

In the opinion of the authors of this book, there is seldom any valid reason for not using correct compound interest methods in analyzing *proposed* investments. A great deal of time and effort often goes into the making of estimates for economy studies relative to proposed investments. Only a few minutes more time are needed to apply methods of computing rate of return that are correct in principle than are needed to apply any of the various competing incorrect methods.

However, several incorrect methods of computing prospective rates of return on proposed investments are in common use in industry. Although these methods all have their origins in the type of calculations of rate of return on past investment illustrated in Examples 10–1 and 10–2, we shall see that the methods give results that differ greatly from one another. Sometimes these methods are used in the belief that they are good approximations to correct compound interest methods; sometimes they are used under the illusion that they are correct in principle. Some of the weaknesses of these methods are illustrated and discussed at the end of this chapter.

Before we can describe and evaluate these "approximate" methods, we must first examine the most common methods of depreciation accounting.

General Comment on All Methods of Depreciation Accounting. As brought out in the quoted definition of depreciation accounting, it is the *cost* of tangible assets, less prospective salvage value, that is written off on the books of account. In effect, the cost of capital assets is viewed as a prepaid expense to be apportioned among the years of service of the assets "in a systematic and rational manner."

There are many different methods of writing off cost that obviously are "systematic." Moreover, methods that differ greatly from one another have been advocated as being "rational." In the United States the methods in common use have been influenced by changes in income tax laws and regulations, particularly by changes in 1934, 1954, and 1962 that will be mentioned in the following discussion.

One way to classify depreciation accounting methods is as follows:

1. Methods that aim to give a greater write-off in the early years of life than in the final years of life
2. Methods that aim to give a uniform write-off throughout the entire service life
3. Methods that aim to give a smaller write-off in the early years of life than in the final years

In class (1) we shall discuss the declining-balance method, the sum-of-the-years-digits method, and certain multiple-straight-line methods. In class (2) we shall discuss the straight-line method. In class (3) we shall discuss the sinking-fund method. Because of its historical importance, the straight-line method is discussed first.

Straight-Line Depreciation Accounting. In the straight-line method, the full service life of the asset is estimated. The prospective net salvage value at the end of the life is also estimated and expressed as a percentage of first cost. The annual depreciation rate to be applied to the first cost of the asset being written off is computed as follows:

$$\text{Straight-line rate} = \frac{100\% \text{ minus estimated salvage percentage}}{\text{estimated service life in years}}$$

Consider a machine tool with a first cost of $35,000, an estimated life of 20 years, and an estimated net salvage value of $3,500. The salvage percentage is $3,500 \div \$35,000 = 0.10$ or 10%.

$$\text{Straight-line rate} = \frac{100\% - 10\%}{20} = \frac{90\%}{20} = 4.5\%$$

With this straight-line depreciation rate, the depreciation charge every year will be $1,575 (i.e., 4.5% of the $35,000 first cost).

The same $1,575 may be computed without the use of the 4.5% figure, as follows:

Straight-line depreciation charge

$$= \frac{\text{first cost minus estimated salvage value}}{\text{estimated service life in years}}$$

$$= \frac{\$35,000 - \$3,500}{20} = \frac{\$31,500}{20} = \$1,575$$

Prior to 1934, it was common in the manufacturing industries of the United States for cost to be written off in a much shorter period than full service life. For example, the cost of machinery often was written off by a uniform annual charge during the first 10 years of its life. At the expiration of this period the machinery was carried on the books of account as "fully depreciated." It was not uncommon for the full service lives of machines so written off to be 20 or 25 years or even longer. Although in pre-1934 days, this method of write-off was described as "straight-line," we shall see that the method is more accurately described as a special case of multiple-straight-line depreciation accounting.

A change in policy of the U. S. Treasury Department in 1934 and thereafter was intended to force the writing off of cost for tax purposes over the full service life. With the straight-line method applied over full service life, the final years of life receive exactly the same depreciation charges as the initial years of life.

Declining-Balance Depreciation Accounting. It is common for assets to be used for stand-by or other inferior uses during the final years of their lives. The contribution of assets to income often is much greater in the early years of life than in the final years. For these reasons and for other reasons brought out in Chapter 16, it usually is sensible to write off the cost of assets more rapidly in the early years of life than in the later years.

Several ways of making this more rapid write-off in the early years were authorized for income tax purposes in the United States in 1954. The use of these liberalized methods for tax purposes was restricted to assets having lives of three years or more that were acquired new by the taxpayers in 1954 or thereafter. One of these methods was the so-called double-rate declining-balance method.

In any declining-balance depreciation accounting, a given depreciation rate is applied each year to the remaining book value, that is, to that portion of the cost of an asset (or assets) that has not already been written off in a previous year. For example, if a 10% rate is applied to an asset that cost $35,000, the depreciation charge in the first year is $0.10(\$35,000) = \$3,500$. In the second year the charge is $0.10(\$35,000 - \$3,500) = 0.10(\$31,500) = \$3,150$. In the third year it is $0.10(\$31,500 - \$3,150) = 0.10(\$28,350) = \$2,835$. And so on.

In the double-rate declining-balance method authorized for income tax purposes in the United States in 1954, the depreciation rate is computed as 200% ÷ (estimated life in years). This rate is double the straight-line rate that would be allowed for an asset that has an estimated zero salvage value and the given estimated life. In computing the permissible declining-balance rate, any prospective terminal salvage value is disregarded.

Consider, for example, the $35,000 machine tool for which we computed the 4.5% straight-line rate. This had a 20-year estimated life and a $3,500 estimated salvage value. The permissible declining-balance rate for this asset is $200\% \div 20 = 10\%$. The application of a 10% rate for 20 years will lead to a book value of $4,255 at the end of the 20th year.

If P represents the first cost of an asset and f represents the declining-balance rate expressed as a decimal, the book value at the end of r years obviously will be $P(1-f)^r$. At this point in our discussion, the so-called textbook method of computing a declining-balance rate requires a brief mention. Assume that a rate f is desired that will make the book value at the end of an n-year life exactly equal to an estimated terminal salvage value, L. Then

$$L = P(1-f)^n$$

and

$$f = 1 - \sqrt[n]{\frac{L}{P}}$$

However, this method of setting a declining-balance rate is rarely if ever used. It cannot be used with zero salvage value. Small differences in estimated salvage value make a great difference in the computed rate. For example, consider two $1,000 assets each with a 20-year estimated life, both with small prospective salvage values. Asset X has an estimated salvage value of $50; asset Y has an estimated salvage value of $1. The declining-balance percentage computed for X is 13.91% and for Y is 29.20%.

In the actual use of the declining-balance method, it is better to select a depreciation rate that seems appropriate, all things considered, than to compute a rate from the textbook formula. The declining-balance rates permitted by the 1954 tax laws and regulations in the United States are intended to permit a write-off of about two-thirds of the cost of an asset in the first half of the estimated life.

Sum-of-the-Years-Digits Depreciation Accounting. This method, authorized in the United States by the 1954 tax law, apparently was never used in actual accounting practice before that date. The digits corresponding to the number of years of estimated life are added together. For example, consider our $35,000 machine tool with its estimated life of 20 years. The sum of the digits from 1 to 20 is 210. The depreciation charge for the first year is 20/210 of the depreciable cost (i.e., of the first cost minus the estimated salvage value). This is 20/210($35,000 − $3,500) = 20/210($31,500) = $3,000. In the second year the charge is 19/210($31,500) = $2,850. In the third year it is 18/210($31,500) =

$2,700. And so on. The charge decreases by $150 (i.e., by 1/210 of $31,500) each year until it is $150 in the 20th year.

This method writes off about three-fourths of the depreciable cost in the first half of the estimated life.

Sinking-Fund Depreciation Accounting. This method visualizes an imaginary sinking fund established by uniform end-of-year annual deposits throughout the life of an asset. These deposits are assumed to draw interest at some stated rate, such as 6%, 4%, or 3%, and are just sufficient so that the fund will equal the cost of the asset minus its estimated salvage value at the end of its estimated life. The amount charged as depreciation expense in any year consists of the sinking-fund deposit plus the interest on the imaginary accumulated fund. The book value at any time is the first cost of the asset minus the amount accumulated in the imaginary fund up to date. The sinking-fund method is also known as the present-worth method; the book value at any time is equal to the present worth of the uniform annual cost of capital recovery for the remaining years of life plus the present worth of the prospective salvage value.

For example, assume that our $35,000 machine tool is to be depreciated by the 6% sinking-fund method. The annual sinking-fund deposit is ($35,000 − $3,500)(A/F,6%,20) = ($31,500)(0.02718) = $856.2. This will also be the depreciation charge in the first year. In the second year the depreciation charge will be $856.2 + $856.2(0.06) = $907.6. In the third year it will be $856.2 + ($856.2 + $907.6)(0.06) = $962.0. And so on.

The book value at any age can be computed without year-by-year calculations by finding the amount in the imaginary sinking fund and subtracting this amount from the first cost. For instance, the sinking fund at the end of 12 years will amount to $856.2(F/A,6%,12) = $856.2-(16.870) = $14,444. The book value at this time is therefore $35,000 − $14,444 = $20,556. This book value may be checked by computing the present worth at date 12 of the annual cost of capital recovery for the remaining 8 years plus the present worth of the terminal salvage value. The annual capital recovery cost is ($35,000 − $3,500)(A/P,-6%,20) + $3,500(0.06) = ($31,500)(0.08718) + $3,500(0.06) = $2,746.2 + $210.0 = $2,956.2. The sum of the present worths of remaining capital recovery and terminal salvage value is $2,956.2(P/A,6%,8) + $3,500-(P/F,6%,8) = $2,956.2(6.210) + $3,500(0.6274) = $18,358 + $2,196 = $20,554. (The interest tables in this book are not carried to enough significant figures for this calculation to check to the nearest dollar.)

Book values with the sinking-fund method are always greater than they would be with the straight-line method. The difference is greater for long-lived assets than for short-lived ones, and is greater with high interest rates than with low ones. The straight-line method has sometimes been described as the limiting case of the sinking-fund method in which the interest rate has been assumed to be 0%.

Although the sinking-fund method was used in certain industries a few decades ago, it has ceased to be of much importance in actual accounting practice. It is explained here primarily because of the use of so-called sinking-fund depreciation in certain engineering economy studies in a manner explained later in this chapter.

An Illustration of Depreciation Charges and Book Values by Various Methods. Table 10–2 shows the year-by-year write-offs that would be made for our $35,000 machine tool by the four methods that have been explained. The table also shows end-of-year book values. In the de-

TABLE 10–2

Comparison of Depreciation Charges and Book Values by Four Methods of Depreciation Accounting

(Asset has first cost of $35,000, estimated life of 20 years, and estimated salvage value of $3,500.)

	Depreciation Charge for Year				End-of-Year Book Value			
Year	Declining Balance	Years Digits	Straight Line	6% Sinking Fund	Declining Balance	Years Digits	Straight Line	6% Sinking Fund
0					$35,000	$35,000	$35,000	$35,000
1	$3,500	$3,000	$1,575	$ 856	31,500	32,000	33,425	34,144
2	3,150	2,850	1,575	908	28,350	29,150	31,850	33,236
3	2,835	2,700	1,575	962	25,515	26,450	30,275	32,274
4	2,551	2,550	1,575	1,020	22,964	23,900	28,700	31,254
5	2,297	2,400	1,575	1,081	20,667	21,500	27,125	30,173
6	2,067	2,250	1,575	1,146	18,600	19,250	25,550	29,027
7	1,860	2,100	1,575	1,215	16,740	17,150	23,975	27,812
8	1,674	1,950	1,575	1,287	15,066	15,200	22,400	26,525
9	1,506	1,800	1,575	1,365	13,560	13,400	20,825	25,160
10	1,356	1,650	1,575	1,447	12,204	11,750	19,250	23,713
11	1,221	1,500	1,575	1,533	10,983	10,250	17,675	22,180
12	1,098	1,350	1,575	1,626	9,885	8,900	16,100	20,554
13	998	1,200	1,575	1,723	8,897	7,700	14,525	18,831
14	890	1,050	1,575	1,827	8,007	6,650	12,950	17,004
15	801	900	1,575	1,936	7,206	5,750	11,375	15,068
16	720	750	1,575	2,052	6,486	5,000	9,800	13,016
17	649	600	1,575	2,175	5,837	4,400	8,225	10,841
18	584	450	1,575	2,306	5,253	3,950	6,650	8,535
19	525	300	1,575	2,444	4,728	3,650	5,075	6,091
20	473	150	1,575	2,591	4,255	3,500	3,500	3,500

clining-balance and the 6% sinking-fund methods, the book values have been rounded off to the nearest dollar for listing in the table; the figures shown in the table for yearly depreciation charges have been made consistent with the figures shown for book value.

It is evident that "systematic" ways of writing off cost can differ greatly from one another. Comment on the rational basis of a choice among the different methods is deferred until later in the chapter.

Some Other Methods of Depreciation Accounting. Some types of capital assets can be identified with the production of specific units of output. For such assets, depreciation can be charged in proportion to units of production provided it is reasonable to estimate life in production units. The method has been used for assets associated with exhaustible natural resources where the factor limiting the life of the assets is the quantity of the natural resource in question. Thus the cost of a sawmill might be depreciated at so much per thousand board feet sawed, or the cost of a coal mine tipple might be depreciated at so much per ton of coal mined. Frequently the unit-of-production method is used for motor vehicles with depreciation charged in proportion to miles of operation. The method is rarely used in diversified manufacturing because of the difficulty of finding any suitable production unit.

It is possible to use depreciation accounting methods where two or more straight lines are needed to show the decline in book value from first cost to estimated salvage value. Such a scheme may be described as a multiple-straight-line method. Under the United States 1954 tax law, multiple-straight-line methods may be used for tax purposes subject to the restriction that the amount written off at any time during the first two-thirds of life is not more than would have been permitted under the declining-balance method. For example, our $35,000 machine tool might be written off at $2,250 a year for the first 10 years and at $900 a year for the final 10 years.

A special case of the multiple-straight-line method is the one in which the entire first cost (less estimated salvage value, if any) is written off on a straight-line basis in some period shorter than the life. As previously stated, this was the common situation in the United States before 1934. When an asset with a 25-year life was written off at 10% a year for 10 years and 0% for the remaining 15 years, this was really a multiple-straight-line method with one of the straight-line rates as 0%.

Under the 1954 tax law in the United States, it is permissible to switch from the declining-balance method to the straight-line method at any time before an asset is retired. For example, Table 10–2 shows the book value of our machine tool by the declining-balance method to be $8,897 at the end of 13 years. If the estimated remaining life on this date is still

7 years and the estimated salvage value is still $3,500, a straight-line write-off of $\dfrac{\$8,897 - \$3,500}{7} = \$771$ a year could be used for the final 7 years.

Estimates of Service Life and Salvage Value for Tax Returns, for Business Accounting, and for Economy Studies. Certain types of assets, such as automobiles, may have several owners before reaching the scrap heap. For each owner, the "life" for accounting purposes ordinarily is the expected period of service to the owner himself. In general, service life for accounting purposes is viewed as the number of years elapsing from an asset's acquisition to its final disposal, regardless of the different uses to which the asset may have been put during these years. Since 1934, the foregoing view of service life has governed the administration of income tax laws in the United States.

Estimates of terminal salvage value used for accounting and tax purposes should be consistent with estimated lives. For example, if automobiles are regularly purchased new and disposed of at the end of 3 years, the salvage percentage used in connection with the estimated 3-year life should be an estimated salvage percentage for 3-year-old automobiles.

Where sufficient data are available, various types of statistical studies may be made to estimate average service lives. In many cases such studies lead to survivor curves of the type illustrated in Figure 10–1. Statistical studies made year after year for a particular class of assets often indicate that the average realized life has been changing.

In 1962 the United States Treasury Department made available "guideline lives" for many broad classes of business assets.[7] The use of these lives for income tax purposes in the United States was subject to certain restrictions. Some aspects of the use of the guideline lives for tax purposes are discussed in Chapter 16. In many cases, taxpayers who elected to use these relatively short lives for tax purposes were using considerably longer estimated lives for the same assets in their business accounting.

An economy study relative to acquiring a proposed asset involves a somewhat different viewpoint from the keeping of the depreciation accounts for the asset once it is acquired. It may be reasonable to assume a shorter life in the economy study than the one that will be used for accounting or tax purposes. It is the economic life that is relevant in the economy study; the estimated full service life, which

[7] Internal Revenue Service Publication No. 456, *Depreciation—Guidelines and Rules,* Government Printing Office, Washington, D.C., 1962. This publication contains Revenue Procedure 62–21, the formal authorization for the use of the guideline lives.

often is the life deemed relevant for accounting and tax purposes, may be considerably longer than the economic life. Moreover, an economy study usually relates to the primary or initial type of service of an asset; it is rarely appropriate in an economy study to consider possible stand-by or other inferior services very much during the final years of an asset's life.

In some cases an economy study may relate to a shorter period than the expected economic lives of the various proposed assets; if so, it is necessary to estimate residual values at the end of the study period rather than terminal salvage values at the end of the economic lives. The use of such residual values in economy studies was illustrated in Example 9–1 and is discussed in Chapter 13.

Distinction Between Single-Asset and Multiple-Asset Depreciation Accounting.[8] Assume a group of assets that have the mortality distribution shown in Figure 10–1. Although the average service life of these assets is 20 years, retirements occur all the way from the first to the 45th year. For the sake of simplicity in the following illustration, assume that the expected salvage value is zero and that each asset, when retired, actually has a zero salvage value. Assume that straight-line depreciation is to be used; the 20-year average service life and zero salvage value requires a 5% depreciation rate.

Now assume that each asset has its own account and that the depreciation on each asset is computed separately. (This is referred to as *single-asset* or *item* depreciation accounting.) Approximately half of the assets will be retired before they are 20 years old. Every such asset will have some book value when retired; with no realized salvage value, the books of account will show a "loss" for each retirement. The half of the assets that survive for more than 20 years will be fully written off at age 20; no further depreciation charges will be made against them during their period of service from years 20 to 45.

In contrast, assume that one account is used to include the investment in all of these assets; each year the depreciation charge is made against the group of assets rather than against the individual asset and the book value at any time applies to the group with no identifiable separate figure applicable to each asset. With the assets considered in a group and with the fact of mortality dispersion recognized, it will be evident that the retirements at ages short of 20 years are not "premature" in the sense that they are inconsistent with the estimate of a 20-year *average* service life. If a set of unequal numbers are averaged, some of the numbers must be less than the average and others must be greater. The recognition of this point in multiple-asset depreciation accounting

---

[8] For a more complete discussion of this topic, see Grant and Norton, *op. cit.*, particularly chaps. 6, 7, 8, 10, and 19.

eliminates the "loss on disposal" entry under normal circumstances. However, in multiple-asset accounting, depreciation charges continue beyond the average service life.

In the language used in publications of the U. S. Internal Revenue Service, a distinction is made among three general types of multiple-asset accounts, as follows:

1. *Group accounts.* Examples of such accounts would be passenger automobiles, punch presses, office desks.
2. *Classified acounts.* Some examples are transportation equipment, machinery, furniture and fixtures.
3. *Composite accounts.* As an example, transportation equipment, machinery, and furniture and fixtures might be included in a single account.

Particularly in the manufacturing industries, the most common practice is to use classified accounts for income tax purposes. Often, the use of item accounts is limited to such assets as buildings and structures.

In this book the most important use of depreciation accounting is in connection with the calculation of cash flow for income taxes. In most of our examples and problems illustrating such calculations, our computations of the tax aspects of depreciation are made as if item accounts were to be used. This assumption of single-asset accounting is made chiefly for reasons of simplicity—to avoid the need to devote space to an explanation of the numerous technical details of multiple-asset accounting. In many studies, particularly those relative to proposed new assets, it makes no difference whether single-asset or multiple-asset accounting is assumed.

An economy study for a proposed retirement is one type of study in which the timing of cash flow for income taxes with single-asset accounting may differ greatly from the timing with multiple-asset accounting. Often the critical point in this type of study is whether a "loss on disposal" will be allowable for tax purposes. This topic is discussed in Chapter 17.

Certain Types of Assets Not Subject to Depreciation Charges in the Accounts. It is a convention of accounting that land is carried on the books at its original cost regardless of changes in its market value. No depreciation or appreciation on land is shown in the books of account. Of course, if land is finally sold at a price above or below its original cost, a "gain" or "loss" assigned to the year of the sale is shown on the books. But for accounting purposes, it is not necessary to make an estimate of the future sale price of land.

In the absence of any basis for a different forecast, some economy studies may follow the lead of orthodox accounting and assume—in effect

—that investments in land will have 100% salvage values. But cases occur where this is not an appropriate assumption. Sometimes there is good reason to forecast that at the end of a study period land will be sold for much more or much less than its original cost. If so, this forecast is relevant in any analysis to guide the decision on whether or not to invest in the land; the estimated future sale price of the land is one element of cash flow to include in the economy study.

Many economy studies relate to the investment in plant to permit the sale of a new product or expanded sale of an existing product. In addition to the investment in physical plant, such a project usually requires an outlay for *working funds*. The working fund investment will usually include inventories of materials, work in process, and finished goods. It will also include the excess of accounts receivable associated with the project over accounts payable similarly associated. For certain types of product there may also be an inventory of returnable containers to be considered.

The working fund investment is not subject to depreciation on the books of account. For purposes of an economy study an outlay for working funds should ordinarily be treated as if it were an investment that had a prospective 100% salvage value at the end of the study period. That is, it usually is reasonable to expect that when a product is discontinued the accounts receivable will be collected and the inventories will be liquidated. This treatment was illustrated in Example 8–3. Comments on certain aspects of the estimation of working fund requirements are made in Chapter 15.

Economy-Study Estimates of Cash Flow for Income Taxes Based on Certain Simplified Assumptions. Many of the examples and problems in Chapters 6, 7, and 8 included estimates of the differences in cash flow for income taxes that would be caused by a choice among stated alternatives. In those studies applicable to competitive industry, these estimates were made under the following simplified assumptions:

1. The same estimated lives and salvage values used in the economy study will also be used for tax purposes and will be acceptable to the taxing authorities.

2. Straight-line item depreciation accounting will be used for tax purposes.

3. Throughout the period of the economy study, the effective tax rate on an increment of taxable income will be 50%.

4. Except for capital items, receipts and disbursements before taxes in any year apply to the calculation of the taxable income for that year. (Capital items include first costs and salvage values of depreciable

plant. They also include assets such as land and working capital that are not subject to depreciation charges in computing taxable income.)

5. Recovery of investments in nondepreciable assets such as land and working capital does not give rise to any tax consequences.

Both the absolute total amount and the timing of prospective income taxes are important in the after-tax evaluation of proposed investments. A reasonable question about the foregoing simple assumptions is whether they give results that are good enough for practical purposes in investment evaluation.

The answer is that sometimes these assumptions are fairly good ones in competitive industry in the United States and sometimes they are not good at all. In Chapter 16 we take a critical look at various matters that influence the amount and timing of the income tax consequences of decisions in competitive industry. In the intervening chapters, the simplified assumptions permit us to make a number of examples and problems more realistic by including differences in estimated cash disbursements for income taxes.

The treatment of prospective income taxes in economy studies for regulated public utilities in the United States is a specialized topic that is related to the way in which public utility rates are regulated. This topic is not discussed until Chapter 20.

Verification of Income Tax Differences Given in Examples 6–1 and 6–2. Consider the application of the foregoing assumptions to the data of Examples 6–1 and 6–2. The following estimates were made for the three plans compared in these two examples:

	Plan A	Plan B	Plan C
First cost	$0	$15,000	$25,000
Life	10 years	10 years	10 years
Terminal salvage value	$0	$0	$5,000
Annual before-tax disbursements	$9,200	$5,100	$4,300

These were alternatives with reference to production methods; the receipts from the sale of the product or service would not be influenced by the choice among the three plans. Therefore, the difference in estimated income taxes depends only on the differences in estimated tax deductions. The deductions from taxable income each year are as follows:

	Plan A	Plan B	Plan C
Straight-line depreciation	$0	$1,500	$2,000
Before-tax disbursements	9,200	5,100	4,300
Total deductions	$9,200	$6,600	$6,300

Because Plan B has $2,600 less deductions from taxable income than Plan A, it will involve higher annual income tax disbursements of $1,300,

50% of $2,600. This $1,300 was the income tax figure given in the statement of Example 6–1.

Because Plan C has $2,900 less deductions from taxable income than Plan A, it will involve higher annual income tax disbursements of $1,450, 50% of $2,900. This $1,450 was the income tax figure given in the statement of Example 6–2.

Explanation of the Method of Estimating Each Year's Income Taxes Given in Example 8–3. The third paragraph of Example 8–3 ended as follows:

The specific estimates of net positive before-tax cash flow from operations year by year are: 1, $100,000; 2, $300,000; 3, $400,000; 4 through 11, $500,000; 12 and 13, $400,000; 14, $300,000; and 15, $200,000. These positive cash flows will be diminished by yearly disbursements for income taxes estimated to be 50% of the amount that each year's figure exceeds $100,000.

The depreciable investment in plant and equipment in this example was $1,500,000 made over a period of two years. The depreciation charge for accounting and tax purposes would not start until date 0 when the construction would be completed and the plant put in service. Because the estimated life was 15 years with no terminal salvage value, the annual straight-line depreciation is $1,500,000 ÷ 15 = $100,000. It is this $100,000 deduction from taxable income that was referred to in the second sentence quoted from the statement of Example 8–3.

The reader will note that Example 8–3 differs from Examples 6–1 and 6–2 in that the choice between the alternatives (accepting the project or rejecting it) involves differences in annual receipts. Moreover, because the estimated before-tax positive cash flow varies from year to year, the estimated disbursements for income taxes also vary from year to year.

According to the conventions of accounting and income taxation, the $300,000 outlay for land and the $200,000 outlay for working capital are nondepreciable and therefore have no influence on estimated disbursements for income taxes during the 15-year operating period of the project. Because it is assumed that these investments will be recovered without increase or decrease at the end of the 15-year operating period, the cash flow incident to their recovery at date 15 has no influence on income taxes in the 15th year, the terminal date of the project.

Some Economy-Study Methods That Appear to Tie Annual Capital Recovery Costs to the Depreciation Accounts. One of the topics presented in Chapter 6 was the conversion of a first cost, P, into an equivalent uniform annual figure over a life or study period. To make this conversion, it is necessary to have a stipulated minimum attractive rate of

return or interest rate, i^*, an estimated life or study period, n, and an estimated salvage value, L, at the end of the life or study period.

Throughout this book, we use the following equation to compute this annual cost of capital recovery with a return:

$$CR = (P - L)(A/P,i^*,n) + Li^*$$

This equation, which involves the use of the capital recovery factor, obviously is independent of the depreciation accounts.

In some economy studies that use the method of annual costs, various combinations of depreciation figures and interest figures are used. The total of depreciation plus interest is intended to serve the same purpose as our annual cost of capital recovery with a return. Three methods that sometimes are used are as follows:

1. Sinking-fund depreciation plus interest on first cost
2. Straight-line depreciation plus interest on first cost
3. Straight-line depreciation plus average interest

These methods give satisfactory results in some cases and misleading results in others.

Sinking-Fund Depreciation Plus Interest on First Cost. This is a correct compound interest method that gives the same annual cost of capital recovery as our conventional method provided the assumed interest rate on the sinking fund is equal to the stipulated minimum attractive rate of return. Sometimes the method is referred to as *interest plus amortization*.

As explained in Chapter 4, the capital recovery factor is always equal to the sinking fund factor plus the interest rate. An alternate way of writing our basic equation for capital recovery at interest rate i is therefore:

$$CR = (P - L)(A/F,i^*,n) + (P - L)i^* + Li^*$$
$$= (P - L)(A/F,i^*,n) + Pi^*$$

In effect, the method of sinking-fund depreciation plus interest on first cost is based on this latter formula. A numerical example will help to show the relationship between this method and the conventional method. Let us assume an asset with a first cost of $22,000, an estimated life of 10 years, and an estimated salvage value of $2,000. We shall use a minimum attractive rate of return of 10%. By the conventional method that is used throughout this book:

$$CR = (\$22,000 - \$2,000)(A/P,10\%,10) + \$2,000(0.10)$$
$$= \$20,000(0.16275) + \$2,000(0.10) = \$3,255 + \$200 = \$3,455$$

Assuming the use of a 10% interest rate in computing sinking-fund depreciation, the calculation by the method of sinking-fund depreciation plus interest on first cost reaches an identical result, as follows:

Sinking-fund depreciation $= (P - L)(A/F,i^\circ,n) = \$20,000(0.06275)$ $\qquad = \$1,255$
Interest on first cost $= Pi = \$22,000(0.10)$ $\qquad = \underline{2,200}$
Total annual cost of capital recovery with a 10% return $\qquad = \$3,455$

It should be noted that the figure for so-called sinking-fund depreciation in the foregoing calculation of capital recovery cost is not the full depreciation charge that would be made in the books if the sinking-fund method should be used; it is merely the *annuity* portion of the depreciation charge. If we should calculate year-by-year depreciation charges in the manner illustrated in Table 10–2, we would see that the sinking-fund depreciation charge for our $22,000 asset would vary from $1,255 in the first year to $2,959 in the 10th year; in our calculation of sinking-fund depreciation plus interest on first cost, only the $1,255 figure was used.

This annuity portion of the sinking-fund depreciation charge is sometimes referred to as *amortization*.[9] (The verb *amortize* comes from the same root as *mortal* and literally means "to make dead or destroy." It is applied to the provision for extinguishment of a debt or other obligation, particularly through periodic payments into a sinking fund.)

If the interest rate used on the amortization fund differs from the interest rate on first cost, the capital recovery cost obtained by this method obviously will differ from the one obtained by a conventional calculation using only one interest rate. For example, assume that a 10% rate is used to compute interest on first cost and a 3% rate is used in the sinking fund calculation. The capital recovery cost for our $22,000 asset will then appear to be:

Sinking-fund depreciation $= (\$22,000 - \$2,000)(A/F,3\%,10)$
$\qquad = \$20,000(0.08723)$ $\qquad = \$1,745$
Interest on first cost $\qquad = \$22,000(0.10)$ $\qquad = \underline{2,200}$
Total $\qquad = \$3,945$

Some Pros and Cons on the Method of Sinking-Fund Depreciation Plus Interest on First Cost. Although this method has not been common in economy studies in competitive industry, it has been widely used in economy studies for regulated public utilities and for governments. In such studies it is usual to assume the same interest rate on first cost and on the sinking fund.

Where used in this manner with a single interest rate, the method gives exactly the same annual cost figure as the method employing the

---

[9] For some reason this word is often mispronounced. The correct division into syllables is a-mor-ti-za-tion, with the second and fourth syllables accented. The common mispronunciation assumes the first syllable is *am* and accents the *am*.

capital recovery factor, which is used throughout this book. The choice between these two methods of computing annual cost must therefore be based on other grounds than the correctness of the results given by the two methods.

If sinking-fund depreciation accounting were actually to be used in the accounts, the use in economy studies of sinking-fund depreciation plus interest on first cost would serve the purpose of helping to reconcile economy studies with the accounts of the enterprise. But this method of depreciation accounting, once used by a few regulated public utilities, has largely been abandoned. This method is subject to the objection that it gives an unrealistically high proportion of the total write off in the final years of the life of an asset.

Or sinking-fund depreciation plus interest on first cost might tie an economy study to the financial policies of an enterprise if an actual sinking fund were to be established to recover an investment (less salvage, if any) in a fixed asset at the end of its life. But such sinking funds are rarely used.

In most cases, therefore, this method should be viewed as a compound interest conversion unrelated to the accounts or to the establishment of any actual fund. Viewed in this way, the method of sinking-fund depreciation plus interest on first cost does not seem to the authors to have any advantage over the conventional method of computing the annual cost of capital recovery with a return illustrated throughout this book. Often the method using sinking-fund depreciation is harder to explain than the conventional method because critics may make such comments as "There will be no actual sinking fund" or "We are not actually using this method of depreciation accounting." It is hard to give a satisfactory answer to these comments.

Valid objections may be raised to this method where two interest rates are used. A discussion of these objections follows the explanation of the method of straight-line depreciation plus interest on first cost because this latter method is really a special case of the analysis using two interest rates.

Straight-Line Depreciation Plus Interest on First Cost. If this method were used, the annual capital recovery cost of our $22,000 asset would be computed as follows:

$$\text{Straight-line depreciation} = \frac{P - L}{n}$$

$$= \frac{\$22,000 - \$2,000}{10} = \frac{\$20,000}{10} \qquad = \$2,000$$

$$\text{Interest on first cost} = Pi^* = \$22,000(0.10) \qquad\qquad = \underline{\ \ 2,200}$$

$$\text{Total} \qquad\qquad\qquad = \$4,200$$

Except in the special case of a salvage value of 100% (or more), this method invariably gives too high a figure for equivalent annual cost. The $4,200 a year that the method indicates is needed to recover our proposed $22,000 investment with a 10% return is in fact sufficient to permit recovery with a return of about 14.5%.

It has been pointed out that the straight-line method of depreciation accounting may be thought of as a limiting case of the sinking-fund method in which the interest rate on the sinking fund has been assumed to be 0%. Similarly, straight-line depreciation plus interest on first cost may be viewed as a special case of sinking-fund depreciation plus interest on first cost in which the sinking-fund interest rate is 0%.

Objection to Annual Cost Calculations Using Two Interest Rates. We have computed three different figures for the annual cost of capital recovery with a 10% return for our proposed $22,000 investment in equipment. The conventional method using the capital recovery factor gave us a figure of $3,455; this same figure was obtained with 10% sinking-fund depreciation plus 10% interest on first cost. But 3% sinking-fund depreciation plus 10% interest on first cost gave us an annual capital recovery cost of $3,945. And straight-line depreciation plus interest on first cost gave us $4,200.

The usual objective of comparing equivalent annual costs in an economy study is to judge whether or not certain proposed investments will yield at least a minimum attractive rate of return. Assume that our proposed $22,000 asset is expected to be responsible for increased receipts (or reduced disbursements) of $3,800 a year for 10 years. This annual $3,800 plus the final $2,000 salvage value will in fact be sufficient to recover the $22,000 investment with interest at 12.1%.

If we should compare this annual figure of $3,800 with our computed annual capital recovery cost of $3,455, we would obtain the correct conclusion that the asset would yield more than a 10% return. But if we should compare the $3,800 with $3,945 or with $4,200, we would obtain the incorrect conclusion that the proposed investment was not justified because it would not yield 10%.

The reader may recall our discussion in Chapter 8 of the misleading conclusions obtainable from the calculation of an unknown rate of return by the Hoskold method, where reinvestment was assumed in an imaginary sinking fund bearing a low interest rate. The fallacy in the annual cost calculation using two interest rates (i.e., 3% and 10%, or 0% and 10%) is the same one that we examined in Chapter 8 in our discussion of the Hoskold method.

Consider the following possible interpretation of a comparison of the $3,800 annual receipts with the $3,945 figure obtained by the method of 3% depreciation and 10% interest on first cost: "To judge whether our proposed $22,000 investment will give us a 10% return, the positive cash flow that it will cause is divided into two parts. One part, $2,200, is 10% on our investment. The other part must be enough so that we can invest it at 3% and (with the prospective terminal salvage value) have $22,000 back at the end of the 10 years. As the $3,800 will not be enough to permit us to do this, we should view this proposed investment as yielding less than 10%."

The error here is that the merits of *one* investment, the proposed $22,000 asset, are to be judged on the basis of the combined consequences of *two* investments, the asset and the 3% sinking fund. It is true that the asset, yielding 12.1%, and the sinking fund, yielding 3%, will not combine to give an over-all rate of return of 10%. A total of $3,945 a year will be needed for the combined rate of return to be 10%; $3,800 is not enough. But, unless there is to be an actual 3% sinking fund investment that *must* be made if the asset is acquired, this deficiency of the combined rate of return below 10% has no bearing on the merits of the proposed investment in the asset.

The foregoing two paragraphs may be altered so that they become a comment on the method of straight-line depreciation plus interest on first cost if 0% is substituted for 3% and $4,200 for $3,945.

Straight-Line Depreciation Plus Average Interest. This method of computing the annual cost of capital recovery with a return was widely used in economy studies in the United States in the 1930's and 1940's. Its use was illustrated in many examples and problems in the second (1938) and third (1950) editions of this book. Where straight-line depreciation was actually to be used in the accounts and where the assumed life and salvage value in the economy study were the same as used in the accounts, the method had the advantage of helping to reconcile economy studies with the accounts of an enterprise. The method is a close approximation to true equivalent annual cost in certain cases but a poor approximation in others.

With the decline in the application of straight-line depreciation accounting to new assets that started in 1954 in the United States, the use of this method no longer is justified on the basis of reconciling economy studies with the accounts except in a minority of cases.

A good way for the reader to compare this method with the conventional method is to look back at Table 3–1 (page 26) which compares different schemes of repaying (or recovering) $10,000 in 10 years with interest at 6%. Plan III in this table corresponds to the conventional viewpoint on computing the annual cost of capital recovery with a return. It is evident that the $1,358.68 a year for 10 years will exactly repay $10,000 with 6% interest.

Plan II is representative of another approach to the annual cost of capital recovery with interest. In this plan the annual payment on principal is uniform but the interest paid each year diminishes. With $10,000 paid in 10 equal installments, each installment is $1,000. Interest the first year is $600, which is 6% of the full $10,000, but diminishes by $60 each year as the principal is repaid until in the tenth year it is only $60. The average interest is $330.

These interest payments form an arithmetic progression the first term of which is Pi and the final term of which is $(P/n)i$. The average interest is the average of the first and last terms or $\dfrac{Pi}{2}\left(\dfrac{n+1}{n}\right)$.

The method of straight-line depreciation plus average interest always computes an *average* (rather than an equivalent) annual figure for a repayment plan devised along the lines of Plan II in Table 3–1. In the general case with a first cost, P, an estimated terminal salvage value, L, an estimated life of n years, and an interest rate, i, straight-line depreciation is $\dfrac{P-L}{n}$ and average interest is $(P-L)\left(\dfrac{i}{2}\right)\left(\dfrac{n+1}{n}\right) + Li$. As applied to our $22,000 asset, the calculation is:

$$\text{Straight-line depreciation} = \frac{\$22,000 - \$2,000}{10} = \$2,000$$

$$\text{Average interest} = \left[(\$22,000 - \$2,000)\left(\frac{0.10}{2}\right)\left(\frac{11}{10}\right)\right]$$
$$+ \$2,000(0.10) = \$1,100 + \$200 = \underline{\quad 1,300\quad}$$
$$\$3,300$$

This is somewhat less than the exact equivalent uniform annual cost, which we computed to be $3,455.

Limitations of Methods of Straight-Line Depreciation Plus Average Interest. Wherever the prospective terminal salvage is less than 100% of first cost, this method yields a figure for capital recovery cost that is too low. The method is an approximate one because it assumes the simple average of a diminishing series of payments to be the equivalent uniform annual payment. The error involved in its use increases with the length of the period of time considered and also increases with an increase in the interest rate. This variation is illustrated in Table 10–3.

Where annual cost methods are used to compare assets having approximately the same lives, where the lives are not too long, and where the minimum attractive rate of return is low, this method often gives satisfactory results. The greater the disparity in the lives of assets being compared and the higher the minimum attractive rate of return, the more likely it is that economy studies using this method will yield misleading conclusions.

TABLE 10–3

Capital Recovery Factors by Exact and Approximate Methods

Recovery Period, Years	4% Interest			8% Interest		
	Exact Method	Approx. Method	% Error	Exact Method	Approx. Method	% Error
n	$\dfrac{i}{(1+i)^n-1}+i$	$\dfrac{1}{n}+\dfrac{i}{2}\left(\dfrac{n+1}{n}\right)$		$\dfrac{i}{(1+i)^n-1}+i$	$\dfrac{1}{n}+\dfrac{i}{2}\left(\dfrac{n+1}{n}\right)$	
5	0.22463	0.22400	− 0.3	0.25046	0.24800	− 1.0
10	0.12329	0.12200	− 1	0.14903	0.14400	− 3
15	0.08994	0.08800	− 2	0.11683	0.10933	− 6
20	0.07358	0.07100	− 4	0.10185	0.09200	−10
50	0.04655	0.04040	−13	0.08174	0.06080	−26
100	0.04081	0.03020	−26	0.08004	0.05040	−37

Recovery Period, Years	12% Interest		
	Exact Method	Approx. Method	% Error
n	$\dfrac{i}{(1+i)^n-1}+i$	$\dfrac{1}{n}+\dfrac{i}{2}\left(\dfrac{n+1}{n}\right)$	
5	0.27741	0.27200	− 2.0
10	0.17698	0.16600	− 6
15	0.14682	0.13067	−11
20	0.13388	0.11300	−16
50	0.12042	0.08120	−33
100	0.12000	0.07060	−41

Three Common Methods of Computing So-Called Rates of Return on Proposed Investments. There are many different ways in which prospective figures from the accounts are used to compute ratios that are alleged to be prospective rates of return. George Terborgh in the chapter entitled "Popular Rule-of-Thumb Tests of Investment Merit," in *Business Investment Policy* [10] reports attending a conference where 14 companies reported 14 different methods of this type of calculation.

The numerous schemes that the authors of this book have observed all seem to be variants of the following three methods:

1. The ratio of prospective average annual profit after depreciation to original investment is alleged to be the prospective rate of return

[10] George Terborgh, *Business Investment Policy* (Washington, D.C.: Machinery and Allied Products Institute, 1958), p. 33.

on investment. Often this is referred to as the "original book" method.

2. The ratio of prospective average annual profit after depreciation to the average book value is alleged to be the prospective rate of return on investment. Often this is referred to as the "average book" method. In many instances it gives a figure for rate of return that is double the figure given by the original book method.

3. The figures for prospective profit after depreciation for each year are divided by the prospective book value figures for the start of the respective year in the way that was illustrated in Table 10–1. This division gives a series of ratios that are alleged to be year-by-year prospective rates of return. Conceivably, these rates might be averaged to give an over-all figure for rate of return.

All these methods may be used to compute so-called rates of return either before or after income taxes. To simplify matters a bit, our present illustrations deal with the computation of rates of return *before* income taxes. The same objections that will be raised to the use of these methods to calculate rates of return before income taxes are equally applicable to their use for after-tax calculations.

Two Competing Investment Proposals.   To illustrate these three methods and to demonstrate that all of them are inferior to correct compound interest methods, it is helpful to use some numerical examples. The following is adapted with some modifications from an illustration used by Horace G. Hill, Jr.,[11] for many years Budget Director of The Atlantic Refining Company.

Two investment proposals, a vacuum still and a product terminal, are competing for limited funds in an oil company. Each requires an immediate disbursement of $110,000, all of which will be capitalized on the books of account. In both cases the expected life is 10 years with zero salvage value. Straight-line depreciation will be used in the accounts.

The estimated positive cash flow resulting from the vacuum still will be $38,000 the first year, $34,000 the second, and will diminish by $4,000 a year until it is $2,000 in the tenth year. The estimated positive cash flow resulting from the product terminal will be $5,000 in the first year, $9,000 in the second, and will increase by $4,000 a year until it is $41,000 in the tenth year. With a trial-and-error present worth solution and with the aid of Table E–27, the respective rates of return are computed as follows:

[11] Horace G. Hill, Jr., *A New Method of Computing Rate of Return on Capital Expenditures,* a pamphlet published privately by the author (Berwyn, Pa., 1953).

Vacuum Still

PW at 15% $= -\$110,000 + \$38,000(P/A,15\%,10) - \$4,000(P/G,15\%,10)$
$= -\$110,000 + \$38,000(5.019) - \$4,000(16.9795) = +\$12,806$
PW at 20% $= -\$110,000 + \$38,000(4.192) - \$4,000(12.8871) = -\$2,252$

Interpolation indicates a rate of return of slightly over 19%.

Product Terminal

PW at 10% $= -\$110,000 + \$5,000(P/A,10\%,10) + \$4,000(P/G,10\%,10)$
$= -\$110,000 + \$5,000(6.144) + \$4,000(22.8913) = +\$12,285$
PW at 12% $= -\$110,000 + \$5,000(5.650) + \$4,000(20.2541) = -\$734$

Interpolation indicates a rate of return of slightly less than 12%. The vacuum still therefore has a much higher prospective rate of return than the product terminal.

The straight-line depreciation for each project will be $11,000 a year for 10 years, 10% of the original $110,000 investment. Let us assume that all cash flow except the original investment will affect the profit or loss figure on the books of accounts in the year when the cash flow occurs. Then the influence of each project on the prospective enterprise profit each year will be the positive cash flow minus the $11,000 depreciation charge. A tabulation of the estimated year-by-year influences of the two projects on the profit to be shown by the accounts is as follows:

Year	Vacuum Still	Product Terminal
1	+$27,000	−$ 6,000
2	+23,000	−2,000
3	+19,000	+2,000
4	+15,000	+6,000
5	+11,000	+10,000
6	+7,000	+14,000
7	+3,000	+18,000
8	−1,000	+22,000
9	−5,000	+26,000
10	−9,000	+30,000
Total profit	+$90,000	+$120,000
Average annual profit	+$ 9,000	+$ 12,000

Rate of Return (So-Called) by Original Book Method. In this method the average annual estimated profit is divided by the estimated original investment. The calculations for the two projects are:

$$\text{``Rate of return'' on vacuum still} = \frac{\$9,000}{\$110,000} = 0.082 \text{ or } 8.2\%$$

$$\text{``Rate of return'' on product terminal} = \frac{\$12,000}{\$110,000} = 0.109 \text{ or } 10.9\%$$

It is evident that this method of calculation ranks the rates of return from our two projects in the wrong order. This error is due to the failure of the method to give any weight whatsoever to the *timing* of the consequences of a project. The figure for "average profit," the *numerator* of the fraction, fails to reflect the difference between a dollar in the near future and one in the distant future.

It also is evident that the method has given us figures for rates of return that are less than the rates that we computed by correct compound interest methods. In most cases the original book method will understate the true rate of return. The difficulty here is that the *denominator* of the fraction, the full original investment, is too large since it fails to reflect the concept that the year-by-year positive cash flow should be viewed in part as a recovery of the money originally disbursed.

Rate of Return (So-Called) by Average Book Method. In this method the average annual estimated profit is divided by the average book value over the life of the project (or possibly over the period of the economy study). As the book value in both of our projects declines uniformly from \$110,000 to \$0 over the 10-year period, the average book value in each is \$55,000. The calculations for the two projects are:

$$\text{"Rate of return" on vacuum still} = \frac{\$9,000}{\$55,000} = 0.164 \text{ or } 16.4\%$$

$$\text{"Rate of return" on product terminal} = \frac{\$12,000}{\$55,000} = 0.218 \text{ or } 21.8\%$$

This method also ranks the rates of return from our projects in the wrong order. Just as in the original book method, the numerator of the fraction gives no weight to the timing of the consequences of a project.

The difference between the average book and original book methods is entirely in the denominator of the fraction that gives the computed rate of return. The use of an average figure in the denominator recognizes the viewpoint that the investment is being recovered throughout the life of a project rather than on the date the project terminates.

In our example, the denominators in the average book method are half those in the original book and the computed rates of return are double those of the original book. However, this two-to-one relationship between the two methods does not always exist. For example, it will not exist for a project that does not have zero salvage value. In the special case where the salvage value is 100%, the two methods give the same figure for rate of return.

Rates of Return (So-Called) from Year-by-Year Estimated Profits and Book Values. In this method the estimated profit to be shown by the books for each year is divided by the computed book value for the start of the year in question (or in some cases by the average of the start-of-year and end-of-year book values). Both the profit figures and the book values depend on the method of depreciation accounting to be used. This point is illustrated in Tables 10–4 and 10–5, which show the application of this method of computing rate of return to our two competing projects. The tables show calculations using straight-line depreciation and also using years-digits depreciation.

Several aspects of this method of computing prospective rates of return make its use undesirable for economy studies. Some objections to this method, illustrated by Tables 10–4 and 10–5, are as follows:

1. Even if the year-by-year computed rates of return had any validity as a guide to decision making on proposed investments, the rates would be difficult to interpret. The many different rates computed for a single project are confusing; it is much better to have a single figure indicating an over-all rate of return. It is evident from Tables 10–4 and 10–5 that this difficulty cannot be resolved in a satisfactory manner by taking an average of the year-by-year rates. The vacuum still project, shown by correct methods to have a 19% return, has an average return of less than 2% when straight-line depreciation is assumed; the product terminal

TABLE 10–4

Apparent Yearly Rates of Return from Vacuum Still Project Assuming Two Methods of Depreciation Accounting

(All dollar figures in thousands)

| Year | Profit Before Depreciation | Straight-Line Depreciation | | | | Years-Digits Depreciation | | | |
		Year's Depreciation	Profit	Start-of-Year Book Value	Rate of Return	Year's Depreciation	Profit	Start-of-Year Book Value	Rate of Return
1	$ 38	$ 11	+$27	$110	+24.5%	$ 20	+$18	$110	+16.4%
2	34	11	+23	99	+23.2%	18	+16	90	+17.8%
3	30	11	+19	88	+21.6%	16	+14	72	+19.4%
4	26	11	+15	77	+19.5%	14	+12	56	+21.4%
5	22	11	+11	66	+16.7%	12	+10	42	+23.8%
6	18	11	+7	55	+12.7%	10	+8	30	+26.7%
7	14	11	+3	44	+6.8%	8	+6	20	+30.0%
8	10	11	−1	33	−3.0%	6	+4	12	+33.3%
9	6	11	−5	22	−22.7%	4	+2	6	+33.3%
10	2	11	−9	11	−81.8%	2	0	2	0.0%
Totals	$200	$110	+$90		+17.5%	$110	+$90		+222.1%
		Average rate of return			+1.7%	Average rate of return			+22.2%

TABLE 10-5

Apparent Yearly Rates of Return from Product Terminal Project Assuming Two Methods of Depreciation Accounting

(All dollar figures in thousands)

Year	Profit Before Depreciation	Straight-Line Depreciation Year's Depreciation	Profit	Start-of-Year Book Value	Rate of Return	Years-Digits Depreciation Year's Depreciation	Profit	Start-of-Year Book Value	Rate of Return
1	$ 5	$ 11	−$ 6	$110	−5.5%	$ 20	−$ 15	$110	−13.6%
2	9	11	−2	99	−2.0%	18	−9	90	−10.0%
3	13	11	+2	88	+2.3%	16	−3	72	−4.2%
4	17	11	+6	77	+7.8%	14	+3	56	+5.4%
5	21	11	+10	66	+15.2%	12	+9	42	+21.4%
6	25	11	+14	55	+25.5%	10	+15	30	+50.0%
7	29	11	+18	44	+40.9%	8	+21	20	+105.0%
8	33	11	+22	33	+66.7%	6	+27	12	+225.0%
9	37	11	+26	22	+118.2%	4	+33	6	+550.0%
10	41	11	+30	11	+272.7%	2	+39	2	+1,950.0%
Totals	$230	$110	+$120		+541.9%	$110	+$120		+2,879.0%

| | | Average rate of return | +54.2% | | Average rate of return | +287.9% |

project, shown by correct methods to have a 12% return, has an average return of nearly 290% when years-digits depreciation is assumed.

2. A method of computing rate of return before income taxes should not be influenced by the arbitrary time-allocation of the investment among accounting periods. Both Tables 10-4 and 10-5 bring out the point that the foregoing principle is violated by this method of computing rate of return. Both of our projects seem to look much better with the years-digits method than with the straight-line method of depreciation accounting.

(In Chapter 16 we shall see that when years-digits or declining-balance depreciation is used for income tax purposes, the rate of return *after* income taxes usually will be a little higher than when straight-line depreciation is used for tax purposes. This after-tax difference in rate of return results from the influence of the depreciation accounting method on the *timing* of cash flow for income taxes. However, the effect of a depreciation accounting method on the timing of tax payments is an entirely different topic from the analysis of various methods of computing so-called rates of return.)

3. Like the original book and average book methods, the method of computing year-by-year rates of return fails to array proposals cor-

rectly in the order of their merit. All three methods make the low-return project, the product terminal, seem to have a greater return than the high-return project, the vacuum still.

General Comment on the Foregoing Three Methods of Computing Rate of Return. Our calculations of rates of return for our two projects have demonstrated that these methods, sometimes described as "approximate," may give figures that actually are very poor approximations to the rate of return that would be computed by correct compound interest methods. We have also seen that the various methods give quite different answers. Although the correct figure for the vacuum still project was about 19%, our different calculations gave us answers of 8.2%, 16.4%, 1.7%, and 22.2%. Although the correct figure for the product terminal project was about 12%, our answers here were 10.9%, 21.8%, 54.2%, and 287.9%.

We also noted that all of the methods ranked our two projects in the wrong order; the low-return project seemed to be better than the high-return one. Of course it is not always true that these methods will give an incorrect ranking of proposed investments. Ordinarily the chief cause of an incorrect ranking is the failure of the methods to give proper weight to the timing of cash flow. Our example comparing the vacuum still with the product terminal was chosen to stress this particular weakness of these common methods of computing rates of return; the vacuum still had most of its positive cash flow in the early years of its life whereas the product terminal had the largest part of its positive cash flow in the final years of its life.

However, our example comparing the vacuum still and the product terminal did not illustrate a quite different weakness of these three methods. In a correct calculation of rate of return before income taxes by compound interest methods, it is immaterial whether a cash disbursement is to be capitalized on the books of account or whether it is to be charged as an expense in the year when it occurs. But the three methods that we have discussed all use book value (original or average or the current year's) as the denominator in a fraction stated to be the rate of return. "Book value" ordinarily refers only to items that are capitalized on the books of account. Thus two projects having identical cash flows might appear to have quite different rates of return if the two projects are to be treated differently in the accounts. This type of error may lead to incorrect ranking of projects and may also increase the inherent errors in the rates of return computed by these three methods.

Why Are Incorrect Methods of Computing Rates of Return in Common Use? A reader of this book who is not already employed in an organization using one of these methods may well ask why methods of analysis that are so erratic and unreliable are so widely used. This is a good question to which the authors are unable to give a fully satisfactory answer. George Terborgh [12] refers to these and similar methods of analysis as "really industrial folklore, handed down from one generation of management to the next. They have no scientific rationale, no legitimate intellectual parentage."

In some instances it doubtless is true that the methods are used because the people who use them are not aware that any better methods are available. But there are many cases where analysts consciously reject compound interest methods of computing rates of return in favor of the original book or average book method. The choice of book methods usually is defended by the following arguments:

1. Book methods are alleged to be easier to apply.
2. Book methods are alleged to be easier to explain to others.

The greater ease of application of book methods is not a valid argument for their use. There are many economy studies in which compound interest methods can be applied as easily as book methods, once the compound interest methods are understood by the analyst. Moreover, even where compound interest methods require, say, an extra half-hour of an analyst's time, this extra time usually is trivial in relation to the many hours of time that have been spent on the gathering of data to be used in the economy study.

In many organizations it is true that the book methods are easier to explain. Unless managers and engineers have some understanding of compound interest, methods that seem to be tied to the books of account can be explained more readily than methods that use the mathematics of compound interest. The answer to this argument is that, as we have pointed out, book methods lead to erratic and unreliable answers that cannot be trusted as a basis for action; compound interest methods should be used in spite of the greater difficulty of explaining them.

A pertinent comment on this subject is made by Ray I. Reul as follows: [13]

Another obstacle to the acceptance of an objective method (of computing rate of return) is the desire of nearly all business executives to find a method of evaluation that will be directly comparable to accounting evaluations of current operations. I would like to, too! But I know it cannot be done. It is time the inevitable was faced. The search for such a method is like looking for a pot of gold at the end of the rainbow—foredoomed to failure. It is an impossibility which has been given the cloak of plausibility by the use of the same

[12] Terborgh, *op. cit.*, p. 28.
[13] Ray I. Reul, "Profitability Index for Investments," *Harvard Business Review,* XXXV, No. 4 (July–August, 1957), 116–32.

words, "rate of return on investment," to describe . . . entirely different concepts.

What Meaning Shall Be Attached to the Phrase "Rate of Return" as Applied to Proposed Investments? In our initial discussion of equivalence in Chapter 3, we examined a loan transaction in which an investor exchanged an initial cash disbursement of $10,000 for the prospect of end-of-year cash receipts of $1,358.68 a year for 10 years. It was shown (in the tabulation for Plan III, Table 3–1) that this series of receipts enables the investor to recover his investment with exactly 6% interest per annum. It might also be stated that he is scheduled to recover his investment with a 6% rate of return.

This is the only sense of rate of return that is a sound and consistent guide to action regarding proposed investments, and it is the only sense in which the phrase is used in this book. Where one of the methods based on the depreciation accounts is employed, we use the phrase "so-called rate of return."

(It may be of interest to apply the various methods based on the books of account to our simple case of the $10,000 investment recovered at 6% interest by $1,358.68 a year for 10 years. By the original book method, the rate of return appears to be 3.59%. By the average book method, it appears to be 7.17%. The year-by-year method depends on the scheme used for a time allotment of the investment among the 10 years; if a straight-line allotment is used, the return appears to vary from 3.59% the first year to 35.87% the 10th year.)

Arguments on the silly and unanswerable question "What does rate of return really mean?" have been so heated in some industries that certain industrial writers have tried to avoid the question by coining other phrases for rate of return obtained by correct compound interest methods. Thus Reul uses the phrase "Profitability Index" or "PI" in this meaning. Weaver and Reilly have suggested the phrase "interest rate of return" to be used in this same sense.[14]

Some Aspects of Depreciation Accounting Not Developed in This Book. We have already mentioned that the various types of statistical analysis of physical property mortality are not explained here, and that most of the technicalities of multiple-asset accounting have been avoided. Some other topics that we have omitted are as follows:

1. Assets generally are acquired during a fiscal year rather than exactly at the start of a year. For example, consider an asset acquired on March 31 in a business enterprise having the calendar year as its

14 J. B. Weaver and R. J. Reilly, "Interest Rate of Return for Capital Expenditure Evaluation," *Chemical Engineering Progress*, LII, No. 10 (October, 1956), 405–12.

fiscal year. The question arises regarding the depreciation charge to be made for the remainder of the year. Because 9 months of the year remain, it might seem reasonable to charge 9/12 of the depreciation computed for the first full year of life under the depreciation accounting method selected. However, such a practice would require the application of a different fraction to each new asset, depending on its date of acquisition.

A more common practice is to use some type of *averaging convention*. The so-called half-year convention is a common one; all assets are given a half-year's depreciation charge during their acquisition year regardless of the time of the year when they were acquired. Another convention is to charge a full year's depreciation for the acquisition year for the assets acquired during the first half of the year and no depreciation for those acquired during the second half.

In our examples we have, in effect, assumed that all assets are acquired at the start of a fiscal (and tax) year and that a full year's depreciation is charged during the year of acquisition.

2. There are various possible accounting treatments of gross amounts realized from salvage values and of costs of removing assets when retired. The way these matters are to be treated may influence the depreciation rate to be used and will determine the type of entry to be made on retirement.

3. There are differences between depreciation accounting where each year's acquisitions of a particular class of asset are kept in a separate account and where all year's acquisitions of the class of asset are merged together in a so-called open-end account.

4. It will rarely be true that average lives and salvage values will turn out exactly as estimated. Various problems arise associated with re-estimates of remaining lives and salvage values for existing assets. These problems differ with different depreciation accounting methods.

One purpose of mentioning the foregoing topics is to make it plain to our readers that our approach to depreciation accounting here is necessarily a simplified one—that there are many facets to the subject that we do not have space to explore. Another purpose is to suggest depreciation accounting and the tax aspects of depreciation as appropriate subjects for study by persons who are responsible for making or reviewing economy studies. Although an introduction to engineering economy can be made with simplified assumptions about depreciation accounting, a more sophisticated understanding of the subject will be helpful in certain types of economy studies.

The authors' views regarding the selection of a method of depreciation accounting are briefly stated in Chapter 16, following the discussion of certain income tax aspects of depreciation.

PROBLEMS

10–1. An asset has a first cost of $13,000, an estimated life of 15 years, and an estimated salvage value of $1,000. Using the straight-line method, find (a) the annual depreciation charge, (b) the annual depreciation rate expressed as a percentage of first cost, and (c) the book value at the end of 9 years. (*Ans.* = (a) $800; (b) 6.15%; (c) $5,800.)

10–2. An asset has a first cost of $22,000, an estimated life of 30 years, and an estimated salvage value of $2,000. Using the sinking-fund method with a 4% interest rate, find (a) the depreciation charge in the first year, (b) the depreciation charge in the 6th year, and (c) the book value at the end of 20 years. (*Ans.* = (a) $356.60; (b) $433.85; (c) $11,381.)

10–3. An asset has a first cost of $5,000. It is to be depreciated by the declining-balance method using a rate of 12.5%. (a) What will be the book value at the end of 5 years? What will be the depreciation charge (b) in the first year, and (c) in the 6th year? (*Ans.* = (a) $2,564.55; (b) $625; (c) $320.57.)

10–4. An asset has a first cost of $9,000, an estimated life of 12 years, and an estimated salvage value of $1,200. It is to be depreciated by the sum-of-the-years-digits method. What will be the depreciation charge (a) in the first year and (b) in the 7th year? (c) What will be the book value at the end of 6 years? (*Ans.* = (a) $1,200; (b) $600; (c) $3,300.)

10–5. Project A has an initial investment in depreciable property of $100,000. The prospective life is 10 years with zero salvage value. Estimated excess of receipts over disbursements before income taxes is $33,000 the first year, $29,500 the second, and decreases uniformly by $3,500 each year to $1,500 in the 10th year. Straight-line depreciation will be used in the accounts. Estimate the rate of return before income taxes by the following methods:
  (a) Interest rate that makes the present worth of net cash flow equal to zero
  (b) Ratio of average annual book profits to initial investment
  (c) Ratio of average annual book profits to the average of the start-of-year book values
  (d) Ratio of average annual book profits to the average of the book values throughout the 10-year period
  (e) Average of the year-by-year profit rates computed from each year's estimated book profits divided by the start-of-year book value for the year in question.
  (*Ans.* = (a) +17.4%; (b) +7.25%; (c) +13.2%; (d) +14.5%; (e) −0.1%.)

10–6. Like Project A in the preceding problem, Project B has a first cost of $100,000, an estimated life of 10 years, zero salvage value, and will be subject to straight-line depreciation. The total estimated excess of receipts over disbursements for the 10-year life is the same as in Problem 10–5. However, the first year's positive cash flow is only $1,500 and this increases by $3,500 a year to $33,000 in the 10th year. Estimate the rate of return before income taxes by the same five methods used in Problem 10–5. (*Ans.* = (a) +8.3%; (b) +7.25%; (c) +13.2%; (d) +14.5%; (e) +42.6%.)

10–7. What generalizations about the four methods of finding so-called rates of return used in parts (b) to (e) of Problems 10–5 and 10–6 are suggested by a comparison of the results of the two problems?

10–8. In Example 6–3 (page 77), it was stated that the extra annual income taxes for Plan E as compared to Plan D would be $1,250. Show the calculations that were needed to determine this $1,250 figure.

10–9. In Problem 6–1 (page 84), it was stated that the extra annual income taxes for Mill N as compared to Mill M would be $320. Show the calculations that were needed to determine this $320 figure.

10–10. For the data of Problem 6–2 (page 84), show the necessary calculations to check the stated year-by-year differences in income taxes.

10–11. For the data of Problem 6–3 (page 85), show the necessary calculations to check the stated $750 annual difference in income taxes between Machines V and W.

10–12. For the data of Problem 6–4 (page 85), show the necessary calculations to check the stated $1,300 annual difference in income taxes between the steam and Diesel plants.

10–13. Compare the annual costs of Plans A, B, and C of Examples 6–1 and 6–2 (pages 69 to 74) using the method of straight-line depreciation plus average interest.

10–14. Compare the annual costs of Plans D and E of Example 6–3 (page 77) using the method of straight-line depreciation plus average interest.

10–15. Compare the annual costs of Machines V and W in Problem 6–3 (page 85) using the method of straight-line depreciation plus average interest.

10–16. Solve Problem 6–8(b) using the method of straight-line depreciation plus average interest.

10–17. The following estimates were made to compare a timber trestle with a steel bridge for a certain highway drainage crossing:

	Trestle	Steel Bridge
First cost	$9,000	$24,000
Life	10 years	60 years
Annual maintenance cost	$ 500	$ 350

Salvage values are assumed to be negligible.
A comparison of annual costs using an $i°$ of 8% was made as follows:

	Trestle	Steel Bridge
Depreciation	$ 900	$ 400
Average interest	396	976
Annual maintenance	500	350
Total annual cost	$1,796	$1,726

Assuming all estimates (i.e., first cost, life, salvage value, maintenance cost, and $i°$) to be acceptable, is this a satisfactory comparison of the economy of these two alternatives? Explain your answer. If you disagree with this comparison, give your solution of this problem.

10–18. An asset has a first cost of $40,000, an estimated life of 18 years, and an estimated salvage value of 10% of first cost. Using the straight-line method, find (a) the annual depreciation charge, (b) the annual depreciation rate expressed as a percentage of first cost, and (c) the book value at the end of 10 years.

10–19. An asset acquired by a manufacturing company has a first cost of $14,400, an estimated life of 12 years, and an estimated salvage value of $2,700. Compute the depreciation charge for each of the first 2 years of life as it would be made in the company's accounts by each of the following four methods. (Assume that a full year's charge is made in the first year of ownership.)

(a) Straight-line method
(b) Years-digits method
(c) Double-rate declining-balance method
(d) 4% sinking-fund method

10–20. A machine has a first cost of $80,000, an estimated life of 8 years, and an estimated salvage value of $8,000. How much depreciation will be written off during the second year of life by the (a) straight-line method, (b) years-digits method, (c) double-rate declining-balance method?

10–21. A building has a first cost of $270,000, an estimated life of 40 years, and an estimated salvage value of $24,000. Compute the depreciation charge for each of the first 2 years and the book value at the end of 20 years by the (a) straight-line method, (b) years-digits method, (c) double-rate declining-balance method, and (d) 6% sinking fund method.

10–22. A manufacturer has the policy of paying the delivery costs on certain parts that a group of good customers order for emergency replacements. Many of these deliveries are by air express. An increased inventory of parts kept in a certain branch warehouse will require an investment of $50,000. It is estimated that this investment will make it possible to reduce annual delivery costs by $4,000. Assume that this increased inventory will be maintained for 10 years and then disposed of for 100% salvage value. Show your computations for prospective rate of return on investment (before income taxes) by (a) compound interest methods, (b) original book method, (c) average book method, and (d) method of year-by-year rate of return. What important point regarding these different methods of computing rate of return is illustrated by your answers in this problem?

10–23. What declining-balance rates will give a book value of (a) 30%, (b) 10%, and (c) 1% of the first cost at the end of 20 years?

10–24. Example 8–2 analyzed a proposed investment in a rental machine having a first cost of $12,000, an estimated life of 8 years, and an estimated $1,200 salvage value. Table 8–3 (page 112) gives the year-by-year estimates of receipts and disbursements. Prepare a table similar to Table 10–5 showing the apparent yearly rates of return from this investment using (a) straight-line depreciation and (b) years-digits depreciation. Compute the averages of these two sets of rates. How do these rates compare with the correct figure of 12% computed in Chapter 8?

10–25. A building has a first cost of $100,000, an estimated life of 50 years, and an estimated zero terminal salvage value. It is to be depreciated by the 6% sinking-fund method. Without computing year-by-year depreciation charges, find its book value at the end of 30 years. Using 6% interest, compute its annual capital recovery cost over its 50-year life. Assume that when it is 30 years old, a purchaser buys it for a price equal to its then existing book value and that he estimates its remaining life to be 20 years. Using 6% interest, compute the capital recovery cost over this remaining life. Comment on the results of these two calculations of capital recovery cost.

11

Choice of a Minimum
Attractive Rate of Return

> "Well, in *our* country," said Alice, still panting a little, "you'd generally get to somewhere else—if you ran very fast for a long time as we've been doing."
>
> "A slow sort of country!" said the Queen. "Now, *here*, you see, it takes all the running *you* can do, to keep in the same place. If you want to get somewhere else, you must run at least twice as fast as that!"—LEWIS CARROLL [1]

In many examples and problems up to this point, we have stipulated a figure for i^*, the minimum attractive rate of return, without any discussion of why the particular value of i^* was selected. In this chapter we examine some of the troublesome issues that arise in selecting a minimum attractive rate of return. We start with two examples that will help to emphasize that decision criteria often are related to a limitation on the funds available for capital investment.

EXAMPLE 11–1. CRITERIA FOR INVESTMENT EVALUATION IN A CERTAIN CLOSELY HELD CORPORATION

Facts of the Case. Three members of a family held slightly more than half of the stock of a successful small company which we shall call the ABC Manufacturing Company. This company had no long-term debt. These controlling stockholders were active officers of the corporation. As the company made capital goods, its profits fluctuated considerably; although its over-all profit record had been excellent, there had been occasional loss years.

The proposal was made to expand by manufacturing certain new products. An analysis of the proposal indicated that there was a good prospective rate of return. However, all the moneys for plant investment that became available each year from retained earnings and depreciation charges were being absorbed by replacements and plant modernization in connection with the present product line. A substantial investment in plant and equipment was needed to undertake the new product line. Therefore, it was necessary to raise new capital if this proposal for business expansion were to be accepted.

Investigation disclosed that this capital could be raised either by the sale

---

[1] Lewis Carroll, *Through the Looking Glass*, chap. 2.

of new stock to certain persons interested in the company or by a 10-year loan from an individual investor. The proposal to make the new products was finally rejected by the three controlling stockholders on the grounds that neither type of financing was acceptable to them.

The objection to the sale of stock was that the three stockholders would no longer have a majority stock interest that made it certain they could control the company's affairs. The 10-year loan also involved certain restrictions on their control through stipulations (such as one limiting dividend payments while the loan was outstanding). However, their chief objection to the loan was that the required annual payments of principal and interest made them much more vulnerable to any business recession that might cause one or more loss years.

In effect, this decision, based on considerations related to financing, caused the rejection of an investment proposal (plant expansion) yielding a high prospective rate of return even though other investment proposals (replacements and modernization) were being accepted yielding lower rates of return.

EXAMPLE 11–2. CRITERIA FOR INVESTMENT DECISIONS IN AN UNDERFINANCED MANUFACTURING BUSINESS

Facts of the Case. Two partners purchased a small manufacturing enterprise. They used their entire personal savings for a payment to the former proprietor of half the purchase price. The remainder of the purchase price was to be paid from a stipulated percentage of the profits.

During its initial years, the partnership was always short of cash. The partners saw many chances to reduce production costs by moderate outlays for new equipment or for changes in existing equipment. Because of the cash shortage and because it was impracticable to bring new money into the business, every proposal had to be judged primarily with relation to its effect on the short-term cash position of the business. During the first year, it was not possible to adopt any proposal that—in terms of cash flow—would not "pay for itself" in three months.

The Concept of Capital Rationing in Relation to the Minimum Attractive Rate of Return. Resources available for new investment in capital assets during any given period of time usually are limited even though the constraints may not be as severe as those in Examples 11–1 and 11–2. Also, technological progress and an expanding economy make it common for the total of the proposals for investment in new assets to be considerably greater than the total of available funds. For example, assume that the manufacturing company of Example 11–1 had $90,000 of funds for its capital budget for a given year and that there were investment proposals for plant modernization and expansion totaling $207,000 as listed in Table 11–1.

In this simple example it is evident that the $90,000 of available funds would have been exhausted by Projects U, Y, Z, and S. It follows that the minimum rate of return that was attractive was 15%, the prospective rate on Project S. If an investment had been made in any project yielding less than 15% (X, T, V, W, or some other project not tabulated),

TABLE 11–1

Proposals for Capital Expenditures in ABC Manufacturing Company for a Certain Year

(Available funds limited to $90,000)

Project	Investment Required	Prospective Rate of Return After Taxes	Cumulative Total of Investments
U	$12,000	40%	$ 12,000
Y	45,000	20%	57,000
Z	8,000	18%	65,000
S	25,000	15%	90,000
. . . . . .			
X	22,000	12%	112,000
T	30,000	10%	142,000
V	55,000	9%	197,000
W	10,000	8%	207,000

the effect would have been to eliminate the possibility of investing in some project that was expected to yield 15% or more.

Validity of the Capital Rationing Concept. Matters are rarely as simple as implied by the foregoing discussion. For example, the alternative of securing new outside capital often is available. Moreover, it may be impracticable to array all the proposals for capital expenditures during the coming year and to be sure that no other good proposals—now unforeseen—will develop during the year. Even without outside financing, the total funds that can be made available for capital expenditures may not be fixed absolutely but may be related to the attractiveness of the proposed projects. In choosing among available projects, it often is desirable to apply supplementary criteria in addition to prospective rate of return. The differences in the duration of the consequences of the various proposals may be deemed to be an important consideration. There may be no group of projects that will exactly absorb the available funds. Various aspects of these topics are discussed throughout the remainder of this book and the whole subject is considered more critically in Chapter 21.

Nevertheless, the principle is entirely sound that the minimum attractive rate of return ought to be chosen with the objective of making the best possible use of a limited resource. This resource is, of course, the money that can be made available for investment in capital assets and closely related items. If the consequence of making an investment yielding 10% is to forego some other investment that would yield 20%, it is not sensible to make the 10% investment. The high figures for i^* that so often are used in competitive industry are based in part on this principle.

Moreover, as emphasized throughout this book, it is prospective *differences* among alternatives that are relevant in their comparison. The prospective rate of return from a proposed investment should be based on the difference between making the investment and not making it.

The "With or Without" Viewpoint with Reference to Prospective Rates of Return on Investments in Competitive Industry. The president of a large manufacturing company in a highly competitive industry was discussing various matters with the engineer responsible for review and analysis of investment proposals. The president made comments along the following line:

In our company, we approve many proposals for investments aimed at cost reduction. Generally speaking, the proposals approved show prospective rates of return of 16% or more after income taxes. When we post-audit the results of these investments, we conclude that the cost reductions realized have been, on the average, somewhat greater than we forecast in computing the prospective rates of return. Nevertheless, our average overall rate of return on investment is only about 8% after taxes and does not seem to be improved by these numerous cost reduction investments that individually seem to be so successful.

The president was, in fact, describing a condition that reasonably may be expected to be the normal state of affairs in competitive industry. The difference between *making* the investments in cost reduction equipment and *not making* these investments was measured by the 16% rate of return. However, under the stress of competition, the favorable consequences of these good investments were shared among the owners of the enterprise, its employees, and its customers. Wage and salary rates to the company's employees were increased from year to year; prices of the industry's product were reduced (if measured in monetary units of constant purchasing power) and the quality of the product was improved.

In spite of the fact that the owners of the enterprise did not keep all the return yielded by the cost reduction equipment, the 16% rate was a valid measure of the productivity of this equipment from their point of view. If their company had *not* installed the modern equipment but its competitors had done so, competition would still have made it necessary to reduce prices and improve product quality; it would also have been necessary to raise wage and salary rates because such rates are responsive to industry-wide conditions, not merely to conditions in one particular company. Under conditions of competition the over-all rate of return of 8% could not have been maintained unless there had been cost reductions that, considered on a "with or without" basis, yielded rates of return of much more than 8%.

Why Consider the Time Value of Money in Economy Studies? Objections are sometimes raised to the giving of any consideration whatsoever to interest in the making of decisions between technical alternatives. A brief answer to the question "Why recognize interest in connection with engineering economy studies?" may be phrased as follows: "Interest exists as a business fact; if you borrow money it is necessary to pay interest; if you have money you can earn a return by investing it. Where a choice is to be made between alternatives that involve different money receipts and disbursements at different times, it therefore is essential to consider interest. Engineering economy studies generally involve decisions between such alternatives."

This statement of the reason for recognizing interest in decision making seems to imply a slight difference in the explanation between the situation in which money is actually borrowed and the situation in which it is available without borrowing. Since businessmen sometimes reason differently about these two situations, it is worth while to examine them separately at this point.

Distinction Between Equity Funds and Borrowed Funds. Assume that you buy a $30,000 home by paying $7,500 in cash and securing a long-term loan for the remaining $22,500. Your *equity* in the $30,000 property is then $7,500. Your home ownership has been financed one-fourth by equity funds and three-fourths by borrowed funds.

In business the equity funds are the funds provided by the owners of the enterprise. In corporate business the owners are the stockholders of the corporation. A corporation may also finance in part by long-term borrowings, frequently through the sale of bonds. The bondholders are *creditors* of the corporation; their legal relationship to the corporation differs greatly from that of the stockholders. Where funds are borrowed, there is generally an agreement to pay interest and principal at stipulated dates. No such obligation exists in connection with equity funds.

Some of the problems caused by doing business on borrowed money are discussed briefly in Chapter 18. At the present point in our discussion, it needs to be brought out that the less stable the earning power of a prospective borrower, the less desirable it is to borrow. Many business enterprises in competitive industry are financed largely or entirely from equity funds. Authorities on finance recognize that it is appropriate for many regulated public utilities to secure from one-third to one-half of their capital from long-term borrowing. In certain types of government projects the entire first cost of a project is financed by borrowing.

Considering the Time Value of Money for Proposals To Be Financed by Equity Funds. Engineering structures and machines may be built or acquired by individuals, partnerships, private corporations, and governmental bodies. Unless they are financed by borrowing, they must necessarily be financed out of money belonging to the owners of the enterprise.

These equity funds may come from various sources. In private corporations, for instance, they may come from the sale of stock, or from profits that are "plowed back" into the business rather than paid out as dividends to the stockholders, or from the recovery of capital previously invested in other machines and structures. In governmental bodies, equity funds may come from direct assessments or taxation (e.g., the gasoline tax used to finance highway improvement).

Where capital assets are financed entirely by equity funds, it is not necessary to pay out interest to any creditor. Here interest is a cost in the economists' sense of *opportunity cost*. When funds are invested in any particular capital goods, the opportunity is foregone to obtain a return from the investment of the funds elsewhere. Interest is a cost in the sense of an opportunity foregone.

In deciding whether to invest equity funds in specific capital assets, an important question is how good an opportunity will be foregone. In other words, if the investment in the specific capital assets is not made, what return is likely to be obtainable from the same funds invested elsewhere? In principle the interest rate (minimum attractive rate of return) used in an economy study ought to be the rate of return obtainable from the opportunity foregone, as nearly as can be determined.

What Investment Opportunity Is Being Foregone? The opportunity foregone may be either within the business enterprise or outside of it. In Table 11–1 earlier in this chapter, the minimum attractive rate of return was 15% because any investment yielding less than 15% would cause the ABC Manufacturing Company to forego the opportunity to earn 15% in Project S.

The appropriate figure for minimum attractive rate of return is generally higher when the opportunity foregone is within the enterprise. Two circumstances, both illustrated in Table 11–1, are generally present when a within-the-enterprise figure is controlling. One circumstance is the presence of many good opportunities for investment within the enterprise. The other circumstance is the limitation of available funds. High minimum attractive rates of return are common in competitive industry because both of these circumstances occur so frequently.

If new equity capital cannot be secured for a business enterprise and no new money is to be borrowed, the available funds for investment in new fixed assets are usually limited to current earnings retained in the business (if any) and to capital recovered from previous investments in fixed assets. (This latter source of funds is discussed in Chapter 18.) But even where new equity funds *can* be secured, the management of a business enterprise may deem it unwise to obtain them. In many small and moderate-sized enterprises that are owned by a few individuals, the securing of new equity capital may involve a sacrifice of control by the present owners. This condition was illustrated in Example 11–1. In large corporations in competitive industry where no question of control is involved, boards of directors often find other reasons that influence them against the raising of new equity capital.

In determining a minimum attractive rate of return in a given business enterprise or other sphere of activity, it always is appropriate to consider possible opportunities for return that may be foregone outside of the enterprise as well as within it. For example, corporate stockholders have opportunities for personal investments outside of their corporation; the board of directors should not withhold part of the current earnings from the stockholders unless the prospective return from the reinvestment of these earnings within the enterprise is as great as the return the stockholders could obtain from personal investments elsewhere. A similar line of reasoning may be applied to government projects financed by current taxation; the collection of these taxes requires the taxpayers to forego an opportunity to earn a return from personal investment of the moneys collected.

Relationship of the Minimum Attractive Rate of Return to the Cost of Borrowed Money. Consider an economy study to judge the justification of a project to be financed entirely by borrowing.

Persons who have not given the matter much critical thought often assume that the interest rate to be used in such a study ought to be the bare cost of borrowed money. Although this view is particularly common in governmental projects and in personal economy studies, the same view is sometimes advanced in connection with projects in competitive industry. The following paragraphs relate solely to competitive industry.

The reasons why the minimum attractive rate of return to be used in such an economy study should be greater than the cost of borrowed money may be summarized as follows:

1. Decisions made for business enterprises engaged in competitive industry are presumably made from the viewpoint of the owners of the enterprise. If the prospective return to be obtained from investing borrowed funds in capital assets is just equal to the cost of the borrowed

money, the owners will gain no advantage from the borrowing. The prospective return needs to be greater than the cost of borrowed money in order to justify the risks and other disadvantages to the owners associated with fixed obligations to pay interest and to repay principal at stated dates. This topic is explored further in Chapter 18.

2. Even though it may *seem* as if certain types of assets can be financed entirely by borrowing (e.g., certain machinery purchased on the installment plan), the amount of possible borrowing by any business enterprise depends on the amount of equity capital in the enterprise. Generally speaking, the cost of new capital to an enterprise ought to be viewed as a weighted average of the cost of borrowed capital and equity capital. This weighted average will nearly always be considerably higher than the cost of borrowed money.

3. If there is a limit on the total funds available for investment in capital assets from all sources including borrowing, and if there are many proposals for investments in assets that seem likely to yield high returns, the type of reasoning illustrated in Table 11–1 is applicable. If the $90,000 of available funds in Table 11–1 had come entirely from borrowing at, say 7%, rather than from equity sources, the minimum attractive rate of return for the ABC Manufacturing Company would still have been 15% after income taxes. The controlling element in determining the minimum attractive rate would still have been the fact that the selection of any project yielding less than 15% would cause the elimination of some project that would yield 15% or more; the 7% cost of the borrowed money would not have been relevant.

The Element of Risk in Relation to the Minimum Attractive Rate of Return. In some types of loan transactions the risk of loss is recognized to be greater than in other types. (A good measure of risk of loss would be obtained by finding the actual losses sustained by lenders on different types of loans over a long period of years.) The risk of loss influences the interest rate. Generally speaking, the poorer the credit rating of a borrower, the greater the interest rate he will have to pay.

In a similar way the standard of attractiveness applied to proposals for capital expenditures in industry may be related to estimated risk of loss. For example, there are four major divisions in the petroleum industry, production, refining, transportation, and marketing. There are obvious differences in risk associated with investment proposals in the different divisions. One large integrated oil company has recognized these differences by requiring a minimum attractive rate of return of 18% after income taxes for certain types of proposals in the production division, 14% for proposals in the refining division, and 10% for proposals in the transportation and marketing divisions.

Often the element of risk is recognized at the level of decision making by top management without the use of any such formal rules. For example, in Table 11–1 the management of the ABC Manufacturing Company might deem Project X to be considerably less risky than Project S. Project X might therefore be preferred even though its rate of return is only 12% compared to the 15% estimated for Project S.

Analysts disagree on the question of whether it is better to recognize this element of risk of loss in setting a minimum attractive rate of return or to introduce the matter into economy studies in some other way. This topic is discussed further in Chapters 13, 14, and 21.

Shall Minimum Attractive Rate of Return in Competitive Industry Be Before or After Income Taxes? Decisions in business enterprises engaged in competitive industry are presumably made from the viewpoint of the owners of the enterprise. Obviously it is to the owners' advantage to obtain the best possible rate of return *after* income taxes rather than *before* income taxes.

Where analysts responsible for economy studies in competitive industry make studies before income taxes, the implication is that the same choices among alternatives will be made by studies made before taxes or after taxes. This point may be illustrated by a reference to Table 11–1, which gave prospective rates of return after taxes for eight projects. Assume that a table is made showing rates of return before income taxes rather than after, and that all prospective rates of return before taxes are approximately double the after-tax rates shown in Table 11–1. The new table would array the projects in the same order as Table 11–1, and the same four projects—U, Y, Z, and S—would be selected. The minimum attractive rate would appear to be 30% before income taxes rather than 15% after taxes, but there would be no difference in the action resulting from the economy studies.

If it were invariably true that an array of projects in order of rate of return would be the same before and after income taxes, the conclusions of economy studies would not depend on whether the studies were made before or after taxes. Under such circumstances the greater simplicity of making studies before taxes would be a valid basis for always using before-tax studies and merely increasing the minimum attractive rate of return (or interest rate used) enough to recognize the effect of income taxes.

However, it frequently happens that the best projects after income taxes are not the same as the best ones before income taxes. Usually this circumstance arises because of differences in rate of write-off for tax purposes applicable to different investments or because of different tax rates applicable to different investments. A number of such cases are described in Chapter 16 and thereafter. For this reason, it is desirable that most economy studies in competitive industry be made after income taxes.

Need for a Uniform Criterion of Attractiveness of Proposed Investments at All Levels of Decision Making Throughout an Enterprise. A common condition in industry is described by Robert F. Barrell as follows: [2]

> Most companies have some definite sum of money available for investment purposes. Since the amount of available capital is limited, decisions must be made with respect to alternative uses such that the company will maximize its earnings on this added investment. Furthermore, a company's budget director and executives must set up some base for evaluating the returns on alternative uses for capital before such decisions can be made. Generally, a company will establish some minimum acceptable rate of return, below which it feels the return is insufficient to justify the risk assumed by the company on that particular venture.
>
> It has been observed that under present practices in industry, decision making pertaining to investments is based upon time-rate-use of money only in the higher echelons of top management. For example, decisions pertaining to amounts set aside for expansion programs, research and development, are usually made on this basis. However, the decisions which are made by the lower echelons of management and by engineering, scientific and manufacturing personnel, pertaining to the actual expenditure of these funds, are not based on time-rate-use of money, but rather on hunch decisions and value judgments. Although these decisions may be fortified by rough computations based upon reasonable assumptions, they often yield misleading results. Furthermore, due to the lack of uniformity in such approximations from one person to the next, these decisions cannot possibly reflect top management policy for the optimum use of invested capital.
>
> It would appear that this is a serious defect in our industrial planning structure. Decisions are based on sound calculations up to the point where the detailed expenditures are made, and at this point the basis for decision making suddenly changes. What would it mean to a company if each of the purchases of machines, tools, molds, dies, or plant modifications were all judged on a minimum acceptable rate of return for the additional investment set by top management for that particular plant or division?

Our Table 11–1 represented an analysis of a group of separate projects such as might be prepared by a budget director for submission to top management. As pointed out in the foregoing quotation, it is desirable that the economic decisions within each project be made on substantially the same basis as the top management decisions among the projects. Otherwise, desirable elements that would yield high returns may be

[2] In an unpublished paper, "Analog Computers for Calculating the Rate of Return on Added Investment," submitted to fulfill the requirements of the management training program of the University of Buffalo. Mr. Barrell is an engineer for a large manufacturing company.

eliminated from some projects and other projects may be overdesigned in the sense that thay include unjustifiable increments of investment.

This topic of obtaining uniformity in criteria for investment decisions at all levels of decision making within an organization is explored further in Chapter 21.

Representative Values for Minimum Attractive Rate of Return. Whether one wishes to discuss what in fact is being done or what ought to be done in selecting a value of i^*, it is helpful to give separate consideration to the following four types of activity:

1. Business enterprises in competitive industry where, for one reason or another, the capital budget is limited to funds generated within the enterprise.
2. Business enterprises in competitive industry that regularly or occasionally acquire new funds for plant investment either by acquiring new equity capital (in the case of a corporation, selling new stock) or by making new long-term borrowings, or both.
3. Regulated public utility companies (selling electricity, gas, water, telephone and telegraph service, transportation service), particularly those operating under the rules of rate regulation that have developed in the United States.
4. Governmental activities.

It will be pointed out in Chapters 19 and 20 that the distinctions among these four groups are in fact not always clear. However, for the purpose of the following preliminary comments on what ought to be done and on what actually seems to be done, we shall arbitrarily assume that these are four distinct categories.

1. In principle, opportunity costs within the enterprise normally should determine the choice of i^* when the capital budget is limited to internally generated funds. Clearly, no generalizations can be made about where the cut-off point is likely to come under these conditions; it is all a matter of the estimated productivity of the various investment proposals and the aggregate capital budget that is available. Sometimes, as in Table 11–1, the cut-off point may come at 15% or even lower. In other cases, such as the one described in Example 11–2, the cut-off point may be very high indeed because of the availability of many good investment opportunities in combination with a severe limitation of funds.

In the special case where few good investment opportunities exist within the enterprise, opportunity costs outside the enterprise may establish the appropriate value of i^*.

2. This is the type of case about which much has been published by writers on economics and finance. In general, the view is expressed that

the value of i^* ought to be the weighted average "cost of capital" to the enterprise, considering both long-term borrowings and equity capital. For example, if the cut-off point based on internally generated funds is 15%, as in Table 11–1, and the overall cost of capital is, say, 9%, there should be enough new financing to permit the approval of all projects with prospective rates of return greater than 9%. One difficulty with this approach that is discussed in Chapter 21 is that there is seldom any clearly-defined and agreed-on figure for the "cost" of equity capital that can be weighted with the computed cost of borrowed capital to find the over-all cost of capital to the enterprise.

When one tries to find out about the actual practice of industry in the United States, he finds that a number of studies by questionnaire have been made, usually for doctoral dissertations or other research papers. In the opinion of the authors of this book, the questionnaire technique has limited usefulness for this purpose (a) because, as pointed out in Chapter 10 (page 179), industry uses so many different definitions of rate of return, and (b) because the authors have observed that, on this matter, the answers given to questionnaires do not necessarily describe the actual practices of the particular business enterprises answering the questions.

It seems to the authors that no one really knows the relative frequencies of values of i^* selected by those enterprises in the United States that make annual cost studies, present worth studies, or rate of return studies by compound interest methods along the lines described in this book. However, the authors have discussed this question with a number of analysts in competitive enterprises that do use these methods. The impression obtained from these conversations is that the use of an after-tax i^* less than 8% is extremely rare, that rates of 10% or 12% after income taxes are more common than 8%, and that it is not unusual to find a figure of 15% or even more. Further comment on this topic is made in Chapter 21.

3. It is suggested in Chapter 20 that for many regulated public utilities in the United States, the minimum attractive rate of return ought to be equal to or slightly greater than the "fair return" permitted by the regulatory agency. This concept seems to be fairly widely applied. It has led to values of i^* in the range 6½%–8% for utilities furnishing electricity, gas, water, and telephone service. For transportation utilities, where there nearly always is direct competition with other transportation agencies, the appropriate i^* tends to be a little higher, possibly 10% or even more.

4. Many government agencies in the United States make economy studies using as the interest rate some assumed average cost of borrowed money. Historically there have been many economy studies that have,

in effect, assumed a minimum attractive rate of return from 2½% to 3½%. In many other economy studies, particularly for highway agencies financing highway projects from current taxation, a 0% interest rate has been used. In the opinion of the authors, it usually is unsound public policy to select such very low values of i^* in the economic analysis of government projects; low rates in the 0%–3% range disregard opportunity costs and tend to cause overdesign of public works projects. This topic is discussed in Chapter 19.

Explanation of Interest in Economic Theory. We have answered the practical question, "Why consider the time value of money in decision making?" by saying that interest is a business fact. It is also desirable to consider the answer to the more fundamental question, "Why does interest exist as a business fact?"

In answering this question, the economist explains interest, as he explains any other sort of price, by examining the supply and demand situations for investment funds. On the supply side he points out that interest is necessary as an incentive to saving; on the demand side he points out that interest is possible because capital is productive.

Explanation of the Necessity of Interest. On the supply side the economist points out that if you lend money at interest you deprive yourself of immediate satisfactions. You cannot use your money to buy consumers' goods now if you lend it to somebody else, or if you spend it yourself on engineering machines or structures (i.e., producers' goods), or if you buy stock in a corporation that spends it this way, or if you pay it to the government, which uses it for public works. We all of us have a low present estimation of the utility of future goods; for instance, the prospect of a square meal next year does not look as good to us as a square meal today. Thus we need some sort of incentive to defer consumption, a compensation for waiting or putting off immediate satisfactions.

However, in recent years it has been recognized that this explanation is not quite complete, and that the desire for security might serve as an incentive for a good deal of saving even though there were no interest. Moreover, there are numerous individuals with sufficiently large personal incomes so that the incentive to spend all their incomes immediately for consumers' goods is so small that they will invest a substantial part of their incomes regardless of the size of the interest rate. Nevertheless, the higher the interest rate, the greater the motive for putting off consumption in order to earn a return on invested money; it is reasonable to believe that if the prospect of a return (i.e., interest) on invested capital were removed, the stimulus for its investment would also disappear.

Explanation of the Possibility of Interest. On the demand side, how is it possible to pay interest? That is, how can business enterprises find it profitable to borrow money and pay the interest required by lenders; how is it possible for corporations to pay dividends that are in effect a return upon the stockholders' invested capital? The answer is that capital goods (i.e., producers' goods such as engineering machines and structures) are productive.

The economist in his explanation of interest will take you back to primitive society and illustrate the productivity of capital by the situation of primitive man trying to hunt and fish without any tools other than his hands. He finds that by making tools (such as spears, canoes, bows and arrows) he may greatly increase his catch. These capital goods are not anything that can be eaten; he must defer consumption for a while when he makes these instruments of production. But after he has gone hungry for a time while making these "producers' goods," he can catch more fish and kill more game; thus, he makes a return on the investment of his time.

In the same sense present-day engineering machines and structures are productive. It is possible to invest money in plant and machinery, in the fixed-capital goods of business enterprise, and to do things better than could be done otherwise. It is because of this that enterprises can borrow money and pay interest, or can secure money for the investment of ownership funds and pay dividends that are greater than the interest that the stockholder could otherwise receive by lending them.

So we have the twofold explanation of interest. Interest can exist because capital is productive, and it is probably necessary that interest exist if there is to be any substantial incentive for voluntary saving.

Implications of the Theoretical Explanation of Interest. It has been stated that interest is possible because capital goods (i.e., producers' goods) are productive. A better statement might be that under favorable circumstances specific capital goods may be sufficiently productive to earn a return.

Whether in fact specific capital goods in a given set of circumstances promise to be productive enough to earn a return is a problem in engineering economy. Each situation must be examined with respect to the specific prices that apply to the given circumstances. The technical considerations that usually enter into such a problem make an engineering training necessary for its solution.

For instance, consider the selection of the steam pressure for a steam-electric power plant. The higher the pressure the greater the initial investment in boilers, valves, piping, etc.; but—within limits—the less the amount of fuel required to produce a given quantity of electric energy.

The point beyond which it is not a productive investment of capital to increase steam pressure depends on many circumstances (such as the extra cost of the equipment necessary for higher pressures, the cost of fuel, and the amount and time distribution of the load). There is no particular pressure that is inherently the most economical regardless of circumstances. And the question of just what pressure is economical in a given set of circumstances cannot be decided apart from the technical considerations involved.

The engineer is thus in a position where he is called upon to make recommendations as to the economic wisdom of specific capital expenditures for machines and structures; he determines whether they are likely to be productive enough under the circumstances to earn a return (interest) sufficient to justify an investment in them.

Engineering Economy Studies from the Social Viewpoint. Because engineers are in a position to propose some capital expenditures and veto others, they indirectly exercise a considerable influence in the distribution of the social energies between consumers' goods and producers' goods; and they directly exercise an influence in the distribution of the social energies between various alternative producers' goods. Decisions between alternatives are necessarily dependent on the expression of otherwise incommensurable quantities (e.g., hours of unskilled labor, hours of various kinds of skilled labor, pounds of steel, tons of coal, barrels of fuel oil, board feet of lumber, acres of land) in a common unit—money value. Each money value is a result of a complex interaction of forces of supply and demand that reflects the utility and the scarcity of the commodity involved. To the extent that the price system so arrived at may be defended as weighing, as well as can be done, the sacrifices involved in the production of various commodities and the satisfactions obtainable from their use, the requirement that any capital goods to be created show the prospect of earning a return (interest) on the investment in them should tend toward a wise distribution of our social energies. In other words, not only is the recognition of the time value of money in economy studies by private individuals and corporations the only sensible policy for such individuals and corporations, but it is also sound policy from the collective viewpoint.

Differences Between Engineering and Accounting Viewpoints on the Time Value of Money. Engineering economy studies generally deal with *proposed* investments in machines or structures. As long as an investment is only proposed but not yet made, it is necessary to recognize interest in any calculations relative to the decision whether or not to make it; there is always offered the alternative of an investment at interest.

The engineer's usual viewpoint here is in contrast to that of the accountant. Accounting records deal generally with *past* investments, receipts, and disbursements. Once money is invested in machines and structures it is not necessarily true that the alternative exists of investing the money productively elsewhere; in fact, there is generally no such alternative. Thus in calculations relative to past expenditures and disbursements the time value of money may or may not be considered, depending upon the questions that it is desired to answer by means of the calculations. Many of the questions that the accounts of a business are called on to answer do not require the consideration of interest; thus interest on ownership capital (i.e., where there is no actual interest payment to a creditor) is not generally considered as a cost in accounting, although there are some exceptions.

This difference between the engineer's viewpoint before the event and the accountant's viewpoint after the event often creates problems in trying to reconcile the calculations made for engineering economy studies with accounts of a concern; some of these problems were discussed in Chapter 10, others are discussed in later chapters. Often controversies arise between the engineers and the accountants of a concern owing to their conflicting views of cost; such controversies generally reflect a mutual misunderstanding of the legitimate objectives of procedures designed to serve different purposes. What is needed is a recognition by both engineers and accountants of the difference in the objectives of their calculations.

A Concluding Statement on Part II. In studies to determine a prospective rate of return (the subject matter of Chapter 8), the lowest rate of return deemed sufficient to justify a proposed investment may obviously be described as the minimum attractive rate of return. In annual cost comparisons (Chapter 6), present worth comparisons (Chapter 7), or benefit-cost comparisons (Chapter 9), the interest rate selected for use in equivalence calculations is—in effect—a minimum attractive rate of return regardless of whether or not it is so described.

The choice of a minimum attractive rate of return obviously has a great influence on decision making at all levels at which decisions are made between alternative investments in fixed assets. Proposed investments that look attractive at 3% appear to be undesirable at 7%; proposals that look good at 7% are properly vetoed at 15%. Further comments on the choice of a minimum attractive rate of return are made at various places in Part III. In the meantime the major point to keep in mind is that the controlling element in the choice of a minimum attractive return should ordinarily be either the return on the investment opportunity foregone or the over-all cost of capital, all things considered. There is no one figure for minimum attractive rate of return that is appropriate to all circumstances; it is reasonable that this figure should be much higher in some cases than in others.

PROBLEMS

11–1. Examine the financial page of the daily newspaper or current issues of some financial journal to determine the current yields on United States government bonds and on representative municipal, public utility, and industrial bonds. What are current rates of interest on home loans and on loans on commercial property in your locality? Discuss possible reasons for the differences in these interest rates.

11–2. Find some index of the yield of high-grade corporate bonds that has been in existence for 25 years or more. Find a comparable index for medium-grade corporate bonds. Plot the two indexes on coordinate paper, showing the year-by-year figures for the past 25 years. Note the variations in the general level of interest rates and also the differences between the variations of the rates of high-grade and medium-grade bonds.

11–3. A number of years ago, some leading citizens of the town of Q agreed that their community was badly in need of a modern hotel that would cost approximately $250,000. To meet this need they organized the Civic Hotel Company. By strenuous solicitation they were able to raise $150,000 by selling 1,500 shares of stock at $100 a share. The other $100,000 necessary to build the hotel was provided by a building and loan association on a 10-year, 8% mortgage that called for uniform annual payments sufficient to pay interest and extinguish the debt at the end of the 10 years.

After the hotel was completed, the board of directors of the Civic Hotel Company leased it to a company that operated a national chain of hotels. The lease ran for 20 years and contained a clause permitting the operating company to purchase the hotel for $100,000 at the end of the 20-year period. The operating company agreed to furnish the hotel and pay all taxes (including income taxes) and operating expenses, and was to receive all revenues from the operation of the hotel. It also agreed to meet the rather high interest and repayment obligations on the mortgage during the first 10 years of the lease. During the last 10 years of the lease, the operating company agreed to make payments sufficient to permit annual dividends of $8 per share. No payments at all were to be made to the stockholders during the first 10 years. This was the most favorable operating contract that the directors of the Civic Hotel Company were able to secure anywhere.

When the local stockholders, many of whom had bought stock under considerable pressure, learned that there was no prospect of dividends for 10 years, they were very much disappointed, and a number of them were anxious to sell their stock. Henry Smart, one of the businessmen in the original group that promoted the project, was reported to be buying stock from some of these disgruntled stockholders at $75 a share.

This resulted in local comment to the effect that Henry Smart was a "shrewd old skinflint" who was taking advantage of his public-spirited fellow citizens. There were remarks regarding the "fat dividends" he would be receiving after the mortgage was paid off. One man was reported to have turned down Smart's offer of $75 a share and to have commented publicly to the effect that the "old Shylock" would not get his stock unless he paid him what it was worth.

Was $75 a share really too low a price for this stock? Make the necessary assumptions and the necessary financial calculations to place a value on this stock. Discuss your conclusions.

11–4. In discussing the relevance of the time value of money in the evaluation of certain proposed investments in manufacturing, a writer comments that when a manufacturer ties up capital in his own business, he is prevented from investing this capital in secure investments such as government bonds. The writer implies that the manufacturer's minimum attractive rate of return ought to be the same as the rate of interest that he can obtain on government bonds.

Do you agree? If so, why? If not, why not?

III

TECHNIQUES FOR
ECONOMY STUDIES

12

Some Aspects of the Analysis of Multiple Alternatives

The logical order of procedure in the case of any new enterprise—which is, first, to determine whether or not the project is a sound one, and to be carried out; and secondly, to make the necessary studies as to the manner of carrying it out—is not necessarily followed in order of time: often it cannot be, for the final decision as to the former often depends on the results of the latter, or on unknown future events. Nevertheless, although subsequent events may cause a revision of such assumptions, the mere initiation of the study of details implies a pro-forma conclusion, that the project as a whole is a wise one if wisely carried out, and can only fail by bad judgment in details. This premise must be from the beginning, therefore, under all circumstances, the basis of the engineer's action. From this it follows:

No increase of expenditure over the unavoidable minimum is expedient or justifiable, however great the probable profits and value of an enterprise as a whole, unless the INCREASE can with reasonable certainty be counted on to be, in itself, a profitable investment. Conversely,

No saving of expenditure is expedient or justifiable, however doubtful the future of the enterprise as a whole, when it can with certainty be counted on that the additional expenditure at least will, at the cost for the capital to make it, be in itself a paying investment.—A. M. WELLINGTON [1]

A first step in learning how to reason clearly about choosing among many possible courses of action is to learn how to choose between *two* alternatives. Moreover, general principles of decision making often are clearer when only two alternatives are involved. For these reasons most of the examples and problems up to this point have dealt with alternatives in pairs.

Why Discuss Multiple Alternatives? Obviously, many decisions call for a choice among a number of different proposals. Do these involve

[1] A. M. Wellington, *The Economic Theory of Railway Location*, 2d. ed. (New York: John Wiley & Sons, Inc., 1887), p. 15.

special problems or difficulties that differ in any way from the analysis of only two possibilities? The answer to this question is "Yes and no."

The answer is "No" in the sense that the same principles of analysis apply to multiple alternatives that apply to comparison of only two alternatives. Any multiple-alternative problem can be analyzed by considering alternatives in pairs.

But the answer is "Yes" because it is helpful to use various mathematical techniques to find optimal solutions for multiple-alternative types of problems and because it is desirable for analysts to be aware of certain pitfalls and limitations in the use of such techniques. Also the answer is "Yes" because certain types of errors in reasoning have been common when either the rate-of-return method or the benefit-cost-ratio method have been used in the analysis of multiple-alternative problems.

A Classification of Multiple-Alternative Problems in Engineering Economy. For purposes of discussion, it is helpful to divide multiple-alternative problems into two classes:

1. Cases where only *one* of the alternatives will be selected, usually (although not always) because the alternatives are physically mutually exclusive. A convenient subclassification is:

(a) Cases where differences in estimated cash flows are entirely (or almost entirely) in disbursements. Many design alternatives and many cost-reduction alternatives are of this type. Examples 12–1 to 12–4 all fall within this group.

Although Example 12–1 does not involve any special complications, it does illustrate a common state of affairs in which an increase in required investment in one place is accompanied by a decrease in required investment in another place. It also illustrates the treatment of income taxes in a multiple-alternative analysis that is based on equivalent uniform annual costs.

Examples 12–2 to 12–4 deal with problems that are of great historical interest (as well as of continuing applied interest) in engineering economy. These examples are simplified by using comparisons before income taxes. They serve here as an introduction to the use of mathematical models in dealing with multiple alternatives.

(b) Cases where there are also prospective differences in cash receipts (or in benefits). Decisions among alternate levels of development in a new project generally fall into this class. Examples 12–5 and 12–6 illustrate, respectively, rate-of-return analysis and benefit-cost-ratio analysis as applied to this type of problem.

2. Cases in which proposals are sufficiently independent so that two or more can be accepted but some constraint (such as a limitation in finances or a limitation in manpower) controls the aggregate of the

proposals that can be accepted. Some aspects of this common type of capital-budgeting problem were discussed in Chapter 11; other aspects are considered in subsequent chapters.

The present chapter is limited to consideration of the first class of case, namely, the case in which only one alternative is to be selected.

EXAMPLE 12–1. PRELIMINARY STUDY TO DETERMINE THE ECONOMIC DIAMETER OF AN OIL PIPE LINE

Facts of the Case. Table 12–1 shows preliminary estimates and calculations of annual costs in connection with a proposed pipe line. Four diameters of pipe are under consideration. The larger the diameter of the pipe, the lower the friction loss in the line. An increased size of pipe therefore reduces the necessary investment in pumping stations and reduces the amount of energy to overcome friction in the line.

In this preliminary study the estimated life of both the pipe line and the pumping stations is taken as 15 years with zero salvage value. The minimum attractive rate of return is 8% after income taxes. Income tax differences are computed using the simplified assumptions explained in Chapter 10. Estimated average annual property taxes and insurance are 3% of first cost. The comparison by equivalent uniform annual cash flow is shown in Table 12–1.

TABLE 12–1

Comparison of Annual Costs for Different Diameters of Proposed Oil Pipe Line

(All figures in thousands of dollars)

Pipe Diameter	8-in.	10-in.	12-in.	14-in.
A. First cost of pipe line	$ 9,600	$12,000	$14,300	$16,700
B. First cost of pumping stations	3,600	2,400	1,360	700
C. Total investment	$13,200	$14,400	$15,660	$17,400
D. Capital recovery cost ($i^* = 8\%$)	$ 1,542	$ 1,682	$ 1,830	$ 2,033
E. Annual pipe line maintenance	294	325	364	390
F. Annual pumping station maintenance and attendance	320	225	108	70
G. Annual fuel cost for pumping	780	450	290	140
H. Annual property taxes and insurance ..	396	432	468	522
I. Extra annual income taxes over 8-in. line	0	139	198	194
J. Total equivalent annual cost	$ 3,332	$ 3,253	$ 3,258	$ 3,349

The table indicates that the 10-in. and 12-in. pipes have approximately equal annual costs. Both are clearly more economical than the 8-in. and 14-in. sizes. The choice between the 10-in. and 12-in. sizes should not be made without careful detailed cost estimates for both. If such estimates continue to show the two sizes as having almost the same annual costs, the choice should be made on the basis of irreducible data. One important matter to consider would be the possibility of an increase or decrease in flow during the life of the pipe line.

This example illustrates a characteristic of many design problems involving alternative levels of investment. It will be noted that the larger the investment in the pipe line, the smaller the investment in the pumping plant. Moreover, certain operation and maintenance costs are increased by increased diameter whereas others are decreased.

It is a common condition that an increased investment in one place will reduce the necessary investment somewhere else. Whenever possible, this should be indicated directly in the cost estimates of total investment as has been done here.

Formulas for Minimum-Cost Point. Example 12–1 dealt with a case in which cost varied with a certain variable of design, namely, pipe diameter. Some elements of cost increased and others decreased with an increase in the value of the design variable. In this common type of case there is presumably some value of the design variable that makes the sum of all costs a minimum.

Wherever the variation of cost as a function of a design variable can be expressed by an algebraic equation, it is possible to use calculus to find the value of the design variable that results in minimum cost. The literature of engineering economy is full of formulas for minimum-cost points arrived at in this way.

The simplest case is one in which one element of cost varies in direct proportion to the variable of design, a second element of cost varies inversely as the variable of design, and all other costs are independent of this variable. Although minimum-cost point formulas may, of course, be developed for situations much more complex than this, some of those that have traditionally been used by engineers did actually deal with situations of this type. A general solution of the problem of finding the minimum-cost point in such circumstances is as follows:

Let

$$y = \text{total cost}$$

and let

$$x = \text{the variable of design}$$

The situation of cost variation just described may be expressed by the equation

$$y = ax + \frac{b}{x} + c$$

Taking the first derivative, we find

$$\frac{dy}{dx} = a - \frac{b}{x^2}$$

Equating this to zero, and solving for x,

$$x = \sqrt{\frac{b}{a}}$$

This is the value of the design variable that makes cost a minimum.

When $x = \sqrt{\frac{b}{a}}$, the directly varying costs equal the inversely varying costs. This may be demonstrated as follows:

$$ax = a\sqrt{\frac{b}{a}} = \sqrt{ab}$$

$$\frac{b}{x} = \frac{b}{\sqrt{\frac{b}{a}}} = \sqrt{ab}$$

The formula, $x = \sqrt{\frac{b}{a}}$, can be applied to a number of different kinds of problems, but it should be obvious that certain precautions should be taken in the applications. For example, the statement that the minimum-cost point occurs when the directly varying costs equal the inversely varying costs is not correct unless the line representing the directly varying costs goes through the origin. Also, the cost represented by ax must actually vary directly with x and the cost represented by $\frac{b}{x}$ must actually vary inversely. In the following example the cost per pound of wire must be the same for all different sizes of wire (which usually is not true), and the costs of energy losses must vary inversely with the wire size. A variable rate for electric energy or the existence of leakage loss and corona loss (such as occur in high voltage transmission lines) interfere with the second assumption. Moreover, the analysis disregards any possible adverse consequences of voltage drop on the operation of electrical equipment. A lower limit on wire size may exist because of electrical code requirements.

EXAMPLE 12-2. ECONOMICAL SIZE OF AN ELECTRICAL CONDUCTOR

Facts of the Case. The greater the diameter of an electrical conductor, the less the energy loss that will take place in it. (Power loss in watts is I^2R, where I = current in amperes and R = resistance in ohms. This may be converted to kilowatts by dividing by 1,000. Power loss in kw. multiplied by the number of hours it occurs in a given period will give energy loss in kw-hr.) Thus an increased investment in conductor metal will save an operating expense for electric energy.

Assume that a conductor is to be selected to carry 30 amperes for 4,200 hours per year, with the cost of wire at 48 cents per pound and electrical energy purchased at 2.3 cents per kw-hr. The life is estimated as 25 years with zero salvage value. The minimum attractive rate of return before income taxes is 12%, and average annual property taxes are estimated at 1.75% of first cost. These charges proportional to investment—namely, capital recovery cost of 12.75% and property taxes of 1.75%—are lumped together as investment charges of 14.5%.

The cross-sectional area of a copper conductor is expressed in circular mils, and the weight of the conductor is directly proportional to the cross-sectional area and the resistance to the flow of current is inversely proportional to the area. Therefore, let x represent the cross-sectional area in circular mils, and x_e represent the most economical size for the stated conditions. The resistance, R, for a conductor of 1,000 ft. in length and 1 circular mil in cross-sectional area is approximately 10,580 ohms at 25°C, and the same conductor will weigh approximately 0.00302 pounds.

The investment in the conductor will be

$$\$0.48(0.00302)x$$

The annual cost will be $\$0.48(0.00302)(0.145)x$. Let

$$\$0.48(0.00302)(0.145) = a = \$0.000210$$

The annual cost of power loss is

$$\frac{I^2R(4{,}200)(\$0.023)}{1{,}000}$$

but

$$R = \frac{10{,}580}{x}$$

Therefore, the cost of power loss is

$$\frac{(30^2)(4{,}200)(\$0.023)(10{,}580)}{1{,}000x}$$

Let

$$b = \frac{(30^2)(4{,}200)(\$0.023)(10{,}580)}{1{,}000} = \$919{,}800$$

From the formula developed in the previous article we know that the most economical value of x, x_e, occurs when

$$x = \sqrt{\frac{b}{a}}$$

$$x_e = \sqrt{\frac{\$919{,}800}{\$0.000210}} = 66{,}180 \text{ circular mils}$$

By examining a table of wire sizes (American Wire Gage, B & S) the closest available conductor is Gage No. 2, with 66,400 circular mils.

Comments on Example 12–2. In this example the size of the conductor was treated as a continuous variable. Actually, the conductors available are discrete sizes, increasing by a geometric progression at the rate of 1.123^2 for the cross-sectional area. The fact that there are specific sizes of wire available and that tables giving the resistance, weight, cross-sectional area, etc., are also available makes another method of solution attractive.

In Table 12–2 five successive wire sizes that might be used for this application have been selected and the annual cost of each size was computed. The table shows that wire size No. 2 gives the lowest annual cost. This table also emphasizes the fact that one type of cost increases as the other decreases, as happens in many problems involving multiple

TABLE 12–2

Comparison of Annual Costs of Various Wire Sizes in the Selection of an Electrical Conductor

(Investment in wire at 48 cents/lb.; current of 30 amperes for 4,200 hrs./yr.; all calculations based on 1,000 ft. of copper wire)

	00	0	1	2	3
A. Size of wire (AWG)	00	0	1	2	3
B. Weight of wire in lb.	403	319	253	201	159
C. Investment in wire	$193.40	$153.10	$121.40	$96.50	$76.30
D. Resistance in ohms	0.0795	0.100	0.126	0.159	0.201
E. Power loss—kw.	0.0716	0.090	0.113	0.143	0.181
F. Annual energy loss in kw-hr.	301	378	475	601	760
G. Investment charges at 14.5%	$ 28.04	$ 22.20	$ 17.60	$13.99	$11.06
H. Cost of lost energy at 2.3 cents/ kw-hr.	6.92	8.69	10.92	13.82	17.48
I. Total annual cost assumed to be variable with wire size	$ 34.96	$ 30.89	$ 28.52	$27.81	$28.54

alternatives. Furthermore, note that at the most economical alternative the investment charges approximately equal the cost of lost energy. This is characteristic of problems in which the total costs can be represented by the equation

$$y = ax + \frac{b}{x} + c.$$

It was first pointed out by Lord Kelvin in 1881 that the economical size of conductor is that for which the annual investment charges just equal the annual cost of lost energy. This is well known in electrical engineering as Kelvin's Law. The costs in Figure 12–1 illustrate its application.

The Problem of Economic Production Quantities in Manufacturing. Possibly there has been more written about methods of determining the economic size of a manufacturing lot than about any other single problem

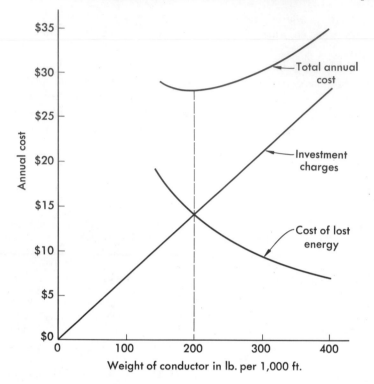

FIGURE 12–1. Comparison of Annual Costs in the Selection of an Electrical Conductor

of engineering economy. This common problem in manufacturing arises whenever a machine or group of machines is capable of being shifted from one part or product to another. A machine will be set up for a "run" on a certain product; when the stock on that product has been built up to a desired point, it will be shifted to the production of something else. Thus, whenever a factory production order is made out, a decision must be made on the matter of lot size.

Ordinarily, any run on a given product will involve a preparation cost which is independent of the number of pieces to be produced in the lot. This will include such items as the cost of tool preparation and the cost of the machine setup. Preparation cost—expressed either as an annual total or as a unit amount per piece—will vary inversely with lot size. For instance, if the sizes of lots are doubled, annual expenditures for preparation will be cut in half.

On the other hand, a doubled lot size means a doubled inventory with resulting doubled costs of storage, taxes, and insurance for that inventory. It also means that the money outlay at the time a lot is manufactured will be doubled; thus, more of the concern's funds will be used for the financing of inventories. If such extra investment of funds is to be justified, it must yield a return commensurate with the risk. This should be reflected in the economic lot size calculations (which, in effect, are to determine whether the savings in reduced preparation costs minus the additional costs for storage, taxes, and insurance resulting from larger lot sizes, represent an adequate return on the extra investment in inventories) by an "interest" charge against the inventory investment at the desired rate of return on funds invested in working capital.

EXAMPLE 12–3. A TABULAR COMPARISON TO DETERMINE ECONOMIC LOT SIZE

Facts of the Case. The comparison of costs for various lot sizes is relatively simple if uniform demand for the manufactured product or piece is assumed. Table 12–3 shows such a comparison for the following situation:

S, the total preparation cost for each lot, is $4.60.

P, the total number of pieces which can be made per day with the machine operated at full capacity, is 100.

U, the total number of pieces used per day, is 10.

N, the number of days worked per year, is 300.

C, the variable outlay per piece, is $0.44. This consists of direct material cost per piece, $0.20; direct labor cost per piece, $0.16; and variable overhead or burden per piece, which is estimated as 50% of direct labor cost. This variable burden includes such items as indirect labor, indirect material, power, and repairs.

T, the total apportioned cost per piece, is $0.56. This includes direct material and direct labor as before, and indirect manufacturing expense apportioned by a burden rate of 125% of direct labor cost. This burden rate, which is based on the assumption of "normal" output, includes not only the "variable" indirect expenses but also those "fixed" indirect expenses which are independent of the rate of production within wide limits of variation—for instance, taxes, insurance on plant and machinery, and most of the cost of superintendence, heat, light, building upkeep, and depreciation.[2]

A, the cost of storing one piece for one year, is $0.04. (It is generally more convenient to consider storage cost on such a rental basis, than in any other way. In this case it is to be based on the maximum inventory anticipated, as with storage of the pieces in bins, sufficient storage space must be

[2] The implications of the 125% total burden rate that includes a 50% variable burden rate, about the variation of indirect manufacturing expense with output are as follows: With a normal direct labor cost of $20,000, indirect manufacturing expense will be $25,000. Of this $15,000 is "fixed," and $10,000 "variable." With direct labor cost at $12,000, indirect manufacturing expense would, therefore, be $21,000 (i.e., $15,000 plus 50% of $12,000). While any such separation of indirect manufacturing expense into "fixed" and "variable" elements may fall short of an accurate description of how such expenses really vary, it is generally closer to the facts than the assumption that indirect expenses vary in proportion to direct expenses.

TABLE 12-3

Minimum-Cost Point in the Selection of the Size of a Manufacturing Lot—Comparison of Annual Costs Variable with Lot Size

	Q	100	200	300	400	500	600
(1) Lot size							
(2) Lots manufactured per year	$\dfrac{NU}{Q}$	30	15	10	7½	6	5
(3) Maximum inventory-pieces	$Q\left(1-\dfrac{U}{P}\right)$	90	180	270	360	450	540
(4) Investment (variable) in maximum inventory	$CQ\left(1-\dfrac{U}{P}\right)$	\$ 39.60	\$ 79.20	\$118.80	\$158.40	\$198.00	\$237.60
(5) Interest on investment in average inventory	$\dfrac{ICQ}{2}\left(1-\dfrac{U}{P}\right)$	3.96	\$ 7.92	\$ 11.88	\$ 15.84	\$ 19.80	\$ 23.76
(6) Book value of maximum inventory	$TQ\left(1-\dfrac{U}{P}\right)$	\$ 50.40	\$100.80	\$151.20	\$201.60	\$252.00	\$302.40
(7) Taxes and insurance on average inventory	$\dfrac{BTQ}{2}\left(1-\dfrac{U}{P}\right)$	\$ 0.38	\$ 0.76	\$ 1.14	\$ 1.51	\$ 1.89	\$ 2.27
(8) Storage cost	$AQ\left(1-\dfrac{U}{P}\right)$	\$ 3.60	\$ 7.20	\$ 10.80	\$ 14.40	\$ 18.00	\$ 21.60
(9) Total annual cost of carrying inventory	$\dfrac{IC+BT+2A}{2}\,Q\left(1-\dfrac{U}{P}\right)$	\$ 7.94	\$ 15.88	\$ 23.82	\$ 31.75	\$ 39.69	\$ 47.63
(10) Annual preparation cost	$\dfrac{SNU}{Q}$	\$138.00	\$ 69.00	\$ 46.00	\$ 34.50	\$ 27.60	\$ 23.00
(11) Total annual cost variable with lot size	$(9)+(10)$	\$145.94	\$ 84.88	\$ 69.82	\$ 66.25	\$ 67.29	\$ 70.63

dedicated to the particular product to take care of the maximum inventory requirements.)

B, the annual rate for inventory taxes and insurance, based on the book value (i.e., total apportioned cost including the full burden rate) of the inventories, is 1.5%, or 0.015.

I, the before-tax minimum attractive rate of return on investment, is 20%, or 0.20. This rate is intended to reflect the risk of inventory obsolescence that exists whenever inventories are large.

It will be noted that Table 12–3 gives *annual* costs *variable* with lot size.

The same comparison might have been made on the basis of unit costs; in that case items (5), (7), (8), (9), (10), and (11) would all have been divided by the annual production, NU. The relative values would, of course, have been unchanged. However, it is somewhat easier to see the magnitude of the differences in cost involved in any choice, if annual costs are used rather than unit costs.

Only those costs variable with lot size have been compared. No advantage is gained by including in the comparative cost study all of the production expenses for labor, material, and overhead which are unaffected by the choice of lot size. Similarly, no carrying charges have been included for the minimum inventory required regardless of lot size.

The following comments relate to the numbered lines of Table 12–3:

1. Note the use of the symbol Q to designate lot size.

2. The number of lots per year is obviously the total annual production NU divided by the lot size.

3. If a day's production P is 100 units and a day's use U is 10 units, 90 units from each day's production remain to increase inventory; thus we get the factor $\left(1 - \dfrac{U}{P}\right)$. Where P is large in proportion to U, the omission of this factor will simplify the calculations with little influence on the final result. Moreover, unless the use is fairly uniform from day to day, the entire lot produced may be an addition to inventory; in such cases it is better to omit the $\left(1 - \dfrac{U}{P}\right)$ entirely.

4. A point of difference between this exposition of the lot size problem and the usual treatment of the problem in management literature, lies in the "valuation" here of inventories for the purpose of calculating "interest" (i.e., minimum attractive return) at the increment cost of their production rather than at the total cost apportioned by the cost system. Like all economy studies, the determination of an economic lot size is a problem in measuring differences between alternatives. In comparing one alternative, Large Inventory, with another alternative, Small Inventory, the difference between the expenditures necessary to procure them will not include any of the "fixed" indirect manufacturing expenses. It is only this increment of expenditure necessary to get the larger inventory which is relevant in calculating "interest" or return.

5. As in all economy studies, interest should be figured at the minimum attractive rate of return on investment in the light of the risk rather than at the bare cost of borrowed money. Because the risks involved in inventory investment are substantial, the difference between these two figures may be large. Many published discussions on economic lot sizes have used an interest rate such as might be paid on bank loans (usually 6% or thereabouts); this gives a lot size that is too high.

The assumption behind the calculation of interest on *average* inventory rather than on maximum inventory is that many different items are being produced in intermittent lots. The peak inventory for one item will occur at the time of the minimum inventory for another; the net "investment" by the manufacturer will be based on the average of all peaks and minimums.

6. Both fire insurance and taxes will be based on the total allotted cost of production rather than on increment cost.

7. The same reasoning about averages used in (5) applies here.

8. Whether storage costs should be based on average inventory or on maximum inventory is a matter of fact to be determined in any specific instance. Where storage is in bins, it is generally necessary to provide space for maximum requirements. Where it is not, as in the furniture industry, it is often more reasonable to base storage costs on average inventory.

9. This is the sum of interest (i.e., return on investment), taxes, insurance, and storage cost, on the inventory.

10. The annual preparation cost is obviously the preparation cost for a lot multiplied by the number of lots manufactured per year.

11. Although a lot of 400 pieces appears to be the most economical, the difference in cost from 300 to 600 seems so small as to be negligible. This might well result in the selection of 300 as the desirable lot size for production.

The irreducibles in the lot size problem are almost always on the side of the selection of smaller lot sizes. They may include any or all of the following: (1) risk of obsolescence of part or product due to style changes or design changes, (2) desirability of conserving working capital, and (3) avoidance of risk of loss on inventory declines as a result of falling prices.

Larger lot sizes mean larger inventories. Where changes in design or style come suddenly, the manufacturer with large inventories is likely to have difficulty in disposing of them except at a loss. Moreover, where a concern's funds are not adequate to finance large inventories without substantial bank loans that may involve possible difficulties of repayment in the event of business recession, the desire to keep working capital requirements to a minimum is a motive toward small inventories.

In view of these irreducibles it is often desirable to look not for the minimum-cost point but rather for the minimum-cost range (i.e., the range through which the choice of a lot size has little effect on cost) and then to select the lot size at the lower end of that range. The selection of a lot size of 300 on the basis of the calculations of Table 12–3 would be an example of this policy.

EXAMPLE 12–4. USE OF A FORMULA TO DETERMINE ECONOMIC LOT SIZE [3]

Facts of the Case. The minimum-cost formula developed earlier in this chapter is applicable to the economic lot size problem, because one cost element varies directly with some variable under investigation and another element of cost varies inversely with this variable. The problem of finding the

---

[3] The symbols that have been used throughout the economic lot size discussion are those employed by Professor Paul T. Norton, Jr., in his pamphlet, *Economic Lot Sizes in Manufacturing*, Virginia Polytechnic Institute Engineering Extension Division Series, Bulletin No. 31. With minor points of variation, the formula given here is that developed by Professor Norton. The reader will note that certain of the symbols (*P* and *A*) have been used with quite different meanings in our development of the mathematics of compound interest.

economic size of a manufacturing lot involves the carrying charges on inventory that vary directly with lot size, and the preparation or setup costs which vary inversely. Hence the formula for minimum-cost point developed earlier in this chapter may be used to find the lot size for which the sum of these costs is a minimum.

It was shown that the design variable, x, should equal $\sqrt{\dfrac{b}{a}}$ for minimum cost, where a is the coefficient for the directly varying costs and b is the coefficient for the inversely varying costs. Lines (9) and (10) of Table 12–3 indicate the values of these coefficients as

$$a = \frac{IC + BT + 2A}{2}\left(1 - \frac{U}{P}\right)$$

$$b = SNU$$

Q, the lot size, corresponds to x

The economic lot size is therefore given by the expression

$$Q = \sqrt{\frac{2SNU}{(IC + BT + 2A)\left(1 - \dfrac{U}{P}\right)}}$$

The application of this formula is illustrated by its use for the problem solved by direct calculation in Table 12–3, as follows:

$$Q = \sqrt{\frac{2(\$4.60)(300)(10)}{[(0.20)(\$0.44) + (0.015)(\$0.56) + 2(\$0.04)]\left(1 - \dfrac{10}{100}\right)}} = 417$$

If the factor $\left(1 - \dfrac{U}{P}\right)$ is eliminated [for reasons explained in the discussion of line (3) of Table 12–3], and the minor item of taxes and insurance on inventory is neglected, this simplifies to

$$Q = \sqrt{\frac{2SNU}{IC + 2A}}$$

Some Comments About the Use of Mathematical Models in Engineering Economy.

Many mathematical models have been developed to guide decisions among investment alternatives. Certain general statements may be made that are applicable to many of the complex models as well as to simple models such as the ones leading to Kelvin's Law and to our economic lot size formulas.[4] These statements may be illustrated with reference to our two simple examples.

[4] Not all formulations of the economic lot size problem are as simple as the one in Examples 12–3 and 12–4. In his 375-page book about economic lot sizes, *Quantity and Economy in Manufacture* (New York: McGraw-Hill Book Co., Inc., 1931), F. E. Raymond used some 150 different symbols to represent parameters that appeared in his various formulas! Many modern formulations of this problem assume that certain relevant estimates should be treated as random variables; these models therefore make use of the mathematics of probability. A brief discussion of the probabilistic approach to this type of problem is given in Chapter 14.

One generalization is that whenever a particular type of problem of economic comparison occurs fairly often, a rule or formula is a time saver in finding the most economic value of a variable of design. In the case of finding economic lot size, it has been fairly common to use a nomographic chart or special purpose slide rule as a tool for time saving. With many of the complex mathematical models developed by operations researchers and systems analysts, the modern high-speed electronic computer takes the place of the chart or slide rule that could be used to solve the simpler formulas.

The saving of time through the solution of a formula that gives a single "optimal" value for a variable sometimes has a hidden penalty associated with it. The single value has the limitation that it does not show the range of variation of the design variable through which cost (or some other chosen economic measure) will change very little. What often is needed is a minimum-cost *range* rather than a minimum-cost *point*. If this range is known, it is much easier to give weight to the irreducibles that enter into most economy studies. Thus Table 12–3 which indicated a negligible variation in cost from a lot size of 300 to one of 600, gave more useful information than the solution of the formula in Example 12–4, which told us only that the minimum cost would take place with a lot size of 417.

The analyst who uses a formula to guide an economic decision ought to understand the assumptions underlying the mathematical model that generated his formula. Mathematical models describing economic matters generally require the model builder to make some compromises with reality. Sometimes these compromises are made so that the mathematics can be simplified; sometimes a mathematical treatment is impossible without a few compromises. These compromises are found in complex mathematical models as well as in simple ones.

Compromises may take the form of the omission of certain matters. For example, the derivation of Kelvin's Law disregarded the possible existence of leakage and corona losses and also disregarded any possible adverse consequences of voltage drop. Compromises may also take the form of a simplification of the relationship between certain relevant quantities that appear in the model. For example, in the derivation of Kelvin's Law it was assumed that the investment in an installed conductor is a linear function of the weight of conductor metal and that the appropriate rate of investment charges is the same for all wire sizes. These assumptions do not necessarily fit the facts of particular cases. Also it was assumed that wire size is a continuous function whereas in fact the function is discontinuous.

When an analyst decides whether or not to use a particular formula, the real issue that he should consider is whether or not his *decision* will be sensitive to the omissions and/or simplifications that exist in the mathematical model. The topic of tests for sensitivity is discussed in Chapter 13.

The attempt to devise a mathematical model to describe a type of problem calling for an economic decision can lead to a clearer understanding of the nature of the problem and the relevant matters that need to be considered. There have been many cases where this has occurred; one of them is examined throughout Appendix D.

Relationship of Subsequent Chapters and Appendixes to the Construction and Interpretation of Mathematical Models Dealing with Investment Decisions. Chapter 13 on sensitivity analysis deals with a topic of great importance both in the design of mathematical models and in the interpretation of formulas derived from them. The application of the mathematics of probability to investment-type decisions is the subject matter of Chapter 14; a number of the mathematical models developed by operations researchers and systems analysts involve probability mathematics.

Chapter 15 on increment costs and sunk costs develops the concept, first mentioned in this book near the end of Chapter 1, that it is only prospective *differences* among alternatives that are relevant in their comparison. Over the years, many published formulas for the solution of problems in engineering economy have given dangerously misleading guidance to decision makers because the authors of the formulas have not recognized this concept. Such misleading formulas have, generally speaking, made uncritical use of figures derived from the accounting systems of business enterprises.

Appendix D contains a brief discussion of the various "MAPI systems" for investment evaluation. These systems were developed by George Terborgh, Research Director for the Machinery and Allied Products Institute, with the aid of his associates; they are described in a series of MAPI publications issued from 1949 to 1967. Although the original MAPI models were aimed particularly at decisions about *replacements* of industrial assets, this objective was broadened considerably in the later writings by Terborgh. An examination of the changes in the MAPI systems over a period of years throws light on certain types of problems that seem likely to arise in the design of mathematical models for decision making that are intended to be widely useful in industry.

Some Special Aspects of Comparing Mutually Exclusive Multiple Alternatives Using Rates of Return or Benefit-Cost Ratios. Certain examples in Chapters 8 and 9 brought out the point that in comparing three mutually exclusive proposals, each proposal should be able to sustain

TABLE 12-4

Prospective Rates of Return on Total Investment and on Successive Increments of Investment for Ten Alternative Plans for Development of a Commercial Rental Property

(All dollar figures in thousands)

	Plan 1	Plan 2	Plan 3	Plan 4	Plan 5	Plan 6	Plan 7	Plan 8	Plan 9	Plan 10
A. Investment in land	$200	$200	$200	$200	$200	$200	$200	$200	$ 200	$ 200
B. Investment in building	68	120	184	256	340	428	504	648	800	1,000
C. Total investment	$268	$320	$384	$456	$540	$628	$704	$848	$1,000	$1,200
D. Annual receipts	$ 48.7	$ 68.4	$ 94.0	$130.7	$164.8	$188.3	$212.9	$242.2	$ 266.0	$ 293.6
E. Annual disbursements other than income taxes	20.4	25.0	30.2	38.7	47.3	56.6	69.5	88.0	105.2	125.4
F. Annual disbursements for income taxes	13.3	20.2	29.6	42.8	54.5	60.5	65.4	69.0	70.4	71.6
G. Annual net positive cash flow	$ 15.0	$ 23.2	$ 34.2	$ 49.2	$ 63.0	$ 71.2	$ 78.0	$ 85.2	$ 90.4	$ 96.6
H. After-tax rate of return on total investment	5.5%	7.1%	8.8%	10.8%	11.6%	11.3%	11.0%	9.9%	8.7%	7.7%
J. Increment of investment over plan with next lower investment		$ 52	$ 64	$ 72	$ 84	$ 88	$ 76	$144	$ 152	$ 200
K. Increment of annual net positive cash flow over plan with next lower investment		8.2	11.0	15.0	13.8	8.2	6.8	7.2	5.2	6.2
L. After-tax rate of return on increment of investment ..		(15.7%)	(17.1%)	20.8%	16.4%	9.0%	8.6%	3.3%	(1.6%)	(1.1%)

its economic challenge as compared to the best of the other two proposals. Specifically, it was pointed out that it is insufficient for each proposal for change to be compared only with the continuation of a present condition.

In using the rate of return method of analysis or the benefit-cost ratio method, there seems to be a special temptation for analysts to give undue weight to comparisons made with inappropriate alternatives. This temptation seems to be greatest when there are many alternative proposals. Example 12–5 illustrates the use and possible misuse of the rate of return method in examining a number of mutually exclusive proposals for private investment. Example 12–6 illustrates the use and possible misuse of the benefit-cost ratio method in examining a number of mutually exclusive proposals for a government project.

EXAMPLE 12–5. RATE OF RETURN ANALYSIS OF A SET OF MUTUALLY EXCLUSIVE ALTERNATIVES

Facts and Estimates. Ten different plans are under consideration for the construction of a building for commercial rentals on a piece of city property. As shown on line A of Table 12–4, the investment in land will be $200,000 regardless of which plan is selected. Line B gives the required investment as estimated for each building design; the investments vary from $68,000 for a very simple single-story building in Plan 1 to $1,000,000 for a luxurious multi-story building in Plan 10. The total investment shown in line C is the sum of the land and building investments.

The estimated annual receipts from rentals for each plan are shown in line D. The estimated total annual disbursements for operation and maintenance, property taxes, and insurance—in fact, all items except income taxes—are shown in line E. The estimated life of the project is 40 years with an estimated zero net terminal salvage value for the building. The income taxes shown in line F are calculated using the simple assumptions described in Chapter 10 (a 50% incremental tax rate, the use of straight-line depreciation for tax purposes with the same estimated life and salvage value used in the economy study, and financing entirely from equity funds). The annual net positive cash flow in line G is found by subtracting the total disbursements (lines E and F) from the receipts (line D).

Calculated Rates of Return. The rates of return shown in line H assume that the land will be sold for its original cost, namely, $200,000, at the end of 40 years. (With the simple assumptions about income tax matters that we are making at this point in the book, this is the only practicable assumption that will permit calculation of income-tax consequences for an after-tax study. However, the calculated rates of return are relatively insensitive to fairly large changes in the estimated terminal value of the land.)

The rates of return in line H are found by computing present worths and making interpolations in the manner that was explained in Chapter 8. For example, for Plan 6:

PW at 12% = $71,200($P/A$,12%,40) + $200,000($P/F$,12%,40) = $589,100
PW at 10% = $71,200($P/A$,10%,40) + $200,000($P/F$,10%,40) = $700,700

Interpolation using the $628,000 investment indicates that the prospective rate of return is approximately 11.3%.

A rate of return analysis of multiple alternatives calls for consideration of incremental rates of return as well as total rates of return. Lines J and K give the cash flow figures needed to calculate these rates. Line L gives the prospective rate of return on each increment of investment. Because all the increments of investment apply only to the building and therefore have zero terminal salvage values, it is possible to compute these incremental rates by interpolating between capital recovery factors. For example, to compute the incremental rate of return of Plan 6 over Plan 5:

$$A/P = \$8,200/\$88,000 = 0.09318$$

An interpolation between the 40-year capital recovery factors for 10% and 8% (0.10226 and 0.08386) gives the approximate incremental rate of return of 9.0%.

We shall draw our conclusions from Table 12–4 on the assumption that the primary criterion for the choice among the alternatives is that the minimum attractive rate of return is 8% after income taxes. Of course this criterion should be applied not only to the total investment but also to each separable increment of investment.

However, none of the figures for rates of return in lines H and L depend on the stated i^* of 8%. Nevertheless, because the incremental rates for Plans 2, 3, 9, and 10 are not required in applying this i^* criterion, these rates have been shown in parentheses in line L.

The Challenger-Defender Viewpoint in Analyzing a Set of Mutually Exclusive Multiple Alternatives. In using Table 12–4 as a guide to decision making, it needs to be recognized that an untabulated alternative is to accept none of the plans. Plan 1 cannot sustain its challenge against this do-nothing alternative because its prospective 5.5% rate of return is less than the stipulated i^* of 8%. Neither can Plan 2 because 7.1% < 8%.

The do-nothing alternative should be the defender against Plan 2 because Plan 1 was eliminated when it failed to sustain its challenge. Similarly, the elimination of Plan 2 makes the do-nothing alternative the defender against Plan 3. But Plan 3, with its 8.8% overall rate of return, eliminates the do-nothing alternative from the competition because 8.8% > 8%.

At this point in the analysis, incremental rates of return become relevant. Plan 3 now becomes the defender. Plan 4 is successful in its challenge to Plan 3 because the extra $72,000 will yield 20.8% and the overall rate of return is 10.8%; both of these rates exceed the stipulated 8%. Similarly, Plan 5 succeeds in its challenge to Plan 4 because the incremental rate of return of 16.4% and the overall rate of return of 11.6% both exceed 8%.

In spite of the fact that the overall rate of return decreases after Plan 5, Plan 6 succeeds in its challenge to Plan 5, and Plan 7 succeeds in its challenge to Plan 6. The extra investment of $88,000 in Plan 6 over Plan 5 has a prospective after-tax rate of return of 9.0%; because 9.0% exceeds the stipulated 8%, this extra investment is attractive. Similarly, the 8.6% on the extra investment of $76,000 in Plan 7 meets the given standard of attractiveness.

Beyond Plan 7, the proposed increments of investment are not attractive. Plan 8 does not succeed in its challenge to Plan 7 because the $144,000 extra investment yields only 3.3%. If we consider Plan 9 as a challenger to Plan 7, an extra investment of $296,000 is required to obtain an extra annual after-tax cash flow of $12,400 for 40 years; the approximate rate of return is 2.8%. (The 1.6% rate of return shown in line L for the extra investment in Plan 9 over Plan 8 is not relevant because Plan 8 was eliminated when it was compared with Plan 7.)

Plan 10 clearly fails to meet the 8% standard of attractiveness because its over-all rate of return is only 7.7%.

The conclusion of the foregoing analysis is that the stipulation of an after-tax i^* of 8% leads to the selection of Plan 7.

Two Possible Types of Error in Interpreting Prospective Rates of Return on a Set of Mutually Exclusive Alternatives. If lines J, K, and L had been omitted from Table 12–4, the rates of return in Line H would not have been a sufficient guide for making a choice among the alternatives. There are two types of error that sometimes are made in drawing conclusions from such a curtailed table. Some persons who examine such a table will make the mistake of selecting the alternative that has the highest total rate of return; this is Plan 5 in Table 12–4. Other persons will make the mistake of selecting the alternative with the highest investment that will yield at least the stipulated i^*; this is Plan 9 in Table 12–4.

If it is stipulated that the minimum attractive rate of return is 8%, presumably it is believed that the consequences of *rejecting* a proposed increment of investment will be to *accept* an unspecified investment elsewhere that will yield 8%. If Plan 5 should be selected in Example 12–5 on the grounds that it has the highest over-all rate of return, the rejection of Plans 6 and 7 is, in effect, a choice of unspecified investments yielding 8% rather than specified ones yielding, respectively, 9.0% and 8.6%.

Also an i^* of 8% implies that the consequence of *accepting* a proposed increment of investment will be to *reject* an unspecified investment elsewhere that will yield 8%. If Plan 9 is chosen on the grounds that it has the highest total investment with an over-all yield of at least 8%, an implied consequence of this choice is to reject an investment of $296,000 elsewhere that will yield 8% in favor of an avoidable extra investment in this project that will yield only 2.8%.

When a Calculated Incremental Rate of Return is Irrelevant. The discussion of Example 12–5 pointed out that certain rates of return on increments of investment in line L of Table 12–4 were shown in parentheses to emphasize the point that these rates were not relevant in the choice among the stated alternatives. In general, if an alternative is rejected because it fails to meet the decision criteria, it should not be viewed as the defender against subsequent alternatives that require higher investments.

Occasionally there is an irregularity in the pattern of incremental rates of return that may lead to an error in interpretation. As an example, add Plan 7a in Example 12–5; this plan requires a total investment of $812,000 ($200,000 for land and $612,000 for the building) and has an estimated annual net positive cash flow of $81,600. The rate of return on total investment will be approximately 9.9%, an acceptable figure. But the rate of return on the $108,000 increment of investment over Plan 7 will be only 1.5%, clearly an unacceptable figure.

Now imagine that Table 12–4 is changed to add Plan 7a and that in lines J, K, and L, Plan 8 is compared with the new 7a. Plan 8 will continue to have a 9.9% rate of return on total investment and line L will now show a rate of return of nearly 9.8% on the increment of investment. A superficial view of the matter might lead to the incorrect conclusion that Plan 8 is acceptable because both of these rates exceed the stipulated i^* of 8%. Such a conclusion would be incorrect because an incremental rate of return over an unacceptable alternative is not relevant. The defender against the challenge of Plan 8 should be the plan with the next lower investment that is *acceptable*, namely, Plan 7. The addition of an unacceptable Plan 7a does not change the fact that Plan 8 is an unattractive alternative to Plan 7 because its $144,000 increment of investment over Plan 7 promises an after-tax yield of only 3.3%.

EXAMPLE 12–6. USE OF BENEFIT-COST RATIOS IN ANALYSIS OF A SET OF MUTUALLY EXCLUSIVE ALTERNATIVES FOR A PUBLIC WORKS PROJECT.[5]

Facts and Estimates. A certain section of highway is now in location A. A number of proposed designs at new locations and proposed improvements at the present location are to be compared with a continuation of the present condition at A. For purposes of analysis, continuing the present condition is designated as A–1.

Three possible new designs in the present location are referred to as A–2, A–3, and A–4, respectively. Two new locations B and C are also considered for this section of highway. There are five new designs to be analyzed at location B and four at location C. These 13 proposals, A–1 to A–4, B–1 to B–5, and C–1 to C–4, are mutually exclusive in the sense that only one proposal will be selected. Of course the various designs at each location contain a number of common elements.

Table 12–5 gives the investments and the estimated annual maintenance costs for the various locations and designs. It also gives estimates of the annual costs to the road users for each alternative. It is assumed that there are no differences in other consequences that can be expressed in money terms.

[5] This example is adapted from one given in a paper "Economy Studies for Highways" by E. L. Grant and C. H. Oglesby published in Highway Research Board Bulletin 306, *Studies in Highway Engineering Economy*, Washington, D.C., National Academy of Sciences—National Research Council, 1961.

In order to concentrate the reader's attention on the special problems involved in the comparison of multiple alternatives for a public works project, the facts of this example have been simplified in certain ways. It is assumed that road user costs will be uniform throughout a 30-year study period and that all alternatives will have zero terminal salvage values at the end of that period. (The reader may recall that when we used a highway example to introduce the benefit-cost ratio in Example 9–1, we assumed that annual traffic and road-user costs would increase and that certain alternatives would have substantial residual values at the end of the analysis period.) Our economic comparisons of the 13 alternatives are made assuming a minimum attractive rate of return of 7%.

TABLE 12–5

Estimates and Annual Cost Comparison for
Certain Mutually Exclusive Highway Alternatives

(All figures in thousands of dollars)

Alter- native	First Cost	Annual CR Cost ($i^* = 7\%$)	Annual Main- tenance Cost	Annual Highway Costs	Annual Road User Costs	Total Annual Costs Influenced by Choice
A–1 [a]	$ 0	$ 0	$60	$ 60	$2,200	$2,260
A–2	1,500	121	35	156	1,920	2,076
A–3	2,000	161	30	191	1,860	2,051
A–4	3,500	282	40	322	1,810	2,132
B–1	3,000	242	30	272	1,790	2,062
B–2	4,000	322	20	342	1,690	2,032
B–3	5,000	403	30	433	1,580	2,013 [b]
B–4	6,000	484	40	524	1,510	2,034
B–5	7,000	564	45	609	1,480	2,089
C–1	5,500	443	40	483	1,620	2,103
C–2	8,000	645	30	675	1,470	2,145
C–3	9,000	725	40	765	1,400	2,165
C–4	11,000	886	50	936	1,340	2,276

[a] Continuation of the present condition.
[b] Minimum total annual cost.

Analysis Based on Minimum Annual Costs. The total annual costs of the 13 alternatives are compared in the final column of Table 12–5. For each alternative, this total is the sum of the capital recovery cost of the investment using an n of 30 and an i^* of 7%, the annual highway maintenance cost, and the annual costs to road users. The total annual cost is a minimum for design B–3, which requires an investment of $5,000,000.

Analysis Based on Benefit-Cost Ratios. In Table 12–6 the 12 alternatives to A–1, a continuation of the present condition, are arranged in order of in-

TABLE 12-6

Benefit-Cost Ratios as Compared to Continuation of a Present Condition (A–1) and Relevant Incremental Benefit-Cost Ratios for Alternatives of Table 12–5

(Alternatives are listed in order of increasing annual highway costs. Annual benefit and cost figures are in thousands of dollars.)

Alternatives	A–2	A–3	B–1	A–4	B–2	B–3	C–1	B–4	B–5	C–2	C–3	C–4
Road user benefits as compared to A–1	$280	$340	$410	$390	$510	$620	$580	$690	$720	$730	$800	$860
Highway costs in excess of costs for A–1	$96	$131	$212	$262	$282	$373	$423	$464	$549	$615	$705	$876
B/C ratio as compared to A–1	2.92	2.60	1.93	1.49	1.81	1.66	1.37	1.49	1.31	1.19	1.13	0.98
Incremental analysis compared to which defender	A–1	A–2	A–3	A–3	A–3	B–2	B–3	B–3	B–3	B–3	B–3	B–3
Increment of benefits	$280	$ 60	$ 70	$ 50	$170	$110	–$ 40	$ 70	$100	$110	$180	$240
Increment of costs	$ 96	$ 35	$ 81	$131	$151	$ 91	$ 50	$ 91	$176	$242	$332	$503
Incremental B/C ratio	2.92	1.71	0.86	0.38	1.13	1.21	Negative	0.77	0.57	0.45	0.54	0.48
Decision in favor of	A–2	A–3	A–3	A–3	B–2	B–3	B–3	B–3	B–3	B–3	B–3	B–3

creasing highway costs. Because each alternative first is to be compared to A–1, the highway costs shown are the annual costs in excess of the $60,000 maintenance cost for A–1; for example, the highway cost figure for A–2, shown as $156,000 in Table 12–5, is $96,000 in the third line of Table 12–6. The benefits shown in the second line of the table are the estimated reductions in annual road user costs below the $2,200,000 that will continue if A–1 is selected; thus the benefit figure of $280,000 shown for A–2 is found by subtracting $1,920,000 from $2,200,000.

The fourth line of Table 12–6 gives the **B/C** ratio for each alternative as compared to A–1. All except the $11,000,000 C–4 design show **B/C** ratios greater than unity.

However, it is necessary to compare the 12 designs with one another as well as with the continuation of the present condition. The relevant incremental **B/C** ratios for this comparison are developed in the final five lines of Table 12–6. Of course, a consideration of these benefit-cost ratios leads to the same conclusion as the annual cost comparison in Table 12–5; B–3 turns out to be the best of all the alternatives.

It is of interest to note the challengers and defenders in the incremental comparison. A–2 is successful in its challenge to A–1 with an incremental **B/C** ratio of 2.92. Then A–3 eliminates A–2 with an incremental **B/C** ratio of 1.71. Neither B–1 nor A–4 can sustain their challenges to A–3; their respective incremental ratios are 0.86 and 0.38. Then B–2 eliminates A–3 and is in turn eliminated by B–3. In all of the subsequent comparisons, B–3 remains the defender; no design that has higher highway costs than B–3 can justify them by an increase in benefits that is greater than the increase in highway costs.

Some Comments on the Use of Rates of Return and Benefit–Cost Ratios in Comparing Mutually Exclusive Multiple Alternatives. Even though the techniques of analysis were different, the reader will doubtless have observed a similarity between the types of reasoning used in Examples 12–5 and 12–6. In the rate of return analysis in Example 12–5 is was not enough to compare each plan with a do-nothing alternative; the plans also needed to be compared with one another. And in using the **B/C** ratios in Example 12–6, it was not enough to compare each design with a continuation of a present condition; the comparison of the designs with each other was also essential. The same general type of reasoning applied to choosing the appropriate challengers and defenders in the incremental comparisons. The temptations to incorrect reasoning were similar in the two examples.

The reader should recognize that the selection of a minimum attractive rate of return is of critical importance in analysis based on the benefit-cost ratio just as in the various other types of analysis. Problems 12–11 to 12–16 illustrate certain aspects of the importance of the chosen value of i^* in Example 12–6 as well as some other aspects of benefit–cost analysis not brought out in the example.

Consideration of Multiple Irreducibles in the Analysis of Multiple Alternatives. Even with only two alternatives to be compared, it often happens that certain irreducible data favor one alternative whereas other irreducibles favor the other alternative. (This was illustrated in the story at the end of Chapter 2 about the choice between two proposed total energy systems.) When there are many alternatives to be compared and when there are a number of irreducibles with different impacts on the different alternatives, the problem of giving suitable weight to irreducibles may be particularly troublesome.

If there are multiple alternatives and if irreducibles need to be given weight in the final choice, it is helpful to examine alternatives in pairs. It is much easier to reach a conclusion about the impact of a variety of irreducibles, some favorable to one alternative and some favorable to another, when the decision maker looks at only two alternatives at a time. In Example 12–5, which applied the rate-of-return method, and in Example 12–6, which applied the B/C ratio method, we illustrated the technique of considering multiple alternatives in pairs, always viewing one as a defender and another as a challenger. Whenever a number of irreducibles are present, a similar technique can be applied with any method of analysis of multiple alternatives.

A systematic procedure for organizing and using data regarding multiple irreducibles is discussed at the end of Chapter 19. This is in connection with the "community factor profile" developed by C. H. Oglesby, A. B. Bishop, and G. E. Willeke to help with the problem of comparing alternate locations for urban freeways.

The System Viewpoint in a Choice among Multiple Alternatives. In a choice among major alternatives, it is common for each alternative to have subalternatives, for each subalternative to have subsubalternatives, and so on. This point was stressed in the presentation of basic concepts in Chapters 1 and 2.

To reach sound decisions about the subalternatives, an analyst needs to recognize the interrelationships between the choices among subalternatives and the choices among major alternatives. Insofar as practicable, it is desirable to take a system viewpoint in making decisions about subalternatives.

Where a choice among major systems must be made, one difficulty may be the existence of too many possible alternatives for an economical and convenient analysis. Often a complex problem of making a choice among possible systems can be reduced to workable dimensions by first considering the component subsystems. An instance where this was done is described in Examples 12–7 and 12–8.

EXAMPLE 12–7. CONSIDERATION OF RELEVANT SUBSYSTEMS IN PLANNING AN ECONOMY STUDY FOR THE SELECTION OF A MATERIALS HANDLING SYSTEM.

Facts of the Case. One of the nation's largest independent drug distributors has 8 distribution centers covering a major part of the country. It is now planning to remodel one of its warehouses that serves a population center of about 10 million people in an area about 200 miles wide by 500 miles long.

Each distribution center carries about 30,000 items in stock from which it fills several thousand orders per day. Most of the orders involve less-than-case lots of 10 to 50 different items. About 2,000 items account for 50% of its volume and another 2,000 items account for the next 30% of its volume. The company maintains its own fleet of trucks on which it delivers all its orders within a radius of 50 miles (about 6 million people) on a daily basis. Daily shipments are made to more distant points by way of commercial carriers. About 80% of its volume is delivered by its own trucks.

The company has experimented with a number of different materials handling systems for filling orders and has warehouses in which the order selection is performed entirely by hand, others involving some mechanization, and one in which the most important 2,000 items are stored in a completely automatic, electronically controlled order-picking machine, with the other items being picked by hand and placed on a conveyor system for accumulating orders. The company is now trying to decide just what combination of methods to use in this installation.

The majority of the orders to this distribution center are telephoned in by the individual drugstores. A clerk types out a temporary invoice as she takes the order over the telephone. The items on the preliminary invoice must be picked from the stock in the warehouse and moved to the packing area. The items are checked against the invoice and any unfilled items are marked off. A final invoice in four copies is typed, with one copy serving as a shipping list, one as a receipt to be signed by the receiving clerk at the drugstore, one for the accounts receivable office for billing purposes, and the fourth for the inventory control section for use in maintaining stock levels.

It is important to visualize the interrelationships of the various activities. Prompt and complete shipments are essential for customer satisfaction. Errors, short shipments, and delays drive customers to competing distributors. Drugstores typically maintain only limited stocks of drug items and expect to be able to replace stock within 5 to 10 hours from local distributors.

This example deals primarily with the materials handling system, but it was found that the paperwork systems were so closely tied to the materials handling system that they must be considered simultaneously. Three major systems must be integrated: (1) the materials handling (receiving, storing, order picking, and packing); (2) customer paperwork (taking order, preparation of invoice and shipping list, and end-of-month billing); and (3) inventory control (maintaining perpetual inventory, determination of order points, and writing purchase orders).

Identification of the alternatives available can best be done for the different subsystems individually. The physical handling system can be subdivided into three subsystems:

    A. Receiving and storing
    B. Order picking and assembly
    C. Packing for shipment

Subsystem A. The products are always received in cases or in multi-case lots, and must be transported to the proper storage area in the warehouse and stacked in the shelves and bins. The alternative methods that appear feasible are:

A1. A completely manual system, using 4-wheeled shop trucks for transportation

A2. A pallet-fork truck system. Manually palletize at the dock. Small-volume items would require manual separation and stacking at point of storage.

A3. Under floor tow chain towing 4-wheeled trucks through the warehouse. Requires manual loading, unloading, and stacking.

A4. Powered belt or roller conveyors running from dock to storage area. Requires manual loading, unloading, and stacking

A5. Completely automatic conveyorized system, employing live storage of cases on gravity roller conveyors and electronic dispatching and control

Subsystem B. A typical order consisting of from 1 to 12 bottles, jars, tubes, small boxes, etc., of 10 to 25 items. Most of the items are relatively small. The order picking and assembly can be performed in a number of ways:

B1. Completely manual system, employing 4-wheeled shop trucks, with one person picking all the items for one order

B2. A belt conveyor system, nonautomatic, with manual picking and manual regulation of the placement of orders on the belt for transport to the packing tables

B3. Under floor tow chain with 4-wheeled shop trucks, performing in same way as conveyors in B2

B4. Overhead chain conveyor system with independent, dispatchable carriers, but with manual picking

B5. Completely automatic order picking of the large-volume items and any of the other alternatives for the low-volume items

Subsystem C. The packing function is basically a manual job, allowing only minor variations in the arrangement of the work places to accommodate the order-picking system selected. The packing operation should include the final accuracy check on the shipment and the initiation of the customer paperwork.

Subsystem D. The records system dealing with the customer can be operated in a number of different ways, with a wide choice of actual equipment under each general alternative:

D1. Completely manual system

D2. Basically manual, but including a duplicating process to eliminate the retyping of invoices in multiple copies

D3. Basically manual, but including semiautomatic accounting machine to prepare invoices, shipping lists, and monthly bills

D4. An automatic system involving electronic data processing equipment, punched cards, automatic printers, etc.

Subsystem E. The inventory control system must maintain a perpetual inventory for each item and see that an adequate supply is on hand at all times. Thus, it must not only have daily records of receipts and sales of each item, but must continuously analyze sales trends, market fluctuations, and prices in order to set the best purchasing policies. The available methods are similar to those dealing with the customer:

E1. Completely manual system

E2. Basically manual, but including some semiautomatic accounting machines to summarize daily sales and receipts, compute inventories, and compare balances with order points

E3. Fully automatic system, using electronic data processing equipment to perform the operations

The complete system in this warehouse must contain one of the alternatives from each of the five subsystems. With 5 alternatives each for subsystems A and B, 1 for C, 4 for D, and 3 for E, there are a total of 300 possible combinations from which the most economical should be chosen. It is theoretically possible to estimate the expenses involved and the effects on receipts of each of the 300 possible alternatives, but it is doubtful that attempting to do so would be worth the effort.

In the first place, many of the 300 combinations can be eliminated as impracticable. For example, it would obviously be foolish to install subsystem A3, the under floor tow chain, for handling incoming materials and then use subsystem B2, the belt conveyor, for order picking. This would involve two separate systems covering the same floor area, two large investments in equipment, and would increase the complications of layout, because the conveyor would permanently occupy space and interfere with the layout of the tow chain system. Similarly, the choice of subsystem D3, the use of semiautomatic accounting machines for processing customers' orders and invoices, would make system E1 a foolish choice, because a great deal of the information needed by inventory control would be readily available from subsystem D3 in a form that could best be handled by semiautomatic machines rather than by hand. Furthermore, the selection of a fully automatic order-picking system for the large-volume items, subsystem A5, would practically demand the use of either subsystem D3 or D4 and either E2 or E3, because the information to the order-picking machine would have to be in a form that the machine could understand and be available at speeds that could not be possible with manual insertion.

Consequently, the selection of the system for this remodeled distribution center can best be made by making up a set of combinations for the materials handling problem and another set for the paperwork. Each alternative combination for the materials handling should be chosen so that the two subsystems will be compatible and so that the specific information needs (restrictions imposed by the handling system on the information system) will be known. Then the alternative combinations for the information and paperwork systems should be selected to make most economical use of whatever equipment is involved in that combination. One or more combinations should be devised to meet the information needs of each handling alternative. Thus, suboptimization can be employed to simplify the problem. Equivalent annual costs can be computed for each alternative combination, and the best pair of alternatives can be selected.

Comments on Example 12–7. This example illustrates a number of important concepts that must be understood by the person undertaking a complex economy study. The systems viewpoint is important to this case. If an attempt had been made at the beginning to identify only those complete systems that would be feasible, it is unlikely that all the alternatives would have been recognized. By breaking the whole system into subsystems and examining each individually, the analyst helped assure that he would not overlook some important alternative. Furthermore, the analysis of the subsystems tends to bring the requirements of an acceptable whole system into proper focus.

The company had other distribution centers and many of the alternatives had been used in various forms. Cost data were available from the other centers, but the data could not be used in the existing form. Differences in such items as taxes, labor rates, insurance rates, and volumes to be handled among the different locations required adjustment of the cost data to suit the conditions at this location. None of the other distribution centers have a system that is considered to be ideal, and this remodeling presents another opportunity to try to develop the best possible system. Consequently, the new system should be a composite of many of the ideas from different plants in addition to some entirely new ideas. This is really a new problem and requires a complete analysis rather than dependence on past solutions. The final analysis of this problem is summarized in Example 12–8.

EXAMPLE 12–8. ECONOMY STUDY TO SELECT A MATERIALS HANDLING SYSTEM

Estimates and Analysis. After study of the many possible combinations of subsystems described in Example 12–7, eight different combinations were chosen for preliminary economic analysis. Three of these combinations were eliminated by this initial analysis and the following five combinations were selected for detailed analysis:

Combination 1 consists of manually operated 4-wheel shop trucks for both handling incoming shipments and order picking, along with a manual system for records keeping and inventory control. It includes a duplicating process for multiple copies.

Combination 2 consists of underfloor tow chain with 4-wheel shop trucks for both handling operations and semiautomatic accounting equipment for all records keeping and inventory control.

Combination 3 employs an underfloor tow chain with 4-wheel trucks for incoming materials, an overhead chain conveyor with independent dispatchable carriers for order picking, and an automatic electronic data processing system for records keeping and inventory control.

Combination 4 employs fork lift trucks for handling incoming materials, a completely automatic order-picking system for the 2,000 high volume items and manual picking for all other items, and an automatic electronic data processing system.

Combination 5 is the same as *combination 4* except that it has automatic order picking for 4,000 high volume items.

The monetary comparison is shown in Table 12–7 using a before-tax i^* of 15%. This is a case where the choice among the alternatives does not affect the estimated revenues of the enterprise.

TABLE 12–7
Cost Comparison of Alternative Materials Handling Systems for Wholesale Drug Distributor

Combination	1	2	3	4	5
A. Total first cost	$ 5,000	$ 22,320	$ 42,160	$200,000	$250,000
B. Estimated economic life, years	15	10	10	10	10
C. Estimated salvage value at end of economic life	0	$ 5,000	$ 7,000	$ 25,000	$ 30,000
D. Capital recovery factor, $i^* = 15\%$	0.17102	0.19925	0.19925	0.19925	0.19925
E. Equivalent annual cost of capital recovery	$ 855	$ 4,200	$ 8,060	$ 38,650	$ 48,400
F. Average annual labor cost	158,400	123,200	110,000	52,800	44,000
G. Average annual fuel and power costs	100	600	800	1,600	1,900
H. Average annual maintenance costs	900	1,500	1,800	3,600	4,500
I. Average annual taxes and insurance	150	670	1,265	6,000	7,500
J. Annual rental on data processing equipment ...	0	1,200	12,000	18,000	20,500
K. Total equivalent annual costs	$160,405	$131,370	$133,925	$120,650	$126,800

There are a number of irreducibles that need to be considered in the final decision. With combinations 3, 4, and 5 the invoices, bills, purchase orders, and reports will be available earlier than with a manual system. The combinations 4 and 5 will provide capacity to handle more orders per day with very little added expense, while all the other combinations can only be expanded by adding additional people (and increasing labor costs). The automatic systems will no doubt require a somewhat greater development and "debugging" period than the other systems. Also, a greater number of errors will probably be made in both order filling and billing during the initial period, but eventually the automatic systems should operate with fewer errors than the other combinations.

Table 12–7 reveals that combination 4 has the lowest prospective annual cost with a minimum attractive rate of return of 15% before income taxes. Combination 4 is only $6,150 better than combination 5, however, and consideration of such irreducibles as prospective increases in business, less dependence on labor, and the prospect of fewer errors might lead the management to select combination 5.

Summary. This chapter has dealt with certain aspects of economic analysis in comparisons of multiple alternatives, with special reference to cases where only one alternative can be chosen. The first part of the chapter illustrated and discussed the use of simple mathematical models to obtain an optimal solution in this type of problem. The second part of the chapter illustrated and discussed certain dangers of misinterpretation of an analysis of multiple alternatives whenever rates of return or benefit–cost ratios are calculated. The final part of the chapter illustrated a complex problem in which it was desirable to recognize a variety of subsystems before selecting the particular combinations to be compared in the detailed economy study.

PROBLEMS

12–1. A manufacturing company has been cited by the local air pollution authority for allowing too much smoke to issue from its chimney. Investigation shows that there is no chance to meet the authority's requirements by better control of combustion because part of the "smoke" is a form of dust inherent in the manufacturing process. It will be necessary to install a precipitator to remove the solids from the hot gases before they leave the chimney. The plant engineer has made the following estimates:

| | *Precipitators* | | | |
	A	B	C	D
First cost installed	$6,000	$7,600	$9,000	$10,300
Life (years)	10	10	10	10
Salvage value	$ 0	$ 0	$ 0	$ 0
Annual operating disbursements:				
Power and water	$1,280	$1,280	$1,000	$ 950
Cleaning	1,200	1,200	860	800
Maintenance	600	500	600	500
Labor extras	400	370	260	240
Property taxes and insurance	120	150	180	210
	$3,600	$3,500	$2,900	$ 2,700

Estimate the annual income tax differences using the simple assumptions illustrated in Chapter 10. Compare the economy of the four precipitators using an after-tax i^* of 8%. Which one would you recommend? (*Ans.* = Precipitator C.)

12–2. Prepare a table similar to Table 12–2 comparing the annual costs of wire sizes 00 to 3, both inclusive, assuming the investment in copper wire at 55 cents/lb., the price of electric energy at 2 cents/kw-hr, investment charges at 16.2%, for a current of 40 amperes flowing for 2,500 hours per year. Which size has the lowest annual cost? (*Ans.* = Size 3.)

12–3. In a certain manufacturing plant, schemes for cost-reducing machinery are judged on the basis of the "gross return," which is computed as the ratio of the annual saving in direct materials and labor to the investment. To justify the investment of funds in such projects, there must be a gross return of 30%. This 30% covers capital recovery (interest and depreciation), property taxes, insurance, and income taxes. Funds are available to finance any projects that meet this standard of attractiveness. On a certain operation, six alternative proposals for cost reduction are made. On the basis of the stated criterion, which one of these should be chosen? Why?

Proposal	Required Investment	Annual Saving in Direct Materials and Labor
A	$ 6,000	$1,500
B	8,000	2,500
C	12,000	4,100
D	13,000	4,200
E	18,000	6,000
F	25,000	7,600

(*Ans.* = Proposal E.)

12–4. Six alternative proposals have been made for the development of a commercial rental property. The land is available on option at a price of $500,000. The following estimates have been made for the six plans:

	Investment in Building	Annual Excess of Receipts Over All Disbursements Except Those for Income Taxes
Plan I	$ 400,000	$142,000
Plan II	700,000	258,000
Plan III	1,000,000	316,000
Plan IV	1,400,000	380,000
Plan V	1,800,000	442,000
Plan VI	2,500,000	532,000

The estimated life of the building is 50 years with zero terminal salvage value. For purposes of this analysis it is to be assumed that the land will be sold for its original cost at the end of a 50-year analysis period. Estimated annual disbursements for income taxes are to be based on the simplified assumptions illustrated in Chapter 10.

Prepare a table similar to Table 12–4 showing prospective rates of return on total investment and on successive increments of investment. If the stipulated after-tax i^* is 10%, which plan should be selected? (*Ans.* = Plan III.)

12–5. In a proposed flood control project, there are two possible sites, A and B, for a dam and storage reservoir. One or the other of these sites may be used but not both. Certain channel improvement is also considered; this will increase the capacity of the stream to carry flood discharge. Estimated first costs, lives, and annual operation and maintenance costs are as follows:

	Site A	Site B	Channel Improvement
First cost	$6,000,000	$8,000,000	$1,000,000
Life	75 years	75 years	25 years
Annual O & M	$100,000	$140,000	$230,000

Annual capital recovery costs are to be computed using an i^* of 5½%. Assume zero salvage values at the end of the estimated lives.

The average annual amount of damages due to floods are estimated under various possible plans of development, as follows:

No flood control works at all $1,200,000
Development at Site A alone 380,000
Development at Site B alone 260,000
Channel improvement alone 520,000
Site A plus channel improvement 200,000
Site B plus channel improvement 120,000

Compute a benefit-cost ratio for each of the five plans of development as compared to the alternative of having no flood control. Assume that the annual costs of a dam and reservoir plus channel improvement will be the sum of the costs of the dam and reservoir alone and channel improvement alone. Compute any incremental **B/C** ratios that you believe are relevant. Which plan of development, if any, would you recommend? Why? (*Ans.* = Development at Site A alone.)

12–6. (a) Use the economic lot size formula to determine the economic size of a manufacturing lot under the following conditions: Preparation cost is $10; variable outlay per piece is 20 cents; annual rental of storage space per finished piece is 0.5 cents; minimum attractive rate of return is 12%; annual demand (250 working days per year) is 10,000 pieces; machine output per working day is 500 pieces. (*Ans.* = 2,529.)

(b) Calculate a table similar to Table 12–3, using lots that are multiples of 1,000.

12–7. (a) Use the economic lot size formula to determine the economic size of a manufacturing lot under the following conditions: Preparation cost is $225; variable outlay per piece is 6 cents; annual rental of storage space per finished piece is 1.5 cents; minimum attractive rate of return is 12%; annual demand (250 working days per year) is 300,000 pieces; machine output per working day is 5,000 pieces. (*Ans.* = 69,100.)

(b) Calculate a table similar to Table 12–3, using lots that are multiples of 10,000.

12–8. A small machined part is used more or less uniformly throughout a 200-day working year in a certain plant. The preparation cost for each production run is $65, and the variable cost of each piece is 48 cents. The annual rent of storage space per finished part is 6 cents and the minimum attractive rate of return on investment in working capital is 20%. If 8,000 pieces are needed per year and the machine produces 96 pieces per day, how many pieces should be produced in each production run? Use the economic lot size formula.

Solve the same problem by calculating a table similar to Table 12–3, starting with 2,000 pieces per lot and increasing the lot size by 500 each time until the minimum cost point is found.

12–9. Approximately 400 complicated castings are used per year of 200 days. The setup to machine the castings costs $300 and the rent on storage space per year is $4 per casting. The variable outlay per casting is $80, and 4 can be machined per day. The minimum attractive rate of return is 20%.

Determine the economic lot size for this casting both by the formula and by the tabular method illustrated in Table 12–3.

12–10. Determine the economic size of a manufacturing lot under the following conditions: Preparation cost is $50; variable outlay per piece is 40 cents; annual rental of storage space per piece is 2 cents; minimum attractive rate of return is 15%; annual demand (250 working days per year) is 10,000 pieces; machine output per working day is 400 pieces.

How would a change in the use rate to 20,000 pieces per year affect the economic lot size?

12–11. Using the data of Example 12–6, compute the excess of annual road user benefits over annual highway costs for each of the 13 plans. Which alternative gives the largest excess of benefits over costs? Use your figures as a basis for discussing the relationship between methods of analysis that aim to maximize $(B - C)$ and the methods of analysis that were illustrated in Tables 12–5 and 12–6.

12–12. Assume that the only alternatives in Example 12–6 are A–1, A–3, B–2, B–3, B–4, C–3, and C–4. Find the prospective rate of return for the final 6 of these 7 alternatives as compared to A–1, the continuation of the present condition. Find any rates of return on increments of investment that you consider relevant in relation to a stipulated i^* of 7%. Which alternative is favored by a comparison based on rates of return using this i^*? Use your figures as a basis for discussing the relationship between methods of analysis based on computing rates of return and incremental rates of return and the methods of anlysis that were illustrated in Tables 12–5 and 12–6.

12–13. Assume that in Example 12–6 the stipulated i^* is 3½%. Prepare an annual cost comparison similar to the one shown in Table 12–5. Which alternative is now favored?

12–14. Assume that in Example 12–6 the stipulated i^* is 3½%. Prepare a table similar to Table 12–6 showing B/C ratios as compared to continuing a present condition and showing relevant incremental B/C ratios. (Note that the change in i^* may change the order of listing the alternatives as well as changing the appropriate challengers and defenders in the incremental comparison.) Which alternative is now favored?

12–15. Solve Problem 12–14 using an i^* of 0%. (A questionnaire by a Highway Research Board committee in the mid-1960's disclosed that approximately one-third of the state highway agencies in the United States were, in effect, still using an i^* of 0% in economy studies of this type.)

12–16. Solve Problem 12–14 using an i^* of 20%. (A computerized study in one state that was described in a Highway Research Board paper in the mid-1960's indicated that, considering the various proposals for highway improvement in the state and the limitation of available funds, the acceptance of any project that had a prospective rate of return of less than 20% would cause the rejection or deferment of some other proposal that had a prospective rate of return of more than 20%.)

12–17. The subscription rates to a certain weekly publication are $12 for 1 year, $18 for 2 years, $23 for 3 years, and $30 for 5 years, payable in advance in all cases. What is the rate of return on the extra investment in a 2-year subscription as compared to two 1-year subscriptions? On the extra investment in a 3-year subscription as compared to three 1-year subscriptions? On the extra investment in a 5-year subscription as compared to five 1-year subscriptions? Discuss the significance of these rates of return as a guide to a decision on the length of the subscription period. Compute any other rates of return that might reasonably be considered by someone who expects to continue to subscribe for many years and who wishes to choose among these four available subscription periods. What irreducibles or other matters do you think might reasonably influence such a subscriber's decision on his subscription period?

12–18. In a proposed flood control project, there are two possible sites for a dam and storage reservoir, designated as the Willow and Cottonwood sites. One or the other of these sites may be used but not both. A small hydroelectric power development may be added at the Willow site. Certain channel improvements are also considered. Seven alternate projects are set up for analysis and average annual damages due to floods under each plan estimated as follows:

Plan		Damages
A	Willow dam and reservoir alone	$110,000
B	Willow dam, reservoir, and power plant	130,000
C	Willow dam and reservoir, with channel improvement	40,000
D	Willow dam, reservoir, and power plant with channel improvement	60,000
E	Cottonwood dam and reservoir alone	180,000
F	Cottonwood dam and reservoir, with channel improvement	90,000
G	Channel improvement alone	330,000

With no flood control works at all, the average annual amount of flood damages is estimated as $680,000.

The estimated first cost of the Willow dam and reservoir is $5,000,000. The power plant will increase this first cost by $1,000,000. The estimated first cost of the Cottonwood dam and reservoir is $3,000,000. The estimated first cost of the channel improvement is $800,000. In the economic analysis a 100-year life with zero salvage value is to be used for the two dams and reservoirs, a 50-year life with zero salvage value is to be used for the power plant, and a 20-year life with $300,000 salvage value is to be used for the channel improvement. All equivalence calculations are to use an i^* of 5%.

On the basis of the cost of equal power from a steam electric plant, the "benefits" from the hydroelectric power are estimated to be $70,000 a year. Annual operation and maintenance costs will be:

Willow dam and reservoir	$60,000
Power plant	25,000
Cottonwood dam and reservoir	50,000
Channel improvement	70,000

Compute a benefit-cost ratio for each of the seven plans of development. Make any other calculations that you think are desirable to aid a choice among the different plans. Do you recommend that one of these plans be adopted? If so, which one? Why?

12–19. The XYZ Manufacturing Co. has funds available for investment in machinery and tools to reduce direct manufacturing costs. All proposals for such investment are judged on the basis of "gross return." It has been decided that no avoidable investment is to be considered attractive that does not show a gross return of 25%. This is intended to cover capital recovery at the company's i^* over a stipulated service period plus property taxes, income taxes, and insurance.

A group of engineers has analyzed six different mutually exclusive proposals for investment in machinery and tooling to reduce costs on a certain operation. They have prepared the following table to provide a basis for comparing these proposals:

Proposal	Investment	Annual Saving in Direct Mfg. Costs	Gross Return on Inv.	Extra Inv.	Extra Annual Saving	Gross Return on Extra Inv.
A	$ 2,000	$ 200	10.0%			
B	8,000	2,320	29.0%	$ 6,000	$2,120	35.3%
C	16,000	4,800	30.0%	8,000	2,480	31.0%
D	18,000	5,340	29.6%	2,000	540	27.0%
E	24,000	5,760	24.0%	6,000	420	7.0%
F	40,000	10,240	25.6%	16,000	4,480	28.0%

At this point the engineers disagree on the question of which of these proposals is to be recommended to the management. Smith prefers C on the grounds that it has the greatest gross return on total investment. Jones chooses B because it has the greatest gross return on the extra investment. Johnson is inclined toward F as representing the maximum investment on which both the gross return on total investment and the gross return on the extra investment are over 25%.

Which of these six proposals would you recommend? Explain why.

12–20. Assume that the installed prices and the resistances of various sizes of single-core, low-tension, lead-sheathed electrical cable are as follows:

Size	Resistance in Ohms per 1,000 Ft.	Installed Price per 1,000 Ft.
0	0.0983	$ 970
00	0.0779	1,090
000	0.0618	1,200
0000	0.0490	1,390
250,000 circ. mils	0.0416	1,590

The cost of electric energy to a certain user of this cable is 1.35 cents per kw-hr. Annual costs of capital recovery of the investment are to be based on an after-tax $i°$ of 7% and a 25-year life with zero net terminal salvage value. Annual income tax differences are to be computed using the simple assumptions illustrated in Chapter 10. Annual disbursements for property taxes will be 1.1% of installed cost. Make the necessary calculations to find the most economical section to transmit 200 amperes 2,200 hours per year. Assume that the only relevant costs are capital costs (including property taxes and extra income taxes) and costs of lost energy.

12–21. Five alternative proposals have been made for the development of a commercial rental property. The required land is available on option at a price of $100,000. The following estimates have been made for the plans:

	Investment in Building	Annual Receipts	Annual Disbursements (Not Including Income Taxes)
Plan A	$ 80,000	$ 38,900	$14,700
Plan B	160,000	65,800	24,200
Plan C	260,000	96,300	33,800
Plan D	364,000	117,800	41,900
Plan E	520,000	145,200	55,000

The estimated life of the building is 40 years with zero terminal salvage value. For purposes of this analysis it is to be assumed that this land will be sold for its original cost of $100,000 at the end of a 40-year analysis period. Estimated annual disbursements for income taxes are to be based on the simplified assumptions illustrated in Chapter 10.

Prepare a table similar to Table 12–4 showing prospective rates of return on total investment and on successive increments of investment. If the stipulated after-tax i^* is 8%, which plan should be selected?

12–22. Many valves are required in a certain pipe line that carries a corrosive chemical. In the past, cast iron valves have always been used and have required replacement every 2 years. Now valves of two corrosion-resistant alloys, A and B, are available. Estimates of installed first costs, lives, and salvage values for these three types of valve are as follows:

	Cast Iron	Alloy A	Alloy B
First cost	$2,000	$4,000	$6,000
Life	2 years	5 years	10 years
Salvage value	zero	$1,000	zero

The only differences in annual disbursements for the three types of valve are in disbursements for income taxes. For purposes of this analysis use the simplified assumptions illustrated in Chapter 10 to estimate the income tax differences.

(a) At what value of i will the after-tax cost of 10 years of service with the cast iron valve have exactly the same present worth as the after-tax cost of 10 years of service with valves of Alloy A? Assume that replacement costs will be the same as original costs.

(b) At what value of i will the after-tax cost of 10 years of service with the cast iron valve have exactly the same present worth as the after-tax cost of 10 years of service with valves of Alloy B? Assume that replacement costs will be the same as original costs.

(c) At what value of i will the after-tax costs of 10 years of service with Alloy A valves have exactly the same present worth as the after-tax cost of 10 years of service with valves of Alloy B? Assume that replacement costs will be the same as original costs.

(d) If the stipulated after-tax i^* is 8%, which type of valve do you recommend? Would your answer be changed if the stipulated after-tax i^* should be 12%? Explain your reasoning.

12–23. In a certain manufacturing company, decisions regarding approval of proposals for plant investment are based on a stipulated minimum attractive rate of return of 20% before income taxes. The mechanization of a certain costly hand operation has been proposed. Machines from six different manufacturers are under consideration. The estimated investment for each proposal and the estimated reduction in annual disbursements are given below. Approximate rates of return before income taxes on total investment and on each increment of investment are also given. These rates of return have all been computed assuming a 10-year life and zero salvage value for each machine.

Which one, if any, of these six mutually exclusive proposals should be accepted? Explain the reasons for your answer and show any additional calculations that are necessary to support your answer.

Machine	Investment	Reduction in Annual Disburse-ments	Rate of Return on Total Investment	Rate of Return on Increment of Investment
Onondaga	$30,000	$11,000	34.8%	
Oneida	50,000	14,100	25.2%	8.9%
Cayuga	55,000	16,300	26.9%	42.7%
Tuscarora	60,000	16,800	25.0%	0.0%
Seneca	70,000	19,200	24.3%	20.2%
Mohawk	75,000	21,100	25.1%	36.3%

12–24. A warehouse and terminal company is planning to build a subzero storage warehouse for frozen foods. The refrigeration engineer, employed by the architect, made a study of four different types of insulation that might be used and the effects on the cost of refrigeration equipment and operating costs to determine the most economical plan. The more money that is spent on insulation material in the walls and roof, the less money that must be spent on refrigerating equipment and power. The engineer's estimates are as follows:

Plan	A	B	C	D
First cost of insulation material	$25,000	$35,000	$50,000	$70,000
First cost of compressors	22,000	17,000	14,000	12,000
First cost of refrigerant piping and coils	20,000	18,000	14,000	10,000
Annual power cost	5,600	4,200	3,200	2,600

The insulation materials are estimated to have a 20-year life with no terminal salvage value. The compressors, piping, and coils are estimated to have a 10-year life with no terminal salvage value. Property taxes plus insurance will require annual disbursements of 2% of first cost. The extra annual income taxes for B, C, and D above those for A are to be computed using the simplified assumptions illustrated in Chapter 10. The stipulated after-tax i^* is 12%.

(a) Compare the after-tax equivalent uniform annual costs for the four alternatives.

(b) Analyze the choice among the alternatives by computing rates of return on increments of investment in B, C, and D as compared to A, as well as any other rates of return on increments of investment that you believe are required to guide a decision. Explain which plan you favor and why you have chosen it.

12–25. A chain of grocery stores operates its own meat cutting and packaging center to supply precut packaged meats to its various retail stores. One of the cutting and packaging operations is that of cold cuts, cheeses, and other sliced products. The items such as cheese, bologna, salami, etc., are purchased in large quantities, sliced on semi-automatic machines, assembled into units of approximately one pound or one-half pound, placed between two sheets of plastic film by girls, and then heat sealed in a special vacuum sealing machine. The manual operation of tearing off two sheets of plastic film from a roll and arranging the slices (unit) between them for the heat-vacuum sealer is performed by 7 girls, each earning $3,500 a year (including fringe benefits).

The company's industrial engineers have been studying this task and have found that the process of tearing off the sheets of plastic film is the real time consumer. They have proposed two possible improvements. The first is to design and build an automatic film cutter that will, at the press of a button, cut off two sheets in such a way that the girl can place the product on one sheet and, grasping the second sheet with the other hand, place it over the product. The second method involves a completely automatic wrapping machine. The estimates of the various cost factors are as follows:

	5 Sheet Cutters	Automatic Wrapping
First cost, installed	$5,000	$32,000
Estimated life	5 years	10 years
Terminal salvage value	zero	$2,000
Required operators	5 @ $3,500	2 @ $4,000
Saving per year in plastic film	$500	$800
Annual cost of electric energy	$100	$250
Repairs, maintenance, and property taxes ..	$150	$400

If the company requires an after-tax i^* of 10%, should either of the proposed changes be made? If so, which one? Explain your analysis. In estimating additional income taxes as compared to a continuation of the present condition, use the simplified assumptions illustrated in Chapter 10.

12–26. Line G of Table 12–4 gives the after-tax annual net positive cash flow for each of the ten plans. For each plan, subtract from the figure given in line G the sum of 8% of the land investment and the annual capital recovery cost of the building investment in 40 years with an i^* of 8%. Which plan gives the highest value of the figure obtained from this subtraction? Could this type of calculation be used to guide a choice among the ten plans? Discuss the relationship between this type of analysis and the rate of return analysis given in Example 12–5.

12–27. Solve Problem 12–4 using an after-tax i^* of 8%.

12–28. Solve Problem 12–5 using an i^* of 3½%.

13

Sensitivity Analysis in
Economy Studies

What's to come is still unsure.—SHAKESPEARE

The examples and problems in the preceding chapters have involved choosing among alternatives with a single set of forecasts given. Presumably in each case the stated forecasts represent someone's best judgment on the way in which future receipts and disbursements and other matters will be influenced by the choice among the stated alternatives.

There is always uncertainty about the future; it will rarely if ever turn out that events occur exactly as forecast. This uncertainty in itself is not a reason why we should not make the best forecasts that we can and then be governed by our analysis of these forecasts. Nevertheless, a decision among alternatives often can be made more sensibly if we can see whether the conclusion of our economy study is sensitive to moderate changes in certain forecasts.

The Concept of Sensitivity. All of the examples and problems of the previous chapters have involved estimates of such cost elements as fuel, power, labor, taxes, repairs, maintenance, and insurance, and some have involved estimates of revenue, salvage value, life, and other factors affecting the economic analysis of the particular proposal. Recommendations for or against a proposal were the result of the economy studies making use of those estimates or forecasts, and possibly some irreducible factors. It is obvious that if the estimates in some of the examples had been different, the decisions would also have been different. In some examples, however, it would have been possible to alter one of the elements quite radically without changing the decision resulting from the economy study.

Sensitivity refers to the relative magnitude of the change in one or more elements of an engineering economy problem that will reverse a decision among alternatives. Thus, if one particular element can be varied over a wide range of values without affecting the decision, the

251

decision under consideration is said not to be sensitive to uncertainties regarding that particular element. On the other hand, if a small change in the estimate of one element will alter the decision, the decision is said to be very sensitive to changes in the estimates of that element.

Since all estimates are subject to some amount of uncertainty, the sensitivity approach may be very helpful in analyzing a proposal or set of proposals. The application of the sensitivity concept becomes an intermediate step between the numerical analysis based on the best estimates for the various elements and the final decision. Each element can be tested to see how sensitive the decision is to variations from the best estimate, and the results used in the final decision-making process. Several examples will be given in this chapter to illustrate how the sensitivity concept can be applied.

The Concept of the Break-Even Point. Often we have a choice between two alternatives where one of them may be more economical under one set of conditions and the other may be more economical under another set of conditions. By altering the value of some one of the variables in the situation, holding all of the other points of difference between the two alternatives constant, it is possible to find a value for the variable that makes the two alternatives equally economical. This value may be described as the break-even point.

It frequently happens that a knowledge of the approximate value of the break-even point for some variable of design in the comparison of two alternatives is a considerable help in preliminary engineering studies and designs.

The term "break-even point" is also used in management literature to describe the percentage of capacity operation of a manufacturing plant at which income will just cover expenses.

The literature of engineering economy contains many formulas to determine break-even points, although such formulas are not necessarily described by this name.

Break-even-point formulas deal with such matters as the investment justified by a prospective cost saving, annual hours of operation necessary before a proposed extra investment is profitable, the period of time in which a proposed investment will "pay for itself" (i.e., the life to break even). In general, although such formulas may appear to be complicated, the only mathematics involved in their preparation is elementary algebra. The formulas are merely expressions of cost situations in symbols rather than in figures; the apparent complexity is the result of a large number of symbols.

Break-even formulas do not really save much time as compared to direct calculations for the break-even point. Moreover, the mistake is often made of using such formulas as substitutes for direct comparisons of the costs of specific alternatives under specific circumstances. When they are so used—a choice between alternatives being based on the relation between a calculated break-even point and the hours per year (or life or investment or whatever the break-even point has been calculated for) actually expected—the estimator is less apt to give intelligent weight to irreducibles than if he had made a direct comparison of alternative costs. Just as in the minimum-cost-point situations described in Chapter 12, the use of the formulas as a time saver may be at the sacrifice of desirable information. Where a choice is to be made between specific alternatives, a direct comparison of the expected costs for each is likely to be more illuminating than any break-even-point calculation.

The break-even-point calculation may be particularly useful in the situation where a decision is very sensitive to a certain variable. If the break-even point for that variable can be calculated, it may be possible to estimate on which side of the break-even point the operations may fall even though there may be considerable uncertainty regarding the exact value of the variable. Even in this use, however, it is desirable to investigate the range of values of the variable that would permit that alternative to be attractive, and to estimate the consequences of its occurring outside that range.

The Influence on Economy of the Amount of Utilization of Fixed Assets. Subject to certain exceptions,[1] the annual cost of capital recovery with a return is independent of the amount of utilization of fixed assets. So also are the other investment charges of taxes and insurance. Many other current disbursements may be practically independent of the amount of utilization. Examples are space charges and attendance costs on some machines and maintenance costs on some structures. Moreover, machinery is often considerably less efficient operating at fractional load than at full load; energy costs per unit of output will therefore be less at full load than at partial load.

Hence, in the majority of cases, the greater the utilization of fixed assets, the less the unit cost of product or service. As a result, the attractiveness of many proposed investments in machines and structures de-

---

[1] In some cases accelerated use of machinery—for example, on three shifts rather than on one—will increase maintenance costs to the point where replacements will be economical sooner than would otherwise be the case. Thus, economic life will be shortened by increased utilization. But the important economic factors causing most retirements (such as improved alternatives and changes in service requirements) are likely to be independent of the amount of utilization of machines and structures. Therefore it is reasonable in most instances to consider the capital recovery period to be independent of the amount of operation—at least within a fairly wide range.

pends on the prospective amount of utilization. The variation of the unit costs with the amount of utilization is illustrated in Example 13–1. This example, with Figure 13–1, also illustrates the use of the break-even concept in analyzing the prospective differences among several alternatives.

EXAMPLE 13–1. EFFECTS OF HOURS OF OPERATION ON THE CHOICE OF A LIGHTING SYSTEM

Statement of Alternatives. A company is planning the construction of service and repair shops of a standardized design to be constructed at a number of different locations. The following estimates are made for three types of electric lighting systems any one of which will provide the desired level of illumination:

	Incandescent	Fluorescent Type I	Fluorescent Type II
First cost installed (including lamps)	$150	$1,200	$1,400
Number of fixtures required	25	40	15
Number of lamps per fixture	1	2	4
Cost per lamp	$1.25	$1.75	$3.50
Rated life of lamps in hours	1,000	4,000	5,000
Watts per fixture	500	90	200

The investment in wiring is determined by other considerations and in this case will be independent of the type of fixture selected. The unit cost of labor for each lamp replacement is estimated as 20 cents, regardless of the type. Electric energy is estimated to cost 2.6 cents per kw-hr. Capital recovery on the original investment is desired in 10 years with a minimum attractive rate of return before income taxes of 15%. Insurance and property taxes are estimated at 2.5% of the first cost.

Differences in the climatic conditions of the several locations indicate that lighting needs will vary considerably in daylight hours, and also the volume of business will vary with the locations. Some locations may consistently require two or three-shift operation while some may require only one shift. The amount of utilization of the lighting system will obviously affect the annual cost of providing the required illumination.

Table 13–1 compares the equivalent annual cost of the three systems at 1,000 and at 4,000 hours per year. The annual investment costs are independent of the amount of utilization of the systems. These costs are fixed by the decision to select one of the systems. On the other hand, both the lamp replacement costs and the power costs vary directly with the amount of utilization. Figure 13–1 shows graphically the comparison of the equivalent annual costs of the three systems as the number of hours of utilization increases. The cost curves for the incandescent and the Type I fluorescent systems intersect at approximately 1,000 hours. This is the break-even point between the two systems. If the prospect is that the average utilization will be more than 1,000 hours per year, the Type I fluorescent system should be chosen over the incandescent system. The break-even point between the two types of fluorescent systems occurs at approximately 5,000 hours. Similarly, if the prospect is that the average annual utilization will be greater than 5,000 hours, the Type II fluorescent system should be chosen over Type I. It

TABLE 13–1

Comparison of Annual Costs for Three Lighting Systems

	1,000 Hours per Year			4,000 Hours per Year		
	Incand.	Fluor. Type I	Fluor. Type II	Incand.	Fluor. Type I	Fluor. Type II
Annual investment charges	$ 33.26	$266.10	$310.45	$ 33.26	$266.10	$310.45
Lamp replacement	36.25	39.00	44.40	145.00	156.00	177.60
Annual power cost	325.00	93.60	78.00	1,300.00	374.40	312.00
Equivalent annual cost	$394.51	$398.70	$432.85	$1,478.26	$796.50	$800.05

should be noted that difference in equivalent annual cost of the two fluorescent systems is very small, and irreducibles might easily alter the decision.

Comments on Example 13–1. This example provides a good illustration of several important points. The first point to be emphasized is that the estimate of the amount of utilization is the key factor in making the decision. It is assumed that the other factors (such as installed cost, lamp costs, and power costs) can be estimated with considerable confidence that the estimates will be reasonably accurate. The amount of utilization, however, will vary with the number of cloudy days, weather, and the amount of business for the service and repair shops. Variations in the economic conditions in the various localities are more likely to affect the volume of business than to affect the price of power or lamps.

The break-even charts in Figure 13–1 show that between 1,000 and 5,000 hours of operation the Type I fluorescent system is more economical than either of the others. They also show that there is a large difference between the incandescent lights and the Type I fluorescent at all levels of utilization, while there is a relatively small difference between the two types of fluorescent systems. This information makes it somewhat easier to make a decision because the probable minimum utilization can be estimated with reasonable confidence. For example, if a shop is expected to work on a single shift basis during daylight hours and the average number of cloudy days per year (obtained from weather bureau records) is 125, then 1,000 hours per year (8 × 125) can be expected. The prospect of increasing business to the point of adding overtime work or a second shift would tend to indicate that the Type I is preferable to the incandescent system.

Similarly, if the shop were to operate 5 days a week on a three-shift basis, there would be about 250 working days per year (excluding holidays). Lights could be assumed necessary on the second and third shifts and on the 125 cloudy days for day shifts. The maximum number of hours per year would probably not exceed $250(8)(2) + 125(8) = 5,000$. Thus the chance of needing more than 5,000 hours per year is rather small. The possible range of utilization has now been reasonably well established as between 1,000 and 5,000 hours, and the decision is obvious. Type I fluorescent lighting should be selected.

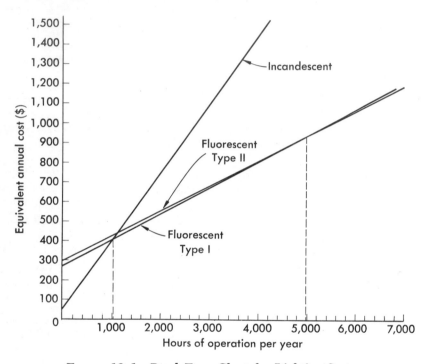

FIGURE 13–1. Break-Even Chart for Lighting Systems

This design problem might also be used to illustrate the sensitivity of a decision to several aspects of the original estimates. For instance, how sensitive is the decision to changes in such matters as price of lamps or price of energy?

EXAMPLE 13–2. SENSITIVITY OF DECISION IN EXAMPLE 13–1 TO CHANGES IN PRICE OF ELECTRIC ENERGY

Facts of the Case. The present electric power rates are such that it is believed that 2.6 cents per kw-hr is a fair price to use in making the decision as to which lighting system to select for the standardized service and repair shops. However, it is believed that there is some possibility of changes in rate structures so that the price in a few years will be reduced. How sensitive is the problem to changes in the cost of energy per kw-hr? One way to determine the sensitivity is to compute the break-even points between the Type I fluorescent system and the incandescent system at various rates.

The break-even points can be computed directly. Let x equal the number of hours of utilization per year at which the equivalent annual cost of the incandescent will equal the equivalent annual cost of the fluorescent system. At 2.6 cents per kw-hr, the equation is:

$$\$150[(A/P,15\%,10) + 0.025] + \frac{(\$0.026)(500)(25)x}{1,000} + \frac{(\$1.45)(25)x}{1,000}$$

$$= \$1,200[(A/P,15\%,10) + 0.025] + \frac{(\$0.026)(90)(40)x}{1,000} + \frac{(\$1.95)(80)x}{4,000}$$

Substituting the value of the capital recovery factor into the equation and solving for x, we find that the break-even point is 1,018 hours per year. This corresponds with the value found in Figure 13–1. Repeating this operation for successively smaller prices for electric energy gives the break-even points shown in Table 13–2. It will be noted that the decision is not very sensitive to the price of energy in this case.

If the same comparison is made between the two types of fluorescent systems, only one calculation is necessary to find that the break-even point increases and that we are not interested in considering a choice between Types I and II if a prospective reduction in the price of energy will make it more difficult to justify the selection of Type II. The break-even point at 1.8 cents per kw-hr is 8,212 hours per year.

TABLE 13–2

Break-Even Points for Incandescent and Type I Fluorescent Lighting Systems at Different Prices of Energy

	Price of Energy (Cents per Kw-Hr)				
	2.6	2.4	2.2	2.0	1.8
Break-even points (hours of utilization per year)	1,018	1,084	1,206	1,328	1,479

Sensitivity of Decisions to Estimates About Cash Flow in the More Distant Future. For an after-tax i^* of 10%, a dollar of estimated cash flow 25 years away has a present worth of only a little over nine cents; a dollar 50 years away has a present worth of less than one cent. In general, the higher the stipulated minimum attractive rate of return, the less likely it is that the conclusions of an analysis will be changed by a moderate change in an estimate of cash flow in the more distant future. Because good estimates for the distant future are harder to make than good estimates for the near future, it is fortunate that it is often true that *decisions* will be insensitive to substantial changes in the distant estimates.

Lack of sensitivity to distant estimates is illustrated in Example 13–3 and in a number of problems at the end of this chapter.

EXAMPLE 13–3. EFFECT OF MODIFYING CERTAIN DISTANT ESTIMATES IN EXAMPLE 6–3

Data of Example 6–3. Our first example of a comparison of alternatives with different lives was Example 6–3, in which the estimates were as follows:

	Plan D	Plan E
First cost	$50,000	$120,000
Life	20 years	40 years
Salvage value	$10,000	$20,000
Annual O & M disbursements	$9,000	$6,000
Extra annual income tax disbursements		$1,250

Using an after-tax i^* of 8%, equivalent uniform annual costs were calculated (on page 77) as $13,874 for Plan D and $17,236 for Plan E. On the assumption that the 20-year structure in Plan D would be replaced by one that had the same first cost, salvage value, and annual disbursements as the initial structure, the present worths of the net disbursements for 40 years were computed (on page 93) to be $165,440 for Plan D and $205,540 for Plan E. On the same assumption, the prospective after-tax rate of return on the extra investment in Plan E was computed (on page 121) to be approximately 2.7%.

Effect of Change in Estimated Life or Estimated Salvage Value for Plan E. There is *no* estimated life for Plan E that will give this plan annual costs below the $13,874 computed for Plan D. The annual capital recovery cost for Plan E was $9,986 with a 40-year estimated life, a $20,000 salvage value, and an i^* of 8%. If an infinite life should be assumed, this cost would be $9,600 (i.e., 8% of $120,000), a reduction of only $386. Moreover, with *any* assumed life and the estimated salvage value increased to $120,000 (rather than the original figure of $20,000), the capital recovery cost would still be $9,600.

Incidentally, the extra annual income taxes for Plan E were stated as $1,250. This difference was obtained using the simplified assumptions described and illustrated in Chapter 10, namely, a 50% tax rate and straight-line depreciation used for tax purposes with the same lives and salvage values used in the economy study. With this assumption, a change of salvage value from $20,000 to $120,000 would eliminate a $2,500 annual tax deduction for Plan E and therefore increase the extra income taxes with Plan E from $1,250 to $2,500. Therefore an after-tax comparison assuming a $120,000 salvage value in Plan E would be even more unfavorable to that plan than the original comparison in Example 6–3 where only a $20,000 salvage value was assumed. (Our simplified assumptions about income taxes are not necessarily the best ones to make in all cases.)

Effect of Change in Estimated Disbursement for Replacement of Plan D at the End of 20 Years. The comparison in Chapter 7 of the present worths of 40 years of service assumed that a $40,000 net disbursement would be made at the end of 20 years to replace Plan D's initial structure. This figure was based on the assumption that the second 20-year structure, like the first one, would require an initial total outlay of $50,000, and that the net outlay would be $10,000 less than $50,000 because of the receipt from salvage of the first structure.

Assume that a 40-year service is expected and that it is desired to minimize the present worth of the estimated net disbursements during the 40-year period. For the stipulated i^* of 8%, the single payment present worth factor for 20 years is 0.2145. With our arbitrary conventional assumption that costs for the second structure in Plan D would be the same as those for the first structure, Plan D had approximately $40,000 lower net present worth of disbursements than Plan E. It therefore is evident that a fairly large increase in the estimated disbursement for Plan D at date 20 would not change the conclusions of the economy study. In this particular case, the *decision* between the two plans is relatively insensitive to the estimated replacement cost at date 20.

A change in the estimated first cost of the second 20-year structure in Plan D will also have income tax consequences. Nevertheless, any estimated income tax differences from years 21 to 40 will have relatively low present worths. Certain income tax aspects of this matter are illustrated in Problem 13–5.

Prospective Rate of Return on Extra Investment Viewed as a Break-Even Point. Example 6–3 was one of a number of examples in this book in which alternatives were compared by equivalent uniform annual costs and by present worths, both at a stipulated i^*, and then compared by rate of return on extra investment. In this particular case, the analysis indicated that the extra $70,000 investment required for Plan E would yield an after-tax rate of return of about 2.7%.

It was brought out in Chapter 11 that the choice of a value of i^* is not necessarily a simple straightforward matter subject to no legitimate differences of opinion. Any calculation of an unknown rate of return may be viewed as a special case of sensitivity testing. Where two alternatives are being compared at a stipulated i^*, and where the monetary calculation (by equivalent uniform annual cost or by net present worth) favors one of them and the irreducibles favor the other, a rate of return calculation may be a great help to the decision maker.

For instance, in Example 6–3 asume that certain irreducibles favored Plan E. These irreducibles would need to carry very great weight to justify an avoidable $70,000 investment that promised only a 2.7% return in an enterprise in which the normal expectation was at least 8%. On the other hand, if the prospective rate of return on the extra investment had been, say, 6% or 7%, the irreducibles might well be sufficient to tip the balance in favor of Plan E.

Using Estimated Residual Values in Place of Estimated Terminal Salvage Values in Certain Economy Studies. In Example 9–1, two alternate possible new locations for a rural highway, designated as J and K, were compared with the resurfacing of the present location, designated as H. The study period (sometimes also called the *analysis period*) was chosen as 20 years. In a highway economy study, the study period may be the longest period for which it seems reasonable to estimate traffic volumes and related road user costs. The useful lives of the proposed highway facilities at either J or K were expected to be longer than 20 years. It therefore was necessary to estimate residual values as of date 20 at both J and K and to use these residual values in the economy study in computing the capital costs at these two locations.

Whenever a study period is chosen that will end before the end of the expected useful lives of all the proposed assets that are being compared, it is necessary to estimate some residual values rather than final salvage values. In principle, such residual values should be what the assets are expected to be worth to their owners for continued use beyond the end of the study period. In practice, often the best that an analyst can do is to make fairly arbitrary estimates, appreciably below first costs and appreciably above estimated terminal salvage values. The use of such arbitrary estimates may be defended on the grounds that the conclusions of the economy study are relatively insensitive to substantial changes in the estimated residual values. This is a valid defense provided the study period is long enough and i^* is large enough. Problem 13–3 illustrates a sensitivity study dealing with the estimated residual values in Example 9–1.

Because Example 9–1 was a comparison of public works alternatives, it did not involve income taxes. We shall not be in a position to illustrate the use of residual values in after-tax studies until we take a more sophisticated look at income tax matters in Chapter 16. Our simplified assumptions about income taxes that were explained in Chapter 10 required the same lives and salvage values in computing tax depreciation that the analyst used in his economy study. These assumptions are not valid in economy studies that use estimated residual values.

Some Representative Indexes of Price Changes. Sensitivity analysis may be useful when an economy study is to give consideration to possible future price changes. There are two quite different aspects of changes in prices. One is a change in the general level of prices; this is really a change in the purchasing power of the monetary unit. The other is differential price change; the prices of some goods and services rise with reference to the general price level while the prices of other goods and services are falling with reference to the general level.

Figure 13–2 shows in a general way how price levels have behaved in the United States over a period of nearly 170 years. It shows the wholesale price index of all commodities of the United States Bureau of Labor Statistics. (This index started in 1890; the figures before 1890 are based on less complete information.) The base period, to which an index number of 100 has been assigned, is 1957–59. Because any price index is an average, and because different prices may be used as the components of an average and different schemes of weighting may be used, there are a number of different price indexes that give somewhat different conclusions about the amount of price level change. Two other important general indexes in the United States are the consumer price index and the gross national product (GNP) implicit price deflator.[2]

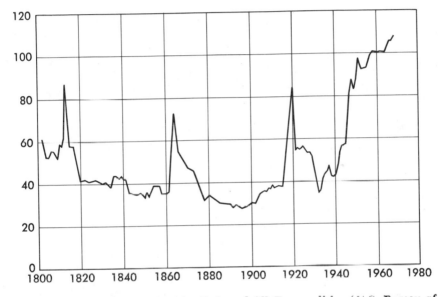

FIGURE 13–2.   **Wholesale Price Index of All Commodities (U.S. Bureau of Labor Statistics)**

Figure 13–3 is included here to emphasize the point that the pattern of variation of different elements of cost is influenced by technological change as well as by changes in wage rates and material costs. This figure shows the indexes of price trends for excavation, surfacing, and structures, for federal-aid highway construction in the United States over a period of more than 40 years. (As in Figure 13–2, the base period is 1957–59.) By comparing Figures 13–2 and 13–3, the reader can observe that the changes in the costs of surfacing and structures were roughly similar to the changes in the general level of wholesale prices.

[2] For a general discussion of price indexes and their relationship to economy studies, see a paper "Inflation and Highway Economy Studies" by R. R. Lee and E. L. Grant. This is published in *Highway Research Record No. 100*, Highway Research Board of the National Academy of Sciences–National Research Council, Washington, D.C., 1965, pp. 20–37.

In contrast, during most of the 45-year period in Figure 13–3, the unit cost of excavation was somewhat less than it had been near the start of the period despite the fact that the general level of prices had doubled. The great technological improvement in earth moving machinery that took place particularly during the first half of the 45-year period was responsible for this differential price change.

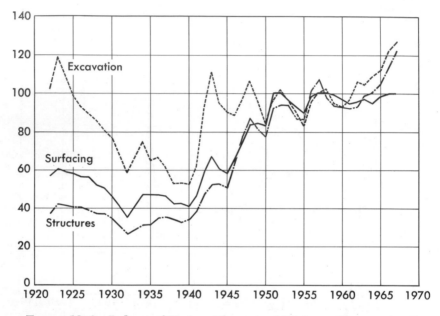

FIGURE 13–3. Indexes of Various Elements of Highway Construction Costs (U.S. Bureau of Public Roads)

Forecasting Changes in the General Price Level. In Chapter 1 we pointed out that one reason for expressing expected consequences of decisions in terms of money is that money units make unlike things commensurable with one another. However, because the purchasing power of any monetary unit varies from time to time, it is evident that money units are imperfect units for certain kinds of comparisons that involve consequences over extended time periods.

A deterrent to making long-run forecasts of price level changes is the evident fact that good long-run forecasts have been fairly rare in the past. For example, consider an estimator in the United States during the period 1921–29, a period when prices seemed to be on a level plateau. It is unlikely that he would have correctly forecast the substantial fall in prices of the 1930's followed by the moderate rise during the early

1940's and then followed by a steep rise in the late 1940's. (The authors have not heard of anyone who made this prediction in the 1920's.)

Short-run forecasts of price level changes often are made with considerable confidence and with considerable success. If, say, price levels have been rising at 3% per year and the same conditions of government fiscal policy and monetary policy seem likely to continue for the next year or two, there may be good grounds for expecting that such inflation will continue at about the same rate. In estimating the funds that will be needed to finance a construction project that will not start at once or that will continue over, say, a year or more, it is essential to make such a short-run forecast.

Generally speaking, price levels in the United States and elsewhere have tended to move upwards since the 1930's. Governmental policies and other influences have combined to create a "creeping" inflation in the United States and in many other countries; in certain countries there has been a "galloping" inflation. During the 1950's and 1960's, it was common for decisions to be made with an expectation of an upward trend in price levels.

Influence on Engineering Economy Studies of a Prediction that All Prices Will Change by the Same Percentage. Certain general principles may be illustrated to advantage by a simple numerical example. Consider the following series of estimated disbursements before income taxes that was given in Example 6–1 (page 69):

Year	Plan A	Plan B
0		$15,000
1	$9,200	5,100
2	9,200	5,100
3	9,200	5,100
4	9,200	5,100
5	9,200	5,100
6	9,200	5,100
7	9,200	5,100
8	9,200	5,100
9	9,200	5,100
10	9,200	5,100

Now let us make one assumption and one stipulation. The assumption (a reasonable one) is that the estimates of disbursements are based on prices applicable to zero date of the study. The stipulation (also reasonable) is that it is desired to make the economic analysis in units of constant purchasing power; to this end, estimates of future cash flows are to be expressed in the purchasing power units applicable to zero date before they are used in calculations of equivalent uniform annual costs, present worths, or rates of return.

Let us assign an index number of 100 to the price level at zero date. (This arbitrary assumption simplifies our arithmetic; any other number for the index at zero date will give us the same final conclusion.) Let us estimate the corresponding price indexes for dates 1, 2, 3, 4, and 5 to be 100, 104, 108, 112, and 116, respectively, and let us estimate that the price index will increase by 2 each year for years 6 to 10. If we assume that *all* cash flows except those for income taxes will increase in the same ratio as these indexes, the estimated series of before-tax disbursements expressed in the dollar units of each particular year will be as shown in Table 13–3.

TABLE 13–3

Revised Estimates of Before-Tax Disbursements of Example 6–1 Assuming that all Disbursements Increase in Proportion to a Predicted Increase in General Price Levels

Year	Plan A	Plan B
0		$15,000
1	$9,200(100/100) = $ 9,200	$5,100(100/100) = 5,100
2	9,200(104/100) = 9,568	5,100(104/100) = 5,304
3	9,200(108/100) = 9,936	5,100(108/100) = 5,508
4	9,200(112/100) = 10,304	5,100(112/100) = 5,712
5	9,200(116/100) = 10,672	5,100(116/100) = 5,916
6	9,200(118/100) = 10,856	5,100(118/100) = 6,018
7	9.200(120/100) = 11,040	5,100(120/100) = 6,120
8	9,200(122/100) = 11,224	5,100(122/100) = 6,222
9	9,200(124/100) = 11,408	5,100(124/100) = 6,324
10	9,200(126/100) = 11,592	5,100(126/100) = 6,426

The dollar figures in Table 13–3 are subject to the objection that the disbursements at different dates are expressed in dollar units of different purchasing power. In Table 13–4, the estimated disbursements at the various dates are stated in terms of dollars of uniform purchasing power by multiplying each figure by the ratio of the zero year price level index to the estimated price level index in the year of the particular disbursement.

Tables 13–3 and 13–4 may seem to many readers to be an unnecessarily elaborate way for the authors to make a fairly simple point. This point of course is that it is sufficient to base estimates of future cash flow on the prices in effect at zero date provided it is forecast that *all* prices will move up and down at the same rate and provided it has been decided that the engineering economy analysis is to be made before income taxes and in units of constant purchasing power.

TABLE 13-4

Estimated Disbursements of Table 13-3 Expressed in Dollars of Purchasing Power of Zero Date

Year	Plan A	Plan B
0		$15,000
1	$ 9,200(100/100) = $9,200	$5,100(100/100) = 5,100
2	9,568(100/104) = 9,200	5,304(100/104) = 5,100
3	9,936(100/108) = 9,200	5,508(100/108) = 5,100
4	10,304(100/112) = 9,200	5,712(100/112) = 5,100
5	10,672(100/116) = 9,200	5,916(100/116) = 5,100
6	10,856(100/118) = 9,200	6,018(100/118) = 5,100
7	11,040(100/120) = 9,200	6,120(100/120) = 5,100
8	11,224(100/122) = 9,200	6,222(100/122) = 5,100
9	11,408(100/124) = 9,200	6,324(100/124) = 5,100
10	11,592(100/126) = 9,200	6,426(100/126) = 5,100

Nevertheless, all prices do not actually move up and down together. These tables will be helpful in examining the problem of how to consider differential price change.

Forecasting Differential Price Changes. Even though the before-tax relative economy of proposed alternatives may not be altered by the prospect of the same percentage of change in the prices of *all* goods and services, prospective *differential* price changes are relevant in many economy studies. Moreover, there often is a rational basis for predicting certain types of differential price change.

For example, the growth of population tends to increase land prices more rapidly than the increase of prices in general. Technological progress tends to increase wages and salaries relative to the general price level. On the other hand, particular technological improvements may cause certain prices to decline relative to the general price level. For example, the price of electric energy has generally declined relative to the general price level ever since the development of the electric central station shortly before the turn of the century. Our discussion of Figure 13-3 pointed out how unit excavation costs were reduced by technological progress in earth moving machinery.

In making estimates for specific economy studies, it should be emphasized that the relevant matter is the prospect of a change in some specific price rather than the prospect of some general differential price change. For example, consider an economy study involving a possible purchase of certain land. It may be evident that a particular parcel of land is presently overpriced; if so, it may be reasonable to expect that the subsequent resale price of this land will be less than its present cost even though land prices in general are expected to increase.

One source of possible differential price change in any after-tax study is the item for difference in estimated cash flow for income taxes. The depreciation deduction used in computing taxable income is based on the cost of the assets being written off regardless of changes in price levels. Each year's taxes, however, are paid in dollars that have the particular year's purchasing power.

In the common case where the same tax rate is assumed throughout the analysis period, the conclusions of an economy study are likely to be insensitive to the prospect of a differential price change in income taxes. The sensitivity may be much greater if a change is expected in the applicable tax rate.

A special case of differential price change occurs whenever general price levels are changing but certain future cash flows are fixed in dollars (or in other relevant monetary units). Such cash flows may be fixed by contract, by government regulation, or for some other reason. Payments of interest and principal are commonly fixed in debt financing; payments may also be fixed in financing by long-term leases. It follows that prospective price level changes are of great importance in financing decisions. In Chapter 18, where we examine certain relationships between engineering economy, business finance, and public finance, there is a brief discussion of this topic.

Testing the Sensitivity of the Conclusions of an Economy Study to Changes in Specific Items of Cash Flow. Consider the listed items of annual disbursements in Example 6–1 (page 70), which were as follows:

Plan A		*Plan B*	
Labor and labor extras	$9,200	Labor and labor extras	$3,300
		Power	400
		Maintenance	1,100
		Property taxes, insurance	300
		Extra income taxes	1,300
		Total	$6,400

Assume that these estimates are applicable only to year 1 on our time scale. Let us now estimate that the cost of labor and labor extras will increase by $460 each year with Plan A and by $165 each year with Plan B.[3] It also is estimated that the annual disbursements for power, maintenance, property taxes, and insurance in Plan B will not change

---

[3] The assumption of a 5% arithmetic rate of increase is made here for the sake of simplicity in our illustration. In some cases an analyst might prefer to assume a geometric rate of increase or to make some other less uniform type of assumption based on present and prospective trade union contracts.

throughout the 10-year study period. No change in the general price level is forecast. Under the simplified assumptions about income taxes that were explained in Chapter 10, the extra income taxes with Plan B will increase by $147.50 each year (i.e., by 50% of the difference between $460 and $165). Our revised estimates of year-by-year comparative disbursements are shown in Table 13–5.

TABLE 13–5

Revised Estimates of After-Tax Disbursements of Example 6–1 Assuming New Figures for Labor, Labor Extras, and Income Taxes

Year	Plan A	Plan B
0		$15,000
1	$ 9,200	6,400
2	9,660	6,712.5
3	10,120	7,025
4	10,580	7,337.5
5	11,040	7,650
6	11,500	7,962.5
7	11,960	8,275
8	12,420	8,587.5
9	12,880	8,900
10	13,340	9,212.5

Using the after-tax i^* of 8% that was stipulated in Example 6–1, the comparative equivalent uniform annual disbursements for Plan A are $9,200 + $460(A/G,8%,10) = $9,200 + $460(3.87) = $10,780. The corresponding figure for Plan B is the capital recovery cost of $2,235 + $6,400 + $312.5(A/G,8%,10) = $9,844. Whereas the comparison in Example 6–1 showed that Plan B had an annual cost advantage of $565, this revised comparison increases its advantage to $936. The prospective after-tax rate of return on the $15,000 investment in Plan B is now approximately 17.2% as contrasted with the 13.4% rate calculated in Example 8–5 (page 117).

In this particular case, Plan B already was economically superior to Plan A without any prediction of an increase in labor costs. Moreover, it was evident without any calculation that a change that increased estimated disbursements for Plan A more than for Plan B was bound to increase the margin of superiority of Plan B. But if the original comparison had favored Plan A, such a sensitivity study would have given the decision maker an indication as to how rapidly unit labor costs would have to increase to shift the advantage from one plan to the other.

The reader will have noted that an estimated year-by-year increase in the extra income taxes with Plan B partly offset the estimated year-by-year increase in the extra labor costs with Plan A. It should be recognized that the estimate about income taxes assumes that the business enterprise will continue to be successful enough to have taxable income that will be taxed at a 50% rate.

Introducing Both Prospective Price Level Changes and Prospective Differential Price Changes into an Economy Study. Now let us combine the assumptions about the changing purchasing power of the dollar that we applied to the data of Example 6–1 earlier in this chapter with the assumptions about rising labor costs and the resulting income tax differences that we have just made. Estimated disbursements for the two plans converted into dollars of purchasing power of zero date are shown in Table 13–6.

TABLE 13–6

Estimated Disbursements of Table 13–5 Expressed in Dollars of Purchasing Power of Zero Date Using the Same Predicted Changes in General Price Levels that Were Assumed in Tables 13–3 and 13–4

Year	Plan A		Plan B	
0				$15,000
1	$ 9,200(100/100) = $	9,200	$6,400(100/100) =	6,400
2	9,660(100/104) =	9,288	6,712.5(100/104) =	6,454
3	10,120(100/108) =	9,370	7,025(100/108) =	6,505
4	10,580(100/112) =	9,446	7,337.5(100/112) =	6,551
5	11,040(100/116) =	9,517	7,650(100/116) =	6,595
6	11,500(100/118) =	9,746	7,962.5(100/118) =	6,748
7	11,960(100/120) =	9,967	8,275(100/120) =	6,896
8	12,420(100/122) =	10,180	8,587.5(100/122) =	7,039
9	12,880(100/124) =	10,387	8,900(100/124) =	7,177
10	13,340(100/126) =	10,587	9,212.5(100/126) =	7,312

Comparative equivalent uniform annual disbursements expressed in dollars of purchasing power of zero date are $9,672 for Plan A and $8,939 for Plan B. (These equivalence conversions continue to use an i^* of 8%.) The advantage for Plan B is now $733. This may be compared with the $565 advantage computed in Example 6–1 in which no price changes were forecast, and with the $936 advantage computed from the figures in Table 13–5, which assumed the same rise in labor costs but no change in general price levels.

In comparing any two alternatives, the question may arise of the likelihood of some particular differential price change. If this particular change will have more impact on one alternative than on the other, a recognition that the change may occur is relevant in any economy study comparing the alternatives. The greater a predicted differential price change, the greater its importance in the choice between the alternatives.

In the foregoing comparisons of Plans A and B under somewhat different assumptions, the influence of the estimated change in prices was less in Table 13-6 than in Table 13-5. In Table 13-6 the *differential* price change was less because of the expected rise in general price levels even though the estimated year-by-year disbursements were exactly the same in the two tables.

Sensitivity Analysis Applied to Possible Price Changes. The reader will doubtless have recognized certain practical obstacles to making the type of analysis illustrated in Table 13-6. To prepare such a table, an analyst must make specific forecasts of the changes, if any, expected in all prices that will influence the estimated cash flow figures for the entire study period. He also must make year-by-year forecasts of some chosen index of price levels that is believed to reflect the coming change in the purchasing power of the dollar or other relevant monetary unit. Another obstacle that has not been evident from our discussion is that there is no one perfect price index that reflects changes in the purchasing power of money; a choice must be made among competing indexes that tend to behave in somewhat different ways.

The reader therefore should not interpret Tables 13-3 to 13-6 as models for everyday economy studies. These tables with their discussion have been included to bring out certain relationships among economy studies, predictions of changes in general price levels, and predictions of differential price changes. These relationships apply to economy studies in general as well as to sensitivity studies.

A predicted change in a specific price should not be viewed as solely a matter for sensitivity analysis. Often such a change will be part of the original set of estimates for an economy study. This might occur, for example, where an expected increase in the price of certain land would be a major consideration in a particular economy study.

Nevertheless, sensitivity analysis can be helpful whenever a decision maker raises the question of how much a possible differential price change will influence the relative advantages of proposed alternatives. In the absence of a formal sensitivity analysis, the likelihood of a particular type of differential price change often is treated by a decision maker as if it were part of the irreducible data. For instance, in the choice between a labor-intensive and a capital-intensive alternative (such as Plans A and B of Example 6-1), the expectation that labor costs will rise more rapidly than general price levels is viewed as a nonquantified factor that favors the capital-intensive alternative.

Use of Computers in Sensitivity Analysis. High-speed electronic digital computers often are used for trial-and-error calculations of prospective rates of return. In such cases, it is a simple matter to give a decision maker almost any information about sensitivity that he may desire. That is, the computer can be programmed to calculate the rate of return with a number of different estimates. If it is desired to consider, say, three different estimates for certain stipulated components of cash flow, the computer can calculate the rate of return with all the desired combinations of estimates of the various components.

Analogue computers can be particularly helpful when economy studies dealing with proposals for major investment projects are being presented orally to review committees or other groups of executives. It is common for executives to ask how the conclusions of such a study will be changed by specific changes in various input parameters and to want rapid answers to their questions. David W. Gillings describes a computer suitable for this purpose as follows: [4]

Significant assistance to the evaluator may be given by use of a small, special-purpose analogue computer which has been developed at the Central Instrument Research Laboratory, Imperial Chemical Industries, Limited, near Reading, England. This equipment has been usefully applied to practical evaluation problems, investigations of method, and training course work in this field. The computer carries out the main series of discounting calculations which has to be repeated for every alternative investigated in the course of a project evaluation. Analogue operation is used, having certain specific advantages for this application. It is well-adapted to the discounting calculation and its incorporation with the other figures; and sensitivity analysis can be carried out rapidly, so that the effects of a wide range of operating conditions can be explored for a number of alternative plant and process investment possibilities. The easy-access characteristic of analogue computers generally, makes it possible for the engineer to use such equipment personally, and very flexibly, without having to put technical data for repetitive evaluations onto the data tape—or other input—of a large digital computer which may be remotely located and not continuously accessible.

The computer can be programmed by setting the values of annual cash inputs or outputs for the project, using the rows of digital divided switches, from which the inputs can be read directly, each for the correct year in the expected life of the plant. The rate of interest used can be adjusted, and results for the evaluation derived either as present worth of the project at the completion of life, at selected interest rates, or as the "discounted cash flow" rate, that is, the rate resulting in zero present worth at the completion of project life. All the inputs can be changed rapidly so that a series of explora-

[4] The quotation is from the abstract of Dr. Gillings' paper "Analogue Computing for Project Evaluation," in the Papers and Discussions of the Fourth Summer Symposium of The Engineering Economy Division, American Society for Engineering Education, published by *The Engineering Economist*, Stevens Institute of Technology, Hoboken, N.J., 1966, p. 102. The paper was published in its entirety in *The Engineering Economist*, vol. 11, no. 2, Winter 1966.

tory evaluations can be carried out without loss of time for repetitive calculation. In the case of chemical process industry projects, factors which have a marked influence on profitability include any potential changes of unit price realized for products, unit costs of raw materials, changes in production volume, and amount and timing of capital investment. By rapid exploration, the factors with the most significant influence can be readily identified, and estimated quantitatively.

Figures 13–4 and 13–5 show pictures of the computer described in the foregoing quotation.

Some General Comments Regarding the Sensitivity Point of View. In any particular economy study, there will usually be certain estimates for which a moderate change will have a relatively small influence on the conclusions of the study, and there will be other estimates for which a moderate change will have a relatively large influence. When an analyst is aware of this relationship, he can put his maximum effort on the estimates that are of the greatest importance. It follows that it is helpful to have an awareness of sensitivity in the initial stages of any economy study.

In the final or decision-making stage of a study, the sensitivity viewpoint continues to be desirable. The first two chapters of this book stressed the importance of defining alternatives, estimating their consequences, expressing the consequences in money terms, and analyzing the monetary figures with reference to a chosen decision criterion. But it was pointed out that such an analysis does not necessarily settle the problem of choice. Finally, someone must make a selection among the

FIGURE 13–4. CONIAC Economic Estimating Analogue Computer (Photograph by courtesy of Imperial Chemical Industries Ltd.)

FIGURE 13–5. CONIAC Computer in Use (Photograph by courtesy of Imperial Chemical Industries Ltd.)

alternatives giving due consideration to matters that for one reason or another were left out of the formal economic analysis. One aspect of the decision maker's assignment is that he often needs to recognize that "What's to come is still unsure" (as pointed out in the Shakespearean quotation that started this chapter). Sensitivity analysis may well help him to make up his mind. Various types of calculation using the mathematics of probability may also be useful to him in contemplating an unsure future; this topic is discussed in Chapter 14.

At the capital budgeting level in a business enterprise, it is possible to establish certain formal secondary decision criteria based on the concept of sensitivity; such criteria will be discussed briefly in Chapter 21.

In Chapter 12, we made certain comments about the use of mathematical models for making or influencing economic decisions. It was pointed out that when a general class of economic decisions is described by a mathematical formula, it often is necessary to make certain omissions and simplifications. In making new mathematical formulations, it is desirable to restrict omissions and simplifications so that decisions will be relatively insensitive to the matters omitted or simplified. Moreover, in deciding whether or not to apply an existing mathematical model to a particular decision, it is a good idea to evaluate the model in part from the viewpoint of sensitivity. Some comments illustrating this type of evaluation are made with respect to several models that are briefly described in Appendix D.

PROBLEMS

13–1. Following Table 13–5 it was stated that the new disbursement series in that table raised the prospective after-tax rate of return to approximately 17.2%. Show the calculations to obtain this 17.2% figure.

13–2. Following Table 13–6 it was stated that the comparative equivalent uniform annual disbursements expressed in dollars of purchasing power of zero date were $9,672 for Plan A and $8,939 for Plan B. Make the necessary calculations to check these figures.

13–3. In Example 9–1 (page 138), residual values were estimated as $300,000 for location J and $550,000 for location K, both at the end of the 20-year analysis period. The **B/C** ratio of J as compared with continuing the present location at H was computed as 1.94; the incremental **B/C** ratio of K as compared to J was 0.57. To test the sensitivity of these **B/C** ratios to the estimated residual values, recompute the two ratios (a) increasing each residual value by 50%, and (b) decreasing each residual value by 50%. (*Ans. a.* 2.17; 0.61; *b.* 1.75; 0.54.)

13–4. In Example 8–6 (page 117), the prospective rate of return on the extra investment in Plan C over Plan B was computed to be approximately 1.9%. This calculation assumed a $5,000 salvage value for Plan C at the end of the 10-year study period. To judge the sensitivity of this comparison to the estimated terminal salvage value, recompute this rate of return assuming a $10,000 salvage value for Plan C. Compute the changed difference in annual income taxes using the simplified assumptions explained in Chapter 10. (*Ans.* = 4.0%.)

13–5. The latter part of Example 13–3 discussed the extent to which the comparison of the costs of 40 years of service for Plans D and E was sensitive to the estimated disbursement for renewal of Plan D at the end of 20 years. However, the example gave only a qualitative consideration to income tax differences in the final 20 years of the 40-year study period.

In the original comparison, in which the second 20 years for Plan D was assumed to require the same disbursements as the first 20 years, the present worth of the after-tax disbursements was $40,100 less for Plan D than for Plan E. (Present worths were computed using an after-tax i° of 8%.) Recompute the difference in present worth assuming that the first cost of the renewal of Plan D after 20 years will be $100,000 and that the salvage value of this second structure will be $20,000 on the terminal date of the study period (i.e., 40 years from zero date). Assume no change in O & M disbursements during the final 20 years but alter the income tax differences to reflect the changed depreciation deduction using the assumptions about income taxes that were explained in Chapter 10. (*Ans.* = Recomputed disbursements for 40 years of service now have approximately $32,000 less present worth for Plan D than for Plan E.)

13–6. Assume that a $50,000 structure having an estimated life of 25 years is to be compared with a $100,000 structure having an estimated life of 50 years. Both will have zero terminal salvage values. Assume that except for the difference in lives the two structures will provide exactly the same service. The total of the annual disbursements for operation, maintenance, property taxes, and insurance will be the same for the two structures. Using our simplified assumptions about income taxes, there will be no difference in annual disbursements for income taxes. (Why?) At what after-tax i^* will the two have equal annual costs? (*Ans.* = 0%.)

13–7. In Problem 13–6 assume that it is desired to compare the present worths of the costs of the two structures for a 50-year service. Change the data so that the estimated renewal cost of the shorter-lived structure at date 25 is $75,000 even though the investment at zero date remains at $50,000. A consequence of the higher renewal cost will be an extra $500 of annual disbursements for income taxes for the longer-lived structure during years 26 to 50, both inclusive. Explain how our simplified assumptions about income taxes lead to this $500 estimate. At what after-tax i^* will the present worths of disbursements for 50 years be equal for the two structures? (*Ans.* = at a little less than 1%.)

13–8. The private branch exchange telephone switchboard of a certain company is so designed that all interoffice calls must be handled by manual switching. It is proposed that the necessary changes in the company's telephone system be made to permit direct dialing on all interoffice calls. This will require an immediate investment of $6,000 by the company and will increase the monthly telephone bill by $110. At present two operators are required. Each receives $320 per month (including salary extras). It is thought that when manual switching on interoffice calls is eliminated, equally good service on incoming and outgoing calls can be provided with a single operator plus one-fourth time of another employee who receives the same salary as part-time relief operator and part-time typist. It is believed there will be a time saving on the completion of interoffice calls. If no money value is placed on this time saving, how many years are required for this $6,000 investment to pay off? Assume a minimum attractive rate of return before taxes of 12%. How many years if the time saving is valued at $50 per month? (*Ans.* = (a) 5.5 years; (b) 3.8 years.)

13–9. In the design of a 2-story municipal office building, the question arises whether provision should be made for the addition of 2 more stories at a later date. The architect makes two designs; the one that provides for this possible expansion involves an estimated first cost of $69,500; the one without this provision involves an estimated first cost of $63,000.

If the former plan is adopted, it is estimated that the subsequent addition of 2 stories will cost $42,000. Without the additional strength of columns and footings provided by this plan, it is likely that if it were ever decided to add the 2 stories, the necessary reconstruction and strengthening of the lower stories would cost at least $15,000 in addition to the cost of the 2 new stories.

Assume the life of the building as 50 years from now, either with or without the additions. How soon must the additional stories be needed in order to justify the selection of the $69,500 design? Assume i^* as 5%. Building upkeep will be the same with either design. Since this is a government building, there will be no taxes.

13–10. In the construction of a hydroelectric power plant, it is planned to install only 4 turbo-generators at the start, although the ultimate design calls for 10. The question arises in the design whether to provide foundations, draft tubes, and other necessary facilities to permit the installation of the additional turbo-generators when needed merely by the purchase and installation of the machines, or to defer the investment in these facilities until the turbo-generators are about to be installed.

The extra cost now to provide these facilities for all 6 future turbines will be $100,000. It is contemplated that 2 more turbo-generators will be needed in 6 years, 2 in 11 years, and the final 2 in 15 years. The installation of these facilities at the time they are required is estimated to cost $90,000 per pair of turbines.

With interest at 10% and annual taxes at 1.8% of investment, compare the present worth of the disbursements for 15 years under the plan calling for the present investment and the plan calling for the deferred investment. Which has the lower cost? What implied money advantage of the present investment plan is omitted from this comparison?

13–11. Tanks to hold a certain chemical are now being made of Material A. The first cost of a tank is $30,000 and the life is 8 years. When a tank is 4 years old it must be relined at a cost of $10,000. It has been suggested that it might be preferable to make the tanks from Material B. Accelerated tests give the estimate that the life using Material B will be 20 years and that no relining will be needed. The first cost of the tanks using Material B is not yet known. If the minimum attractive rate of return is 15% before income taxes, what is the greatest amount that it would be justifiable to spend for a tank constructed of Material B? Assume zero salvage value for tanks made of either material.

13–12. A manufacturing company guarantees its product against defects in workmanship and materials for a certain period of time. Whenever a customer finds a defective unit within the warranty period, he returns it to the factory for free repair. Current records show that approximately 15% of the company's output is returned once and another 5% is returned twice, due to defects in manufacture. The total cost to repair a unit amounts to about $100.

The company's quality control director thinks the percentage of returned items can be reduced by an intensive quality control program. He estimates that the expenditure of $85,000 a year for labor and salary expense and $100,000 for improved inspection and quality control equipment will reduce the number of returned items to 8% of the output and that none will be returned a second time.

(a) Determine the annual production rate that would be required to justify the quality control director's proposal. Assume that the minimum attractive rate of return is 15% before income taxes and that the quality control equipment will have a life of 10 years with no salvage value.

(b) Assuming i° at 15%, 10-year life for equipment with no salvage value, and an annual production rate of 10,000 units, determine the maximum percentage of the products that the company could afford to have returned one time and still justify the quality control director's proposal.

13–13. Example 8–3 (page 113) deals with an analysis of a proposed investment to produce a new product. The prospective after-tax rate of return turned out to be 9.1%. The estimate assumed that the before-tax cash flow would not reach its peak of $500,000 until year 4 on the chosen time scale. The manufacturer's budget review committee asks how much the prospective rate of return would be increased if the before-tax cash flow could be increased from $100,000 to $300,000 in the first year and if the peak of $500,000 could be maintained from the 2nd to the 12th year, both inclusive. Compute the changes in after-tax cash flow that would be caused by these changes and make the necessary calculations to answer the committee's question.

13–14. In Example 8–3 (page 113), how much would the prospective after-tax rate of return be decreased if the estimated annual before-tax cash flow should be decreased from $500,000 to $400,000 in years 4 to 11, both inclusive?

13–15. A hotel owner in a developing country depends on tourism for most of his business, and, in order to maintain a high occupancy rate, advertises "Pure Drinking Water" on all of his bill boards, letterheads, and business cards. At present he is providing bottled water for his guests at a cost of #1 per gallon, but occasionally some guest drinks the tap water and becomes ill. (The symbol # represents the *adler*, the currency unit of the country.) Because he believes that every such illness is bad for his business, he is seeking an economical means of providing pure water for all guest consumption. There is an ample supply of water available in the town through a reasonably reliable pipe system, and at very low rates. That system is now being used for all sanitary and guest purposes except for drinking.

A visiting civil engineer has proposed to him that he install an automatic filtration and chlorination plant and process all the water he uses. After careful investigation he finds that he can buy such a unit in either of two sizes, 2,500 or 5,000 gallons per day. The 2,500 unit will be adequate for his immediate needs and for the next 5 years. After 5 years he expects to double the size of the hotel and will need to double the purification capacity.

The smaller unit will cost about #32,000 installed and will require maintenance and repairs costing about #500 a year. The larger unit will cost about #48,000, and annual maintenance and repairs will cost #750. Both units have estimated lives of 15 years with zero salvage value. The owner has decided to purchase one or the other of these units.

Chlorine is available in steel cylinders for #350 per cylinder. Each cylinder will treat 150,000 gallons of water. Diatomaceous earth, used in the filter, costs #60 per 100 pounds. A hundred pounds will filter 75,000 gallons of water. The foregoing rates apply to both units. However, electric energy to pump the water through the units will cost #20 per 100,000 gallons for the smaller unit and #15 per 100,000 gallons for the larger.

The owner wishes to select the unit under the assumption that he will need 1,000 gallons per day next year and that the need will increase by 350 gallons per day each year for the following 10 years. Thereafter it will remain constant at 4,500 gallons per day. The owner wants an i^* of 15% on any investment that can be deferred. There will be no income taxes.

Use the present worth method to determine whether he should buy a small unit now and another one in 5 years or buy a large unit now. Make some type of sensitivity analysis to judge how sensitive your conclusion is to the i^* used and to the estimated rate of growth in demand for water.

13–16. In Problem 7–7 (page 103) which compares a full program and a stepped program of development of a certain public water supply, it is evident that the prospect of a differential price rise in waterworks construction cost will favor the full program. Assume that the estimates given in Problem 7–7 are all based on prices in effect at zero date. If there should be a differential price increase in construction costs at a compounded rate of 3% a year, the required investment outlay in 10 years in the stepped program would be $300,000(1.344) = $403,200; in 20 years the outlay would be

$300,000 (1.806) = $541,800. The solution in Problem 7–7 favored the stepped program of development. Would this prospective price rise be sufficient to tip the balance in favor of the full program? Assume no change in the differences in annual disbursements stated in the problem.

At what compound rate of differential price increase would the full program and the stepped program just break even on capitalized costs using the stated i^* of 7%?

13–17. It is evident that a comparison such as the one in Problem 7–7 (page 103) will be sensitive to the chosen value of i^*. Using the estimates given in the problem, find the value of i^* that will make the full program and the stepped program have equal capitalized costs.

13–18. In the project described in Problem 8–12, the analysis assumed that the land would be sold for its initial cost of $400,000 at the end of the 15-year analysis period. The question is raised as to the sensitivity of the prospective after-tax rate of return (computed as 7.3%) to moderate changes in the estimated resale value of the land. Compute the rate of return assuming (a) that the net after-tax resale value is $600,000, and (b) that it is $200,000.

13–19. A $10,000 investment is proposed. It is expected that this investment will eliminate a certain manual operation that now costs $2,000 a year before income taxes. It is estimated that the life of the investment will be 10 years with no terminal salvage value. The after-tax i^* is 10%.

(a) Using the simplified assumption about income taxes explained in Chapter 10, make calculations to determine whether the investment is justified if the estimated before-tax saving will be $2,000 for each year of the 10 years.

(b) Wage rates have been rising. Assume that it is estimated that the before-tax saving will be $2,000 in the first year, $2,100 in the second, and will increase by $100 each year thereafter. Assume no change in general price levels. Make an economy study to determine whether these revised estimates lead to the justification of the proposed investment.

13–20. Modify Problem 13–19(b) by assuming that the general price level index, 100 for zero date and year 1, will increase to 102 in year 2, 104 in year 3, and will continue to increase by 2 each year thereafter. It is desired to make the economy study in dollars of the purchasing power of zero date. With this stipulation, is the proposed investment justified?

13–21. A small utility company is considering the purchase of a power-driven post hole auger mounted on a truck, to dig holes for posts used in the extension of its electric distribution system. This machine will cost $15,000 new, including the truck. Its life is estimated as 8 years with $2,000 salvage value. Annual cost of storage, maintenance, painting, insurance, and taxes is estimated at 16% of first cost regardless of the amount the equipment is used. Costs incident to its operation are:

Operators—2 men at $25 per day each
Fuel and lubricants—$12 per day

Observation of similar machines indicates that it can dig 25 post holes per day. At present, holes are being dug by hand labor. An average laborer requires 1½ days to dig a hole. Labor costs $18 per day.

Assuming an i^* of 8%, how many holes must be dug per year to make this machine an attractive investment?

13–22. In the purchase of land for the construction of a manufacturing plant, the question arises regarding the desirability of purchasing certain adjoining unimproved land for possible use for plant expansion. At present this land is available at a price of $40,000. On the assumption that the land will not be needed for 15 years and that average property taxes will be 2% of cost, what must be the prospective price of the land 15 years hence to make it pay to purchase the land now? Assume no income tax differences and use an i^* of 8%. What are some of the irreducible data that should enter into a decision on such a matter?

13–23. Two 10-HP motors are under consideration for a certain application. Motor A costs $340 and has a full-load efficiency of 85.2%. Motor B costs $290 and has a full-load efficiency of 92.1%. Electric energy is purchased at 2.3 cents per kw-hr. (1 HP = 0.746 kw.) Estimated lives of both motors are 20 years with no salvage value. The stipulated i^* is 12% before income taxes. Annual property taxes and insurance will be 2.5% of first cost. When the motors are operated, it always will be at full load. Compute the break-even point in number of hours of operation per year at which the two motors will be equally economical.

13–24. A maintenance operation on a plating tank consists of installing a new lining. The type of lining now being used costs $1,800 installed and has an average life of 3 years. A new lining material has been developed that is more resistant to the corrosive effects of the plating liquid. Its estimated cost installed is $3,100. With a stipulated i^* of 10%, how long must the new type of lining last for it to be equally economical with the present type? (In this case the before-tax and after-tax rates of return are approximately the same; the circumstances under which this is true are illustrated later in Example 16–4.)

13–25. An engineer who is on a 5-year assignment in a certain city is contemplating the purchase of a home for $40,000. However, he believes that this is a highly inflated price and that prices may be considerably lower in 5 years when his job will require him to move to a different city. If he buys this house he estimates annual property taxes as $700, annual insurance as $150, and annual repairs and maintenance as $400. His other alternative is to rent a house of about the same size and desirability on a 5-year lease for $375 a month. He considers 6% to be a minimum attractive rate of return on an investment in a home. What is the net resale value (after commissions and other selling expenses) 5 years hence that will make his annual cost of home ownership just break even with the annual cost of renting?

14

Use of the Mathematics of
Probability in Economy Studies

What can we say about the future behavior of a phenomenon act-
ing under the influence of unknown or chance causes? I doubt,
that, in general, we can say anything. For example, let me ask:
"What will be the price of your favorite stock thirty years from
today?" Are you willing to gamble much on your powers of prediction in such a case? Probably not. However, if I ask: "Suppose
you were to toss a penny one hundred times, thirty years from today, what proportion of heads would you expect to find?," your
willingness to gamble on your powers of prediction would be of an
entirely different order than in the previous case.

—W. A. SHEWHART [1]

The statement that tomorrow will probably be a rainy day is perfectly clear and understandable, whether you agree with it or not. So
also is the statement that Smith is more likely than Jones to receive a
promotion. In general, the word *probability* and its derivative and related words such as *probable, probably, likelihood, likely,* and *chance*
are used regularly in everyday speech in a qualitative sense and there
is no difficulty in their interpretation.

But consider a statement that the probability is 0.01 that there will
be a runoff of 500 cubic feet per second or more next year at a certain
highway drainage crossing. Or a statement that if a 13-card hand is
selected at random from a standard deck of 52 playing cards, the
probability is 0.00264 that it will contain all four aces. In such statements, *probability* is used in its quantitative or mathematical sense. It
is evident that some special explanation of the meaning of *probability*
is necessary before these statements can be understood. A critical consideration will show that the two statements not only call for more
explanation but that they need somewhat different explanations.

Two different traditional definitions of *probability* in its mathematical

[1] W. A. Shewhart, *Economic Control of Quality of Manufactured Product*, p. 8.
Copyright, 1931 by Litton Educational Publishing, Inc., reproduced here by permission of Van Nostrand Reinhold Company.

sense may be given. One may be described as the *frequency definition,* the other as the *classical definition.*

Definitions of Probability.[2] Probability may be thought of as relative frequency in the long run. This may be phrased somewhat more precisely as follows:

Assume that if a large number of trials be made under the same essential conditions, the ratio of the number of trials in which a certain event happens to the total number of trials will approach a limit as the total number of trials is indefinitely increased. This limit is called the probability that the event will happen under these conditions.

It may be noted that this limit is always a fraction (or decimal fraction), which may vary from 0 to 1. A probability of 0 corresponds to an event that never happens under the described conditions; a probability of 1 corresponds to an event that always happens.

It is because *probability* describes relative frequency in the long run that the concept is so useful in practical affairs. But its use would be severely limited if the only way to estimate any probability were by a long series of experiments. Most mathematical manipulations of probabilities are based on another definition, which may be stated as follows:

If an event may happen in **a** *ways and fail to happen in* **b** *ways, and all of these ways are mutually exclusive and equally likely to occur, the probability of the event happening is* $a/(a + b)$, *the ratio of the number of ways favorable to the event to the total number of ways.*

This is called the *classical definition.* It represents the approach to the subject developed by the classical writers on the mathematics of probability, many of whom wrote particularly about probabilities associated with games of chance. Experience shows that where properly used, this definition permits the successful forecasting of relative frequency in the long run without the necessity of a long series of trials prior to each forecast.

Our statement about the probability of a runoff of at least 500 cu. ft./sec. implies knowledge about past runoff at this or comparable sites; it would be impossible to enumerate a number of equally likely

---

[2] With a few minor changes, our discussion of definitions is taken from pages 195–197 of the third edition of *Statistical Quality Control* by E. L. Grant (New York: McGraw-Hill Book Co., Inc., 1964.). The definitions are included here because it is necessary to make specific reference to them in our discussion of various probability applications in economy studies. However, limitations of space in this book make it impracticable for us to explain the various theorems of the mathematics of probability such as those that are applied in Examples 14–1 and 14–2. Many of our readers will already have been exposed to these theorems elsewhere in the study of algebra, probability, or statistics. If not, the reader can take our simple probability calculations on faith for the time being until he has the chance to read more about this subject elsewhere.

ways in which the runoff could be above or below 500 cu. ft./sec. In contrast, the statement about the probability of the hand with all four aces is based on a counting of equally likely ways in which the hand might contain all four aces or less than four aces; even though not based on the evidence of actual trials, a statement of this sort may be made with strong confidence that the stated probability is really the relative frequency to be expected in the long run.

It is possible to raise philosophical and practical objections to both of the traditional definitions of probability. For example, in the frequency definition how long a series of trials should one have to estimate relative frequency in the long run? In the classical definition, how can one tell which ways are equally likely? Such types of objections have led many of the modern writers on probability to view probability merely as a branch of abstract mathematics developed from certain axioms or assertions. The establishment of any relationship between actual phenomena in the real world and the laws of probability developed from the axioms is viewed as an entirely separate matter from the mathematical manipulations leading to the probability theorems.[3]

The mathematical theorems that deal with the interrelationships among probabilities are the same regardless of the definition that is used. Generally speaking, persons who use probability calculations in economy studies will find it satisfactory to think of probability as meaning relative frequency in the long run.

Probabilities of Extreme Events. One important application of probability theory in engineering economy is in estimating the *expected value* of certain kinds of extreme events. We shall use this type of application to introduce the subject.

First, we shall examine the calculation of expected value in a certain game of chance. Here we can use the classical definition of probability to compute numerical values of extreme probabilities. A study of the gambling game of Keno will help to clarify certain principles even though this is not an engineering economy application. Examples 14–1 and 14–2 refer to this game.

Then in Example 14–3 we shall look at calculations of the expected value of the adverse consequences of extreme natural phenomena such as floods. Here we shall find it necessary to use the frequency definition of probability. We shall see that often it is necessary to use estimates of probability values that clearly are imperfect. Finally, in the same

---

[3] For a clear discussion of the relationship of the axiomatic definition of probability to the two traditional definitions, see G. A. Wadsworth and J. G. Bryan, *Introduction to Probability and Random Variables* (New York: McGraw-Hill Book Co., Inc., 1960), pp. 12–19.

example we shall illustrate the use of such calculated expected values in the analysis of a problem in engineering economy.

The Gambling Game of Keno. This is a variant of a game of Chinese origin. Our description applies to the version of the game played in a Nevada gambling house which we shall call the XYZ Club.

In each game, a mechanical device makes a random drawing of 20 plastic balls from a set of 80 balls that are numbered from 1 to 80. Prior to a drawing, each player chooses certain numbers to have marked on a card for which he pays 60 cents or some multiple thereof. His chosen numbers are called "spots." He may elect to choose from 1 to 15 spots. In effect, he is betting that enough of his spots will be the same as some of the 20 numbers selected by the mechanical device for him to be entitled to a payment by the XYZ Club. The size of his payoff, if any, depends on how many of his spots agree with some of the chosen 20. (A spot that agrees is described as a "winning spot.") The stipulated amounts of payoff for players who elect to choose either 2 or 7 spots are given in Examples 14–1 and 14–2. (Certain other payoff schedules are given in problems at the end of this chapter.)

The number of different sets of 20 numbers that may be selected out of 80 numbers is the number of combinations of 80 things taken 20 at a time. In general, the symbol C_r^n may be used to represent the number of combinations of n things taken r at a time. It is shown in algebra that $C_r^n = \dfrac{n!}{r!\,(n-r)!}$. Here the expression $n!$, read as "factorial n" or "n factorial," is used for the product of the first n integers. By definition, $0! = 1$. $C_{20}^{80} = \dfrac{80!}{20!60!} = 3{,}534{,}816{,}142{,}212{,}174{,}320$. Presumably, if the mechanical device operates in a way so that the 80 plastic balls have equal chances to be selected, each of this large number of combinations is equally likely.

Suppose a player selects 7 spots. To find the probability that he will have exactly 5 winning spots, one first must compute how many of the foregoing combinations will contain exactly 5 out of a set of 7 specified numbers. This computation calls for multiplying C_5^7 by C_{15}^{73}. The classical definition of probability may then be applied to compute the desired probability, as follows: $\dfrac{C_5^7 C_{15}^{73}}{C_{20}^{80}} = \dfrac{7!73!20!60!}{5!2!15!58!80!} = \dfrac{18{,}054}{2{,}089{,}945}$

$$= 0.008638505$$

EXAMPLE 14–1. CALCULATION OF EXPECTED VALUE WITH A SINGLE PAYOFF FIGURE

Calculations for Two-Spot Version of Keno. Suppose a player buys a Keno ticket for 60 cents and elects to have only two spots marked on it. If both of his spots are winning spots, the house will pay him $7.50; otherwise it will pay him nothing. The probabilities of the three possible mutually exclusive results are as follows:

$$\text{Prob. of 0 winning spots} = \frac{C_0^2 C_{20}^{78}}{C_{20}^{80}} = \frac{177}{316}$$

$$\text{Prob. of 1 winning spot} = \frac{C_1^2 C_{19}^{78}}{C_{20}^{80}} = \frac{120}{316}$$

$$\text{Prob. of 2 winning spots} = \frac{C_2^2 C_{18}^{78}}{C_{20}^{80}} = \frac{19}{316}$$

The sum of all of the mutually exclusive probabilities is $316/316 = 1$. (The necessity for the sum of all of the mutually exclusive probabilities to be 1 often supplies a useful check on probability calculations.) These probabilities can be combined with the payoff schedule to obtain the expected value of the payoff on a 60-cent ticket, as follows:

Winning Spots	Probability	Payoff	Expected Value
0	177/316	$0.00	$0.00000
1	120/316	0.00	0.00000
2	19/316	7.50	0.45095
Totals	316/316		$0.45095

EXAMPLE 14–2. CALCULATION OF EXPECTED VALUE WITH SEVERAL DIFFERENT PAYOFF FIGURES

Calculations for Seven-Spot Version of Keno. For a player who elects to have 7 spots marked on his 60-cent Keno ticket, the XYZ Club will pay nothing if he has 0 to 3 winning spots, 60 cents for exactly 4 winning spots, $12 for exactly 5, $245 for exactly 6, and $5,500 for exactly 7. To determine the expected value of a player's winnings, it is necessary to add the various expected values for the different possible numbers of winning spots, as follows:

Winning Spots	Probability	Payoff	Expected Value
0 to 3	0.938414048	$ 0.00	$0.0000
4	0.052190967	0.60	0.0313
5	0.008638505	12.00	0.1037
6	0.000732077	245.00	0.1794
7	0.000024403	5,500.00	0.1342
Totals	1.000000000		$0.4486

Comment on the Significance of an Expected Value as Illustrated by Examples 14–1 and 14–2. In the long run, Keno players at the XYZ Club get back as winnings approximately 45 cents per 60-cent ticket purchased. (This is true not only for the two-spot and seven-spot versions of the game but for all versions from one-spot to eleven-spot as well.) From the viewpoint of the XYZ Club, about 75% of the money taken in on 60-cent tickets goes for payment of players' winnings and the other 25% goes for miscellaneous expenses, including taxes, and for profits, if any.

From the viewpoint of the player who buys *one* 60-cent ticket, it is impossible for him to get back exactly 45 cents. If, say, he plays the two-spot version, he either will win nothing or $7.50. Our probability calculations show that if he plays a great many such games, he will win nothing in about 94% of them and will win $7.50 in about 6% of them. The 6% of his games in which he wins $7.50 will give him 45 cents for each 60 cents bet. This is the sense in which $0.45 is his expected value.

Although the arithmetic is somewhat more complicated in analyzing the seven-spot version of Keno, the meaning of the calculated expected value is the same. Nevertheless, there are some important differences between the two-spot version and the seven-spot version from the viewpoint of a prospective gambler. Any reader interested in gambling will doubtless have noted that in any single seven-spot game a player has less than 1 chance in 100 of doing better than getting his 60 cents back. But the low probabilities of having 6 or 7 winning spots are offset by the higher payoffs. We shall have occasion to comment further on this difference between Examples 14–1 and 14–2 after we have examined calculations of expected values of flood damages and used such calculations in an economy study.

Incidentally, it should be noted by the reader that the phrase *expected value* is a mathematicians' phrase referring to the product of a probability and an associated monetary figure and carries no implication about desirability or lack of it. Although a $5,500 payoff for a Keno player who is fortunate enough to have 7 winning spots on his 60-cent ticket will be viewed quite differently by the player and by the XYZ Club, the expected value of this occurrence is the same for the player and the club. In this usage, the word *value* is applied in a neutral sense. Thus one can speak of the expected value of something that is viewed as undesirable, such as the adverse consequences of a flood, as readily as something viewed as desirable, such as a successful gamble.

EXAMPLE 14–3. USING EXPECTED VALUES IN THE COMPARISON OF ALTERNATIVE INVESTMENTS

Determining the Economic Capacity of a Spillway. The following illustration is adapted from one prepared by the late Allen Hazen:[4]

A large public utility company has acquired a recently constructed small hydroelectric plant in connection with the purchase of a small utility property. It seemed probable to the engineers of the large company that the spillway capacity of 1,500 cu. ft. per sec. provided by the dam at the plant was inadequate; if a flow occurred that exceeded the capacity of the spillway, the stream was likely to cut a channel around the power plant. A rough estimate of the cost of the necessary repairs if this should occur was $250,000.

In order to estimate what, if any, increase in spillway capacity was justi-

[4] Allen Hazen, *Flood Flows* (New York: John Wiley & Sons, Inc., 1930).

fied, the engineers estimated the costs of increasing the spillway capacity by various amounts. They also estimated from the available records of stream flow the probabilities of floods of various magnitudes.

Flood Flow in Cu. Ft. per Sec.	Probability of Greater Flood Occurring in Any One Year	Required Investment to Enlarge Spillway to Provide for This Flood
1,500	0.10	No cost
1,700	0.05	$ 24,000
1,900	0.02	34,000
2,100	0.01	46,000
2,300	0.005	62,000
2,500	0.002	82,000
2,700	0.001	104,000
3,100	0.0005	130,000

Annual investment charges on the spillway enlargement were assumed as 10.5%. This figure was the sum of annual capital recovery cost of 7.5% at an $i°$ of 7% over the estimated remaining life of 40 years, property taxes of 1.3%, and income taxes of 1.7%. For each spillway size, the expected value of annual flood damages was the product of the probability that the spillway capacity would be exceeded and the $250,000 estimated damage if this event should occur. The following tabulation shows that the sum of these costs is a minimum if the spillway is designed with a capacity of 2,100 cubic feet per second. This will take care of a flood such as would be expected, on the average, 1 year in 100.

Spillway Capacity	Annual Investment Charges	Expected Value of Annual Flood Damages	Sum of Annual Costs
1,500	$ 0	$25,000	$25,000
1,700	2,520	12,500	15,020
1,900	3,570	5,000	8,570
2,100	4,830	2,500	7,330
2,300	6,510	1,250	7,760
2,500	8,610	500	9,110
2,700	10,920	250	11,170
3,100	13,650	125	13,775

Certain Implications of the Use of Expected Value of Annual Damages in Design Against an Extreme Event. In Example 14–3 the remaining life of the power plant and spillway was estimated to be 40 years. Nevertheless, the economy study indicated that it was desirable to design against a flood that would be expected on the average only once in 100 years.

It is reasonable for such an analysis to give weight to the hazard of events that are so extreme that they may not happen at all during the study period. In effect, the calculations in Example 14–3 recognize that the flood that is expected on the average only once in 100 years is as likely to occur next year (or in any other specified year) as to occur 100 years from now.

It is because it is impossible to predict the *time* at which such extreme events will occur that it is desirable to predict their relative frequency in the long run. One way to look at the solution in Example 14–3 is to say that the analysis leads to the conclusion that it is a better gamble to design against the 100-year flood than against some more frequent or less frequent flood. Another way to interpret the expected values of damages used in the economy study is to say that they would represent a fair charge for flood insurance of $250,000 if such insurance were available at the bare "cost of the risk."

Computing Expected Values When Different Expected Damages Are Associated with Different Probabilities of Extreme Events. In Example 14–3, the damage from a flood exceeding the spillway capacity was estimated to be $250,000 regardless of whether the flood was slightly more than capacity or a great deal more. Under this simple assumption, the expected value (i.e., the prospective average annual damage in the long run) was the product of $250,000 and the probability that the spillway capacity would be exceeded in any year.

Often the damage from an extreme event will vary with the magnitude of the event. For example, in analyzing most flood control projects, it is necessary to recognize that, generally speaking, the larger the flood, the greater the prospective damage.

We may illustrate the way to compute expected values under such circumstances by a slight modification of the data of Example 14–3. Assume that it is estimated the damage will be $0 for any flood less than the spillway capacity, $250,000 if the flood exceeds the spillway capacity by not more than 200 sec. ft., $300,000 if the flood exceeds capacity by from 200 to 400 sec. ft., and $400,000 if the flood exceeds capacity by more than 400 sec. ft. The required calculations for a spillway capacity of 2,100 sec. ft. are as follows:

Damages D	Probability of Stated Damage p	Dp
$ 0	1.00 − 0.01 = 0.99	$ 0
250,000	0.01 − 0.005 = 0.005	1,250
300,000	0.005 − 0.002 = 0.003	900
400,000	0.002 − 0.000 = 0.002	800
Expected value of annual damage		$2,950

Similar calculations for spillway capacities of 1,900 and 2,300 sec. ft. will yield figures for average annual damages of $6,000 and $1,450 respectively. The reader will doubtless recognize that the analysis here is similar to the analysis of the seven-spot Keno game in Example 14–2.

A more general case is one in which the expected damage D varies continuously with the magnitude of the flood flow. In such a case, D can be plotted on rectangular coordinate paper as a function of p; the area under the curve will give the expected value of annual damages.[5] In Example 9-2 and in our various problems dealing with the evaluation of proposed flood control projects, it is assumed that this method has been used.

If the relationship between D and p can be described by a mathematical function, the expected value may be determined by integration.

General Comments on Economic Aspects of Engineering Design to Reduce Risk of Some Undesired Event. Example 14-3 is representative of a type of problem occurring in practically every field of engineering. The selection of a safety factor in structural design implies the balancing of the greater risk of structural failure with a lower safety factor against the larger investment required by a higher safety factor; the design of a sewer that carries storm water implies balancing the damages that will occur if sewer capacities are inadequate in severe storms against the extra cost of building sewers with larger diameters; a similar problem exists in the selection of the waterway area for any highway or railway drainage structure. Similarly, a program of acceptance inspection of manufactured product may require the balancing of the costs associated with the risk of passing defective parts or defective final product against increased inspection costs if more product is inspected; the allotment of public funds to grade-crossing-elimination projects implies balancing the prospective accidents at any crossing against the cost of eliminating that crossing; the design of an electric generating station and distribution system implies weighing the prospective damages from service outages against the cost of reducing the chance of such outages. Illustrations of this sort might be multiplied indefinitely.

If such problems are to be solved quantitatively rather than by someone's guess, estimates must be made of:

1. The expected frequencies of the undesired events under various alternative plans of design and operation
2. The expected consequences if the undesired events occur, expressed in money terms insofar as is practicable
3. The money outlays (both immediate investment and subsequent disbursements) to make various degrees of reduction in the risk
4. Any other future differences—either measurable in money terms or otherwise—associated with alternative designs or operating policies to be compared

---

[5] For a good illustration of this method, see J. B. Franzini, "Flood Control—Average Annual Benefits," *Consulting Engineer*, May, 1961, pp. 107–109.

The practical difficulty lies in evaluating these items, particularly the first two. It is generally easy to recognize cases in which it clearly pays to reduce a risk because the cost of reducing the risk is small, and the risk itself and the prospective damages if the undesired event occurs are large. Similarly, it is easy to recognize cases at the other extreme where the cost of reducing the risk is high, and the risk of the undesired event occurring is very slight.

But often it is not possible to make a quantitative approach to those many troublesome cases in which the answer is not obvious, simply because of the absence of any reliable information as to the frequencies of the events against which it is desired to protect, and as to the amount of the damages that will occur if the events take place. Often this information does not exist merely because of the absence of any systematic effort to get it. In some cases, however, even after such systematic effort is started, the securing of useful data may require the passage of a considerable period of time.

Even though records are available as to the frequencies of undesired events and as to the kinds of damages that have occurred from them, it may be difficult or impossible to place a money valuation on all of the damages. This is particularly true in estimates relative to those types of catastrophe that involve human suffering. Thus irreducibles may play an important part in economy studies of this type, even though the necessary facts are available to take decisions out of the "hunch" class.

Some Difficulties in Estimating Probabilities of Extreme Events. The prediction of an extreme event such as a Keno player having 7 winning spots on a 7-spot card is a fairly simple and straightforward matter. All that is required is to do some arithmetic and to apply the classical definition of probability.

In contrast, if an economy study calls for estimates of the probabilities of infrequent events and the frequency definition of probability must be used, the problem usually is more troublesome. For instance, in our flood spillway example, flood probabilities were estimated as low as 0.0005, that is, 1 year in 2,000. On most streams in the United States, the available records on which such estimates must be based vary from none at all to records extending for approximately 70 years!

In estimating flood frequencies and other extreme hydrologic phenomena, two types of extrapolation may be required. One is an extrapolation in space; in the common case where stream flow records are not available at the particular site in question, it is necessary to draw conclusions from records at some other site on the same stream, or possibly from records on other streams deemed to be comparable. The other is an extrapolation in time, which obviously is required if, say, a 500-year flood is to be estimated from a 25-year record. Different extrapolators can and do reach widely different conclusions about the probabilities of extreme events.

In other engineering fields there are other types of difficulties in estimating the hazard of extreme events. For instance, proposals for changes in highway design often are based on the assertion that a particular location involves more than normal accident hazard and that this hazard can be reduced by a proposed design change. Some practical difficulties in the collection and interpretation of highway accident data are indicated in the following paragraph from a letter written by a distinguished highway engineer: [6]

The identification of an accident-prone location is the bone of contention. Police reports may, at best, provide a guide. They are never complete or conclusive. Seldom do they accurately pinpoint the location and often they err as to cause. A long, straight stretch of road may develop a lot of accidents and thus be identified as an accident-prone location. Actually, the location has nothing to do with it. Poor speed law enforcement and lack of adequate police patrolling may be the cause. I'll bet you that wouldn't show up in the report. There are many dangerous situations where the necessary coincidence of conditions and events has not occurred, and, therefore, no accident record exists. This does not change the hazardous nature. The Angel of Death has merely withheld his hand. I cite the infamous Dansville Hill on our Route 36 as an example. Here is a long steep hill terminating in the main business section of a moderate sized village. To my personal knowledge, at least 20 large trucks have lost their brakes on that hill and roared down into the Village. So far no one has been hit or killed! It took four long years to finally convince the statistics boys that here was a hazardous situation. We now have a relocation under construction. There are many other potential killers of a similar nature.

The Concept of a Constant System of Chance Causes. The following quotations present important ideas that should be helpful in an analyst's decision on whether or not to use probability calculations in any particular economy study.

Wadsworth and Bryan give this clear explanation of the concept of a random variable: [7]

On an abstract level, ordinary mathematics is concerned with independent variables, the values of which may be chosen arbitrarily, and dependent variables, which are determined by the values assigned to the former. In the

---

[6] This letter, dated July 25, 1966, from Robert W. Sweet, Chief Engineer of the New York State Department of Transportation, to A. E. Johnson, Executive Secretary of the American Association of State Highway Officials, was printed in *Highway Research News,* Highway Research Board, Washington, D.C., Winter 1967, pp. 46–49, under the title "Traffic Safety and the Highway Engineer."

[7] G. A. Wadsworth and J. G. Bryan, *op. cit.,* pp. 41–42.

concrete domain, science aims at the discovery of laws whereby natural phenomena are interrelated, and the value of a particular variable can be determined when pertinent conditions are prescribed. Nevertheless, there exist enormous areas of objective reality characterized by changes which do not seem to follow any definite pattern or have any connection with recognizable antecedents. We do not mean to suggest an absence of causality. However, from the viewpoint of an observer who cannot look behind the scenes, a variable produced by the interplay of a complex system of causes exhibits irregular (though not necessarily discontinuous) variations which are, to all intents and purposes, random. Broadly speaking, a variable which eludes predictability in assuming its different possible values is called a *random variable,* or synonymously a *variate.* More precisely, a random variable must have a specific range or set of possible values and a definable probability associated with each value.

In writing about manufacturing quality control, Dr. W. E. Deming made the following observations that have widespread general application: [8]

There is no such thing as constancy in real life. There is, however, such a thing as a *constant-cause system.* The results produced by a constant-cause system vary, and in fact may vary over a wide band or a narrow band. They vary, but they exhibit an important feature called *stability.* Why apply the terms *constant* and *stability* to a cause system that produces results that vary? Because the same percentage of these varying results continues to fall between any given pair of limits hour after hour, day after day, so long as the constant-cause system continues to operate. It is the *distribution* of results that is constant or stable. When a manufacturing process behaves like a constant-cause system, producing inspection results that exhibit stability, it is said to be in *statistical control.* The control chart will tell you whether your process is in statistical control.

The frequency definition of probability given near the start of this chapter began with the clause "Assume that if a large number of trials are made under the same essential conditions." The phrase "constant system of chance causes" coined by Walter Shewhart in his pioneer writings on quality control deals with the issue of whether or not the same essential conditions have existed in the past and are expected to continue to exist in the future. The Shewhart quotation that opened this chapter emphasized the point that some quantities (such as the number of heads in 100 tosses of a penny) seem to behave over long periods of time as if they were random variables, whereas other quantities (such as the price of a favorite stock) do not behave in this way.

Presumably, when an economy study includes expected values obtained by multiplying one or more probabilities by one or more associated money amounts, the analyst who makes the multiplication believes

---

[8] W. E. Deming, "Some Principles of the Shewhart Methods of Quality Control," *Mechanical Engineering,* vol. 66, pp. 173–177, March, 1944.

that he is dealing with a random variable and that a constant system of chance causes will continue to be present throughout his analysis period. Or, at least, he believes that prospective changes in the system of chance causes will be so small that the conclusions of his economy study will be relatively insensitive to these changes.

Expected Values May Be Misleading Guides to Certain Types of Decisions. Even though a constant system of chance causes is anticipated and the estimates of the relevant probabilities are deemed to be entirely satisfactory and the monetary evaluations of the associated events are believed to be correct, it does not follow that it is always reasonable to base economic decisions on expected values. Such values are based on relative frequencies in the long run. Not all decision makers are in a position to take advantage of what is anticipated in the long run. Only one decision may be involved, or, at most, only a relatively few decisions.

Vogt and Hyman [9] illustrate this point by citing the case of a man who is given the choice between two favorable alternatives (a) the certain receipt of $1,000, and (b) the receipt of $10,000 only if the result of a single toss of a fair coin is heads. The expected value of (a) is $1,000 and of (b) $5,000; it therefore appears that (b) is clearly the economic choice. But this man needs exactly $1,000 for an immediate operation to restore his vision and has no other source of this money. His choice therefore is between (a) getting his sight back, and (b) a 0.5 probability of getting his sight back plus an additional $9,000. With this translation of monetary consequences into resulting nonmonetary consequences, it is clear that the sensible choice is (a) in spite of its lower expected money value.

Consider also the case of an automobile owner considering the purchase of liability insurance or a home owner deciding whether or not to take fire insurance. It is clear that only a part of the total premiums that an insurance company receives can be used to pay damage claims. (This is approximately half in the case of many fire insurance companies in the United States.) The remainder must go for sales commissions and operating expenses. If the insurance company has made a good evaluation of the risks associated with each policy, the expected value of the recovery by the insured is bound to be considerably less than the amount paid by the insured.

But the monetary figures used in computing expected values may be an imperfect measure of the favorable or adverse consequences of a particular event. For an individual, an insurance policy can give protection against an extreme event that might mean financial ruin or severe

[9] E. Z. Vogt and Ray Hyman, *Water Witching, U.S.A.* (Chicago: University of Chicago Press, 1959), p. 196.

financial hardship if the event should actually occur. Thus, although large geographically diversified enterprises may find it economical to act as self-insurers, individuals and small business enterprises are well advised to carry fire, casualty, and liability insurance even though a decision to do so does not minimize the expected value of a prospective negative cash flow.[10] Similarly, the public utility company in Example 14–3 might well conclude to design, say, against the 200-year flood rather than against the 100-year flood.

Differences in Personal Attitudes Toward Risk Taking. Jones pays $100 for a fire insurance policy hoping that he will never have a fire that will result in his collecting any insurance. However, considering the probabilities associated with various damaging fires and the payments that will be made to him if a fire occurs, the expected value of his recovery is only $50. Jones' decision to take the insurance policy reflects his aversion to a particular type of risk.

Smith pays 60 cents for a 7-spot Keno card at the XYZ Club, hoping that his card will have 7 winning spots so that the club will pay him $5,500. However, as we saw in Example 14–2, the expected value of his recovery is about 45 cents. Our calculations in that example showed that in the long run, he could expect to win the $5,500 in only 1 game in approximately 41,000 and that he would do better than getting his 60 cents back in only 1 game in approximately 105. Smith's decision to buy the 7-spot Keno card reflects his preference for a particular type of risk.

Johnson, who pays 60 cents for a 2-spot Keno card which also has a 45-cent expected value of recovery, shows still a different attitude toward risk. The XYZ Club has a Keno game every few minutes; if Johnson spends several evenings playing 2-spot Keno, the chances are good that he will win occasionally, that he will end with a reasonable fraction (say, at least half) of his money back, and that he may even get all his money back, paying nothing for his pleasure in gambling.[11] On the other hand, he has only a slight chance of any substantial winning over a long series of games.

The observed fact that different persons have quite different attitudes toward risk has led certain theorists to hunt for ways to quantify such

[10] The authors once knew a brilliant mathematician who refused to buy insurance of any sort on the grounds that the expected value of the recovery by the insured was necessarily less than the cost of the insurance. He seemed to us to be deficient in judgment about practical affairs in spite of his undoubted genius in his special field.

[11] If he wins 4 games out of 100, he will get back half the $60 he has bet; if he wins 8 games, he will get it all back. A student of probability may apply the binomial distribution to find that in 100 games the probability that he will win at least 4 is approximately 0.86, and the probability that he will win 8 or more games is approximately 0.25. But the probability that he will win more than 10 games out of 100 is only 0.04.

attitudes. *Cardinal utility theory,* originally proposed by von Neumann and Morgenstern, provides one approach.[12] Ralph Swalm introduces an explanation of this theory as follows: [13]

According to the theory, each individual has a measurable preference among various choices available in risk situations. This preference is called his utility. Utility is measured in arbitrary units which we will call "utiles." By suitable questioning we can determine for each individual a relationship between utility and dollars which is called his utility function. This plot offers a picture of his attitude toward taking risks.

In any decision involving risk, a man will choose that alternative which maximizes his utility. Once we know his utility function, the odds he assigns to events in a decision-making situation, and the consequences of each possible outcome, we should be able to predict his choice in that situation, since he will attempt to maximize his utility.

It seems to the authors of this book that utility theory may at some future time make useful contributions to engineering economy but that it has not yet reached the point where it is able to do so. Personal attitudes toward risk depend greatly on the surrounding circumstances and are not necessarily fixed for any given individual. Moreover, there are practical difficulties in measuring attitudes toward risk; although an individual may answer questions that define what he *says* he will do in risk situations described to him in terms of known probabilities and expected values, it rarely is possible to measure the risks and expected values associated with his actual decisions. Finally, it is not clear what the appropriate use of a utility function would be as a guide to rational decision making, even though such a function were a valid description of a personal attitude and could be accurately defined.

Use of Estimated Probabilities in Inventory Models. The economic lot size problem, which we discussed in Chapter 12, is one of several interrelated problems that deal with inventory policy. The economic size of purchase orders and the economic size of reserve stock are other common problems in this general class. The reserve stock problem deals with the stipulated "order point" or "reorder level," that is, the minimum size of available stock at which a new production order or purchase order should be initiated.[14]

[12] John von Neumann and Oskar Morgenstern, *Theory of Games and Economic Behavior* (Princeton, N.J.: Princeton University Press, 1947).

[13] In an article "Utility Theory—Insights Into Risk Taking," *Harvard Business Review,* November–December 1966, pp. 123–136. For our readers who have not been exposed to the subject elsewhere, we recommend the Swalm article as a clear brief introduction to utility theory.

[14] See Exhibit 12–4 on page 269 of E. L. Grant and L. F. Bell, *Basic Accounting and Cost Accounting* (New York: McGraw-Hill Book Co., Inc., 2d ed., 1964), for a diagram illustrating the types of forms, records, and operating rules associated with a standard order point and a standard purchase order size.

The economic lot size analysis in Examples 12–3 and 12–4 implied that U, the number of pieces used per day, would be constant throughout the working year. But in most manufacturing operations absolute constancy in such usage would be the exception rather than the rule. The reader might reasonably ask whether a model that assumes a constant rate of use is good enough for practical purposes.

No such question can be answered with a firm "Yes" or "No" that applies to all circumstances. Nevertheless, a fair answer is "Generally speaking, yes." We saw in Example 12–3 that total cost was relatively insensitive to moderate changes in lot size. Of the various classes of costs listed in Table 12–3, only those associated with the size of the maximum inventory would be changed by assuming some variability in daily use with no change in total annual production.

On the other hand, if an analysis is made to determine the economic reorder level, variability in rate of use is extremely important. Such an analysis tries to balance the inventory carrying charges, which increase as the reorder level is increased, against losses due to running out of stock, the probability of which is increased as the reorder level is decreased. The risk of a stockout at any reorder level depends on the expected variability in the rate of use. Formulas that aim to determine an economic reorder level generally make use of the mathematics of probability.[15]

The economic aspects of inventory management are complicated further if there is deterioration in quality of items that are held in storage for considerable periods of time. Also, with reference to purchasing, the appropriate reorder level will depend on the expected time interval (possibly variable) between the issuance of a purchase order and the actual receipt of the items purchased. Models incorporating these matters may require the use of the mathematics of probability.

Intuitive Probabilities. We started this chapter with the classical and frequency definitions of probability. The application of either of these definitions implies the existence of some event for which it is possible to make many trials "under the same essential conditions."

Obviously, not all events in the uncertain future are of this type. Sometimes it is clear that the concept of relative frequency in the long run does not apply because only one trial of a future event will be made under a particular set of conditions. Moreover, it may be evident that there has been no constant system of chance causes operating in the

---

[15] For a clear modern exposition of the various economic aspects of the inventory problem, see B. E. Goetz, *Quantitative Methods: A Survey and Guide for Managers* (New York: McGraw-Hill Book Co., Inc., 1965), pp. 368–419.

past that can be deemed to apply to the future event in question. For example, a proposal is made in a manufacturing company to manufacture and market a product that no one has ever made before.

In circumstances of this type, certain modern writers on operations research and statistical decision theory advocate the use of "probabilities" obtained by intuition.[16] A whole body of mathematical procedures intended to guide economic decisions has been based on the use of such probabilities. The validity of these procedures is currently a matter of controversy. In this book, we have not included any explanations of these procedures.

In the extensive literature pro and con about the use of intuitive probabilities, there is one point adverse to their use that we have never seen mentioned. Consider any formal analysis to be submitted to guide managerial decisions about an event where there will be only one trial. Where there are pressures on analysts to support certain predetermined conclusions, the use of intuitive probabilities may give the analysts an easy way to cheat.[17] It is pointed out in Chapter 21 that there is a chance to post-audit many of the estimates that analysts must make in connection with economy studies. But there can never be a chance to post-audit an intuitive probability where only a single trial is to be made.

Some Special-Purpose Definitions that May Lead to Semantic Confusion. Certain writers on operations research and statistical decision theory classify decisions into three groups, described as (1) decisions under certainty, (2) decisions under risk, and (3) decisions under uncertainty. Where only one set of estimates of the outcome is made for each alternative, the decision is described as being made under "certainty." Where two or more different mutually exclusive estimates of outcomes are made for an alternative, and probabilities (which must

[16] For a clear exposition of the case for the use of such "personal" probabilities, see Robert Schlaifer, *Probability and Statistics for Business Decisions* (New York: McGraw-Hill Book Co., Inc., 1959).

[17] The authors have observed what seemed to them to be cheating even when the conventional concept of mathematical probability was applicable but it was necessary to extrapolate to estimate probabilities of extreme events. On one proposed flood control project, distinguished hydrologists using the generally preferred method of analysis estimated a certain flood, much larger than any that had occurred during the period of record, to be a 1,000-year flood (i.e., to have a probability of 0.001 of taking place in any one year). However, political pressures in favor of the project were very strong. The hydrologists making the official analysis for a certain government agency used an extrapolation technique that contained a "fudge factor" that could be manipulated to give the conclusion that this same flood was a 100-year flood. The expected value of the damages that would be caused by this flood was of course 10 times as great with a probability of 0.01 rather than 0.001. The consequence of the use of the fudge factor in the probability estimate was to change an unfavorable **B/C** ratio to a favorable one.

add to 1) are somehow assigned to each estimate, the decision is described as being made under "risk." (In many instances, such an assignment of probabilities can be made only by intuition.) Where two or more different mutually exclusive estimates are made for an alternative and these estimates are presumed to include all possible outcomes, and where no probabilities are assigned, the decision is described as being made under "uncertainty."

To anyone who is not one of the limited number of professional specialists who have adopted the foregoing terminology, any discussion that assumes these meanings can be extremely misleading because these meanings do not fit the common usage of the words *certainty, uncertainty,* and *risk.* The consequences of a choice among alternatives are rarely, if ever, *certain;* few, if any, decisions of the type we examine in this book can be made under conditions of certainty if the word *certainty* is interpreted as having its usual meaning. The distinction that the special-purpose terminology makes between risk and uncertainty is arbitrary and does not fit any of the common meanings of these two words.

Another possible source of confusion in the use of words exists because of the difference between the meaning of the phrase *expected value* when used in the sense illustrated in Examples 14–1 and 14–2 and its meaning when used in its ordinary sense. The word *expected* used in its popular sense can be applied to any estimate about the future. Therefore, any estimate of future cash flow made for an economy study might conceivably be called an expected value. However, an estimate of future cash flow is not an expected value in the probabilistic sense unless it has been obtained by two or more different estimates of some future cash flow, unless each of the estimates of this future cash flow has been multiplied by its estimated probability and the probabilities add to 1, and unless these products have been added together.

The Troublesome Problem of Making Investment Decisions with Imperfect Estimates of the Future. Our discussion in Chapters 1 and 2 outlined a suggested approach to an engineering economy study. Alternatives should be defined. The differences in their consequences should be estimated and expressed insofar as practicable in commensurable units (i.e., in money units). A primary criterion for decision making should be applied to the monetary figures; this criterion should be chosen with the objective of making the best use of the limited available resources. In some cases, also, secondary decision making criteria should be used; such secondary criteria may be related to the inevitable lack of certainty associated with all estimates of the future. Finally, someone must make a decision among the alternatives. The decision maker should consider the analysis as related to the primary criterion. He should consider the analysis as related to the secondary criteria if any such have been established. He should also give recognition to any prospective differences in consequences that were not expressed in terms of money (i.e., to what we have called the irreducible data).

Where should uncertainties about the future be introduced into the foregoing sequence of procedures? In the view of the authors of this book, there is no one best way to do this under all circumstances.

Moreover, there seems to be no standard practice in this matter either in industry or government. In many types of economy studies there is no formal recognition of uncertainty. But where there is a systematic policy of allowing for uncertainty, the allowance sometimes is made in the estimating, sometimes in the selection of the minimum attractive rate of return where this rate is used as the primary criterion for investment decisions, sometimes through sensitivity analysis (possibly related to formal secondary decision criteria), and sometimes at the final decision making level through viewing uncertainty as one of the irreducibles.

In many economy studies there is a good case for doing nothing at all about the observed fact that an estimate of future cash flow nearly always seems to miss its mark on one side or the other. If experience indicates that the favorable misses tend to be as frequent and as large as the unfavorable misses, and if there is no way to judge in advance which particular estimates will have the favorable misses and which the unfavorable ones, there is nothing useful that can be done about the matter. Of course there should be a sufficient number of estimates involved to give the favorable and unfavorable misses a chance to offset one another. Such a condition might exist, say, with reference to estimates for cost reduction projects in a large manufacturing company or with reference to estimates to guide decisions on alternative designs in an expanding public utility company.

Sometimes, uncertainty is allowed for in estimates for economy studies through the practice of shading estimates to be "conservative" by estimating positive cash flows on the low side and negative cash flows on the high side. Sometimes, there is a formal allowance for uncertainty made in the estimates by using probabilities in connection with associated monetary figures; if so, some of the estimates entering into the economy study will be *expected values* in the sense that this phrase is used in Examples 14-1, 14-2, and 14-3 and in a number of the problems at the end of this chapter. As pointed out earlier in the chapter, a distinction needs to be made between uncertainties that can legitimately be expressed as probabilities and other types of uncertainties.

Where dissimilar types of proposed investments compete for limited funds, and where experience indicates that some types have a considerably greater risk of loss than other types, it is common to require a higher prospective rate of return from the proposals deemed to be riskier. As explained in Chapter 21, such a requirement often is applied at the capital budgeting level without a stipulation in advance of the minimum attractive rate of return for any particular project. However, a case of an advance stipulation was mentioned in Chapter 11; a certain oil company required an after-tax i^* of 10% for projects in marketing and transportation, 14% for projects in refining, and 18% for projects in production.

As pointed out in Chapter 13, sensitivity studies may be a great help to decision makers, particularly where certain constraints put upper and lower bounds on the extent to which actual values will depart from estimated values. Chapter 21 describes a case of the systematic use of secondary decision criteria based on the concept of sensitivity.

A useful piece of advice is not to make allowances for the *same* uncertainties at a number of different stages in the process of analysis and decision making. For instance, do not shorten estimated lives, then shade estimates of cash flow by arbitrary decreases in estimates of cash receipts and increases in estimates of cash disbursements, then require an extremely high i^* because of risk, and then also give weight to the risk at the final step of making the decision. Such a policy of quadruple counting of a recognized hazard may cause a failure to approve many proposed investments that actually would be very productive.

PROBLEMS

14–1. In the one-spot version of Keno at the XYZ Club, a 60-cent ticket pays $1.80 whenever the player's chosen number turns out to be a winning spot. What is the expected value of a player's winnings on each game? (*Ans.* = 45 cents.)

14–2. In the 7-spot version of Keno at the XYZ Club, a $6 ticket pays off according to the following schedule:

Winning Spots	Payoff
0 to 3	None
4	$ 6
5	120
6	2,450
7	25,000

Use the probabilities tabulated in Example 14–2 to compute the expected value of the winnings of a player who buys such a $6 ticket. (*Ans.* = $3.754.)

14–3. Consider the solutions in Example 14–2 and Problem 14–2. Discuss possible reasons why the XYZ Club gives the buyers of $6 tickets relatively less favorable treatment than the buyers of 60-cent tickets. (The club has a policy, announced to all players, of never paying more than $25,000 to the aggregate of the winners in any game.) Do you see any similarity between what you think is the reasoning of the XYZ Club on this matter and the type of reasoning appropriate in decisions about designs intended to reduce the adverse consequences of extreme events such as floods, fires, earthquakes, and tidal waves?

14–4. There is 1 chance in 20 that a certain event will occur in any given year; if it occurs it will require an expenditure of $30,000. With an i^* of 8%, what is the justifiable present expenditure to eliminate this risk for 20 years? What is the justifiable present expenditure to reduce the risk from 1 in 20 to 1 in 50 for the same 20 years. Assume that the expected value of the outlay if the event occurs is deemed to be an appropriate measure of the annual cost of the risk. (Ans. = $14,730; $8,840.)

14–5. In a factory with fire insurance based on a value of $400,000, an engineer suggests the installation of an automatic sprinkler system costing $22,000. This will reduce the annual fire insurance cost from 1.32% to 0.54%. On the hypothesis that insurance rates need to be set high enough so that only half of the total premiums collected by an insurance company will be available to pay for fire damages, the management estimates that the expected value of the damages that would be compensated by insurance will be one-half the insurance premium. It also estimates that on the average the total adverse consequences of a fire will be 3 times the losses on which recovery can be made. The annual cost of operation and maintenance of the sprinkler system is estimated as $150.

Assuming a before-tax i^* of 15% and assuming a 20-year life for the sprinkler system with zero salvage value, make calculations to compare the alternatives (a) continue without sprinkler system, and (b) install sprinkler system. Of course a $400,000 fire insurance policy will be continued either with or without the sprinkler system.

What matters not reflected by the use of expected values do you think might reasonably enter into management's choice between these alternatives?

14–6. The owner of an orange grove in a relatively frost-free area is considering the question whether or not to purchase and operate smudge pots as a protection against frost. An investigation of the weather records in this area shows that during the past 50 years there have been 4 years with freezes sufficiently bad to injure the fruit. It is estimated that on the average such a damaging freeze will reduce the cash receipts from the sale of the crop by about 75%. Average annual gross receipts from this grove during a year without frost are estimated as $12,000.

The initial investment in smudge pots to protect this grove will be $1,500. The life of the pots is estimated as 20 years. Annual labor cost for setting out pots in the autumn, removing in the spring, and cleaning is estimated as $300. Average annual fuel cost will be $50. Assuming that pots will give complete protection against loss due to frost, show calculations to provide a basis for judgment on whether it is desirable to purchase and operate the pots. Assume a before-tax i^* of 10%.

What matters not reflected by the use of expected values do you think might reasonably enter into the owner's decision on this matter? Discuss the sensitivity of the conclusions of your analysis to changes in the various parameters, for example, changes in i^*, in the estimated probability of a damaging freeze, in the price of oranges, and in the labor cost associated with using the smudge pots.

14–7. Two sites are under consideration for a proposed warehouse building. At either site a $500,000 fire insurance policy will be taken on the building and its contents. At site A, the annual insurance rate will be 0.65%; at site B it will be 0.90%. It is estimated that the expected value of the damage that would be compensated by insurance is one-half of the insurance premium. It also is estimated that on the average the total adverse consequences of a fire will be 2.5 times the losses on which recovery can be made from the insurance company. Sites A and B differ only in the cost of land and in risk of fire damage. The estimated life of the warehouse is 40 years with zero salvage value.

Considering the differences in insurance costs and in the expected value of the adverse consequences of a fire that will not be compensated by insurance, and using a before-tax $i°$ of 10%, how much extra could be paid for site A? Assume that there will be no change in land values over the life of the warehouse.

14–8. In the selection of the spillway capacity of a proposed dam, estimates are made of the spillway cost to provide for various flows, and of the probabilities of the flows being exceeded, as follows:

Flow in Cu. Ft. per Sec.	Probability of Greater Flow in Any One Year	Investment in Spillway to Provide for This Flow
8,400	0.08	$200,000
9,900	0.05	225,000
12,200	0.02	260,000
14,000	0.01	300,000
17,000	0.005	330,000
19,000	0.002	360,000

Investment charges on the spillway are to be calculated on the basis of a 75-year life with zero salvage value, an $i°$ of 5½%, and no taxes (as this is a public works project). Operation and maintenance costs will be unaffected by the spillway capacity chosen. The estimated damages are approximately $350,000 if the flow exceeds the spillway capacity.

What spillway capacity makes the sum of investment charges and expected value of damages a minimum? Discuss the sensitivity of this minimum cost capacity to the chosen $i°$, to the estimated damages if spillway capacity is exceeded, and to the estimated probabilities of the extreme floods.

14–9. Compare the sums of investment charges and expected values of damage for the 6 spillway capacities of Problem 14–8 assuming that the damage will be $300,000 if the spillway capacity is exceeded by not more than 1,500 cubic feet per second, and $400,000 if it is exceeded by more than 1,500 cubic feet per second. Estimated probabilities that certain other flood magnitudes (in cubic feet per second) will occur in any year are as follows:

Flow	Probability
11,400	0.03
13,700	0.0115
15,500	0.0075
18,500	0.003
20,500	0.001

14-10. The payoff schedule for a 4-spot 60-cent Keno ticket at the XYZ Club is as follows:

Winning Spots	Ticket Pays
2	$ 0.60
3	2.50
4	70.00

Show the calculations to determine the expected value of the payoff to a player who buys such a ticket.

14-11. (This is adapted from an example in a paper by C. H. Oglesby and E. L. Grant published in Volume 37 of Highway Research Board Proceedings.)

It is desired to select a size for a box culvert for a rural highway in central Illinois. The drainage area has 400 acres of mixed cover with slopes greater than 2%. The culvert will be 200 feet long. As the headroom is critical, the culvert can be only 4 feet high. If the water rises more than 5 feet above the streambed, the road will be overtopped. Damage to highway and adjacent property for each overtopping will be $5,000.

If the project is to be built at all, the minimum acceptable culvert for this location is a simple box 10 x 4 feet, which will be overtopped, on the average, once in 5 years. Four possible designs, with associated initial costs, capacities, and probabilities of overtopping, are as follows:

	First Cost	Capacity Cu. Ft. per Sec.	Probability of Overtopping in Any One Year
A. Single culvert .... 10' x 4'	$11,000	300	0.20
B. Double culvert .... 8' x 4'	$15,000	400	0.10
C. Double culvert .... 10' x 4'	$19,000	500	0.04
D. Triple culvert .... 8' x 4'	$23,000	600	0.02

Which design gives the lowest sum of the annual cost of capital recovery of the investment and the expected value of the annual damage from overtopping? Assume an i^* of 7%. Assume culverts will have lives of 50 years with zero salvage value.

14-12. For the data of Problem 14-11, compute rates of return on increments of investment of B over A, C over B, and D over C. How should these be interpreted with reference to a stipulated i^* of 7%?

14-13. For the data of Problem 14-11, compute incremental benefit-cost ratios for B over A, C over B, and D over C. How should these be interpreted with reference to the choice among the four culvert sizes?

14-14. On page 286, in the discussion of a change in the data relative to estimated damages from floods greater than the spillway capacity in Example 14-3, it is stated: "Similar calculations for spillway capacities of 1,900 and 2,300 sec.ft. will yield figures for average annual damages of $6,000 and $1,450 respectively." Show your calculations to check these two figures.

15

Increment Costs and Sunk Costs

"What is a unit of business?" ... The most important unit is a single business decision.—J. M. CLARK [1]

Throughout this book it has been emphasized that it is always prospective *differences* between alternatives that are relevant in making a choice. In a going concern all past receipts and disbursements and many future ones will be unaffected by a particular decision. It often happens that average costs per unit (sometimes called "unit costs") are misleading guides to choosing between given alternatives.

A critical examination of the influence of a particular decision on receipts and disbursements often is required. Examples 15–1, 15–2, and 15–3 illustrate this point in relatively simple cases. These examples serve the incidental purpose of illustrating some common types of public utility rates.

EXAMPLE 15–1. INCREMENT COST OF ELECTRICITY FOR HOUSEHOLD PURPOSES

Facts of the Case. Consider the purchase of electric energy under the following domestic monthly rate:

Service charge of 50 cents
First 30 kw-hr @ 5 cents per kw-hr
Next 70 kw-hr @ 3 cents per kw-hr
All over 100 kw-hr @ 1.5 cents per kw-hr

A householder's monthly consumption of electricity is about 120 kw-hr, resulting in a monthly bill of $4.40. This is a "unit cost" of 3⅔ cents per kw-hr.

He is anxious to economize, and considers various ways to reduce the monthly electricity bill by eliminating or reducing the use of certain lights or electric appliances. Considering each possibility in turn, it is clear that unless the resulting reduction in monthly consumption is more than 20 kw-hr, the unit saving will be only 1½ cents per kw-hr; this is less than half of the above "unit cost" of 3⅔ cents. This reasoning may be applied to the lights in the living room, to the electric toaster, to the radio, or to any other device using electricity. Thus the average cost or so-called "unit cost" is not relevant to a de-

[1] J. M. Clark, *Studies in the Economics of Overhead Costs* (Chicago: University of Chicago Press, 1923), p. 213.

cision regarding the elimination or reduction of any individual item of use.[2] Similarly, it is irrelevant in the consideration of any proposed addition of load.

EXAMPLE 15–2. INCREMENT COST OF ELECTRICITY FOR INDUSTRIAL PURPOSES

Facts of the Case. A manufacturer purchases electricity under the following rate:

First 50 kw-hr per HP of maximum demand @ 3.0 cents per kw-hr
Next 50 kw-hr per HP of maximum demand @ 2.0 cents per kw-hr
Next 100 kw-hr per HP of maximum demand @ 0.7 cents per kw-hr
All over 200 kw-hr per HP of maximum demand @ 0.6 cents per kw-hr

In a representative month in which he uses 50,000 kw-hr with a maximum demand of 200 HP(149.2 kw.), his bill is computed as follows:

$$
\begin{array}{ll}
\text{10,000 kw-hr @ \ \ 3 cents =} & \$300 \\
\text{10,000 kw-hr @ \ \ 2 cents =} & 200 \\
\text{20,000 kw-hr @ 0.7 cents =} & 140 \\
\text{10,000 kw-hr @ 0.6 cents =} & \underline{\ \ 60} \\
\text{Total bill} & \$700
\end{array}
$$

His average cost per kw-hr is therefore $700 ÷ 50,000 = 1.4 cents.

The manufacturer contemplates installing certain equipment that will reduce labor costs on certain special jobs. This equipment will add 100 HP(74.6 kw.) to the maximum demand. As its average use will be about 10 hours per month, it will add only 750 kw-hr of energy per month. For a study to determine the economy of installing this new equipment, a figure is needed for the "cost" of this extra 750 kw-hr.

Solution: Unlike Example 15–1, the extra costs of extra kilowatt-hours cannot be found merely by examining the rates per kw-hr in the incremental blocks on the rate schedule. Because the size of each block in this rate depends on the maximum demand and because it is planned to change the maximum demand, it is necessary to compute the monthly bill with and without the new load. With the proposed load added to the representative month, the monthly bill is computed as follows:

$$
\begin{array}{ll}
\text{15,000 kw-hr @ \ \ 3 cents =} & \$450.00 \\
\text{15,000 kw-hr @ \ \ 2 cents =} & 300.00 \\
\text{20,750 kw-hr @ 0.7 cents =} & \underline{145.25} \\
\text{Total bill} & \$895.25
\end{array}
$$

This addition of $195.25 to the original $700 monthly bill results from the increase in the proportion of the total energy that is purchased at the higher blocks of the rate. It is of interest to note that the average cost per extra kw-hr is $195.25 ÷ 750 = 26 cents. This is in striking contrast to the previous average cost of 1.4 cents per kw-hr. It is evident that this is a situation in

---

[2] It should be emphasized that this reasoning applies to all the uses of electricity included in the 120 kw-hr. Up to 20 kw-hr, the 1½-cent unit saving may be applied to the elimination or the reduction of each on the assumption that no other elimination or reduction will be made. But the addition of the separate savings figured at the 1½-cent rate is meaningless. This is a simple example of what is called by J. B. Canning, the problem of "non-additive economic valuations."

which it would be decidedly misleading to make the assumption (one very commonly made in industrial economy studies) that additional kilowatt-hours can be purchased at the average unit cost of the energy already being purchased.

However, it would also be misleading to think of the 26-cent figure as an increment cost per unit. A more accurate view is that the additional 100 HP of maximum demand will add $190 to the monthly bill. With this extra demand added, each extra kw-hr of energy will add 0.7 cent to the bill. Thus 750 extra kw-hr add $5.25, making the total addition to the bill $190 + $5.25 = $195.25.

EXAMPLE 15–3. INCREMENT COST OF WHOLESALE GAS

Facts of the Case. A city buys gas for distribution and resale at the following monthly wholesale rate:

A "demand" charge of $3.30 times the maximum number of MCF (thousand cubic feet) used during any 24-hour period during the preceding 12 months, plus

A "commodity" charge of $0.18 times the number of MCF used during the current month

The city's current annual purchase of gas is 280,000 MCF. On the maximum day of the year, 1,600 MCF is used. From these two figures, the city's annual bill may be computed as follows:

Demand charge:	$3.30(12)(1,600) =	$ 63,360
Commodity charge:	$0.18(280,000) =	50,400
Total annual bill		= $113,760

This is an average cost of $113,760 ÷ 280,000 = $0.4063 per MCF.

The distribution system includes a number of old mains from which there is a moderate amount of leakage. Because the pressure in the mains is approximately constant throughout the year and because the leakage depends on pressure rather than on gas consumption, the leakage per day from any main will be approximately constant. In order to make economy studies regarding gas main replacement, it is desired to compute a unit figure per MCF to apply to the estimated gas losses that would be eliminated by the replacement of any particular main.

Solution: The key point here is that, unlike the gas consumption, the gas loss is uniform throughout the year. The loss on the maximum day of a 365-day year will be 1/365 of the annual loss. The amount added to the city's annual gas bill by each MCF of loss may be computed as follows:

Demand charge:	$3.30(12)(1/365) =	$0.1085
Commodity charge		= 0.18
Increment cost of a MCF lost		= $0.2885

This is nearly 30% less than the average cost per MCF purchased. The economy studies for gas main replacement would have given incorrect conclusions if the average cost of gas had been used rather than its incremental cost.

Load Factor and Capacity Factor. Two useful phrases originating in the generation of electricity are *load factor* and *capacity factor*. Load factor is defined as the ratio of average load to maximum load. Average and maximum loads may be taken for any desired period of time. Thus a power company will have a daily load factor each day that is the ratio of the average load for that day to the day's maximum load, and it will have an annual load factor that is the ratio of the average load for the year to the maximum load occurring during the year. A company with a typical daily load factor of 70% might conceivably have an annual load factor of 55% because of seasonal fluctuations in load.

Capacity factor is defined as the ratio of average load to maximum capacity. In comparing entire power systems it is more common to use load factor than capacity factor. This is chiefly because of the difficulty of securing a satisfactory uniform measure of power system capacity. It is appropriate, however, to speak of the capacity factor of an individual generating unit or of a generating station.

Although the terms "load factor" and "capacity factor" have a definite quantitative meaning in the electric power field, they are often used loosely in a qualitative sense in other fields of production. Thus one might say that a factory with a seasonal demand for its product might improve its load factor by taking on another product to be produced in the off season.

Some Aspects of Public Utility Rate Structures. Insofar as practicable, the rate structures of regulated utilities are designed to reflect the behavior of the utility's costs. In many cases a large fraction of a utility's costs are caused by a utility's readiness to serve rather than by the number of service units supplied. For example, a considerable part of the cost of serving natural gas to the city in Example 15–3 depended on the capacity of the pipe line. It was necessary to have sufficient pipe line capacity to supply the demand on the maximum day of the year. (Because of the use of gas for space heating, this was usually the coldest day of the year.) In a similar manner an electric utility's costs are related to the maximum generating and transmission capacity that must be provided. An urban transportation utility's costs depend on the peak loads of traffic when people go to work and return home.

Example 15–3 illustrated a gas rate in which one element was a charge for readiness to serve, based on the measured maximum demand during the year. Such a two-part rate, containing both a demand charge and a commodity charge, is referred to as a *Hopkinson* type of rate. In such a rate, it is obvious that the unit cost decreases as a customer's load factor increases.

Customers may object to direct charges that depend on maximum demand or connected load. The same result is obtained, with less objection because the relation of the maximum demand to the rate is not superficially obvious, by the *Wright* type of demand rate. This is a block rate in which the size of the respective blocks depends on the maximum demand. Example 15–2 illustrated such a rate.

A thorough discussion of the interesting subject of utility rate structures is beyond the scope of this book. The problems at the end of this chapter give a few instances of more complex rates than those illustrated in Examples 15–1 to 15–3. Problem 15–2 illustrates a wholesale electric rate that combines the Hopkinson and Wright types of rate. Problem 15–3 illustrates an electric rate under which off-peak demand (i.e., demand not occurring close to the system peak) is priced at a lower figure than on-peak demand.

Our examples and problems here are from the viewpoint of economy studies made for the purchasers of utility products or service rather than from the viewpoint of a utility company attempting to develop an equitable rate structure. We have used utility rates to emphasize the point that the uncritical use of average costs can lead to an unsound analysis and incorrect conclusions. Because a utility rate provides such a definite basis for predicting how a particular cost will be influenced by a proposed decision, examples involving utility rates provide clear illustrations of why economy studies need to be based on prospective *differences* between alternatives. Presumably such illustrations should be noncontroversial.

Nevertheless, even where utility rates are involved, many persons are inclined to use average costs as a basis for making decisions. For instance, in the case described in Example 15–3, in the initial phases of the replacement studies, the 40-cent average cost of purchased gas was adopted as the "obvious" figure for the unit cost of gas lost.

Relation of Economy Studies to the Accounts of an Enterprise. The tendency to use "unit cost" figures that are readily available, rather than to take a critical look at differences, seems to be even greater when data for economy studies are drawn from the accounts of an enterprise. Many economy studies will combine information obtained from the accounting system with information obtained from other sources, such as time studies or other types of performance tests. The usefulness of accounting information will depend upon the detail of the classification of accounts, the skill with which it has been drawn, and the care with which actual expenditures have been charged to the appropriate accounts.

However, even the best accounting systems may give misleading conclusions if the figures shown by the books of account are uncritically used. The point of view of an estimator for an economy study is necessarily different from the point of view of the accountant. The economy study is concerned with prospective differences between future alternatives. The accounts of the enterprise are a record of past receipts and disbursements. They generally involve apportionments of past costs against future periods of time, and apportionment of joint costs among various services or products; such apportionments are sometimes misleading to estimators who are making economy studies.

Illustrations of Incorrect Inferences from Accounting Apportionments. The following three cases relate to the experience of a city that owned its electrical distribution system, retailing electric energy. Although most of its power was purchased at wholesale rates from a large power system, a small part was generated at peak load periods by its diesel engines (of relatively small capacity) in its own generating plant. In the accounts of this city the expenses of the electric utility were carefully distinguished from the cost of carrying on governmental functions and from the cost of running the municipally owned water utility. The expenses of joint departments were prorated between the city government and the electric and water utilities on an equitable basis; the governmental departments and the water utility were charged by the electric utility for electricity used at rates such as might reasonably have been charged by a privately owned corporation. Three situations arose in which this well-organized plan of accounting served to block an understanding of the true differences between the alternatives which it was desired to compare.

In the first situation some of the councilmen examined the municipal report, which showed the cost of purchased energy at about 1 cent per kw-hr and the cost of generated energy at about 2.5 cents. They concluded from these costs that a substantial saving would result if the diesel plant were shut down and all power were purchased.

It turned out that no such conclusion as this was justified by the facts. Many of the charges included in the 2.5-cent unit cost were allocated charges which would not have been reduced if the generating station were shut down; they would simply have been allotted to some other account than "Power Generation." The crew that operated the diesel engines also operated the substation and the pumping plant for the water department; the labor cost was, therefore, divided uniformly among those three activities. But as it still would have been necessary to run the substation and waterworks, no reduction in labor cost could have been made by discontinuing the operation of the diesels. Another charge allotted against the "Power Generation" account was the depreciation of the diesel engines. This, however, was simply a time allotment against the current year of an expenditure that had been made many years before; no part of that past expenditure could be eliminated or recovered by shutting down the diesels.

Thus the generating costs that were really relevant to the question

"Shall we continue to operate the diesels, or shut them down and purchase all power?" appeared to be merely fuel, lubricants, and maintenance; these totaled about 0.8 cents per kw-hr. As power purchased was on a rate that included a substantial charge for maximum demand, the diesels had been operated only at periods of peak load in order to reduce the demand charge. If the diesels were shut down, the extra cost of purchasing the peak load energy would be considerably greater than the 1-cent average cost for the base load energy. When the councilmen finally recognized this as a problem in determining differences between alternatives, they were able to see that it was clearly economical to continue to generate peak load energy, despite the apparent showing of the accounts that generated energy cost much more than purchased energy.

In the second situation the question arose as to what savings were possible by a proposed temporary reduction of street lighting as a measure of economy. The city-owned electric utility charged the general city government for street-lighting energy at 2.5 cents per kw-hr, a fair rate, all things considered. In estimating the saving from this proposed temporary street-lighting reduction, the engineer making the estimate multiplied the expected reduction in energy consumption of 80,000 kw-hr per year by the 2.5-cent rate and concluded that the saving would be $2,000 a year. Here the engineer used the average cost that he found used in the accounting system and failed to recognize that most of the items that went into the 2.5-cent rate were not variable downward with a small reduction of street lighting.

When the increment cost situation was later recognized, it was apparent that almost the only cost that would be decreased was the cost of energy purchased at wholesale. Because of the structure of the wholesale rate, the last increment of energy cost considerably less than the average of purchased energy; in fact, less than one-third of the 2.5-cent figure previously estimated. When this real net saving to the city of about $600 in the power bill for the year was balanced against several hundred dollars of extra cost for wiring to make the change possible, it was clear that there was little or no real economy possible from the proposed temporary change and the city might as well have the benefit of the existing street lights.

In the third situation the question arose regarding the economy of the city's building its own generating station rather than continuing to purchase power. Here, in estimating the expense of the proposed generating station, the engineer's report included merely direct generating station costs and made no allowances for increased costs in other departments. In justification of this he argued that overhead costs were apportioned in the accounting system in proportion to direct costs and that as direct costs would not be increased with the proposed plant there would, therefore, be no increase in indirect costs as a result of the plant.

A more realistic examination of this situation indicated that his reasoning was in the same class with assuming that the increment cost of extra miles on your automobile was merely the out-of-pocket expense for gasoline; that is, this reasoning took a too short-run viewpoint. It seemed reasonable to believe that doubling the investment in the electric utility, as this would do, would increase the responsibility of the manager of that utility, and in the long run he would be better paid and would require an assistant sooner with the generating station than without it. It also seemed reasonable to believe that the operation of a generating station would involve more of such services as engineering, accounting, purchasing, and storekeeping than would the paying of a single power bill once a month. These conclusions were reinforced by an examination of the experience of other cities, which seemed to indicate quite definitely that expenses of these service departments always tended to move upward with any increase in activity. From such a study, it was possible to make a judgment as to what this long-run increase in expense in indirect departments would be. This item of cost had considerable weight in throwing the final decision against the generating plant which, on the basis of preliminary study, had appeared as if it might be economical.

The "With or Without" Viewpoint and the Concept of Cash Flow as Aids in Decision Making. The three cases just described had one characteristic in common with one another and with Examples 15-1 to 15-3. In each instance one alternative was to make some proposed change from the existing way of doing things and the other alternative was to continue this existing way. A search for the differences between such alternatives calls for a prediction of what will happen *with* the proposed change and *without* it. The phrase "with or without" will sometimes help to clarify the issues in such cases.

Throughout this book we have emphasized that, wherever practicable, the prospective physical differences between alternatives should be converted into prospective differences in cash flow. Although our concentration of attention on cash flow has been aimed particularly at the securing of data permitting the calculation of rates of return on proposed investments, the cash flow viewpoint is also helpful in avoiding the types of estimating errors that are discussed in the present chapter. Once an analyst adopts the cash flow viewpoint, he is likely to take a critical look at all figures based on allocations.

Treatment of Unused Capacity in Economy Studies. In any organization it is likely that various kinds of unused facilities will exist from time to time. Extra space may exist in office or warehouse or factory; extra capacity may exist for various service facilities (such as water, steam, or compressed air). Under such circumstances, a proposal for a new activity needing such facilities (e.g., expanded output, a new product, the production of items previously purchased) may not require any immediate investment to secure the facilities.

A similar, but slightly different, condition exists when it is possible to carry out the proposed new activities using existing facilities at some kind of a cost penalty until the time comes that the need for still further capacity makes it practicable to install a new unit of economic size. For example, the storage of additional material in an existing warehouse, already crowded to its economic capacity, might cause a disproportionately large increase in materials handling costs.

In an expanding organization most unused capacity that now exists is likely to be only temporary. For this reason it usually is incorrect for economy studies to assume that proposed new activities that will use existing unused facilities will never be responsible for investments in new facilities of the types in question. On the other hand, because an immediate investment in such facilities will not be required, it obviously is incorrect to make the economy studies assuming an investment before it will need to be made. Frequently, it should be recognized that the question at issue is the *timing* of an investment that will be required eventually. Ray I. Reul has made the following practical suggestion on this topic: [3]

The solution recommended for this problem is to specify that where facilities are to be provided from surpluses or where acquisition of facilities is to be postponed, the full cost of these acquisitions shall be included in the evaluation as a future requirement but not charged until the time the actual expenditure of these funds is anticipated. To guard against accidental or deliberate overoptimism in postponement, it is further suggested that permissible assumption of deferment be limited to five years or one-third of the life of the project, whichever is the lesser. In this way, such expenditures are included in the total investment specified, but their impact on profitability is lessened.

Figures 21–1 to 21–3 in Chapter 21 include an example of future investment requirements treated in the manner suggested by Reul.

Burden Rates Are Seldom Adapted for Use in Economy Studies. Cost accounting in the manufacturing industries classifies production expense into direct labor, direct material, and indirect manufacturing expense. This latter class may include a wide variety of items (such as

---

[3] R. I. Reul, "Profitability Index for Investments," *Harvard Business Review,* XXXV, No. 4 (July–August, 1957), 122.

salaries and wages of foremen, inspectors, clerical employees, crane operators, and storekeepers; operating supplies; packing and unpacking; shop losses due to defective material or workmanship; purchasing; receiving; shipping; heat, light, and power; plant maintenance; taxes, insurance, and rentals; and depreciation).

Indirect manufacturing expense is called by various shorter names, the most common of which are "burden," "overhead," and "expense." Although there is great variation in cost accounting systems, in many of them each item included in burden is allotted among the various departments (or production centers) on some basis that appears reasonable. Then the total burden allotted against a department is charged against the product of that department in proportion to some "burden vehicle." This burden vehicle will be something that is readily measurable regarding the product (such as its direct labor cost, its total direct cost, its labor hours, or its machine hours). More often than not the burden rate is "predetermined"; that is, it is based on the allotment of estimated indirect manufacturing expenses and on estimated direct labor cost (or other burden vehicle) reflecting estimated production.

In a department in which the vehicle is direct labor cost and the burden rate is 130%, each product is charged with $1.30 for every dollar of direct labor cost. Such burden allocation in cost accounting serves many useful purposes.

It does not follow, however, that a change in production methods that reduces direct labor cost by $100 will reduce indirect manufacturing expense by $130. Or, that if one of two alternative new machines involves $500 less direct labor cost than the other it will also involve $650 less indirect manufacturing expense. The only way to judge the relative effect of two alternatives on burden is to consider their probable effect on each of the individual items of indirect manufacturing expense that have been combined together in the burden rates.

Although the error of assuming that any saving in direct cost will be accompanied by a proportionate saving in indirect cost should be obvious, it appears that this error (which has appeared in several published formulas for determining economy) is often made in industry.

Allocations in Accounting and in Economy Studies. Thus it is necessary that the engineer look beneath the surface of an accounting figure before he uses it in his economy study.

For instance, an engineer for a railway company was called upon to compare the cost of increasing the generating capacity of the power plant serving one of the railway company's shops with the cost of purchasing power. In making the comparison, he found it necessary to recognize that the accounting charges to shop power that the railway made under its accounting routines did not reflect all of the costs that were pertinent to his comparison. For instance, one of the major savings that would result from purchased power was in the cost of coal, and a considerable portion of the coal cost was the cost of its transportation from the mine. But this transportation cost was not allocated to the account showing shop power expense; the railway accounts considered it merely as part of the cost of conducting transportation. Another major advantage of purchasing power as compared with increasing generating capacity was in the lower investment involved, with corresponding lower investment costs of interest, depreciation, and taxes. But none of these investment costs were allocated against shop power expense in the railway's accounts.

Treatment in Economy Studies of an Investment-Type Disbursement Charged as a Current Expense in the Accounts. In tabulating the effect of a decision on cash flow before income taxes, a disbursement is negative cash flow regardless of whether it is capitalized on the books of account or treated as a current expense. It often happens that certain nonrecurrent disbursements that will be "expensed" in the accounts are associated with the acquisition or replacement of physical assets. For example, in considering the replacement of a railway bridge, the cost of handling traffic during the replacement period may be different between alternative replacement structures. This cost of handling traffic will be considered as an operating expense in the railway accounts. Nevertheless, its effect on cash flow before income taxes is just the same as if it were capitalized in the accounts.

However, in any analysis to determine cash flow after income taxes, it is essential to differentiate between disbursements that are to be capitalized and those that are to be expensed. This point is developed in Chapter 16.

Cost Information That Accounting Records Will Not Give. Where the economy of some new process or machine is involved, estimates of operating costs must be obtained by experimental studies rather than from accounting records. Time studies or laboratory studies regarding the characteristics of new machinery may be combined with known wage rates and material costs and with an analysis of indirect costs in order to arrive at cost figures.

Frequently, an economy study requires the consideration of some cost that, by its very nature, cannot be isolated by accounting charges. For instance, in considering the economy of automatic block signal systems for railway trains, an important saving will be in the elimination of train stops. But what is the cost of stopping a train? The railway accounts cannot isolate this cost. It must be determined on the basis of fuel saved from an analysis of locomotive performance curves, and on the basis of the economies resulting from time saved.

In designing any cost accounting system, the question always arises as to the detail to which accounting records ought to be carried. To what extent may approximations be used in allocating costs in place of more precise methods of cost allocation that are more expensive? There is always the conflict between the expense of getting better accounting records and the value of the information obtainable from such records. No cost accounting system is justified that will not pay its way by giving information that is worth more than the cost of getting it. Where cost systems are planned with the idea of simplifying determinations of economy, the question is likely to arise whether it will be more economical to maintain regular continuous records or to make an occasional analysis when a particular sort of cost information is required. There will be, in many organizations, cost information useful to engineers, that must be obtained by analysis, rather than from the accounting records, simply because it does not pay to keep accounting records in such detail as would be required to furnish this information.

Allocation of a Previously Incurred Loss. It is not practicable for accountants to go back into past records and revise past figures when an error is discovered.

Once an industrial engineer made some suggestions of methods aimed to reduce the operating cost of the power plant in a factory. In the course of his investigation he also discovered that the amount of coal in the coal pile was much less than the amount shown by the inventory figure in the books of account.

He was greatly surprised some months later when the factory superintendent told him that the power plant operating costs had gone up rather than down. On investigation he discovered that the accountant had decided to spread the cost of the fuel shortage uniformly over the next 6 months after it was discovered, in order not to make it seem as if expenses had been very high in the month in which the shortage was discovered. This avoided distorting the comparative operating cost statements for various months. But the fuel shortage cost charged subsequent to its discovery more than neutralized the economies resulting from the engineer's suggestions! On superficial examination the situation appeared as if the fuel costs had not been reduced by his suggestions.

Increment Cost. The phrase *increment cost* has been used in this chapter to refer to a prospective difference in cost in certain "with or without" situations. This is not a phrase that can be given a precise definition in general terms; it is a phrase that is useful chiefly in reference to specific alternatives. Other phrases sometimes used in the same meaning are *incremental cost* and *differential cost*.

These phrases are also used in economic literature in connection with discussions of determination of pricing policies. The topic of pricing policy is a complex one that is beyond the scope of this book.

Difficulty in Estimating Increment Costs. Assume that an automobile owner is uncertain whether to use public transportation or his personal automobile for a certain 600-mile trip. Before he makes his decision, he wants to estimate the extra outlays in connection with his automobile if he should use it for this 600 miles.

Two extremes, neither valid, are sometimes observed when estimates of this type are made. One involves calculating a "unit cost" per mile of operation by dividing estimated total costs over the entire period of ownership by estimated total miles during this period; this unit figure is then multiplied by the mileage of a projected trip to find the cost of the trip. If our hypothetical car owner estimates his total costs over his period of ownership to be 15 cents per mile, and if he uses this type of reasoning, he will conclude that his 600-mile trip will involve automobile costs of $90.

Another extreme is to estimate merely the out-of-pocket expense for gasoline during the trip and to view this as the trip's cost for decision-making purposes. If our owner takes this extreme short-run view, and if he estimates his gasoline costs as 2.5 cents per mile, he will conclude that the 600-mile trip will cost him $15.

The reader will recognize that neither type of extreme estimate recognizes the "with-or-without" aspect of the car owner's decision. The total costs of car ownership include many items not affected by the decision to drive the car 600 extra miles. On the other hand, it is unlikely that the $15 for motor fuel covers all the extra long-run outlays that will be caused by the trip. Increased mileage tends to cause increased outlays for lubricants, tires, repairs and maintenance, and possibly accidents, even though no such outlays may happen to occur *during* a particular trip. If our car owner is to base his decision in part on cost, he needs some estimates of how these items are influenced by extra miles. He should recognize that an estimate of increment costs should be his objective, even though he cannot substantiate his estimate by the best possible cost and performance records on a single automobile.

Similarly, even though increment costs are not precisely determinable in industry, they need to be estimated wherever decisions are to be based on cost. As has been pointed out, questions of relative economy of technical alternatives are often complicated by the difference between the short-run and long-run viewpoints. This difference is even more troublesome in cases of increment cost pricing.

Cost Allocations in Accounting in Relation to Economy Studies. Illustrations have been given in situations in which accounting allocations of cost seemed to block a clear recognition of differences between alternatives. This suggests an important problem arising in the management of every business organization having more than one department, that is, "What should be the basis of joint cost allocations and interdepartmental charges?"

Of course, this question cannot be answered in general terms. Interdepartmental charges, for instance, may be established on an average cost basis or on an increment cost basis. (Either permits considerable room for controversy; in fact, the question of interdepartmental charges may be a source of bitter argument between department heads within an organization.) The point to be emphasized here is that no matter what basis is used, there will be some types of decisions in which it will be misleading to use the interdepartmental charges and joint cost allocations as established by the accounting system; no one answer can serve all purposes. No scheme is satisfactory without managerial understanding of its limitations.

The Concept of a Sunk Cost. Once the principle is recognized that it is the *difference* between alternatives that is relevant in their comparison, it follows that the only possible differences between alternatives for the future are differences in the future. The consequences of any decision regarding a course of action for the future cannot start before the moment of decision. Whatever has happened up to date has already happened and cannot be changed by any choice among alternatives for the future. This applies to past receipts and disbursements as well as to other matters in the past.

From the viewpoint of an economy study, a past cost should be thought of as a *sunk cost*, irrelevant in the study except as its magnitude may somehow influence future receipts or disbursements or other future matters. Although this principle that a decision made now necessarily deals with the future seems simple enough, many people have difficulty in accepting the logical implications of the principle when they make decisions between alternatives. This seems particularly true when sunk costs are involved. Although some of the failures to recognize the irrelevance of sunk costs involve a misuse of accounting figures, these mental obstacles to clear reasoning are by no means restricted to people who have had contact with the principles and methods of accounting.

This concept of the irrelevance of past costs is illustrated in a simple way in Examples 15–4 and 15–5.

EXAMPLE 15–4. IRRELEVANCE OF A PAST OUTLAY

Facts of the Case. Four years ago, Green contracted to buy a lot in a new subdivision in a large city with the intention of ultimately building a home on it. The purchase price was $3,000. He made a $300 down payment and has been paying $250 a year plus interest of 6% on the unpaid balance. He has also paid the taxes of $34 a year. He now owes $1,700 on the lot.

Under the terms of his contract, he has not yet secured legal title to the lot. In the event of a default on any payment due, his contract stipulates that he loses all of his past payments; however, he cannot be held for any additional payments through the operation of a deficiency judgment. His contract also permits him to pay off the unpaid balance in a lump sum at any time and thus to secure clear title to the property.

On returning to this city after an absence of two years or so, Green is ready to build his house. He has the funds in hand to pay $1,700 and take title to this lot. He discovers that prices of unimproved property in this city are now greatly depressed, particularly in this subdivision, but this does not alter Green's decision to build his home there. However, before Green has paid his $1,700, Brown, who owns a lot in the same block, offers to sell his lot to Green for $1,200. Brown's lot is the same size as the one on which Green has been making his payments, and, as far as Green can see, it is equally desirable in all respects. Green must therefore decide between (a) rejecting Brown's offer and paying the remaining $1,700 on his contract, and (b) defaulting on his contract and buying Brown's lot for $1,200.

The difference between these alternatives is clear enough. In (a) Green pays $1,700 and acquires title to a lot; in (b) he pays $1,200 and acquires title to an equally good lot. Alternative (b) saves $500 immediately and, as far as can be seen, there are no other differences in future cash flow between the alternatives. It is evident that it is less expensive to buy Brown's lot and default on the original contract.

The type of mental obstacle that so often interferes with correct decisions is also evident. Green has paid out over the past 4 years a total of $1,986 (including interest and taxes) on his original lot. He appears to "lose" this amount if he defaults on his contract. Moreover, this default seems to admit a past error of judgment that would not be admitted if he pays the $1,700 to complete the purchase of the original lot.

The realistic view regarding this past outlay of $1,986 is, of course, that the money has been spent regardless of which alternative is selected for the future. As the past outlay is the same regardless of the alternative selected, it should not influence the choice between the alternatives.

EXAMPLE 15–5. NEED TO CONSIDER PROSPECTIVE RECEIPTS AND DISBURSEMENTS AFFECTED BY THE DECISION ON DISPOSAL IN JUDGING A PROPOSAL TO DISPOSE OF A FIXED ASSET

Facts of the Case. The hobby of a businessman, who for purposes of this example will be called Richard Roe, was the design of houses. Over a period of a number of years, he would design a new house every year or two, contract for its construction, and move his family into it when completed. Because of the original ideas incorporated into his designs, he was always able to sell the previous home at a moderate profit.

During 1941 he completed a new home that, including the land, cost him about $9,500. Early in 1942, a few months after the entrance of the United States into World War II, he was offered $11,000 for this house. He accepted the offer.

While Roe was considering this offer, he discussed the matter with some friends. In the discussion it was pointed out that because of wartime restrictions he would probably not be able to build another house for some time. It also seemed likely that when he did so, it would be at a considerably higher cost; one of the inevitable results of a war seems to be a higher price level. But Roe dismissed these objections with the comment, "You can never go wrong taking a profit!"

As matters turned out, Roe would have been much better off to have rejected the $11,000 offer and to have kept his house for several years. Throughout the succeeding years he and his family had less satisfactory accommodations than they would have had if he had kept the house. When he finally built another house, construction costs had more than doubled. If he had kept the house, he could have sold it several years later at a price that would have been much higher than $11,000.

Just as Green's past outlay of $1,986 in Example 15–4 should not have influenced his decision between the two lots, Roe's $9,500 cost of his house should not have influenced his decision regarding the acceptance of the $11,000 offer. He should rather have asked himself: "What future receipts and disbursements are likely to be affected by this decision? And what matters that are not reducible to money terms will probably be influenced by the decision?"

The difficulty with Roe was that he thought primarily of the "profit" he was making on the sale. His habit of thought was to look backward at past costs rather than to look forward at prospective future differences between alternatives. It was not that Roe did not recognize the likelihood of the events that later occurred (such as higher construction costs and increased restrictions on private building), but rather that he did not recognize that these were the relevant matters for consideration in his decision. He failed to realize that in choosing between alternatives for the future, the important question is not, "Where have we been?" but rather, "Where do we go from here?"

Retirements and Replacements. A decision on a *retirement* is a decision whether or not to continue to own some fixed asset, for example, some machine or structure. In some cases an asset retired may be scrapped, with no salvage value (or even with a negative salvage value if the cost of removal and disposal exceeds any receipts from disposal). In other cases there may be substantial net resale value, even (as in Example 15–5) higher than the original cost.

An asset retired may or may not be replaced. In modern industry, with its frequent improvements in design and changes in service requirements, it is common for the replacement machine or structure to differ in various ways from the machine or structure being retired. Often the new machine or structure may serve other functions in addition to providing the same services that were given by the machine or structure retired.

In some cases a new asset may be acquired to replace the services of an old asset, but the old asset will not be retired. Sometimes the old asset may be used for another purpose, as when an old main-line railroad locomotive was relegated to branch-line service. In other instances the old asset may be continued in the same general type of service but used less frequently than before; for example, an old steam power plant originally used to carry base load might be used only a few hours a year for peak load purposes.

Thus a retirement may be made either with or without a replacement. And the services of an existing old asset may be replaced or augmented by the services of a new one either with or without the retirement of the old asset.

The Question of the Cost of Extending the Service of an Asset Already Owned. In any economy study involving a prospective retirement, it is necessary to consider the money difference between disposing of the old asset at once and disposing of it at some future date. In determining this figure, the past investment in the asset is irrelevant. The current book value is a result of the past investment and the past depreciation charges made in the accounts; this also is irrelevant. So also are the future depreciation charges to be made in the books if the asset is continued in service.

The relevant estimates include the prospective net receipts, if any, from disposal of the asset (1) on the assumption that it is retired immediately, and (2) on the assumption that it is continued in service for the immediate future and retired at some specified later date. Under assumption (2) it is necessary to consider all prospective receipts and disbursements that will take place if ownership is continued but will not take place if the asset is retired immediately. In many economy studies regarding retirements, it may be desirable to consider several different specified future dates on which the asset might be retired if continued in service for the time being. For example, it may be appropriate to consider the cost of keeping the old asset in service for 1 year, for 2 years, for 3 years, etc.

Example 15–6 illustrates the estimates and calculations that are needed relative to the capital recovery costs of extending the service of an asset. This example provides essential background for the discussion in Chapter 17 of practical problems of judging the economy of proposed retirements and replacements. The reader should therefore examine Example 15–6 carefully before starting Chapter 17.

EXAMPLE 15–6. COMPUTING CAPITAL RECOVERY COSTS OF EXTENDING THE SERVICE OF AN ASSET FOR VARIOUS PERIODS

(a) **Capital Recovery Cost of Extending a Service for One Year.** A 2-year-old piece of construction machinery had a first cost of $2,000 and has been depreciated on the books of its owner by the straight-line method at 20% a year. Its present book value is therefore $1,200. Its present net resale value in a second-hand market is $750. It is estimated this resale value will decrease to $500 if the machine is held for another year, to $300 if it is held for 2 years more, and to $200 if held for 3 years more. Interest (minimum attractive rate of return) is at 8%. The question arises whether to dispose of this machine immediately for $750 and to rent a similar machine if one should be needed, or to continue it in service for another year or more.

As a first step in finding the money difference between disposing of the machine at once and disposing of it at some later date, it should be noted that at the present moment it is possible to have either the $750 or the machine but not both. As far as immediate money receipts and disbursements are concerned, the difference is as follows:

Keep Machine	*Dispose of Machine*
No receipts or disbursements	Receive $750

The immediate money difference is just the same as if the question at issue were the purchase of a secondhand machine for $750. In this case the immediate receipts and disbursements would be:

Buy Machine	*Do Not Buy Machine*
Disburse $750	No receipts or disbursements

Whether it is a question of keeping a machine that can be sold for $750 or acquiring one that can be purchased for $750, in either case we have $750 more without the machine than with it. If all future estimates (i.e., annual receipts and disbursements, future salvage values, and irreducible data) are the same,[4] an economy study comparing the alternatives of (a) continuing an asset in service and (b) disposing of the asset at once is identical with an economy study comparing the alternatives of (a) acquiring the same asset at

---

[4] In most cases there would be some differences between the cost estimates that would seem appropriate for a used asset already owned and an apparently identical used asset to be acquired. For example, the net realizable salvage value of a machine already installed in the plant is the secondhand price *minus* the cost of removing it, transporting it to the market, and selling it. In contrast, the installed cost of a purchased secondhand machine is the secondhand price *plus* the costs of buying it, transporting it to the plant, and installing it. Moreover, the appropriate estimates of future repair costs might differ. There might well be a great deal more known about the maintenance history of a used machine already owned than about that of an apparently identical used machine purchased in the secondhand market. Hence the factor of uncertainty might well lead to a higher estimate of repair costs for a purchased machine. The point made in Example 15–6 does not bear on these matters but is simply that a decision to continue an asset in service is, in principle, identical with a decision to acquire the same asset at an outlay equal to the present net realizable value.

a price equal to its present net realizable value if disposed of and (b) not acquiring it. This general principle may be applied in all economy studies regarding proposed retirements.

In all such economy studies the capital recovery costs on any asset already owned should be based on its present net realizable value if disposed of (i.e., on the amount of capital that could be recovered from its disposition). With interest at 8%, the capital recovery cost of extending for one more year the service of the 2-year-old asset in Example 15–6 is:

$$CR = (\$750 - \$500)(A/P,8\%,1) + \$500(0.08)$$
$$= (\$750 - \$500)(1.08) + \$500(0.08) = \$310$$

Another way to express the capital recovery cost of extending the service for one year is as follows:

$$
\begin{aligned}
\text{Depreciation} &= \$750 - \$500 = \$250 \\
\text{Interest} &= \$750(0.08) = 60 \\
\text{Total capital recovery cost} &= \$310
\end{aligned}
$$

This is of course mathematically identical with the preceding calculation. The depreciation figure used here is depreciation in the popular sense of decrease in value; the value figures are market values. In effect this calculation says that by extending the service of the asset 1 year more, we receive $250 less for the asset, and we lose the services of $750 in cash for a 1-year period. With interest at 8%, these latter services are valued at $60. The total is $310, as of a date 1 year hence.

(b) **Equivalent Annual Capital Recovery Cost of Extending a Service for Two or More Years.** Now consider the question of the capital recovery cost of extending the service of the asset for 3 years more. The net realizable value 3 years hence is $200.

$$CR = (\$750 - \$200)(A/P,8\%,3) + \$200(0.08)$$
$$= \$550(0.38803) + \$200(0.08) = \$229.40$$

It is of interest to relate this equivalent uniform annual cost of 3 years to the separate capital recovery costs of extending the service for each of the next 3 years.

$$
\begin{aligned}
\text{CR cost next year} &= (\$750 - \$500) + \$750(0.08) \\
&= \$250 + \$60 = \$310 \\
\text{CR cost 2nd year} &= (\$500 - \$300) + \$500(0.08) \\
&= \$200 + \$40 = \$240 \\
\text{CR cost 3rd year} &= (\$300 - \$200) + \$300(0.08) \\
&= \$100 + \$24 = \$124
\end{aligned}
$$

These separate costs of extending service year by year may be converted into an equivalent annual cost for 3 years by finding their present worths and multiplying the sum of the present worths by the capital recovery factor, as follows:

$$
\begin{aligned}
\text{PW of } \$310 &= \$310(0.9259) = \$287.00 \\
\text{PW of } \$240 &= \$240(0.8573) = 205.80 \\
\text{PW of } \$124 &= \$124(0.7938) = 98.40 \\
\text{Sum of present worths} & = \$591.20 \\
\text{CR} = \$591.20(0.38803) & = \$229.40
\end{aligned}
$$

This of course agrees with the $229.40 figure previously obtained by considering only the $750 present realizable value and the $200 realizable value 3 years hence. The year-by-year capital recovery costs of extending the service of an asset may always be converted into an equivalent annual cost that is equal to the capital recovery cost of extending the service for the entire period of years under study. This is mathematically true regardless of the pattern of year-by-year decline in salvage values.

(c) **Year-by-Year Capital Recovery Costs Throughout the Life of an Asset.** Assume that the asset in Example 15–6 had a net realizable value of $1,100 at the end of its first year of life, and prospective net realizable value at the end of each year from the 2nd to the 10th as shown in Table 15–1. The resulting capital recovery costs of extending service for each year of life are then given in column E of Table 15–1. The first year's cost, $1,060, the sum of $900 depreciation and $160 interest, is the capital recovery cost of one year's service to a *prospective purchaser* of the machine for $2,000 on the assumption that the machine is disposed of for $1,100 at the end of its first year of life. The succeeding figures in column E are of course the capital recovery costs of each successive year's extension of service to a *present owner* of the machine in question. Once the net realizable value has fallen to zero, as it has after 8 years, the capital recovery costs of extending the service are also zero.

Column F gives the present worth at zero date of each year's capital recovery cost of extending service. Column G gives the sum of the present worths of these costs for n years. It will be noted that as soon as the net realizable value has fallen to zero, the sum of these present worths is neces-

TABLE 15–1

Year-by-Year Capital Recovery Costs of Extending Service of a $2,000 Machine, and Equivalent Annual Costs if Held for n Years, with Interest at 8%

Year n	Net Realizable Value at Year- End	Decrease in Realizable Value During nth Year	Interest on Realizable Value at Start of Year	Capital Recovery Cost of Extending Service Through nth Year	Present Worth of Capital Recovery Cost for nth Year	Present Worth of Capital Recovery Costs for n Years	Equivalent Uniform Annual Capital Recovery Cost if Retired After n Years
A	B	C	D	E	F	G	H
1	$1,100	$900	$160	$1,060	$981.50	$ 981.50	$1,060
2	750	350	88	438	375.50	1,357.00	761
3	500	250	60	310	246.10	1,603.10	622
4	300	200	40	240	176.40	1,779.50	537
5	200	100	24	124	84.40	1,863.90	467
6	100	100	16	116	73.10	1,937.00	419
7	50	50	8	58	33.80	1,970.80	379
8	0	50	4	54	29.20	2,000.00	348
9	0	0	0	0	0.00	2,000.00	320
10	0	0	0	0	0.00	2,000.00	298

sarily equal to the first cost, in this case $2,000. Column H shows the annual cost of capital recovery for n years' service computed by multiplying the figure from column G by the appropriate capital recovery factor. (Present worth factors and crfs are taken from the 8% table, Table E–15.) The main purpose of including this calculation is to demonstrate the identity of the capital recovery cost computed in this way with the capital recovery cost computed in the conventional way from first cost and the salvage value at the end of the life.

For example, if the machine is retired at the end of 3 years with a $500 salvage value, the conventional calculation is:

$$CR = (\$2,000 - \$500)(A/P,8\%,3) + \$500(0.08)$$
$$= (\$2,000 - \$500)(0.38803) + \$40 = \$622$$

Or if retired after 6 years with $100 salvage value, it is:

$$CR = (\$2,000 - \$100)(A/P,8\%,6) + \$100(0.08)$$
$$= (\$2,000 - \$500)(0.21632) + \$8 = \$419$$

Or if retired after 10 years with a zero salvage value, it is:

$$CR = \$2,000(A/P,8\%,10) = \$2,000(0.14903) = \$298$$

Irrelevance of Book Value and Current Depreciation Accounting Charges in a Before-Tax Analysis To Guide a Decision on a Proposed Retirement. In Example 15–6 (a) it was stated that the 2-year-old asset in question had been depreciated by the straight-line method at 20% ($400) a year and had a current book value of $1,200. However, these figures were given no weight in the preceding calculation of the cost of extending the service of this asset one or more years. This neglect of the book value and the current annual depreciation charge was entirely proper for this particular purpose.

The original $2,000 purchase price of this asset was spent 2 years ago. This money has already been paid out regardless of whether it is decided to retire the asset at once or to continue it in service. No future decision regarding the disposal or retention of the asset can alter the fact of this past $2,000 disbursement.

As brought out in Chapter 10, the depreciation charges in the accounts are simply a time allotment of this past disbursement, which, when made, was considered in the accounts to be a prepaid expense of service for a number of years. The book value of an asset or group of assets is simply that portion of the cost that has not yet been written off in the accounts as depreciation expense. Regardless of the date of the retirement and regardless of the method of depreciation accounting in use, the first cost less salvage value will all eventually be written off in the books. But, as explained in Chapter 10, the entry made on the books to record a retirement under the single-asset (item) method of depreciation accounting differs from that under multiple-asset methods (group, classified, or composite).

The straight-line item method of depreciation accounting was in common use in the United States prior to 1934, particularly in the manufacturing industries. The accounting entries to record retirements under the item method led to great confusion of thought on the part of many engineers and industrialists regarding the economic aspects of proposed replacements of machinery and other assets.

A Common Error in Reasoning in Economy Studies Involving Prospective Replacements. If the 2-year-old asset in Example 15–6 has been depreciated by the straight-line item method at $400 a year, $800 of the original $2,000 investment has been written off and the current book value (unamortized cost) is $1,200. If the asset is now disposed of for a net $750, the item method requires that $450, the difference between the book value and the net salvage value, be written off at once. This $450 might be charged to an account with some such title as "Loss on Disposal of Fixed Assets."

This "loss on disposal" type of entry, common in the United States up to 1934, proved to be an obstacle to clear thinking on matters of replacement economy. Much of the literature of this subject in the 1920's and 1930's involved formulas or other methods of analysis in which the excess of book value over net salvage value of the old asset was considered as an addition to the first cost of the proposed net asset. For example, if an economy study were to be made to determine whether to replace the 2-year-old asset in Example 15–6 with a new asset costing $2,500, these writers on replacement economy would consider the first cost of the new asset to be $2,950, the sum of the $2,500 purchase price and the $450 "loss on disposal."

The preceding discussion of sunk costs and of Example 15–6 has shown the fallacy of this idea. In further consideration of the unsoundness of this view, it should be pointed out that the loss on disposal entry related only to the timing of the write-off of a prepaid expense. The money spent for an asset already owned was already spent, regardless of the decision on retirement; this fact was not altered by the timing of an accounting write-off. Under straight-line item accounting the need for a loss on disposal entry resulted from the past use of a depreciation rate that turned out to be insufficient to write off the difference between first cost and actual salvage value during the actual realized life.

Need To Consider Book Value and Current Depreciation Accounting Charges in Estimating the Influence of a Proposed Retirement on Cash Flow for Income Taxes. In the 1920's and 1930's, income tax rates in the United States were low enough for most economy studies to be made without examining the income tax consequences of proposed decisions. Like other literature of that period, the incorrect formulas we have mentioned did not consider income taxes.

Because the concept of taxable income corresponds in most respects to the concept of accounting income, matters that affect the accounts usually influence income tax payments. Thus the retirement of an asset under circumstances where the accounts show a "gain" or "loss" will generally have a tax consequence. If the retirement of an asset eliminates a depreciation charge that would continue if the asset were not retired, this also will affect cash flow for income taxes. A discussion of the foregoing aspects of economy studies for retirements is deferred until Chapter 17, where we examine the general problem of estimating the income tax consequences of retirement decisions.

Some Suggested Readings on Topics Introduced in This Chapter. Clark's classic work on overhead costs, published in 1923, is desirable background reading for the subject matter of this chapter. Modern writings by Dean, Goetz, and Reul are excellent. Norton's writings on engineering economy contain helpful examples along these lines. One of the authors of the present book, in collaboration with Norton, has discussed at length the relationship between depreciation accounting and the viewpoint developed in this chapter.[5]

Increment Cost Aspects of the Estimation of Working Capital Requirements for an Investment Proposal.[6] Most of the discussion in this book deals with the economic analysis of proposals involving the flow of business funds for so-called fixed assets (land, buildings and structures, machinery, transportation equipment, furniture and fixtures, and so forth). Many proposals for fixed assets also influence cash flow associated with

[5] Detailed references to the writings cited are as follows: J. M. Clark, *Studies in the Economics of Overhead Costs* (Chicago: University of Chicago Press, 1923). Joel Dean, *Managerial Economics* (Englewood Cliffs, N.J.: Prentice-Hall, Inc., 1951). B. E. Goetz, *Management Planning and Control* (New York: McGraw-Hill Book Co., Inc., 1949). E. L. Grant and P. T. Norton, Jr., *Depreciation* (New York: The Ronald Press Co., 1955), particularly chap. 15. W. G. Ireson and E. L. Grant (eds.), *Handbook of Industrial Engineering and Management*, 2d ed., (Englewood Cliffs, N.J.: Prentice-Hall, Inc., 1970), see particularly the sections by Joel Dean on "Managerial Economics," by P. T. Norton, Jr., on "Engineering Economy," and by R. I. Reul on "Capital Budgeting."

[6] Our exposition of this topic is largely influenced by a paper by J. B. Weaver, Director, Development Appraisal Dept. of Atlas Chemical Industries, given at a conference sponsored by the Engineering Economy Division of the American Society for Engineering Education at Pittsburgh, Pa., in June, 1959. For a more complete presentation of Weaver's viewpoint on this topic, the reader is referred to his articles in the June and August, 1959, issues of *Industrial and Engineering Chemistry*.

such matters as accounts receivable and payable and inventories of raw materials, work in process, and finished goods. It is as important for an analyst to recognize the cash flow associated with working capital, wherever relevant, as to recognize the cash flow associated with proposed investments in physical plant.

It was pointed out in Chapter 10 that economy studies usually treat proposed investments in working capital as if they will have 100% salvage values at the end of the life of a project (or possibly at the end of an assumed study period). Because working capital investments are not depreciated for accounting or income tax purposes, such treatment is consistent with the books of account. Nevertheless, the analyst making an economy study that involves working capital requirements will not find adequate guidance in the standard accounting definition of net working capital as the excess of current assets (chiefly cash, receivables, and inventories) over current liabilities (usually obligations payable within one year). It is essential to apply the "with or without" viewpoint to the influence of a proposal on prospective cash flow in order to make a rational estimate of working capital requirements.

For example, consider the prospective cash flow involved in the financing of additional accounts receivable in a manufacturing business. A company's books will always show accounts receivable at the full selling price. However, the commitment of cash necessary to finance, say, 30 days' accounts receivable is considerably less than the selling price of the product sold in 30 days. The accounts will "value" accounts receivable at the selling price. But this price normally includes such items as allowances for profit and depreciation that have not involved current cash outlays by the manufacturer. Similarly, book values for inventories of finished goods and work in process include depreciation and possibly other noncash items that should be excluded in the estimation of working capital requirements for purposes of an economy study.

The kinds of proposals that obviously call for the estimates of working capital requirements are proposals for a new product or for expanded production of an existing product. But the common use of simple rules of thumb to apply to *all* such proposals in a business organization (e.g., 30 days' accounts receivable; 60 days' inventory) is likely to disregard important differences between different products and between different material sources. For instance, although natural gas and fuel oil are interchangeable for many purposes, they may involve quite different working capital requirements. A user of natural gas generally receives it via a pipe line and therefore carries no inventory; in fact, there may be a negative element in the working capital requirement because of the time lag between the use of gas and the payment for it. In contrast, in many cases the economical way to purchase oil is in tankers or barges, and it may be necessary to carry a considerable inventory at all times to ensure against running out.

Summary. The following points brought out in this chapter may be restated for emphasis as follows:

Average costs per unit, whether generated from accounting records or elsewhere, should not be used uncritically as guides to decision making. It should always be remembered that it is prospective *differences* between alternatives that are relevant to their comparison.

It is particularly important to keep in mind that all economy studies start from the moment of decision. The only possible differences between alternatives for the future are future differences. Past receipts and disbursements and other past events are irrelevant in economy studies except as they may influence future receipts or disbursements or other future events.

For purposes of an economy study to decide whether or not to dispose of assets already owned, capital recovery costs on these assets should be based on the present net realizable value if disposed of rather than on original cost.

PROBLEMS

15–1. A portion of the general power service schedule of a certain utility company is as follows:

Monthly Block Rate in Cents per Kw-hr

HP of Measured Maximum Demand	First 50 Kw-hr per HP of Maximum Demand	Next 50 Kw-hr per HP of Maximum Demand	Next 100 Kw-hr per HP of Maximum Demand	All over 200 Kw-hr per HP of Maximum Demand
25 to 49	2.8	1.8	0.95	0.80
50 to 99	2.4	1.6	0.90	0.75
100 to 249	2.2	1.5	0.85	0.70
250 to 499	2.1	1.4	0.80	0.65

A customer under this rate has a monthly maximum demand of 60 kw. (1 HP = 0.746 kw.) and a monthly energy consumption of 11,000 kw-hr.

(a) What is his monthly bill? What is his average cost per kw-hr? (*Ans.* = $187.48; 1.704¢.)

(b) How much will be added to the monthly bill if a load is added which increases the maximum demand by 10 kw. and increases the monthly energy consumption by 300 kw-hr? What is the average cost per kw-hr of this additional load? (*Ans.* = $17.44; 5.81¢.)

(c) How much will be added to the monthly bill if a load is added which increases the maximum demand by 40 kw. and requires the use of this 40 kw. for 600 hours per month? What is the average cost per kw-hr of this additional load? (*Ans.* = $231.77; 0.966¢.)

15–2. A city which distributes its own electric energy buys the bulk of its power at the following rate:

A monthly demand charge based on measured maximum demand of:

> A flat charge of $90 per month for 50 kw. or less
> $1.50 per kw. for the next 150 kw.
> $1.00 per kw. for the next 300 kw.
> $0.75 per kw. for the next 500 kw.
> $0.60 per kw. for all over 1,000 kw.

Plus an energy charge which is calculated monthly as follows:

> $0.008 per kw-hr for the first block of kw-hr equal to 150 times the month's maximum demand (i.e., the equivalent in a 30-day month of 5 hours per day use of the maximum demand)
> $0.006 per kw-hr for the next block of kw-hr equal to 250 times the month's maximum demand
> $0.0055 per kw-hr for all additional energy

(a) What will be the monthly bill and average cost per kw-hr in a typical month in which the maximum demand is 2,500 kw, and the energy purchased is 1,000,000 kw-hr? (*Ans.* = $8,640; 0.864¢.)

(b) By generating about 40,000 kw-hr per month in its own small diesel plant which is operated only at peak load hours, the city is able to reduce the peak demand for purchased power by about 800 kw. In other words, without this peak load diesel operation, the maximum demand in the typical month cited in (a) would have been 3,300 kw. and the energy purchased would have been 1,040,000 kw-hr. The increment cost of this peak load operation of the diesels is about $650 a month. Does it appear to pay to operate them, or would the city save money to shut them down and purchase all its energy requirements? What would be the increment cost per kw-hr of purchasing the peak load energy which is now being generated? (*Ans.* = It pays to operate diesels; 2.4¢.)

(c) As a matter of accounting between different departments of the city government, the city charges itself 3 cents per kw-hr for all energy used for street lighting. However, in considering a proposal program of improved street lighting, it is desired to know the increment cost of additional energy for street lights. Assume that an increased street-lighting program will use an extra 200 kw. from 5 P.M. till 11 P.M. every night (which includes the peak load period on the electric system), and 100 kw. from 11 P.M. till 5 A.M., all of which will be purchased rather than generated. In a 30-day month such as was described under (a), what would be the increment cost per kw-hr of this street-lighting energy? (*Ans.* = 0.933¢.)

15–3. An electric light and power company offers the following two-part rate for primary (23,000 volt) industrial power, part of which is to be "off-peak" use. There is to be a monthly maximum demand charge of $2 per kw. for the first 200 kw., and $1.50 per kw. for all additional unlimited or "on-peak" service. The on-peak period is defined as the hours between 4 P.M. and 7 P.M. from Monday to Friday, inclusive, during the months from October to

March, inclusive. During the other 6 months the unlimited service charge is at its minimum figure, which is 75% of the maximum on-peak demand recorded in the previous 6-month period. For each kilowatt of additional maximum demand (the difference between the off-peak maximum and on-peak maximum) the customer pays a monthly charge of 75 cents. In addition to the monthly maximum demand charge the customer pays a monthly energy charge, as follows:

1.25 cents per kw-hr for the first 25,000 kw-hr
1.10 cents per kw-hr for the next 25,000 kw-hr
1.00 cent per kw-hr for the next 50,000 kw-hr
0.90 cent per kw-hr for the next 50,000 kw-hr
0.80 cent per kw-hr for the next 50,000 kw-hr
0.70 cent per kw-hr for the next 100,000 kw-hr
0.65 cent per kw-hr for the next 700,000 kw-hr
0.60 cent per kw-hr for all energy in excess of 1,000,000 kw-hr

The maximum demand charge assumes a power factor of 80%. Where the maximum demand is higher or lower, the billed demand equals the measured demand multiplied by 0.80 and divided by the monthly average power factor.

A manufacturing company has an annual load about as follows:

Month	On-Peak Maximum Kw.	Monthly Maximum Kw.	Energy Consumed Kw-hr
January	480	1,600	462,000
February	460	1,400	429,000
March	400	1,400	418,000
April		1,200	372,000
May		1,200	358,000
June		1,000	320,000
July		900	291,000
August		1,100	310,000
September		1,700	465,000
October	440	2,000	562,000
November	440	2,100	567,000
December	480	1,900	540,000

(a) What will be the annual bill assuming an 80% power factor? What is the average cost per kw-hr? (*Ans.* = $59,326; 1.165¢.)

(b) What will be the increment cost per kw-hr of an extra uniform 24-hr. load of 500 kw. to run through June, July, August, and September? (*Ans.* = 0.753¢.)

(c) What will be the increment cost per kw-hr of an extra 500-kw. load used on the average of 4 hours per day including the on-peak hours? (*Ans.* = 1.806¢.)

(d) By installing synchronous condensers, the manufacturing company may raise its power factor to 90% and at the same time reduce the energy losses in its own system by 4,000 kw-hr per month. What will be the annual saving in the power bill? (*Ans.* = $2,177.)

15–4. A manufacturing concern estimates monthly expenses at various percentages of "normal" plant capacity as follows:

	120%	100%	80%	60%	0% (temporary)
Office, sales, etc.	$ 4,020	$ 3,380	$ 3,290	$ 3,250	$1,800
Repairs, maintenance	1,000	640	640	590	280
Indirect costs of operation	4,200	3,580	3,380	3,220	380
Direct costs of operation	13,600	10,280	8,540	6,800	1,200
Overhead charges	4,850	4,800	4,750	4,700	4,680
	$27,670	$22,680	$20,600	$18,560	$8,340

If 100% output represents 100 machines per month, what is the unit cost per machine at each output? What is the increment cost per machine of the first 60 machines? What is the increment cost per machine of each additional 20 machines?

If the selling price is $275 per machine, how many machines must be sold before any profit is made? (*Ans.* = $231, $227, $258, $309; $170; $102, $104, $250; 72 machines.)

15–5. A large chemical company has recently acquired two plants that manufacture a certain chemical. These plants use different production processes, although their products are identical. During the first 6 months of operation neither plant is operated at capacity.

The Los Trancos plant has produced 100 tons per month of output at an average cost of $40 per ton. Of the total monthly costs it is estimated that $2,000 will remain fixed regardless of substantial variations in output either upward or downward, and that the remainder of costs will vary in direct proportion to output. The San Francisquito plant has produced 80 tons per month at an average cost of $38 per ton. Of the total monthly costs it is estimated that $1,200 will remain fixed regardless of substantial variations in output either upward or downward and that the remainder of the costs will vary in direct proportion to output.

(a) If the total amount produced at the two plants is to continue at the present figure of 180 tons per month, does there appear to be any advantage in increasing the production at one of the plants and making an equal decrease at the other? If so, at which plant would you increase production? (*Ans.* = $3 per ton will be saved by increasing production at Los Trancos and reducing it at San Francisquito.)

(b) Assume that for reasons of policy it is not desired to make the production shift indicated in (a). The total required production increases from 180 to 200 tons per month. At which plant would it be more economical to produce the extra 20 tons? (*Ans.* = produce at L.T. since increment cost is $400 compared to $460 at S.F.)

15–6. A certain type of machine has a first cost of $1,000. End-of-year salvage values are as follows:

Year	Salvage Values
1	$530
2	290
3	210
4	160
5	120
6	90

Assuming interest at 10%, what is the capital recovery cost of extending service for each year of life? (*Ans.* = (1) $570; (2) $293; (3) $109; (4) $71; (5) $56; (6) $42.)

15–7. (a) Using only the first cost of $1,000 and salvage value of $90, find the equivalent uniform annual cost of capital recovery for an asset in Problem 15–6 purchased new and disposed of at the end of 6 years. Use interest at 10%. Also find the uniform series for 6 years equivalent to the irregular series of year-by-year capital recovery costs of extending service obtained in the solution to Problem 15–6. These two figures should be the same. (*Ans.* = $217.94.)

(b) A 1-year-old asset is acquired for $530. It is disposed of for $120 when it is 5 years old. Compute the uniform annual cost of capital recovery with interest at 10%. Also find the uniform series for 4 years equivalent to the year-by-year capital recovery costs of extending service for the 2nd, 3rd, 4th, and 5th years obtained in the solution to Problem 15–6. These two figures should be the same. (*Ans.* = $141.34.)

15–8. Assume that you are selling goods on a commission basis. On the sale of a given article you will earn a commission of $100. To date you have spent $80 promoting a certain sale that you have not yet made. You are confident that this sale will be assured by an added expenditure of some undetermined amount. What is the maximum amount (over and above what you have already spent) that you should be willing to spend to assure the sale?

15–9. What differences can you see in the reasoning that ought to influence the decisions of Brown and Green under the following circumstances?

Brown wishes to raise $8,000 immediately to make a down payment on the purchase of a home. He has only two possible sources of funds. (1) He may sell 200 shares of XY Co. stock that is currently paying annual dividends of $2.40 a share. He bought this stock a few years ago for $65 a share; its present market price is $40 a share. Or (2) he may borrow $8,000 at 6% interest from his life insurance company with his life insurance policy as security.

Green also wants to raise $8,000 immediately to make a down payment on the purchase of a home. He also has only two possible sources of funds. (1) He may sell 200 shares of XY Co. stock that is currently paying annual dividends of $2.40 a share. He bought his stock for $25 a share several years before Brown made his purchase; its present market price is $40 a share. Or (2) he may borrow $8,000 at 6% interest from his life insurance company with his life insurance policy as security.

15–10. A machine has a first cost of $3,000 and net realizable salvage values at the end of each of the first 7 years of its life as follows: 1–$1,800; 2–$1,300; 3–$1,000; 4–$800; 5–$600; 6–$500; 7–$400. With an i^* of 10%, show that the capital recovery costs of extending service each year are as follows: 1–$1,500; 2–$680; 3–$430; 4–$300; 5–$280; 6–$160; 7–$150. Using an i^* of 10%, find the uniform annual series for 7 years that is equivalent to this latter year-by-year series. Using an i^* of 10%, compute the annual cost of capital recovery of a machine that has a first cost of $3,000, a life of 7 years, and a terminal salvage value of $400. Compare the figures obtained by these two calculations. What general point relative to compound interest conversions is illustrated by this comparison?

15–11. You have traveled from your home to the city of Z on a 150-day limit round-trip bus ticket for which you paid $57. The one-way bus fare from your home to Z is $33.50; if you do not use the return half of your ticket, the bus company will redeem it at the difference between the round-trip price and the one-way fare.

(a) Assume it is necessary for you to stay in Z until after the return date limit. What is the lowest price at which you could afford to sell the return half of your ticket to a friend rather than turn it in for credit to the bus company?

(b) If you plan to return home by bus before the return date, what is the lowest price at which you could afford to sell the return half of your ticket?

15–12. A family uses 110 kilowatt-hours of electricity per month, purchased under the following rate:

Service charge per month	$0.40
First 35 kw-hr per month	0.035 per kw-hr
Next 65 kw-hr per month	0.024 per kw-hr
Next 100 kw-hr per month	0.016 per kw-hr
All excess kw-hr per month	0.010 per kw-hr

The monthly bill is $3.35, or a little over 3 cents per kw-hr.

(a) The purchase of an electric range is considered. It is believed that this may use 100 kw-hr per month. For the purpose of judging the economy of this range as compared with some other method of cooking, what should be considered as the "cost" of this 100 kw-hr?

(b) It is proposed to economize by using lamps of lower wattage. It is believed that this will save 20 kw-hr per month. For the purpose of deciding whether or not to make this change, what should be considered as the "cost" of this 20 kw-hr?

15–13. A small machine shop with 30 HP of connected load purchases electricity under the following monthly rate:

First	50 kw-hr per HP of connected load at 2.8 cents per kw-hr
Next	50 kw-hr per HP of connected load at 1.8 cents per kw-hr
Next	150 kw-hr per HP of connected load at 1.0 cents per kw-hr
All over	250 kw-hr per HP of connected load at 0.75 cents per kw-hr

The shop uses 2,800 kw-hr per month. The monthly bill is $65.40. This is determined by figuring the first block of $50(30) = 1,500$ kw-hr at 2.8 cents plus the remaining 1,300 kw-hr (which is less than the 1,500 kw-hr that might be included in the second block) at 1.8 cents. The average cost per kw-hr is 2.34 cents, that is, $65.40 divided by 2,800.

(a) Suppose the proprietor of the shop has the chance to secure additional business that will require him to operate his existing equipment more hours per day. This will use an extra 1,200 kw-hr per month. In order to get this business, he must make his bid as low as possible. What is the lowest figure that he might reasonably consider to be the "cost" of this additional energy? What is this per kw-hr?

(b) He contemplates installing certain new machines that will reduce the labor time required on certain operations. These will increase the connected load by 10 HP, but, as they will operate only on certain special jobs, will add only 100 kw-hr per month. In a study to determine the economy of installing these new machines, what should be considered as the "cost" of this energy? What is this per kw-hr?

15–14. A graduate student has been forced by a housing shortage to take a room several miles from his campus. He can ride the city bus to and from the campus, ride a bicycle, or buy a car for his transportation. If he decides to buy a car, he will plan to dispose of it at the end of the school year. What items should he consider in the "cost" of owning and operating the car when trying to reach a decision on the advisability of buying it?

If, after he bought the car, a sudden change in his financial circumstances made it advisable for him to consider disposing of it immediately, what differences would there be between his analysis now and the original analysis before he purchased the car?

15–15. In a period of rising prices a merchant attempted to maintain his stock of goods at a constant physical volume. He had purchased his stock of one item some time ago at $3 per unit. He sold these items at $5 per unit (applying his usual markup) and immediately replaced them by identical ones purchased at the new wholesale price of $6 per unit. What do you think of the profitableness of this transaction?

15–16. A student, arrested for speeding, was given his choice between a $10 fine and a day in jail. He elected the latter. On emerging from jail, he wrote a story about his experience there, which he sold to a newspaper for $15. Commenting on this incident, one of his friends remarked, "Steve made $5 by going to jail, the $15 from the newspaper minus the $10 fine." "No," said another, "he made $15 by the decision to go to jail as he didn't pay the fine." How about it?

15–17. A paperboard manufacturing company has two plants, one in Washington and one in California, producing equivalent grades of "cardboard." The Washington plant has been operating at 75% capacity, producing 2,700 tons per month at a total cost per ton of $77⅓. The California plant has been operating at 60% capacity, producing 3,600 tons per month at a total cost per ton of $85.

Included in the total cost per ton is the cost of waste paper, the major raw material. For each 100 tons of product, 80 tons of waste paper are required. At the Washington plant the local waste paper costs $18.75 per ton (of waste paper), but the supply is limited to 1,440 tons per month. At the California plant, local waste paper costs $20 per ton and is limited to 4,000 tons per month. Additional waste paper must be purchased through brokers at $27.50 per ton (delivered at either plant).

Of the total monthly costs at the Washington plant, $59,400 is estimated to be fixed regardless of production level. The remainder of the costs, with the exception of the cost of waste paper, are expected to vary in proportion to output. The comparable figure for the California plant is $108,000 per month.

(a) If the total production of both is to be continued at the present rate of 6,300 tons per month, would there be any apparent advantage to shifting part of the scheduled production from one of the plants to the other? If so, which plant's production should be increased and by how much? Why?

(b) If production requirements increased to 9,100 tons per month, how much would you recommend be produced at each plant? What would be the total cost per month for each plant in this case?

15–18. Jones and Smith are engineers from the United States employed in a foreign country. Both expect to stay on this assignment for another year or more. Each has just converted $1,000 (U. S.) to the currency of this country at the existing rate of 8 to 1, thus receiving 8,000 currency units in exchange. Suddenly, to the surprise of Jones and Smith, the exchange rate changes to

10 to 1. Now 8,000 currency units changed back into U. S. dollars will bring only $800. A few days later Jones and Smith learn that they are to be transferred back to the United States in two weeks. Each is confronted with the question of what purchases, if any, he will make of various products of the country to take back to the United States. The two men take different attitudes toward this. Jones says that he can get so few dollars for his currency units that he is going to spend them all before going back to the United States. In contrast to this, Smith says that each of his currency units cost him 12½ cents and that he will not spend one unless he believes he is getting 12½ cents worth of goods for it; otherwise he will convert his currency units back into dollars.

Which of these views seems reasonable to you? Or is there some other point of view, not expressed by either Jones or Smith, that seems more sensible than either? If so, what is it? Explain your reasoning.

15–19. A public surveyor owns two transits that he purchased from the Surveyor's Service Co. a year ago for $450 each. He is currently renting a third one from this company at $10 per month. One of his transits becomes damaged in a way not covered by insurance. The S. S. Co. representative estimates the repair cost to be $120. He suggests that the surveyor sell him the two transits "as is" for $540 and rent two more transits at $10 a month. He reasons that his company can rent a transit for less than it costs the surveyor to own one "because we get them wholesale and have our own setup for repairing and adjusting them." He presents the following cost comparison to the surveyor:

Cost of Continuing to Own *Two Transits*		*Cost of Renting Two Transits*	
Depreciation = $900/10	= $ 90	Rental cost = 12($20)	= $240
Taxes and insurance = 3% of $900 =	27	Less	
Repair cost	= 120	Depreciation saved by sale of	
Cleaning and adjustment	= 40	transits = $540/9	60
Net cost	= $277	Net cost	= $180

Criticize the salesman's analysis.

15–20. A power user buys electricity under the following monthly rate:

$1.80 per kw. for each kw. of maximum demand up to 100 kw.
$1.10 per kw. for all maximum demand above 100 kw.
plus
$0.0075 per kw-hr for all energy used

His maximum demand is 120 kw. and his monthly energy consumption is 10,000 kw-hr.

(a) What is his average cost per kw-hr?

(b) What will be the increment cost per month of an additional load that adds 10 kw. to the maximum demand and 2,000 kw-hr to the monthly energy consumption? What is the average cost per kw-hr of this extra load?

15–21. (a) A customer under the power rate given in Problem 15–1 uses 28,800 kw-hr in a 30-day month with a load factor of 20%. What is his monthly bill and his average cost per kw-hr?

(b) Make a similar calculation for a customer who uses 28,800 kw-hr with a load factor of 80%.

15–22. The electric rate described in Problem 15–1 and referred to in Problem 15–21 contains a power factor clause. Under this clause ¼ of 1% is added to the monthly bill for each per cent the customer's average power factor falls below 80% and ¼ of 1% is subtracted for each per cent above 80%.

The customer in Problem 15–21(b) is considering an $1,800 investment in static condensers to raise his present 75% power factor to 90%. His minimum attractive rate of return before income taxes is 15%. Annual disbursements in connection with the ownership of the condensers (e.g., property taxes, insurance) will be 3% of first cost. Should this investment be made if the estimated life of the condensers is 20 years with zero salvage value?

15–23. Electric power is sold under the following rate:

First 40 kw-hr per kw. of maximum demand @ 3¢ per kw-hr
Next 40 kw-hr per kw. of maximum demand @ 2¢ per kw-hr
Next 120 kw-hr per kw. of maximum demand @ 1¢ per kw-hr
All over 200 kw-hr per kw. of maximum demand @ 0.75¢ per kw-hr

What will be the bill in a 30-day month of a customer who uses 216,000 kw-hr with a load factor of 50%?

15–24. Burden rates in a certain factory are on a machine-hour basis. They are established by first apportioning all of the various expected indirect manufacturing expenses of the factory at normal output among all of the machines in the factory; the total estimated indirect manufacturing expense apportioned to any given machine is then divided by the expected normal hours of operation of this machine in order to arrive at a rate per machine-hour. Thus if the estimated indirect manufacturing expense apportioned to a certain milling machine is $1,620, and its expected normal hours of operation are 1,800 per year, the burden rate per hour of operation is 90 cents.

Most of the product of this factory is manufactured to buyers' specifications on contract jobs. In planning many of the operations carried on in this production, the question arises whether they shall be done on general purpose machines or special purpose machines. This involves a comparison of the cost of machine setups and the direct labor and material costs for each given operation on alternative machines. In such comparisons the problem arises as to what use, if any, should be made of the machine burden rates.

Discuss this problem, considering as separate cases (a) the factory operating at about the expected normal hours of operation, (b) the factory operating at greatly curtailed output (such as 30% of normal in a period of business depression), and (c) the factory operating at more than normal output with a large volume of unfilled orders.

15–25. A writer on management subjects discussed the topic of the use of rate of return as a criterion for investment decisions somewhat as follows:

"Prospective rate of return is of limited usefulness as a guide to decision making. For instance, this criterion would be of no use in the following case:

"At the end of his freshman year at the XYZ College, John Doe is offered the campus concession for a certain soft drink. He must pay $900 for the concession and certain equipment. He estimates that the concession will bring him $450 a year for the next 3 years in addition to a reasonable payment for his labor, and that the concession and equipment will be salable for $900 at the end of the 3-year period. He therefore expects a 50% rate of return on his investment.

"However, Richard Roe, who for many years has been concessionaire for a competing soft drink, would prefer less energetic competition than he expects to receive from Doe. Roe therefore offers Doe an outright immediate payment of $100 if Doe will refrain from purchasing this concession. Because Doe will make no investment at all if he accepts Roe's offer, it is evident that his rate of return will be infinite.

"Doe's problem of decision making between the purchase of the concession and the acceptance of Roe's offer illustrates the weakness of the rate-of-return technique. Doe appears to have the choice between a 50% rate of return and an infinite rate of return. But this would also appear to be his choice if Roe had offered him only $1 or if Roe had offered him $1,000. Thus the rate of return technique does not permit Doe to give any weight whatsoever to the size of Roe's offer. No matter how small Roe's offer is, it appears to have a better rate of return than the 50% expected from the purchase of the concession."

Do you agree with the writer that the rate-of-return technique cannot be used by Doe to help him choose between these two alternatives? Or do you see any way to apply the rate-of-return technique to this particular case? Explain your answers fully.

15–26. A land development company tries to buy large tracts of land near growing cities before prices become too inflated. Later the company either sells the land to other developers or develops it itself. The company has purchased several farms containing about 1,600 acres some 8 miles from the city limits of a certain midwestern city. Adjacent to the land is a privately owned golf course containing 60 acres that can be purchased for $80,000. $40,000 of this purchase price is a fair value for the land; the small club house and other improvements account for the remainder of the price. It is estimated that the club house and improvements have a remaining life of 10 years before major reconstruction would be required; the net salvage value of house and improvements will probably be negligible after 10 years. It is estimated that the land value in 10 years will be $90,000.

The management of the land development company does not really want to operate a golf course but recognizes that its presence may help to sell houses or lots when the time comes to develop the adjoining land. The decision has been made to make a separate evaluation of the golf course as an independent investment giving no weight to its possible favorable effect on the company's main activity.

Gross receipts are estimated as $30,000 the first year with an increase of $2,000 each year thereafter. Disbursements for everything except income taxes are estimated as $26,000 the first year with an increase of $1,000 each year thereafter. It is estimated that the project would neither increase nor decrease the company's income taxes in the first year of operation and that income taxes would be increased $500 in the second year; $1,000 in the third; $1,500 in the fourth; and so on. If the land is sold for $90,000 at the end of 10 years, it is estimated that there will be a $15,000 income tax on the capital gain. What is the prospective after-tax rate of return on the investment in this property?

15–27. In the circumstances described in Problem 15–26, the management decided that the irreducible advantages of buying the golf course more than offset any disadvantages. Now the management wishes to know whether or not it should install lights and operate the course in the evenings. After reviewing the operations of some other golf courses at night, the management estimates that the investment to install lights will be $18,000 and that maintenance and lamp replacement will amount to $400 a year. The estimated salvage value at the end of 10 years is negligible. For each night the golf course is lighted, the added operating expenses including labor and electricity will be $40, and the average nightly receipts will be $100. It is estimated that the course will stay open 100 nights a year, and that the added annual income tax will be $1,900.

If the stipulated after-tax i° is 10%, is this an attractive investment?

16

Estimating Income-Tax Consequences of Certain Investment Decisions in Competitive Industry

> Our most important tax problem is to have tax systems at all levels of government that balance one another and are designed so that they promote business enterprise and permit our free-enterprise system to flourish.—H. A. BULLIS [1]

Up to this point we have been using fairly simple assumptions to estimate how much a choice among stated alternatives would influence future cash flow for income taxes. These simple assumptions enabled us to illustrate certain impacts of income taxation on rational decision making. When the assumptions were explained in Chapter 10, it was asserted that in some circumstances these assumptions are good enough for practical purposes but in other circumstances they are not good at all. After a more sophisticated look at certain aspects of income taxation in the present chapter, the reader should have a basis for recognizing some of the cases in which the simple assumptions are not good at all and for finding better assumptions to use in their place. Additional material about the impact of income taxation on certain business decisions is introduced in Chapters 17, 18, and 20.

Distinction Between Taxes on Net Income and Taxes on Gross Income. Where a flat tax is levied on gross receipts (so-called gross income), the estimates of receipts and future tax rates supply an estimate of future tax payments. However, taxes on gross income are subject to a number of serious objections. Therefore income taxes are most commonly levied on net income.

[1] H. A. Bullis, *Manifesto for Americans* (New York: McGraw-Hill Book Co., Inc., 1961), p. 84.

The concept of the net income of a business enterprise for tax purposes is similar to the accounting concept of profit. But in any specific case there may be points of difference between the two concepts because legislative bodies are free to define net income in any way they see fit. The discussion in this chapter relates entirely to taxes on net income.

Widespread Applicability of the General Approach Presented Here. The graduated income tax in various forms is used in most industrialized countries and in many developing countries. However, tax rates and the rules defining taxable income vary from country to country and change from time to time in any given country.

In an introduction to engineering economy, a general approach is needed that can be used with any set of tax laws, regulations, and rates. The authors have tried to develop such an approach in this chapter and in subsequent chapters. It is not our purpose to give detailed up-to-date information on income taxes in the United States or elsewhere. Detailed information would require more space than is available.[2] Up-to-date information would call for annual revision.

Nevertheless, in explaining general principles, it is helpful to refer to some particular set of income tax laws and regulations. Some of the discussion in this chapter is based on the federal tax laws applicable to 1967, 1968, and 1969 income in the United States. The reader who wishes to apply the principles to his own problems must secure up-to-date information about the income tax laws, regulations, and administrative practices that pertain to his specific case.

A General Principle—Income Taxes Are Disbursements. Economy studies deal with prospective receipts and disbursements. In the simplified assumptions that we started to use in Chapter 6, it was recognized that prospective income taxes merely constitute another disbursement to add to those for operation, maintenance, property taxes, insurance, etc.

In this chapter and in the following chapters, we continue to recognize that the inclusion of income taxes in an economy study requires the estimation of the amount and timing of this particular element of future cash flow. But we shall see that our simplified assumptions do not always give us valid estimates. We shall start with a series of examples that bring out the importance of the *timing* of tax consequences of decisions.

A General Principle—The Relationship Between Rates of Return Before and After Income Taxes Depends on the Rules Governing Write-Off for Tax Purposes. To illustrate the foregoing important principle, let us assume four $50,000 proposed immediate disbursements, each ex-

[2] The *Federal Regulations on Income Tax* in the United States contain more than three times as many words as this entire book.

pected to reduce future disbursements (other than those for income taxes) by $12,000 a year for the next 10 years. At 20% interest, the present worth of $12,000 a year for 10 years is $50,300; the prospective rate of return before income taxes is approximately 20.2%.

These four investments yielding 20.2% before income taxes are examined in Examples 16–1 to 16–4. Their returns after income taxes vary all the way from 8.1% to 20.2%. The examples differ only in the manner in which the $50,000 investment is permitted to be written off for income tax purposes.

The higher the tax rate, the greater the importance of the rules governing the write-off of an outlay for tax purposes. In Examples 16–1 to 16–4 we shall assume that a 51% tax rate is applicable throughout the entire period of each study. The circumstances under which this was an appropriate rate are explained later in this chapter.

EXAMPLE 16–1. RATE OF RETURN AFTER INCOME TAXES ASSUMING THAT THE INITIAL OUTLAY IS WRITTEN OFF UNIFORMLY DURING THE PERIOD OF ITS EFFECTIVENESS

Facts of the Case. An outlay of $50,000 for materials handling equipment is proposed. It is estimated that this equipment will reduce disbursements for labor and labor extras by $17,000 a year for 10 years and will increase annual disbursements of $5,000 for maintenance, power, property taxes, and insurance. The estimated life of the equipment is 10 years with zero salvage value; this estimate is acceptable to the taxing authorities. The taxpayer elects to use the straight-line method in reporting depreciation for tax purposes.

Calculation of Rate of Return After Income Taxes. Table 16–1 shows the calculation of the prospective effect of the investment on cash flow after income taxes, assuming a 51% tax rate throughout the entire 10-year period. Under the simple assumptions in this example of uniform annual savings, straight-line depreciation, and a constant tax rate, it is evident that the immediate disbursement of $50,000 will increase net cash receipts after taxes by $8,430 a year for 10 years. The rate of return after taxes may be determined by computing present worth of cash flow after taxes using rates of 10% and 12%.

$$\text{PW at } 10\% = -\$50,000 + \$8,430(P/A,10\%,10)$$
$$= -\$50,000 + \$8,430(6.144) = +\$1,794$$
$$\text{PW at } 12\% = -\$50,000 + \$8,430(5.650) = -\$2,370$$

Interpolation indicates a rate of return of about 10.9% after income taxes. The after-tax rate of return is slightly more than half the before-tax rate.

EXAMPLE 16–2. RATE OF RETURN AFTER INCOME TAXES ASSUMING THAT THE INITIAL OUTLAY IS WRITTEN OFF OVER A CONSIDERABLY LONGER TIME THAN ITS PERIOD OF MAJOR PRODUCTIVITY

Facts of the Case. An outlay of $50,000 for certain machinery is proposed. It is anticipated that the period of primary service of this machinery will be 10 years. During these years it is estimated that the machinery will reduce

TABLE 16-1

Estimation of Cash Flow After Income Taxes, Example 16-1

Year	Cash Flow Before Income Taxes	Write-Off of Initial Outlay for Tax Purposes	Effect of Outlay on Taxable Income $(A + B)$ for years 1 to 10	Effect of Outlay on Cash Flow for Income Taxes $-0.51C$	Cash Flow After Income Taxes $(A + D)$
	A	B	C	D	E
0	−$50,000				−$50,000
1	+12,000	−$5,000	+$7,000	−$3,570	+8,430
2	+12,000	−5,000	+7,000	−3,570	+8,430
3	+12,000	−5,000	+7,000	−3,570	+8,430
4	+12,000	−5,000	+7,000	−3,570	+8,430
5	+12,000	−5,000	+7,000	−3,570	+8,430
6	+12,000	−5,000	+7,000	−3,570	+8,430
7	+12,000	−5,000	+7,000	−3,570	+8,430
8	+12,000	−5,000	+7,000	−3,570	+8,430
9	+12,000	−5,000	+7,000	−3,570	+8,430
10	+12,000	−5,000	+7,000	−3,570	+8,430
Totals	+$70,000	−$50,000	+$70,000	−$35,700	+$34,300

TABLE 16-2

Estimation of Cash Flow After Income Taxes, Example 16-2

Years	Cash Flow Before Income Taxes	Annual Write-Off of Initial Outlay for Tax Purposes	Effect of Outlay on Annual Taxable Income $(A + B)$ for years 1 to 25	Effect of Outlay on Annual Cash Flow for Income Taxes $-0.51C$	Cash Flow After Income Taxes $(A + D)$
	A	B	C	D	E
0	−$50,000				−$50,000
1 to 10	+12,000 per year	−$2,000	+$10,000	−$5,100	+6,900 per year
11 to 25	0	−2,000	−2,000	+1,020	+1,020 per year
Totals	+$70,000	−$50,000	+$70,000	−$35,700	+$34,300

annual disbursements for labor and labor extras by $19,000 a year and will increase annual disbursements by $7,000 for maintenance, power, property taxes, and insurance.

Machinery of this type has an industry-wide average life of 25 years and has, in fact, had such an average life in the service of this particular taxpayer. Therefore, the taxing authorities insist that the write-off for tax purposes be based on a 25-year life. An estimate of zero salvage at the end of this life will be permitted. It is expected that the taxpayer's ownership of this machinery will actually continue for 25 years, with the machinery used for standby purposes during the final 15 years of its life. For purposes of the economy study, the effect of the proposed investment on net cash flow before income taxes will be assumed to be negligible during this final 15 years. The policy of this taxpayer is to use the straight-line method in his depreciation accounting and in reporting depreciation for tax purposes.

Calculation of Rate of Return After Income Taxes. Table 16–2 shows the calculation of the prospective effect of the investment on cash flow after income taxes, assuming a 51% tax rate throughout the next 25 years. Although the algebraic sum of the prospective income tax payments resulting from this $50,000 investment will be $35,700, just as in Example 16–1, the timing of the tax consequences of the investment will be considerably different because of the slower write-off permitted. Table 16–2 has been shortened by showing only one line for the uniform cash flow of years 1 to 10 and another line for the uniform cash flow of years 11 to 25. The totals for this table are, of course, the same as if a separate line had been shown for each year.

The rate of return after taxes may be determined by computing present worth of cash flow after taxes using rates of 8% and 10%.

PW at 8% = −$50,000 + $6,900($P/A$,8%,10) + $1,020[($P/A$,8%,25) − ($P/A$,8%,10)]
       = −$50,000 + $6,900(6.710) + $1,020(10.675 − 6.710) = +$343
PW at 10% = −$50,000 + $6,900(6.144) + $1,020(9.077 − 6.144) = −$4,614

Interpolation indicates a rate of return of about 8.1% after income taxes. This is only about three-fourths of the 10.9% after-tax return obtained in the preceding example from the same series of before-tax cash flows.

EXAMPLE 16–3. RATE OF RETURN AFTER INCOME TAXES ASSUMING THAT THE INITIAL OUTLAY IS WRITTEN OFF OVER A CONSIDERABLY SHORTER PERIOD THAN ITS PERIOD OF MAJOR PRODUCTIVITY

Facts of the Case. The facts and estimates are identical with those in Example 16–2 with one exception. This exception is that, because the product to be made by these proposed assets is deemed to be important to the national defense, the cost of the assets may be written off at a uniform rate over a 5-year period under the terms of a "certificate of necessity" issued by the appropriate government agency.

Calculation of Rate of Return After Income Taxes. Table 16–3 shows the calculation of the prospective effect of the investment on cash flow after income taxes, assuming a 51% tax rate for the next 10 years. The rate of return after taxes may be determined by computing present worth of cash flow after taxes, using rates of 12% and 15%.

PW at 12% = −$50,000 + $10,980(3.605) + $5,880(5.650 − 3.605) = +$1,608
PW at 15% = −$50,000 + $10,980(3.352) + $5,880(5.019 − 3.352) = −$3,393

Interpolation indicates a rate of return of about 13.0% after taxes.

TABLE 16–3

Estimation of Cash Flow After Income Taxes, Example 16–3

Years	Cash Flow Before Income Taxes	Annual Write-Off of Initial Outlay for Tax Purposes	Effect of Outlay on Annual Taxable Income $(A + B)$ for years 1 to 10	Effect of Outlay on Annual Cash Flow for Income Taxes $-0.51C$	Cash Flow After Income Taxes $(A + D)$
	A	B	C	D	E
0	−$50,000				−$50,000
1 to 5	+12,000 per year	−$10,000	+$2,000	−$1,020	+10,980 per year
6 to 10	+12,000 per year	0	+12,000	−6,120	+5,880 per year
Totals	+$70,000	−$50,000	+$70,000	−$35,700	+$34,300

EXAMPLE 16–4. RATE OF RETURN AFTER INCOME TAXES ASSUMING THAT THE INITIAL OUTLAY IS WRITTEN OFF AGAINST CURRENT INCOME

Facts of the Case. The company's industrial engineering department has devised an improved plant layout for existing production equipment in an existing building. An immediate outlay of $50,000 will be required to re-arrange the machinery. It is estimated that the new layout will reduce annual disbursements for materials handling by $12,000 a year for the next 10 years. Because the $50,000 outlay does not involve the acquisition of new assets or the extension of the lives of old ones, the entire amount will be treated as a current expense for accounting and income tax purposes in the year in which it is made (zero year on our time scale).

Calculation of Rate of Return After Income Taxes. Table 16–4 shows the calculation of the prospective effect of the $50,000 outlay on cash flow after income taxes, assuming a 51% tax rate from years 0 to 10. It will be noted that in zero year the increased disbursement of $50,000 for machine rearrangement is partially offset by a decrease in the required disbursements to the tax collector amounting to $25,500. On the other hand, there is no subsequent depreciation deduction that results from the $50,000 outlay, and the tax col-

TABLE 16-4

Estimation of Cash Flow After Income Taxes, Example 16-4

Years	Cash Flow Before Income Taxes	Annual Write-Off of Initial Outlay for Tax Purposes	Effect of Outlay on Annual Taxable Income $(A + B)$ for years 1 to 10	Effect of Outlay on Annual Cash Flow for Income Taxes $-0.51C$	Cash Flow After Income Taxes $(A + D)$
	A	B	C	D	E
0	−$50,000	−$50,000	−$50,000	+$25,500	−$24,500
1 to 10	+12,000 per year		+12,000	−6,120	+$5,880 per year
Totals	+$70,000	−$50,000	+$70,000	−$35,700	+$34,300

lector will therefore take $6,120 each year out of the $12,000 saving in materials handling costs.

The following present worth calculation at 20% shows that the prospective rate of return after taxes is a little more than 20%, the same as the prospective rate before income taxes.

$$PW \text{ at } 20\% = -\$24,500 + \$5,880(4.192) = +\$149$$

The Need for After-Tax Analysis. The four investment proposals in these examples were equally attractive when considered before income taxes. But when tax considerations were introduced, they differed greatly in attractiveness. If funds available for investment had been limited, and if these four proposals had been competing with other proposals and with one another for the limited funds, it is evident that a sound choice among the proposals could not have been made without an after-tax analysis.

Examples 16-1 to 16-4 showed that the way a proposed investment will be written off for tax purposes is an important element in evaluating its attractiveness. Later in this chapter, we shall see other aspects of the tax treatment of projects that need to be considered in comparing investment alternatives.

A General Approach to the Introduction of Income Tax Considerations into Economy Studies. Examples 16-1 to 16-4 illustrate the procedure that is necessary if alternatives in competitive industry are to be compared after income taxes rather than before income taxes. Given two alternatives to be compared, the required steps in the analysis are shown on the following page.

1. The year-by-year prospective differences between the alternatives in cash flow before income taxes must be estimated. (This is an essential step whether alternatives are to be compared before income taxes or after income taxes.) It should be noted that in each of our examples one alternative is a continuation of a present condition and the other alternative is to make an immediate $50,000 outlay to effect a future cost reduction.
2. The year-by-year differences between the alternatives in prospective taxable income must be computed. These differences should be consistent with the estimated differences in cash flow. In Examples 16–1 to 16–4, this computation was a comparatively simple matter of applying the appropriate depreciation charge to the initial cash flow figures. Often the calculation of prospective differences in taxable income is a considerably more complicated matter, requiring a sophisticated understanding of income tax laws and regulations.
3. The applicable income tax rates must be estimated and applied to the estimated differences in taxable income to compute the differences between the alternatives in prospective cash flow for income taxes.
4. The year-by-year figures for differences in cash flow before income taxes should be combined with the year-by-year differences in cash flow for income taxes to obtain the estimated differences in cash flow after income taxes.
5. The cash flow after income taxes may then be analyzed with relation to the selected criterion for decision making. The analysis in Examples 16–1 to 16–4 implied that the criterion in these examples was rate of return after income taxes.

Comment on Certain Simplifying Assumptions in Examples 16–1 to 16–4. In these examples it was assumed that the cost reductions caused by the $50,000 initial outlay would continue at a uniform rate for a stated period of years and then abruptly cease. It was assumed that the depreciation write-off in the first three examples would be at a uniform annual figure. It was assumed that except for the write-off of the initial outlay in the first three examples, all cash outlays affected taxable income in the years in which they were made. The tax payments for each year's taxable income were assumed to be concurrent with the other cash disbursements for the year. The end-of-year convention was assumed in all four examples. It was assumed that all taxable income throughout the period of the study would be taxed at the same rate, 51%. All of these assumptions were intended to simplify the computations and to permit concentration of attention on the two main points at issue, namely, the general approach to comparisons made after income taxes and the importance of the rate of write-off in influencing the ratio between return after taxes and return before taxes.

The general method illustrated in the examples can, of course, be applied equally well when the appropriate assumptions are much more complex. Although many economy studies made after income taxes naturally have more complications than Examples 16–1 to 16–4, each example represents a simplified version of a type of case that occurs frequently in modern industry. Perhaps Example 16–1 represents the most common case, in which the investment is to be written off throughout the period of its expected favorable consequences. Except for the use of the 51% tax rate rather than 50%, the tax assumptions in this example are the same as the ones we have made in the preceding chapters whenever we included estimated cash flow for income taxes in examples and problems applicable to competitive industry.

But the type of case illustrated in Example 16–2 has also been common in the United States; write-off periods for tax purposes have often extended well beyond the date when proposed new assets were expected to have their chief economic usefulness. And many billions of dollars' worth of long-lived assets in the United States were written off for tax purposes in 5 years under "certificates of necessity," just as was illustrated in Example 16–3. And industry had numerous opportunities for productive outlays that like the one in Example 16–4 could properly be charged off immediately for income tax purposes.

The Partnership of the Government in Productive Business Outlays. It is illuminating to examine the totals of the five columns in Tables 16–1 to 16–4 and to note that these totals are identical. In all four examples it is proposed to spend $50,000 at once to avoid spending $120,000 in the future; the prospective total addition to profits before income taxes is $70,000. The government will finally take 51% of this $70,000, leaving $34,300 for the owners of the business enterprise.

Although in all four cases the government's share of the ultimate profits is $35,700, the time at which the government collects its share differs greatly in the various examples. In Example 16–1 the government collects its $35,700 at the rate of $3,570 a year for 10 years. In Example 16–2 it collects $5,100 a year for 10 years, a total of $51,000, and—in effect —refunds $15,300 of this by collecting $1,020 a year less taxes for the years 11 to 25. In Example 16–3, the government collects $1,020 a year for the first 5 years and $6,120 a year for the second 5 years. In Example 16–4 the government reduces its tax collections by $25,500 in the zero year on our time scale and then collects a total of $61,200 at $6,120 a year for the next 10 years. It is the difference in the timing of the collection of the $35,700 of taxes that makes the difference among the rates of return to the taxpayer of 10.9%, 8.1%, 13.0%, and 20.2% from investments that have identical before-tax consequences.

Only in the type of case illustrated in Example 16-4 is the taxpayer's rate of return undiminished by the government's partnership in the profits of the decision to make the $50,000 outlay. The effect of the tax treatment of the $50,000 outlay in Example 16-4 is as if the taxpayer had made an investment of $24,500 from which he receives $5,880 a year for 10 years, a return of 20.2%, and the government had made an investment of $25,500 from which it receives $6,120 a year for 10 years, also a return of 20.2%.

Some Other Advantages of a Rapid Write-Off for Tax Purposes. Examples 16-1 to 16-4 illustrated the point that the more rapid the write-off for tax purposes, the greater the rate of return after income taxes. A rapid write-off for tax purposes has certain other advantages that were not brought out by the calculation of rates of return in these four examples. These advantages are:

1. Generally speaking, if matters turn out badly, they will not turn out so badly with a rapid write-off as they will with a slow write-off.
2. In the common case where enterprise funds are limited, more cash is made available for productive use at an early date by a rapid write-off than by a slow one.

These advantages are elaborated in the next few pages.

The Partnership of the Government in Unproductive Business Disbursements. The government may be a partner in unproductive business outlays as well as in productive ones. For instance, if the new plant layout in Example 16-4 should fail to reduce future disbursements, the government will be a partner in the unproductive $50,000 outlay to the extent of $25,500. (That is, because of the outlay the government will forego taxes of $25,500 that it otherwise would collect.) Or assume that the $50,000 investment in Example 16-1 turns out to be unproductive. If so, the taxpayer will have a $5,000 depreciation deduction for the next 10 years; this deduction will reduce taxable income and will reduce income taxes to be paid during the 10-year period; the government may be viewed as participating in the original investment to the extent of the present worth of future income taxes foregone.

Any partnership of the government in unproductive outlays depends on the taxpayer having taxable income from some other source. Otherwise there is no tax liability that can be reduced by the unproductive outlay. A future depreciation write-off (such as the $2,000 a year for 25 years in Example 16-2) will have value to the taxpayer only if he continues to have taxable income.

In case an outlay turns out to be unproductive (or less productive than was forecast), the more rapid write-off has two advantages over the slower write-off for tax purposes. One advantage is that the tax saving comes sooner and therefore has a greater present worth. The other advantage is that a possible tax saving in the near future is more certain to be realized than a possible tax saving in the distant future.

Influence of Rate of Write-Off on Available Cash. When enterprise funds are limited and have to be rationed among competing proposals, it is helpful to examine the immediate net cash requirements of various proposals and also to look at their net cash requirements in the near future. The cash requirements of proposals are greatly influenced by the rate of write-off. For instance, the proposal to spend $50,000 in Example 16–4 has an immediate net cash requirement of only $24,500,[3] whereas the proposals in the other three examples all have immediate requirements of $50,000.

It is pointed out in Chapter 21 that under certain circumstances it is helpful to compute a figure for crude "payback" after income taxes as a numerical index of the short-term cash aspects of various proposals. This payback is defined as the number of years required for net cash flow to equal zero (without consideration of interest) in a tabulation such as Tables 16–1 to 16–4. Other matters being equal, the more rapid the write-off for tax purposes, the shorter the payback period. This point is illustrated by the following comparison of payback periods in our four examples:

Example	Write-Off Period	Payback Period
16–4	at once	4.2 years
16–3	5 years	4.6 years
16–1	10 years	5.9 years
16–2	25 years	7.2 years

Effect of the Method of Depreciation Accounting Used for Tax Purposes on the Rate of Return After Income Taxes. In Chapter 10 it was pointed out that the double-rate declining-balance method and the sum-of-the-years-digits method, both authorized for federal income tax purposes in the United States in 1954, permit cost to be written off more rapidly than is possible with the straight-line method. Given any particular estimated life and salvage value acceptable to the taxing authorities, either of these 1954 methods will result in a slightly higher return after income taxes than will be obtained with the use of the straight-line method. The differences in return among the different depreciation accounting methods are not nearly as large as the differences

---

[3] For a qualification of this statement, see the discussion later in this chapter of the timing of income tax payments in relation to the timing of taxable income.

in returns illustrated in Examples 16–1 to 16–4 where there were great differences in write-off periods.

Example 16–5 illustrates the calculation of return after taxes with two different depreciation accounting methods in a case where estimated cash receipts differ from year to year and where a prospective salvage value is present.

EXAMPLE 16–5. RATES OF RETURN AFTER INCOME TAXES WITH TWO METHODS OF DEPRECIATION ACCOUNTING

Facts of the Case. In Example 8–2 (pages 111 to 112) we considered a proposed investment of $12,000 in rental machinery. This machinery had an estimated life of 8 years in the service of its first owner and an estimated salvage value of $1,200. On the basis of year-by-year estimates of cash flow before income taxes we found that the prospective rate of return before income taxes was 12%. It is now desired to find the prospective rate of return after income taxes assuming a tax rate of 30%. Two alternate methods of depreciation accounting are to be considered, the straight-line method and the sum-of-the-years-digits method.

Calculation of Rates of Return After Income Taxes. Tables 16–5 and 16–6 show the year-by-year calculations to determine prospective taxable income,

TABLE 16–5

Calculations To Determine Rate of Return After Income Taxes, Example 8–2, Using Straight-Line Depreciation Accounting

Year	Cash Flow Before Taxes	Depre- ciation	Taxable Income	Cash Flow for Taxes	Cash Flow After Taxes	PW at 8%	PW at 10%
0	−$12,000				−$12,000	−$12,000	−$12,000
1	+3,700	−$1,350	+$2,350	−$705	+2,995	+2,773	+2,723
2	+3,000	−1,350	+1,650	−495	+2,505	+2,148	+2,070
3	+2,400	−1,350	+1,050	−315	+2,085	+1,655	+1,566
4	+2,100	−1,350	+750	−225	+1,875	+1,378	+1,281
5	+1,700	−1,350	+350	−105	+1,595	+1,086	+990
6	+1,500	−1,350	+150	−45	+1,455	+917	+821
7	+1,300	−1,350	−50	+15	+1,315	+767	+675
8	+1,150	−1,350	−200	+60	+1,210	+654	+564
8 *	+1,200				+1,200	+648	+560
Totals	+$6,050	−$10,800	+$6,050	−$1,815	+$4,235	+$26	−$750

* Salvage value.

income tax payments, and cash flow after taxes using the two depreciation accounting methods. The tables also show the year-by-year present worths of cash flow after taxes with interest rates at 8% and 10%. Interpolation shows that the prospective rate of return after taxes is 8.1% using straight-line depre-

TABLE 16-6

Calculations To Determine Rate of Return After Income Taxes, Example 8-2, Using Sum-of-the-Years-Digits Depreciation Accounting

Year	Cash Flow Before Taxes	Depre- ciation	Taxable Income	Cash Flow for Taxes	Cash Flow After Taxes	PW at 8%	PW at 10%
0	−$12,000				−$12,000	−$12,000	−$12,000
1	+3,700	−$2,400	+$1,300	−$390	+3,310	+3,065	+3,009
2	+3,000	−2,100	+900	−270	+2,730	+2,340	+2,256
3	+2,400	−1,800	+600	−180	+2,220	+1,762	+1,668
4	+2,100	−1,500	+600	−180	+1,920	+1,411	+1,311
5	+1,700	−1,200	+500	−150	+1,550	+1,055	+962
6	+1,500	−900	+600	−180	+1,320	+832	+745
7	+1,300	−600	+700	−210	+1,090	+636	+559
8	+1,150	−300	+850	−255	+895	+484	+418
8 *	+1,200				+1,200	+648	+560
Totals	+$6,050	−$10,800	+$6,050	−$1,815	+$4,235	+$233	−$512

* Salvage value.

ciation accounting, and 8.6% using sum-of-the-years-digits depreciation accounting.

Use of Gradient Tables To Simplify Compound Interest Calculations with Sum-of-the-Years-Digits Depreciation Accounting. In sum-of-the-years-digits depreciation accounting, the annual depreciation charge decreases by a uniform amount each year. This annual decrease is the product of the so-called depreciable value (first cost minus estimated salvage value) and a fraction having a numerator of one and a denominator equal to the sum of the digits in the estimated life. If it is assumed that the tax rate will not change, the tax effect of the depreciation charge will follow a uniform gradient. Where economy studies are made after income taxes and sum-of-the-years-digits depreciation accounting is to be used, it often is helpful to use the gradient tables, Tables E-26 and E-27, for compound interest conversions. These tables are particularly useful where cash flow before income taxes is assumed to be uniform or to follow a uniform gradient. The use of these tables is illustrated in Example 16-6.

EXAMPLE 16-6.   USE OF GRADIENT TABLES IN COMPUTING RATE OF RETURN AFTER INCOME TAXES

Facts of the Case. Assume the facts of Example 16-1 with the sum-of-the-years-digits method substituted for the straight-line method of depreciation accounting.

Calculation of Rate of Return After Income Taxes. The sum of the digits from 1 to 10 is 55. In the first year, the depreciation write-off is 10/55 of $50,000 or $9,090.91. This write-off will decrease by $909.09 a year, 1/55 of $50,000. The taxable income in the first year will be $12,000 − $9,090.91 = $2,909.09. The income tax disbursement for the first year will be 51% of $2,909.09 = $1,483.64. Each year the income tax disbursement will increase by $463.64 (i.e., by 51% of the $909.09 increase in taxable income).

If a table similar to Table 16–1 should be prepared, the figures in column E (cash flow after income taxes) for years 1, 2, and 3 would be +$10,516.36, +$10,052.72, and +$9,589.08, respectively. Each year, cash flow would decrease by $463.64 down to $6,343.60 in the 10th year. Of course the sum of the figures in column E would be $34,300 just as in Table 16–1.

In the following calculations Table E–27, for present worth of a gradient, has been used in connection with the 12% and 15% interest tables.

$$\text{PW at } 12\% = -\$50,000 + \$10,516.36(P/A,12\%,10) - \$463.64(P/G,12\%,10)$$
$$= -\$50,000 + \$10,516.36(5.650) - \$463.64(20.2541) = +\$30$$
$$\text{PW at } 15\% = -\$50,000 + \$10,516.36(5.019) - \$463.64(16.9795) = -\$5,090$$

The rate of return of approximately 12.0% contrasts with the 10.9% rate of return that was computed in Example 16–1 using the straight-line method.

Economy Studies Where Declining-Balance Depreciation Accounting Is To Be Used. Rates of return after income taxes with double-rate declining-balance depreciation accounting will be very close to those with years-digits depreciation accounting. For example, Table 16–6, which applied the years-digits method to the data of Example 8–2, showed a present worth of cash flow after taxes of +$233 at 8% and −$512 at 10%; interpolation between these figures gave a rate of return of about 8.6%. The corresponding figures using the double-rate declining-balance method are +$277, −$458, and 8.8%.

Prospective rates of return after taxes with double-rate declining-balance depreciation accounting may be slightly more or slightly less than with years-digits depreciation accounting depending on a number of matters, the most important of which are salvage value ratios and the choice among item, group, classified, or composite depreciation accounting. Nevertheless, the differences in rate of return between the two methods will rarely, if ever, be enough to influence the conclusions of an economy study.

It was pointed out in Chapter 10 that the declining-balance method is a simpler method of depreciation accounting than the years-digits method. However, because of the availability of gradient tables (Tables E–26 and E–27) and because the depreciation charge in the years-digits method changes by a constant amount each year, it is easier to make compound interest conversions for economy studies with the years-digits method.

Where double-rate declining-balance depreciation accounting will actually be used and where income tax disbursements are to be introduced into economy studies, a possible simplification is to make the economy study assuming years-digits accounting. This simplification may save considerable arithmetic and will usually make a negligible change in the conclusions of the economy study.

Further Comment on the Selection of a Method of Depreciation Accounting in the United States. For depreciable business assets acquired new after 1954 in the United States, the decision on a method of depreciation accounting may reasonably be made in two steps. First the decision must be made whether it is desired to have a more rapid write-off in the early years than is possible with the straight-line method based on full service life. If the rapid write-off is wanted, it is necessary to choose among the various permissible methods of securing this write-off. Usually the choice is between the declining-balance method and the years-digits method.

The authors of this book believe that in competitive industry the straight-line method based on full service life will rarely give a write-off that is rapid enough for business purposes entirely apart from income tax considerations. Most retirements are made for economic reasons; the same factors that ultimately cause retirements also cause a rapid decline in the competitive value of fixed assets in the early years of their economic lives. Moreover, full service lives are typically much longer than economic lives. Most business decisions influenced by the depreciation accounts will be better made if the depreciation write-off is more rapid in the early years of service life.

The higher the income tax rates, the greater the financial advantage of writing off cost as rapidly as possible. This point has been brought out by the examples and comments so far in this chapter. The only condition where income tax considerations favor a slow write-off is one where the prospective tax rate in the more distant future is considerably greater than the rate in the near future.

Once the decision is made to adopt some depreciation accounting method giving a rapid write-off in the early years, the choice among the different permissible methods may properly be influenced by the convenience, simplicity, and accounting costs associated with the various methods. Particularly for group accounts, and for classified accounts (such as Machinery or Furniture and Fixtures), these considerations favor the declining-balance method. For assets recorded in item accounts and having low estimated salvage values, the advantage of the slightly more rapid write-off may justify the choice of the years-digits method in spite of its somewhat greater accounting complexity and expense.

A study made by the U. S. Treasury Department in 1960 indicated that about 70% of a sample of large corporations used one of the 1954 "liberalized" depreciation methods. About two-thirds of these used double-rate declining-balance and about half used years-digits for some assets. A study made at the same time of a sample of smaller business firms indicated a slightly smaller fraction using the 1954 methods with a somewhat greater preference for the declining-balance method.

Consideration of Differences in Income Tax Disbursements in Comparing Alternatives by Annual Cost or Present Worth. So far in this chapter we have assumed that it was prospective after-tax rate of return that was desired in order to guide investment decisions. In earlier chapters, using the simplified assumptions, we have also illustrated the introduction of outlays for income taxes in annual cost comparisons and present worth comparisons.

If only two alternatives are to be compared, a year-by-year listing of their differences in taxable income should be made and the appropriate tax rates applied to find the year-by-year differences in prospective income tax payments. This series of differences in income tax disbursements is then converted into an equivalent uniform annual figure or into present worth, as the case may be, and added to the cost of the alternative requiring the higher income taxes. This technique was first illustrated in Example 6–1.

If three or more alternatives are to be compared, the alternative having the lowest prospective income tax payments should be selected as a base. The income taxes in excess of this base should be computed for each of the other alternatives. These should be converted to annual cost or present worth, whichever is required, and added to the cost totals for the respective alternatives. This technique was first illustrated in Example 6–2.

Selection of a Tax Rate for Use in Economy Studies. In our examples up to this point we have assumed tax rates of 50%, 51%, and 30% without any explanation of how these rates were determined. In order to examine the question of how to select a tax rate or rates for use in economy studies, it is helpful to consider some specific set of tax laws. The following discussion deals with tax rates applicable to 1967, 1968, and 1969 taxable income in the United States. No attempt is made to explain all the numerous ramifications of the tax laws that need to be understood for the actual preparation of income tax returns.[4]

[4] Two helpful and inexpensive pamphlets that may be purchased from the Superintendent of Documents, U.S. Government Printing Office, Washington, D.C. 20402, are: Internal Revenue Service Publication No. 17, *Your Federal Income Tax—for Individuals;* Internal Revenue Service Publication No. 334, *Tax Guide for Small Business.* These are revised each year.

Tax Rates on Corporate Income. The 1967 federal tax rates on an increment of corporate income were generally 22%, 28%, and 48%, depending on the size of the taxable income and, in some cases, on whether a corporation was a member of a "controlled group." If one disregards the special rules that applied to members of a controlled group, a simple statement of the matter is to say that the first $25,000 of income was taxed at 22% (the "normal" tax rate) and all income above $25,000 was taxed at 48% (because of a "surtax" rate of 26%). For example, the tax on a corporate income of $1,000,000 could be figured as follows:

22% of first $25,000	= $ 5,500
48% of remaining $975,000	= 468,000
Total	= $473,500

The incremental rate therefore was 22% for small corporations that had taxable incomes below $25,000. For the medium-sized and large corporations with taxable incomes about $25,000, the incremental rate was 48%.

The special rules that applied to members of a controlled group of corporations (such as several corporations largely owned by one individual) were too technical to describe here. It is sufficient for our purpose to state that, in some instances, a group of such corporations could minimize their total federal corporate income taxes by paying a 6% "penalty" tax added to the 22% rate that applied to the first $25,000 of taxable income. For all such corporations that had incomes below $25,000, the incremental rate actually was 28%, the 22% normal tax rate plus the 6% penalty tax rate.

For 1968 and 1969, the foregoing 1967 rates were subject to a 10% surcharge. For example, the $1,000,000 corporate income that would have been subject to a $473,500 tax at 1967 rates would be subject to a $520,850 tax at 1968 and 1969 rates. The incremental tax rate in 1968 and 1969 was therefore 52.8% for corporations that had taxable income above $25,000. The 1969 legislation regarding this special surcharge stipulated that the surcharge would be reduced to 5% on January 1, 1970 and would expire on June 30, 1970.

Many of the states of the United States also had corporation income taxes. The rates varied considerably from one state to another.

Tax Rates on Individual Income. There were three 1967 federal tax rate schedules applicable to individual income, namely: Schedule I—for single taxpayers not qualifying for rates in Schedules II and III and for married persons filing separate returns; Schedule II—for married taxpayers filing joint returns and for certain widows and widowers; and Schedule III—for unmarried (or legally separated) taxpayers qualifying as "head of household." Table 16–7 reproduces Schedule I, the basic schedule.

TABLE 16–7

1967 Federal Tax Rates on Individual Income—Schedule I

Taxable Income	Amount of Tax
Not over $500	14% of taxable income
Over $500 but not over $1,000	$70 + 15% of excess over $500
Over $1,000 but not over $1,500	$145 + 16% of excess over $1,000
Over $1,500 but not over $2,000	$225 + 17% of excess over $1,500
Over $2,000 but not over $4,000	$310 + 19% of excess over $2,000
Over $4,000 but not over $6,000	$690 + 22% of excess over $4,000
Over $6,000 but not over $8,000	$1,130 + 25% of excess over $6,000
Over $8,000 but not over $10,000	$1,630 + 28% of excess over $8,000
Over $10,000 but not over $12,000	$2,190 + 32% of excess over $10,000
Over $12,000 but not over $14,000	$2,830 + 36% of excess over $12,000
Over $14,000 but not over $16,000	$3,550 + 39% of excess over $14,000
Over $16,000 but not over $18,000	$4,330 + 42% of excess over $16,000
Over $18,000 but not over $20,000	$5,170 + 45% of excess over $18,000
Over $20,000 but not over $22,000	$6,070 + 48% of excess over $20,000
Over $22,000 but not over $26,000	$7,030 + 50% of excess over $22,000
Over $26,000 but not over $32,000	$9,030 + 53% of excess over $26,000
Over $32,000 but not over $38,000	$12,210 + 55% of excess over $32,000
Over $38,000 but not over $44,000	$15,510 + 58% of excess ovre $38,000
Over $44,000 but not over $50,000	$18,990 + 60% of excess over $44,000
Over $50,000 but not over $60,000	$22,590 + 62% of excess over $50,000
Over $60,000 but not over $70,000	$28,790 + 64% of excess over $60,000
Over $70,000 but not over $80,000	$35,190 + 66% of excess over $70,000
Over $80,000 but not over $90,000	$41,790 + 68% of excess over $80,000
Over $90,000 but not over $100,000	$48,590 + 69% of excess over $90,000
Over $100,000	$55,490 + 70% of excess over $100,000

In Schedule II all dollar figures were double those in Schedule I; for example, the fifth line was:

Over $4,000 but not over $8,000 . . . . $620 + 19% of excess over $4,000

Schedule III for head of household was intermediate between Schedules I and II. For example, the 25% incremental rate, applicable to the bracket of taxable income $6,000–$8,000 in Schedule I and to the bracket $12,000–$16,000 in Schedule II, applied to the bracket $8,000–$10,000 in Schedule III.

Any business income included in personal taxable income was *net* business income; the expenses of the business (including depreciation) were deductible. Taxpayers could also deduct certain "nonbusiness deductions" including certain charitable contributions, interest payments, tax payments, medical expenses, and other specified items.

In lieu of itemizing the nonbusiness deductions, taxpayers could elect to take a "standard deduction." In general, this was 10% of the income before nonbusiness deductions (described as *adjusted gross income*) subject to two constraints. One constraint provided an upper limit; the standard deduction could never exceed $1,000. The other constraint provided a lower limit based on the number of exemptions (explained in the next paragraph). For taxpayers other than married individuals filing separate returns, the lower limit was $200 plus $100 for each exemption allowable to the taxpayer, subject to the restriction that a lower limit so calculated could not exceed $1,000.

The taxable income was the adjusted gross income minus nonbusiness deductions (either itemized or standard) minus one or more exemptions of $600 each. Every taxpayer was entitled to a $600 exemption for himself or herself and for any other person classified as a "dependent" under the law. Extra exemptions of $600 each were allowable if the taxpayer or his wife was over 65 or blind. As an example of calculation of exemptions, a married couple (both under 65 and neither blind) having two dependent children was entitled to an exemption of $2,400.

A simplified tax table, assuming the appropriate standard deduction, was available for taxpayers with adjusted gross incomes under $5,000 who did not elect to itemize their deductions. This simplified table gave the actual tax as a function of taxable income, taxpayer's status (e.g., single person, head of household, married couple filing jointly), and number of exemptions. The tax determined from the simplified table was approximately the same as the tax that would have been computed from Schedules I, II, or III, whichever was applicable, if the standard deduction had been taken.

For 1968, the 1967 individual income tax rates were subject to a 7.5% surcharge.[5] For example, an individual with $10,000 of taxable income would have paid $2,190 at 1967 rates and would pay $2,354.25 at 1968 rates. For 1969, the surcharge rate was 10%. This surcharge was scheduled to be reduced to 5% at the start of 1970 and to expire at the end of June 1970.

The majority of the states of the United States also levied taxes on personal income. Although the tax rate schedules differed greatly from state to state, all used a format similar to the federal schedules in which successive increments of income were taxed at progressively higher rates.

A General Principle—Where a Graduated Income Tax Is in Effect, the Increment Cost Viewpoint Is Necessary. The domestic electric rate quoted at the start of Chapter 15 illustrated the block principle. It was

[5] The surcharge did not apply if taxable income was only in the two lowest brackets; for taxpayers slightly above those brackets the surcharge was at lower rates than 7.5%.

pointed out that for any buyer of electricity under this rate, a determination of the money difference between purchasing more or less electricity involved only those extreme blocks of the rate that would be affected by the difference in consumption.

Graduated income taxes, such as the one illustrated in Table 16–7, employ the block principle in the same manner as electric rates. The major point of difference between block electric rates and a graduated income tax is that the unit price of electricity decreases with increased consumption, whereas the unit tax rate goes up as income increases. The increment cost viewpoint is essential in economy studies involving income taxes just as in studies involving electric rates. The prospective difference in income taxes between a greater and a smaller taxable income depends only on the particular extreme blocks of the tax rate schedule that are affected by the prospective difference in income.

Relationship Between Corporate and Individual Income Taxes in the United States. One subject that has received much discussion by students of taxation is the double taxation of corporate income. If corporations are taxed on their profits, and if that part of the profits remaining after income taxation is subject to a second income tax when received as dividends by the stockholders, this is clearly double taxation.

Over the years, the income tax laws of the United States have varied greatly on this matter of double taxation of corporate income. For 1967, 1968, and 1969, individuals were permitted to exclude from gross income the first $100 of dividend income received during the year from domestic corporations; otherwise, dividends were fully taxable as individual income.

Although corporate income in the United States is taxed as of the year in which it is earned, its second taxation as individual income does not take place until the dividends are received by the stockholders. The tax rates in the upper brackets on the individual income tax are higher than the maximum corporate rate. This leads to the following paradox.

In general, the owners of a business that is incorporated will, in the long run, pay a higher percentage of their profits as income taxes than they would pay if the same business were unincorporated. Nevertheless, under certain circumstances, the corporate form of organization has the possibility of being used as a device to reduce the immediate taxes on business profits. Assume that a corporation is controlled by stockholders whose incomes place them in the upper brackets. If, without penalty, these stockholders could elect to leave all the profits of this corporation in the business, the immediate income tax on these profits would be limited to the corporation tax. If the same profits could be taxed at the rates in the highest brackets of the individual income tax, the government would collect more taxes immediately.

To discourage the use of the corporate form of organization as a means of reducing the immediate payment of income taxes, Sections 531 to 537 of the Internal Revenue Code have imposed an additional tax on "corporations improperly accumulating surplus." A corporation was permitted to accumulate a total of $100,000 of surplus before this additional tax applied. In each year the tax was 27½% of the first $100,000 accumulated beyond the "reasonably anticipated needs" of the business and 38½% on all in excess of $100,000. This particular provision of the tax law was aimed particularly at corporations where a relatively few persons owned a large part of the stock. It exerted strong pressure on many such corporations to distribute a substantial part of their current earnings as dividends each year.

Ordinarily, all the business income of partnerships and sole proprietorships was subject to the individual income tax in the year earned regardless of whether or not any business profits were withdrawn by the owners. However, under certain stipulations, some businesses organized as partnerships or sole proprietorships could elect to be taxed as corporations. Also, under certain restrictions, corporations having 10 or less stockholders could elect to be taxed as partnerships.

What Viewpoint Toward Individual Income Taxes Should Be Taken in Economy Studies for Corporations? In any decision between alternatives made from the viewpoint of the owners of a business enterprise, all receipts and disbursements affecting the owners and influenced by the decision should properly be considered. For this reason the income tax aspects of an economy study for a corporation really involve both the corporation taxes and the individual income taxes to be paid by the stockholders on their dividends.

As a practical matter, prospective income taxes paid by the stockholders are likely to be disregarded in some corporations and considered in others, somewhat as follows:

1. In corporations with many stockholders, in which most policy decisions are made by executives whose personal stock ownership is relatively small, the tendency is to consider only the corporate income tax. Most large corporations fall into this class. Where there are many stockholders whose personal incomes are unknown to the management, it is hardly practicable to consider stockholders' income taxes. Moreover, the performance of hired managers is judged by the profit showing on the corporate books.

2. In corporations with few stockholders, with those stockholders taking an active part in policy decisions, individual income taxes

are much more likely to be considered. In such corporations, Sections 531 to 537 often force distribution of most of current earnings as dividends. Stockholders taking an active part in management are likely to be very conscious of the income taxes they pay on these dividends. Although corporations in this class are generally smaller, they are more numerous.

The Timing of Income Tax Payments in Relation to the Timing of Taxable Income. The payment of federal income taxes by individuals in the United States is so organized that individuals pay their tax throughout the year in which the income is received. Employers are required to withhold income taxes from payments of wages and salaries. Individuals having other sources of income are required to make declarations of estimated income taxes and to make quarterly payments based on these declarations.

During the early 1950's and before, corporate income taxes on a given year's taxable income were paid in the following year. However, a series of changes in tax laws starting in the mid-1950's gradually speeded up the payment of corporate taxes for corporations anticipating taxes over $100,000. Legislation in 1968 was designed so that by 1972, substantially all corporations in the United States would pay their estimated federal income taxes during the year in which the income was earned.

The exact time lag, if any, between the cash receipts and disbursements affecting current taxable income and the quarterly payments of the various income taxes based on this taxable income may be an extremely important matter in the preparation of cash budgets for business enterprises. But in the usual economy studies where the minimum time unit is one year, it generally is good enough for practical purposes in the United States to disregard any short time lag between taxable income and the payment of income taxes. We have done so in Examples 16–1 to 16–6. The column showing cash flow after income taxes in Tables 16–1 to 16–6 was based on the assumption that tax payments would take place in the same year as the current cash flow influencing the year's taxable income.

Special circumstances may arise in which it will be appropriate to assume a time lag in cash flow for income taxes. This matter is illustrated in Problems 16–8 and 16–18.

Combining Income Tax Rates for Different Governmental Units. It often happens that the same income is subject to taxation by two or more governmental bodies. Sometimes income may be taxed by two countries, particularly where an enterprise incorporated in one country does business in another country. In the United States it is common for the same income to be taxed by federal and state governments; many states have both corporation income taxes and individual income taxes. Some cities also have individual income taxes.

Economy studies are simplified where a single effective tax rate can be used to combine the incremental tax rates from the various governmental units that tax the same income. The appropriate rules for combining tax rates depend on the way in which the tax payments to each governmental unit influence the taxable income reported to the other governmental units.

In the United States, state income taxes imposed on corporations are deductible in computing the income to be taxed by the federal government. Individuals who do not take the standard nonbusiness deduction may include income taxes paid to a state among their itemized nonbusiness deductions on their federal tax returns.

A simple formula for combining state and federal incremental tax rates may be given for the common case where the state tax is deductible on the federal tax return but the federal tax is not deductible on the state return, as follows:

Let s represent the incremental state tax rate expressed as a decimal.
Let f represent the incremental federal tax rate expressed as a decimal.

$$\text{Combined incremental rate} = s + (1 - s)f$$

For example, assume that a \$1,000 increment of income is subject to a 6% state tax rate and a 48% federal rate. The state tax on this increment of income will be \$60. As the federal tax will apply only to the difference between the \$1,000 income before taxes and the \$60 state tax, it will be \$451.20, 48% of \$940. The total tax on the \$1,000 increment of income will therefore be \$60 + \$451.20 = \$511.20, or 51.12% of the income. Of course this same combined rate may be obtained from the foregoing formula as $0.06 + (1 - 0.06)(0.48) = 0.5112$.

Where there are two or more taxes to be paid that are independent of one another, the tax rates may be combined by simple addition. For example, consider an individual in the United States who takes the standard deduction rather than itemizing nonbusiness deductions. If his incremental rate on his state tax is 4% and his incremental rate on his federal tax is 25%, a combined rate of 29% will apply to the highest increment of his income.

The most difficult problems of combining tax rates arise where the tax due to each of the taxing units cannot be computed without somehow recognizing the past tax payments or current tax liabilities to the other taxing units. The laws and regulations under which such recognitions occur vary so greatly that no simple rules for combination of tax rates can be given here. But it can be said that, given the specific laws and regulations, it usually is possible to compute an approximate combined incremental rate on an increment of income at any level.

The Concept of an "Effective Tax Rate" as a Net Incremental Rate. Even though income may be subject to two or more taxes with slightly different timing, it usually is good enough for practical purposes in an economy study to combine the taxes into a single rate. The phrase *effective tax rate* used in examples and problems throughout the remainder of this book refers to a single incremental rate to use for a given year or group of years in a particular economy study. Each specified effective tax rate is assumed to have been determined after consideration of all taxes believed to be relevant, both individual and corporate and both federal and state, and after consideration of the interrelationships of these taxes and of the appropriate incremental brackets.

Sometimes the various governmental units taxing the same income have substantially different rules for determining taxable income. If so, it may not be advisable to simplify economy studies by the use of a single effective tax rate.

Consideration of a Prospective Large Change in the Incremental Tax Rate. Our examples up to this point have assumed a single effective tax rate applicable to all of the years of any given economy study. Presumably this is an estimated average rate for the entire study period. The adoption of *one* rate, rather than two or more rates applicable to different years, implies either that the analyst has no basis for estimating different rates for different years or that the expected changes from year to year are not large enough to have a significant influence on the results of the economy study.

Sometimes there is a good reason to forecast an abrupt sharp change in the tax rate applicable to the highest increment of a particular taxpayer's income. For example, it may be expected that a certain corporation with taxable income below $25,000 will soon increase its income so that it will be taxed in the much higher bracket above $25,000. Or a high "excess profits" tax applicable to the final increment of a corporation's income may be scheduled to expire at a definite future date with the effect of dropping the corporation's incremental tax rate. Or an individual may expect considerably higher or lower income with a corresponding change in incremental rates. The same techniques of analysis that have been illustrated for a single effective tax rate can be applied equally well if it is forecast that there will be two or more different tax rates applicable to different years of a study period. Several of the problems at the end of this chapter illustrate the assumption of two effective tax rates during a study period and bring out the point that decisions often are sensitive to this assumption.

Examples 16–1 to 16–4 illustrated the influence of the speed at which certain outlays are written off on the rate of return after taxes, assuming a uniform tax rate throughout the period of the economy study. The advantage of the rapid write-off is increased when it is expected that tax rates in the near future will be greater than in the more distant future. Conversely, the advantage of a rapid write-off is decreased or eliminated when tax rates in the near future are expected to be less than in the distant future.

Selecting Tax Rates for Use in Economy Studies for Corporations. A 50% effective tax rate has often been used in economy studies for corporations in the United States in the common case where it was expected that annual taxable income would continue to be greater than $25,000. Such a rate, which had the advantage of simplicity, allowed for some state tax in addition to a 48% incremental federal tax. Figure 21–2 illustrates a corporate form based on an assumed 50% tax rate. A 50% rate was used in our simplified assumptions in earlier chapters and is specified in a number of problems at the end of this chapter and subsequent chapters.

However, a 50% rate is not a good one to use in textbook examples. Methods of introducing income tax considerations into economy studies can be shown more clearly with rates that do not divide taxable income equally between the taxpayer and the government. For this reason, none of the examples in this chapter assume a 50% rate. (We have noted that the 51% rate, used in several examples, is approximately correct for a combination of a 48% incremental federal rate and a 6% incremental state rate.)

In many small corporations where it was expected that annual taxable income would continue to be below $25,000, effective corporate tax rates between 22% and about 32% were appropriate for use in economy studies made in 1967. The lower of these figures is, of course, the federal rate on the first $25,000 of income for corporations not members of a controlled group; it could be used for such corporations where there is no state corporate income tax. The higher rate combines a 6% state rate and the 28% incremental federal rate appropriate for certain corporations in controlled groups.

In closely held corporations where consideration is given to all taxes on corporate income, both corporate taxes and personal taxes, the appropriate effective tax rates may sometimes be extremely high. For example, assume corporate taxes of 48% and stockholders' incremental tax rates on personal income of 50%. If the income remaining after corporate taxes is distributed as dividends each year, each extra dollar of corporate income before taxes will lead to the payment of 48 cents in corporate taxes and 26 cents in personal taxes; this is an effective tax rate of 74%.

Selecting a Tax Rate in Economy Studies for Individuals. Because of the numerous brackets in both federal and state tax schedules in the United States, the selection of a single effective tax rate is somewhat less appropriate for individuals than for corporations. In many decisions made by individuals where there are prospective differences in taxable income, the best thing to do may be to compute a total taxable income and a total income tax for each alternative under consideration.

Nevertheless, in many economy studies for individuals it is close enough for purposes of decision making to simplify matters by selecting a single rate applicable to the expected highest bracket of the individual's income. In the frequent case where the exact bracket is uncertain, a rate averaging two or more brackets may be used. For example consider a single person who is sole proprietor of a business and who is subject to the federal tax rate schedule shown in Table 16–7. Assume that he expects his annual taxable income to be between $10,000 and $16,000. In decision making related to income taxes, he might use the 36% rate applicable to the bracket $12,000–$14,000. Or if state taxes raised the final increment of his combined tax by about 2% of income, he could make economy studies with an effective rate of 38%.

Need for Consideration in Economy Studies of Laws and Regulations Regarding the Determination of Taxable Income and Tax Liability. Every governmental unit that levies income taxes has its own laws and regulations that govern the way in which taxable income and tax liability are computed. These rules vary considerably from one government to another and change from time to time in any given government. Generally speaking, legislative bodies are free to define taxable income in any way they see fit. Although the concept of taxable income corresponds in a general way to the concept of accounting income, there are likely to be some significant points of difference.

As already mentioned, the discussion in this book is intended to stress the general principles of introducing income tax considerations into economy studies. These principles are not limited to any particular set of tax laws and regulations. The steps outlined in the discussion that followed Example 16–4 are appropriate regardless of the laws and regulations that exist at the time and place of a particular economy study.

Converting Cash Flow Before Income Taxes into Taxable Income.
Among these steps, the most critical one in any analysis is likely to be
the conversion of an estimated difference in cash flow between two
alternatives into an estimated difference in taxable income. In many
cases this is a problem for the tax specialist. Fortunately, however,
there are a number of common types of cases in which this conversion is
reasonably simple and straightforward. Our examples in this chapter
up to this point have dealt with only one aspect of this subject, as they
have concentrated attention on the way in which the depreciation method
used for tax purposes enters into this conversion. Some other aspects of
this conversion are discussed in the next few pages.

It is convenient to examine the conversion of cash flow into taxable
income in two steps, namely, (1) the relationship between cash flow and
accounting income and (2) some possible points of difference between
accounting income and taxable income. In the second of these steps
our illustrations are based on the federal income tax laws and regulations
of the United States (particularly those in effect for 1967, 1968, and 1969).

**A Guide for Nonaccountants in Judging the Influence of Certain
Transactions on Accounting Income.**[6] A common method of presenting
the elements of accounting is by means of the so-called balance sheet
approach. This approach starts with the following rule for obtaining
the valuation placed by the books of account on the owners' equity in a
business enterprise:

Owners' equity = valuation placed by the accounts on what
the enterprise owns minus what it owes

or, expressed more briefly,

Owners' equity = assets − liabilities

The preceding equation is, in effect, simply a definition of owners'
equity. It is important to recognize that owners' equity in the sense
used here is a derived figure. It is the valuation that the accounts place
on the assets and liabilities that determines the valuation that they place
on owners' equity. The equation may be rewritten in the conventional
balance sheet form as follows:

Assets = liabilities + ownership

[6] If persons responsible for the conduct or supervision of economy studies have
not studied accounting at some time in their careers, it is recommended that they read
a text on elementary accounting. Many good standard works on this subject are
available. A short presentation written in part by one of the authors of this book,
aimed particularly at nonaccountants, is: E. L. Grant and L. F. Bell, *Basic Accounting and Cost Accounting* (2d ed.; New York: McGraw-Hill Book Co., Inc., 1964).

As pointed out in Chapter 10, two major statements that always may be derived from the accounts of a business enterprise are the balance sheet and the profit and loss statement (also called the income statement). The balance sheet always applies to a particular date, stating book valuations for the various assets, liabilities, and for the owners' equity as of the stated date. The profit and loss statement applies to a stated period of time (such as a particular year); it serves to summarize the business transactions that have increased or decreased owners' equity during the period (usually excluding certain transactions between the enterprise and its owners—such as the withdrawal of ownership funds or the investment of new funds by the owners).

In converting estimated cash flow into its estimated influence on profit, it is essential to recognize that there are many cash transactions that have no immediate effect on the accounting figure for profit. Thus if the asset, cash, is decreased in a transaction to acquire some other asset given an equal value on the balance sheet, owners' equity is unchanged and the immediate effect on profit is nil. (Examples are the purchase of land for cash, and the purchase of a depreciable asset—such as a building or machine.) Or if cash is increased and some other asset is decreased by an equal amount, there has been no change in owners' equity. (Examples are the sale of land for its original cost and the sale of an old building at exactly its depreciated book value.) Or if cash is increased and there is an equal increase in a liability, owners' equity is unchanged. (An example is the borrowing of money.) Neither is owners' equity changed when cash is decreased and there is an equal decrease in a liability. (An example is the repayment of a loan.)

The student of accounting will recognize that the foregoing simple statements about cash transactions that *do not* make immediate changes in owners' equity cannot be matched by equally simple statements identifying cash transactions that *do* make such changes. Nevertheless, many cash transactions are clearly identifiable as changing owners' equity in the year in which they occur. Fortunately, the use of the year as the time unit in a cash flow analysis for economy studies makes it possible to disregard certain matters that are important in day-by-day accounting. It should be recognized that many incomes (increases in owners' equity) are partially offset by associated expenses (decreases in owners' equity). For example, receipts from the sale of a product or service are offset by the costs of supplying the product or service.

The Difference in the Income Tax Status of Owners' Capital and Borrowed Capital. For accounting purposes, interest paid on a loan is a current expense that reduces the accounting figure for profit (or increases the figure for loss). In contrast, a desired minimum attractive return on money furnished by the owners of an enterprise is not deducted as an expense in the orthodox accounting determination of profit.

In this respect, as in so many others, the income tax concept of taxable income corresponds to the accounting view of profit. Hence, when an enterprise is financed entirely by ownership funds, the entire return on the investment is subject to income taxation. Where part of the financing is by borrowed money, the taxable income is reduced by the interest paid. This topic is discussed and illustrated in Chapter 18.

An assumption that a certain fraction of financing by long-term debt is to be associated with *all* proposed plant investment calls for some modification of the income tax analysis developed in the present chapter. The circumstances under which this assumption may or may not be reasonable are discussed briefly in Chapter 18. The assumption is applied in Chapter 20 in the development of a suggested treatment of income taxes in economy studies for regulated public utilities in the United States.

Carryback and Carryover Provisions of United States Income Tax Laws. It was pointed out in Chapters 8 and 10 that the profitableness of an enterprise cannot be measured exactly until the enterprise has terminated, and that accounting figures for profit or loss should properly be thought of as tentative judgments that may later turn out to have been either too favorable or not favorable enough. This viewpoint, in spite of its obvious soundness, is not a practicable one to adopt in the administration of income taxes. The laws, regulations, and practices governing income taxes are necessarily based on the fiction that there is some determinable correct figure for profit or loss for each year of the existence of an enterprise.

Adherence to this fiction is unfair to business enterprises that are of the feast-or-famine type unless the losses reported in tax returns for some years can be offset against profits reported for other years. Otherwise, two enterprises that have equal net profits over a period of years may have had quite different taxable incomes. For example, Corporation A, producing consumers' goods for which there is a fairly stable demand, may be contrasted with Corporation B, producing capital goods for which there are great fluctuations in demand. Over a 20-year period, each corporation has total net profits before income taxes of $2,000,000. The profits of Corporation A have never fallen below $50,000 or risen above $150,000. In contrast, Corporation B has had total profits of $3,800,000 for 12 profitable years and total losses of $1,800,000 for 8 unprofitable years.

Despite the fact that their accounts show Corporations A and B to be equally profitable over the 20-year period, Corporation B has had nearly twice as much taxable income as Corporation A. In the absence of any provision for using the loss years to offset the profit years in the determination of income tax liability, income taxation places an inequitably large burden on Corporation B.

The income tax laws of the United States have changed from time to time with respect to the use of loss years to offset profit years. Neither a carryback nor a carryover (i.e., a carry forward) of losses was allowed from 1933 to 1939. Therefore the business losses of a number of depression years were never used to offset the profits of earlier or later years in income tax returns. The law was liberalized by degrees, starting in 1940. In 1968, the rule in most cases permitted net operating losses to be carried back to the 3 preceding years or forward to the 5 succeeding years. For certain types of business under certain stipulated conditions, a slightly longer carryback or carryover was permitted.

In contrast to the recent United States laws, income tax laws of many of the states of the United States have not permitted either carryback or carryover of business losses.

Reducing the Adverse Impact of Income Taxation on Capital Formation and Technological Progress. A high standard of living depends on the use of capital goods. Generally speaking, it is technological progress that makes it possible for the standard of living to be improved. Obstacles to capital formation and to technological progress are obstacles to improvements in the standard of living. They may also be obstacles to effective national defense.

Examples 16–1 to 16–6 brought out the point that the tax deterrent to capital investment is greatest when high income tax rates are combined with the requirement that depreciation be written off over a long period of years. Moreover, high income tax rates combined with low depreciation rates often create obstacles in the way of financing capital goods. It is of great social importance that income tax laws be so drawn that this undesirable effect of income taxation be kept at a minimum.

Two changes in 1962 were aimed at reducing this undesirable effect in the United States. One of these, an administrative change, authorized the use of certain "guideline lives" for depreciable business assets that (except for buildings) were considerably shorter than the lives that had commonly been used in tax returns. Various tests were stipulated to ensure that these short lives could not be used indefinitely in tax returns without evidence that the realized average lives for a taxpayer's various classes of assets agreed fairly well with the authorized guideline lives.

The second change established an "investment tax credit." This credit applied from the start of 1962 through the early months of 1969, except for a short period of suspension between October 10, 1966 and March 10, 1967. A law passed at the end of 1969 discontinued this credit effective April 19, 1969.

The Investment Tax Credit Law. When an income tax law contains a provision for an investment tax credit, this provision needs to be recognized in after-tax economy studies. Moreover, the treatment of such a credit in an economy study is quite different from the treatment of other tax matters. It therefore is of interest to examine certain general features of the investment tax credit law as it existed in the United States in 1968, the final full year of its applicability.

1. The tax credit applied to qualified investment in new and used "Sec. 38 property." It was allowed only for the first year in which the property was placed in service by the taxpayer. (However, there was a provision for a carryback and carryover of unused credit.)

2. With certain exceptions, "Sec. 38 property" included tangible personal property subject to depreciation. It also included other tangible depreciable property (not including a building or most of its components) if used as an integral part of manufacturing, extraction, production, or furnishing of transportation, communications, electrical energy, gas, water, or sewage disposal services. Exclusions included property used chiefly outside the United States and property used by or leased to governmental units.

3. The qualified investment in "Sec. 38 property" was equal to the sum of the cost (or other "basis" as defined in tax laws and regulations) of new "Sec. 38 property" plus a limited amount (not over $50,000) of the cost of used "Sec. 38 property." But such basis or cost was limited if the property had a useful life of less than 8 years. Where the life was at least 6 years and less than 8 years, only ⅔ of the basis or cost was taken into account. Where the life was at least 4 years and less than 6 years, only ⅓ was taken into account. Nothing was taken into account where the useful life was less than 4 years. For public utility property, the qualified investment was 3/7 of that allowable on other "Sec. 38 property."

As an example, consider a manufacturing corporation with investments in "Sec. 38 property" during 1968 as follows:

Cost of Property	New or Used	Useful Life	Qualified Investment
$180,000	New	10 years	$180,000
80,000	Used	10 years	50,000
60,000	New	6 years	40,000
30,000	New	4 years	10,000
50,000	New	3 years	0
$400,000			$280,000

If the foregoing corporation had been a public utility, the qualified investment would have been $120,000, ⅗ of $280,000.

4. The amount of the credit was 7% of the qualified investment (subject to the limitation on the maximum investment credit). Thus our manufacturer with a qualified investment of $280,000 would have a credit of $19,600 against his income tax.

5. The investment tax credit in any year could not exceed the tax liability. If tax liability was more than $25,000 the tax credit could not exceed $25,000 plus 50% of the tax liability above that amount.

The manufacturer in our illustration who had a tax credit of $19,600 could use the full tax credit provided his tax liability before the credit was $19,600 or more. However, if his tax credit had been, say, $225,000 and his tax liability before the credit had been $325,000, only $175,000 of the tax credit could have been used in 1968.

6. Any portion of an investment tax credit that could not be used in a current year could be carried back 3 years (but not to tax years ending before 1962) and carried over for 7 years to be used in a year when 7% of the qualified investment was less than the maximum credit allowable under the foregoing rules.

7. Under certain restrictions, a lessor could elect to pass on to his lessee the right to use the investment tax credit on certain eligible property.

8. In general, taxpayers who used estimated lives of 8 years or more in computing qualified investment were expected to keep the assets in question for at least 8 years. Similarly, taxpayers using 6- or 7-year lives for certain assets were expected to keep such assets for at least 6 years; taxpayers using 4- or 5-year lives were expected to keep such assets for at least 4 years. The law contained a recapture clause providing that a "premature" disposal of an asset would increase the tax due for the year of disposal by the difference between the credit originally allowed and the credit that would have been allowed if the credit had been computed using the shorter life that actually was obtained.

The foregoing statement is intended to give the reader a general idea of the effect of a rather complex set of rules. It is not aimed to give enough information to enable the reader to compute what the tax credit would have been under the great variety of different conditions that could arise in practice.

How To Introduce the Investment Tax Credit into Economy Studies. The credit was a reduction of the *tax*, not of taxable income. In fact, it did not affect taxable income. Moreover, under ordinary circumstances the credit reduced the tax in the same year that the investment was made.

If we disregard any slight time lag between the cash flow for the investment and the cash flow for the year's tax payment, the credit appears in any tabulation of cash flow as positive cash flow at zero date on the time scale.

Let us alter Example 16–1 by introducing a 7% investment tax credit. Because the investment is $50,000, the tax credit is 0.07 ($50,000) = $3,500. In revising Table 16–1, the credit would appear as +$3,500 at 0 date in column D, the column showing the effect of the proposed outlay on cash flow for income taxes. The revised figure at 0 date in column E is −$46,500. Other figures in column E are unchanged by the investment tax credit. Interpolation between present worth of cash flow at 12% (+$1,130) and at 15% (−$4,190) gives a prospective rate of return of approximately 12.6%. This may be compared with the 10.9% computed in Example 16–1 without benefit of any assumed tax credit and with the 20.2% before-tax rate of return.

If the estimated life of the assets had been 6 or 7 years, the tax credit would have been 4⅔% of the investment rather than 7%. (This figure results from applying a 7% credit to ⅔ of the investment.) If the life had been 4 or 5 years, the credit would have been 2⅓%. For public utilities, the tax credit was 3% for assets with lives of 8 or more years, 2% for 6 or 7 years, and 1% for 4 or 5 years. (These figures resulted from the stipulation that for public utilities the qualified investment was 3/7 of that allowable on other "Sec. 38 property.")

Some Aspects of the Timing of the Investment Tax Credit. In the common case where an investment tax credit was permitted to be used in the year of the investment, the time lag was relatively short between the negative cash flow due to the investment and the positive cash flow (i.e., reduced income tax payment) caused by the tax credit. The same general considerations applied that we have already discussed with reference to the time lag between the receipt of taxable income and the payment of income taxes.

In some cases, however, there could be a substantial time lag in the influence of the tax credit on cash flow. This lag would be due to the limitation of the amount of the tax credit that could be taken in any year.

In general, the principle that only prospective differences are relevant in comparing alternatives should be applied to the assumed timing of a tax credit in an economy study. Unless a proposed investment will add to the total tax credit that can be used in the year the investment is made, the economy study should assume that the cash flow due to the credit will be deferred for one or more years.

Some Aspects of the Influence of the Investment Tax Credit on Investment Decisions. Any tax reduction makes more money available for various business purposes, including investment in productive assets. Because the tax credit was a tax reduction, it may be viewed in this broad general sense as a stimulus to such investments. But the more interesting aspects of the possible consequences of a tax credit deal with influences that depend on its special features as a unique type of tax reduction.

One obvious feature of the tax credit was that it operated unequally on different types of investment proposals within any given business organization. Proposals for new machinery and equipment (and other "Sec. 38 property") with lives of 8 years or more received the most favorable treatment. Shorter-lived assets received less advantage from the credit. Some types of assets, such as land and buildings, used assets over the $50,000 limit, and all assets with lives of less than 4 years, received no advantage at all. Therefore, the relative attractiveness of different investment proposals was changed by the investment tax credit.

How valuable was the tax credit in the most favorable case where the full 7% could be used without any time lag? Consider a proposed outlay of $10,000 to purchase an eligible asset. In effect, the credit reduced the purchase price by $700. However, the credit was more advantageous to the taxpayer than a mere reduction of the purchase price to $9,300 because depreciation for tax purposes was based on $10,000 rather than on $9,300.[7] Any present worth figure computed to evaluate this $700 greater tax depreciation will depend on the life, the assumed depreciation method, the assumed effective tax rate, and the interest rate used to discount future tax savings. If we assume a 10-year life, straight-line depreciation, a 48% tax rate, and 7% interest, this present worth is ($700/10) $(0.48)(P/A,7\%,10) = \$236$. With these assumptions, the tax credit on the $10,000 asset may be viewed as having been worth $700 + $236 = $936 or 9.36% of the purchase price.

To what extent did the investment tax credit remove or reduce the tax deterrent to investment that is associated with high income tax rates? The answer to this question depends on the extent of the deterrent caused by the applicable tax rate, on the life and depreciation method used for tax purposes, on the amount and time distribution of estimated cash flow before taxes, on the method of financing, and on other matters. The following tabulation, based on application of a 7% immediate tax credit in three of our examples, brings out certain aspects of this subject.

---

[7] The law in 1962 and 1963 stipulated that the depreciation base should be reduced by the amount of the tax credit. This provision of the law was eliminated in 1964.

				Rate of Return	
				After Taxes	After Taxes
		Depreciation	Before	Without	With 7%
Example	Tax Rate	Method	Taxes	ITC	ITC
16–1	51%	Straight-line	20.2%	10.9%	12.6%
16–6	51%	Years-digits	20.2%	12.0%	14.1%
16–5	30%	Straight-line	12.0%	8.1%	10.3%
16–5	30%	Years-digits	12.0%	8.6%	11.0%

With the lower tax rate of 30% in Example 16–5, the combination of
the investment tax credit and the use of one of the 1954 depreciation
methods brought the after-tax rate of return (11.0%) reasonably close to
the before-tax rate (12.0%). Thus nearly all the tax deterrent to this
investment was eliminated.

Because the tax credit applied to the tax rather than to the taxable
income, it could do a more complete job of eliminating tax deterrents
to investment with a tax rate of, say, 30%, than with one of, say 51%. For
the facts of Example 16–1, the before-tax rate of return of 20.2% was
reduced to an after-tax rate of return of 10.9% using straight-line depreciation. The combination of the 7% tax credit and the years-digits depreciation method raised the after-tax rate of return to 14.1%. This was still
considerably short of the before-tax 20.2%.

**Accounting Treatment of "Gains" and "Losses" on the Disposal of
Certain Assets.** It is a convention of accounting that certain business
assets are carried on the books at their original cost regardless of changes
in market value; some examples are land and certain securities (such as
corporate stocks). It was explained in Chapter 10 that the cost of certain
other assets is written off "in a systematic and rational manner." This
systematic write-off applies not only to depreciable physical assets but
also to certain intangible assets (such as patents).

Whenever an asset is disposed of for more or less than its book value,
an increase or decrease occurs in the owners' equity as shown by the
books of account. It is the convention of accounting to assign this so-
called "gain" or "loss" on disposal entirely to the year in which the disposal takes place. For example, if land acquired for $10,000 in 1930 is
sold for $100,000 in 1970, the $90,000 excess over the original cost serves
to increase the profit for 1970. Or if stock purchased for $50,000 in
1956 is sold for $30,000 in 1971, the $20,000 shortage below the original
cost serves to reduce the profit for 1971.

Chapter 15 pointed out that in an economy study dealing with the
influence on future cash flow of a choice between alternatives, past outlays are irrelevant except as they are expected to influence future cash

flow. From the viewpoint of economy studies, the chief importance of a prospective "gain" or "loss" on disposal consists in the effect of this accounting entry on cash flow for income taxes.

Income Tax Treatment of Such "Gains" and "Losses" in the United States. At one time in the United States such gains were included in taxable income and such losses were fully deductible from taxable income in the year in which the disposal of the assets occurred. In the 1930's the law was changed in a way that subjected long-term gains to a lower tax rate than ordinary income and severely limited the extent to which capital losses could be deducted from taxable income except to offset similar gains. The exact rules on this matter have changed many times and have always been full of technicalities. The 1962, 1964, and 1969 tax laws introduced new complications into this already complex subject.

In an economy study in which any alternative involves prospective disposal of assets at more or less than their book values (either immediately or at some future date), it is necessary to consider the effect of the disposal on prospective cash flow for income taxes. To find this cash flow, one must determine the amount of the gain or loss that will be recognized for tax purposes and then determine the applicable tax rate or rates. This matter is discussed in Chapter 17 and illustrated in Examples 17–1 and 17–2.

For tax purposes, *long-term* capital gains and losses were defined as gains and losses on capital assets held for more than 6 months. Net long-term capital gains were taxed at lower rates than ordinary income. Capital losses could be used to offset capital gains; otherwise, the extent to which they could influence current taxable income was limited.

Depreciable assets used in the trade or business were not "capital assets" as defined in the law. However, under certain complex restrictions a part or all of a gain on the sale of certain depreciable assets could be taxed at capital gain rates, with the remainder of the gain, if any, taxed at the higher rates applicable to ordinary income. Under the technical rules of multiple-asset depreciation accounting, ordinary retirements of depreciable assets do not result in either a "loss" or "gain." But where a loss on disposal of depreciable assets used in the trade or business was recognized for tax purposes (because of the use of item accounting or because of certain unusual circumstances), this loss was fully deductible from taxable income in the year of disposal.

Exemption of Certain Interest Income from Income Taxation. Interest received on bonds or other obligations of a state, territory, or the District of Columbia has been completely exempt from federal income taxes in the United States. As a result, states, counties, cities, and the many different types of local improvement districts could borrow at lower rates than would have been possible without this tax exemption.

Chapter 11 pointed out that one element in deciding on a minimum attractive rate of return on a proposed investment is to consider the rate of return foregone on other opportunities to invest the same funds. The return available from tax-exempt bonds tends to establish a lower limit on the before-tax minimum attractive rate of return for many individuals and corporations in the United States. For example, if a taxpayer's effective tax rate is 60% and the yield on tax-exempt bonds is 4.1%, an investment subject to taxation must earn at least 10.25% before taxes to have the same after-tax return as the bonds.

Special Income Tax Treatment of Certain Natural Resources. For accounting purposes, the cost of an exhaustible natural resource (such as a mineral deposit) is written off over the estimated life of the resource. This write-off, usually on a unit-of-production basis, is described as *depletion* rather than as depreciation.

For income tax purposes, the laws of the United States have allowed taxpayers the option of making depletion charges for tax purposes by a method that may permit the total depletion deduction over the life of a resource to exceed its cost. Under the law in 1968, taxpayers could make depletion deductions for certain exhaustible resources equal to a specified percentage of the gross income from the property during the year. Some of the depletion percentages were 27½ for oil and gas wells; 23 or 15 for many metals and minerals, depending on the type of metal or mineral and on whether or not the deposit was in the United States; 10 for coal; and 5 for gravel, sand, and brick and tile clay. The depletion under this percentage method in any year was not permitted to exceed 50% of the net income of the taxpayer from the property in that year computed without the allowance for depletion.

In economy studies relative to the acquisition or disposal of such natural resources, special consideration needs to be given to the income tax treatment of depletion.

Contrast Between Competitive Industry and Regulated Public Utilities (in the United States) with Respect to Economy Studies and Income Taxes. All of our examples and problems relating to competitive industry have assumed that the price of a competitive product or service will be established by market conditions unrelated to an individual producer's decision on alternative types of plant. We have assumed that economy studies for a competitive enterprise should be made from the viewpoint of the owners of the enterprise.

In Chapter 20 we shall see that the assumption that revenues are independent of the choice among alternative production methods is not valid for most regulated privately-owned public utilities in the United States. Under the rules that have evolved to govern the regulation of public utility rates starting in the 1890's, a utility's "revenue requirements" depend, among other matters, on the choice of production methods. Since the establishment of the federal income tax in 1913 (followed by state income taxes in later years), income tax requirements have been a necessary element in total revenue requirements.

It is brought out in Chapter 20 that under most circumstances in the United States, decisions among alternate production methods for regulated public utilities should be made to minimize total revenue requirements as defined under the rules of rate regulation. In effect, decisions are made from the viewpoint of the customers rather than the owners of the enterprise. The implications of this difference in viewpoint with respect to the consideration of prospective income taxes are discussed in Chapter 20.

A Further Comment on the Question of How To Introduce Consideration of Income Taxes into Economy Studies in Competitive Industry. There is no room for debate on the point *that* income taxes need to be considered in choosing between alternatives in competitive industry; the only issue is *how* tax considerations can best be introduced into decision-making procedures. Two methods of considering income taxes in economy studies, both frequently used in industry, are:

1. The first method is to compare alternatives *before* income taxes. In this method, comparisons must be made using a minimum attractive rate of return before taxes that is high enough to yield a desired after-tax rate. Often a stipulated rate of return after taxes is divided by one minus the effective tax rate to find the minimum attractive rate before taxes. For example, if the minimum attractive rate after taxes were 8% and the tax rate were 51%, the before-tax rate would be $8\% \div (1 - 0.51) = 16.3\%$.

2. The second method, illustrated in most of the examples in this book, is to compare alternatives *after* income taxes. The year-by-year differences in disbursements for taxes are estimated, and the analysis is made using a minimum attractive rate of return after taxes.

The first method has two major advantages. It is simpler in the sense of involving less calculation, and it can be applied by persons who are not familiar with the technicalities of income taxation. Nevertheless, the second method clearly is the one that is correct in principle. The first method is appropriate only where it is reasonable to expect that it will lead to the same *decisions* among alternatives that would be reached by applying the second method.

A rough generalization, subject to exceptions, is that the first method often is good enough for practical purposes at the level of decisions on design alternatives but that it will rarely be satisfactory in comparing alternative projects on the level of capital budgeting.

In principle the interest rate used in the first method (the minimum attractive rate of return before income taxes) has the defect of discounting the future too greatly. Therefore the first method places insufficient weight on the more distant consequences of alternatives.

If it is desired to be sure to array investment proposals in their correct order, some circumstances requiring the use of the second method are as follows:

1. Whenever there are substantial differences in the rates of write-off for different alternatives. (This was illustrated in Examples 16–1 to 16–4.)
2. Whenever a substantial change in the applicable tax rate is expected during the period of the study.
3. In the United States, for all investment proposals in the mining and petroleum industries. (This is because of the percentage depletion method permitted for tax purposes. After-tax analyses generally need to be made for all proposals, not merely for those involving percentage depletion, because proposals without this tax advantage must compete for limited funds against proposals that have this advantage.)
4. In the United States, whenever one or more alternatives involve a prospective capital gain or loss or a gain or loss on disposal of real estate or depreciable assets used in the trade or business.
5. Whenever a crude payout after taxes is to be used as a supplementary criterion for investment decisions.

Summary. This chapter has illustrated a rational approach to the introduction of income tax considerations into the making of decisions between alternative investments. In general, this approach has been based on an analysis of alternatives in terms of prospective differences in cash flow and a recognition of income tax payments as a disbursement that should be included in any cash flow analysis.

The reader should recognize that it has been possible to discuss tax matters only in broad general terms. Any brief explanation of such complex matters must necessarily oversimplify certain subjects and omit many details that would be important in the actual preparation of income tax returns.

PROBLEMS

In the following problems, assume 100% equity funds unless otherwise stated. Assume the end-of-year convention. Unless otherwise stated, assume that the cash flow for income taxes that results from each year's taxable income occurs at the end of the respective tax year. Do not assume an investment tax credit unless one is stated.

16–1. A $60,000 investment in machinery is proposed. It is anticipated that this investment will cause a reduction in net annual operating disbursements of $10,000 a year for 15 years. The investment will be depreciated for income tax purposes by the straight-line method assuming a 15-year life and zero salvage value. The forecast of zero salvage value is also to be used in the economy study. The effective income tax rate is 50%. What are the prospective rates of return before and after income taxes? (*Ans.* = 14.5%; 8.0%.)

16–2. Compute the after-tax rate of return in Problem 16–1 assuming years-digits depreciation for tax purposes. (*Ans.* = 8.9%.)

16–3. Compute the after-tax rate of return in Problem 16–1 assuming that the investment is to be written off for tax purposes at $12,000 a year during the first 5 years. (*Ans.* = 10.3%.)

16–4. Compute the after-tax rate of return in Problem 16–1 assuming that the investment must be written off for tax purposes by the straight-line method assuming a 30-year life and zero salvage value, even though the expected operating saving will occur only during the first 15 years of life. (*Ans.* = 6.5%.)

16–5. The solution to Problem 16–4 assumed a positive cash flow during years 16 to 30 due to the depreciation deduction that was assumed to continue through that period. If, for some reason, it is believed that this tax credit in years 16 to 30 will not be realized, what is the prospective rate of return after taxes? (*Ans.* = 5.6%.)

16–6. Change the conditions of Problems 16–4 to assume that the machine will be retired at zero salvage value at the end of 15 years and that the $30,000 "loss on disposal" will be fully deductible from taxable income for the 15th year. (*Ans.* = 7.0%.)

16–7. If the $60,000 disbursement at zero date in Problem 16–1 could be treated as a current expense for tax purposes, and if the tax consequence of this treatment should take place at zero date on our time scale (just as was assumed in Example 16–4), what is the after-tax rate of return? (*Ans.* = 14.5%.)

16–8. If the $60,000 disbursement at zero date in Problem 16–1 could be treated as a current expense for tax purposes but the tax consequence of this treatment should take place at date 1 on our time scale, what is the after-tax rate of return? (*Ans.* = 12.5%.)

16–9. Compute the after-tax rate of return in Problem 16–1 assuming a 7% investment tax credit to be taken immediately. (*Ans.* = 9.2%.)

16–10. Compute the after-tax rate of return in Problem 16–1 assuming a 7% investment tax credit that will not be taken until 3 years after the date of the investment. (*Ans.* = 8.9%.)

16–11. Compute the after-tax rate of return in Problem 16–2 assuming a 7% investment tax credit to be taken immediately. (*Ans.* = 10.3%.)

16–12. A $39,000 investment in machinery is proposed. It is anticipated that this investment will cause a reduction in net annual operating disbursements of $10,500 a year for 12 years. The investment will be depreciated for income tax purposes by the straight-line method assuming a 12-year life and zero salvage value. The forecast of zero salvage value is also to be used in the economy study. The effective tax rate is 55%. What are the prospective rates of return before and after income taxes?

16–13. Compute the after-tax rate of return in Problem 16–12 assuming years-digits depreciation for tax purposes.

16–14. Compute the after-tax rate of return in Problem 16–12 assuming an effective income tax rate of 35%.

16–15. Compute the after-tax rate of return in Problem 16–12 assuming a 7% investment tax credit.

16–16. Compute the after-tax rate of return in Problem 16–12 assuming that the investment must be written off for tax purposes by the straight-line method using a 25-year life and zero salvage value, even though the expected operating saving will occur only during the first 12 years of life. Base the economy study on the assumption that the machine actually will be retired at zero salvage value at the end of 12 years and that the $20,280 "loss on disposal" will be fully deductible from taxable income for the 12th year.

16–17. If the $39,000 outlay at zero date in Problem 16–12 could be treated as a current expense for tax purposes, and if the tax consequences of this treatment should take place at zero date on our time scale (just as was assumed in Example 16–4), what is the after-tax rate of return?

16–18. Alter Problem 16–17 by assuming that the tax cash flow resulting from treating the $39,000 outlay as a current expense would take place at date 1 on the time scale.

16–19. Change the conditions of Example 16–4 so that a 75% effective tax rate is applied to year zero. Assume that this is an "excess-profits" tax rate that is scheduled to expire at the end of the current year and that a 50% rate is forecast for years 1 to 10. Under these assumptions, what is the prospective after-tax rate of return? (*Ans.* = 47%.)

16–20. Make a revised solution of Problem 6–1 (page 84), changing the assumptions about income taxes from the simplified ones used in Chapter 6 as follows:

Use years-digits depreciation for tax purposes based on the estimated lives and salvage values stated in the problem. Continue to assume a 50% effective tax rate.

16–21. Make a revised solution of Problem 6–2 (page 84), changing the assumptions about income taxes as follows:

Years-digits depreciation will be used for tax purposes for the new grinder based on the estimated 10-year life and $4,000 salvage value. A 7% investment tax credit will be taken if the new grinder is chosen. Straight-line depreciation will be used for the second-hand grinder. Assume that because $50,000 of eligible used assets were purchased by this company earlier in the year, no investment tax credit can be taken for the used grinder. Continue to assume a 50% effective tax rate.

16–22. Make a revised solution of Problem 6–12 (page 86), changing the assumptions about income taxes as follows:

Years-digits depreciation will be taken for either heat exchanger based on the respective estimates of life and salvage value. A 4⅔% investment tax credit will be taken for Type Y and a 7% investment tax credit will be taken for Type Z. Continue to assume a 50% effective tax rate.

16–23. Problem 7–11 (page 104) involved a before-tax comparison of the present worths of 12 years of service from two earth-moving machines. Compute the year-by-year differences in cash flow for income taxes under the following assumptions:

Years-digits depreciation will be used for both machines based on the estimated lives and salvage values assumed in the economy study. There will be a 2⅓% investment tax credit if the Trojan machine is selected and a 4⅔% investment tax credit if the Giant machine is chosen. Assume a 50% effective tax rate throughout the 12 years. Assume that the major overhaul costs will be treated as current expenses for tax purposes.

Compare the present worths of the after-tax cash flows for the two alternatives using an i° of 8%.

16–24. Solve Problem 7–20 (page 107) changing the assumptions about income taxes as follows:

Use years-digits depreciation rather than straight-line depreciation. Assume a 55% effective tax rate.

16–25. Recompute the after-tax rate of return in Example 8–3 (page 113) making the following changes in assumptions about income taxes:

The entire $1,500,000 investment in plant and equipment will be depreciated by the years-digits method assuming a 15-year life and zero salvage value. Assume a 55% effective tax rate.

16–26. In 1958, as an aid to small business, the U. S. Congress passed a law allowing "additional first year depreciation" on certain assets for income tax purposes. This law permitted the deduction of 20% of the cost of qualifying property (determined without regard to salvage value) in addition to regular depreciation. The cost of property on which the additional allowance could be taken was limited to $10,000 on a separate return and $20,000 on a joint return. The allowance was applicable to equipment purchased second-hand as well as to new equipment.

Consider a sole proprietor in the construction industry, married, and submitting a joint return. In his depreciation accounting he used an averaging convention under which assets acquired during the first half of the year had a full year's depreciation in the year of acquisition. His fiscal year was the calendar year.

At the start of January, 1959, he had a chance to purchase a used power shovel for $20,000. The estimated remaining useful life of this shovel was 10 years, with a $2,000 terminal salvage value. If he bought this shovel, he could charge $5,400 of depreciation on it in his tax return for 1959. This $5,400 was a combination of $4,000 of "additional" depreciation (20% of the $20,000 first cost) and $1,400 of regular depreciation. This $1,400 was 1/10 of $14,000 (the first cost of $20,000 diminished by the $4,000 additional depreciation and the $2,000 salvage value). The total write-off during the 10-year life would, of course, be $18,000, the difference between first cost and salvage value, just as in any other method.

In the past this contractor had rented a power shovel whenever one was needed for a job. He estimated that owning this shovel would reduce his equipment rental disbursements by $7,000 a year for the next 10 years. This saving would be partially offset by extra disbursements of $2,200 a year for maintenance, storage, property taxes, and insurance.

His taxable income had fluctuated a bit from year to year. However, his highest tax bracket generally fell between 30% and 50%. For purposes of the following questions, assume an effective tax rate of 40% each year for the 10 years starting with 1959.

(a) Compute the prospective rate of return on the proposed investment before income taxes.

(b) Compute the prospective rate of return after income taxes assuming that his right to use 20% additional first-year depreciation would be applied to this power shovel.

(c) Compute the prospective rate of return after income taxes assuming that ordinary straight-line depreciation based on a 10-year life and 10% salvage would be applied to the shovel.

(d) Assuming that money was worth 8% to him after income taxes, what was the present worth (on January 1, 1959) of this right to use additional first-year depreciation rather than ordinary straight-line depreciation throughout the 10 years?

16–27. Consider that two $20,000 assets have been purchased, one with a 10-year estimated life and the other with a 20-year estimated life, both with zero salvage values. Would it be advantageous for a taxpayer to select the shorter-lived or the longer-lived asset for the additional first-year depreciation described in Problem 16–26, or would the length of life be a matter of indifference? Show calculations to support your answer, assuming a tax rate of 40%.

16–28. Consider that two $20,000 used assets have been purchased, both with 10-year estimated lives, one with an estimated zero salvage value and the other with an estimated 30% salvage value. Which would it be advantageous for a taxpayer to select for the additional first-year depreciation described in Problem 16–26 or would the salvage value be a matter of indifference? Show calculations to support your answer, assuming a tax rate of 40%. (Assume that the straight-line method will be used for regular depreciation charges on both assets, because the years-digits and double-rate declining-balance methods are not applicable to used assets.)

16–29. Consider two $20,000 assets, one used and one new, both with 15-year estimated lives and with 10% estimated salvage values. Assume that regular depreciation for the new asset will be by the years-digits method and that regular depreciation for the used asset will be by the straight-line method. Which would it be advantageous for a taxpayer to select for the additional first-year depreciation described in Problem 16–26, or would it be a matter of indifference whether the asset was purchased new or secondhand? Show calculations to support your answer, assuming a tax rate of 40%.

16–30. Solve parts (a), (b), and (c) of Problem 16–26 changing the date from 1959 to 1968 and assuming that the purchase of the power shovel would result in an investment tax credit of 7% of its first cost.

16–31. In Problem 8–1 (page 129), assume that the owner of the unimproved lot itemized his deductions on his personal income tax return and deducted his property taxes each year in reporting his taxable income. Assume a 30% effective tax rate on ordinary income. Assume that his net gain (selling price minus commission minus cost) when he sold the lot at the end of 1969 was taxed at 15%. What was his after-tax rate of return on his investment?

16–32. Recompute the after-tax rate of return in Problem 8–11 (page 130) making the following changes in assumptions about income taxes:

Use years-digits depreciation based on the same estimated life and salvage value assumed for the economy study. Use an effective tax rate of 30% rather than 50%.

16–33. Recompute the after-tax rate of return in Problem 8–12 (page 131) making the following changes in assumptions about income taxes:

Use years-digits depreciation for the $2,250,000 of depreciable investment applied to years 1 to 15, both inclusive, on the assumption of a 15-year life and zero salvage value. Make no change in the assumption of a 50% effective tax rate.

16–34. Find the prospective after-tax rate of return on the investment described in Problem 8–27 (page 132) making the following assumptions about income taxes:

The property will be depreciated for tax purposes on the assumption that $20,000 is the cost of the land (nondepreciable) and $100,000 is the cost of the building. The straight-line method will be used to depreciate the building, assuming a 40-year remaining life with zero salvage value. Throughout the 20 years of ownership, the effective tax rate on ordinary income for this taxpayer will be 40%. When the property is sold at a price above its book value at the end of 20 years, there will be a 25% tax rate on the long-term capital gain.

16–35. Solve Problem 8–38 (page 134) making the following changes in the assumptions about income taxes:

Use years-digits depreciation based on the same estimated life and salvage value used in the economy study. Make no change in the assumption of a 50% effective tax rate.

16–36. Find the prospective after-tax rate of return on the investment described in Problem 8–39 (page 134) making the following assumptions about income taxes:

The property will be depreciated for tax purposes on the assumption that $10,000 is the cost of the land (nondepreciable) and $40,000 is the cost of the building. The straight-line method will be used to depreciate the building, assuming a 20-year remaining life with zero salvage value. Throughout the period of ownership, the effective tax rate on ordinary income for this taxpayer will be 30%. When the property is sold at a price above its book value at the end of 10 years, there will be a 40% tax rate on half of the long-term capital gain.

16–37. During a period of high interest rates, two representative highly rated bond investments were 4.7% bonds of State E and 7.5% bonds of the F & G Electric Co., both available at par. Interest on the state bond was fully exempt from income taxation, whereas interest on the utility company bond was fully taxable. At what effective tax rate did these two bonds have the same after-tax yield? An unmarried taxpayer without dependents was considering the purchase of one or the other of these bonds. If he was subject to the tax rate schedule shown in Table 16–7, how high did his taxable income need to be for the state bond to give him a greater after-tax yield than the utility bond?

16–38. A certain unmarried taxpayer is subject to the tax rate schedule shown in Table 16–7. His taxable income falls in the bracket $26,000 to $32,000. He is considering the purchase of the 4.7% state bond mentioned in Problem 16–37. How high would the before-tax rate of return need to be on a fully taxable investment to yield him the same after-tax rate of return as this state bond?

16–39. The taxpayer in Problem 16–38 also has the opportunity to buy $10,000 par amount of 3% municipal bonds due in 10 years. These bonds are priced at $8,441 to yield a nominal 5% per annum to their maturity date. (Show the calculations required to check this stated yield.) If these bonds are purchased, the taxpayer intends to hold them until they mature 10 years hence. The interest will be exempt from federal income taxation. However, when the bonds mature or are sold prior to maturity, the excess of the amount received over the amount paid for them will be subject to income taxation at the rate applicable to capital gains. Assume that when the bonds mature, the "gain" of $1,559 will be taxed at a 25% rate. What will be the approximate after-tax rate of return on this investment?

16–40. Example 8–4 (page 116) dealt with the calculation of the before-tax rate of return on a $10,000 3.5% government bond due in 25 years, if purchased for $8,140 and held to maturity. Assume that this is a United States government bond the interest on which is fully taxable for federal income tax purposes in the United States. Compute the after-tax rate of return on this bond investment to a buyer whose incremental tax rate on ordinary income is 30% and whose tax rate will be 15% on the "gain" that will be taxable when the bond matures in 25 years.

16–41. The taxpayer in Problem 16–38 is considering a $1,000 gift to a scholarship fund at his university. As his nonbusiness deductions have always exceeded the standard deduction, they have always been itemized on his federal tax returns. The gift will be an additional nonbusiness deduction. How much will he be out of pocket by reason of making this gift?

16–42. An unmarried taxpayer with no dependents expects an adjusted gross income of $37,000 in a given year. His nonbusiness deductions are expected to be $4,400. Answer the following questions assuming 1967 U. S. federal income tax rates to be applicable:

(a) What will be his federal income tax?

(b) He is considering an additional activity expected to increase his adjusted gross income. If this increase should be $6,000 and there should be no change in nonbusiness deductions or exemptions, what will be his federal income tax?

(c) How much of his extra $6,000 of income in (b) will remain after he has paid the additional federal income tax for which it is responsible?

16–43. Answer the questions in Problem 16–42 assuming that the individual is married and has 2 dependent children. Assume the stated income to include the wife's income as well as the husband's.

16–44. On pages 180 to 181 of Chapter 10, two competing investment proposals for an oil company were discussed. Before-tax rates of return were computed as about 19% for a vacuum still and about 12% for a product ter-

minal. Compute the after-tax rates of return for these two proposed investments assuming years-digits depreciation and a 50% effective tax rate.

16–45. Harry Roe receives a salary of $9,600 a year. This is the entire
family income. He and his wife Grace have one dependent child. In their
joint federal income tax return they take the standard deduction rather than
itemizing nonbusiness deductions. Grace is offered a job at $350 per month.
Her acceptance of the job will cause her to spend $100 a month for a baby
sitter and $40 a month for a cleaning woman. She will have to pay 5% social
security taxes for each of these employees. Her salary will be subject to a 5%
social security tax and a 4% state income tax and will, of course, increase the
federal income taxes that must be paid by the Roes. Her payments for the
baby sitter and cleaning woman will not be tax deductible. How much will
Grace's $4,200-per-year employment add to the annual cash resources of the
Roe family? Assume 1967 federal tax rates are applicable. (Note that if
Grace does not work, the Roes' standard nonbusiness deduction will be $960,
10% of the family income. However, this standard deduction cannot exceed
$1,000 regardless of the size of the family income.)

16–46. Solve Problem 16–45 assuming Harry Roe's salary to be $18,000
rather than $9,600.

16–47. Wilma Doe lives in a rented apartment for which she pays $125
a month. She owns a small house that she purchased 2 years ago to give her
a rental income. Her total income consists of her $6,500 a year salary and
the $150 a month that she receives as rental income. The purchase price of
her income property was $15,000. She paid $3,000 down and assumed a
mortgage loan of $12,000 bearing 6% interest. Her annual repayment on this
loan is $500; she now owes $11,000 on the mortgage. Annual upkeep on the
house is about $150 a year. She pays local property taxes on the house of
$200 a year. On her federal income tax returns she has assigned $3,000 of the
$15,000 purchase price of her property as land value; she has depreciated the
$12,000 investment in the house by the straight-line method, using a 2.5%
rate. She itemizes her nonbusiness deductions on her federal return; these
(chiefly charitable contributions and sales taxes) have been about $800 a
year. Wilma is single and has no dependents.

She would prefer to live in her house but has continued her present arrangement because her receipts from rentals are $300 a year more than she
pays for her apartment. Considering only receipts and disbursements in connection with the house, with federal income taxes, and with apartment rental,
what will it cost her next year to give up the apartment and move into her
house? Assume that 1967 tax rates are applicable. (When she rents her
house, interest, property taxes, depreciation, and upkeep are deductions from
her gross rental income; if she lives in her house and itemizes nonbusiness deductions, interest and property taxes will be allowable nonbusiness deductions.)

17

Economy Studies for Retirement and Replacement

The hand of time lies heavy on the works of man, whether ancient or modern.

This is a fact, obviously, of the most practical consequence. It confronts the owners of these nominally "durable" but nevertheless ephemeral goods with two problems. The first is to distinguish the quick from the dead; in other words, to tell whether goods not yet physically exhausted have outlived their economic usefulness, either generally or for the particular function they now perform. The second is to make financial provision against the wastage of durable assets over their service life. The one involves replacement, or reequipment policy; the other, depreciation policy.

—George Terborgh [1]

Chapter 10 listed various types of causes of property retirement, namely: (1) improved alternatives, (2) changes in service requirements, (3) changes in the old assets themselves, (4) changes in public requirements, and (5) casualties. It was pointed out that these causes are not mutually exclusive; for instance, an asset may be retired partly because of obsolescence (cause 1), partly because of inadequacy (an example of cause 2), and partly because of increasing annual disbursements for repairs and maintenance (an example of cause 3).

In modern industry the usual experience is that assets are retired when they are still physically capable of continuing to render service. Someone must make a *decision* to make such retirements. Generally speaking, such decisions should be made on grounds of economy. This chapter discusses the kinds of analysis needed to guide such economic decisions.

Distinction Between Retirement and Replacement. The disposal of an asset by its owner is referred to as a retirement. Not all retirements involve the actual scrapping of the asset retired; many assets, retired by

[1] George Terborgh, *Dynamic Equipment Policy* (New York: McGraw-Hill Book Co., Inc., 1949), p. 1.

their present owners, may be used by one or more other owners before reaching the scrap heap.

If an asset (or group of assets) is retired, and another asset (or group of assets) is acquired to perform the same service, this is a replacement.

It frequently happens that new assets are acquired to perform the services of existing assets, with the existing assets not retired but merely transferred to some other use—frequently an "inferior use" (such as stand-by service). In such cases, the acquisition of the new assets sometimes is also described as a replacement.

Two Words That Are Useful in Discussing Replacement Economy. In Chapter 12 we used George Terborgh's words *defender* and *challenger* with special meanings that were helpful in discussing the problem of choice among multiple alternatives that are physically mutually exclusive. In the present chapter, we use these words with the meanings originally assigned to them in *Dynamic Equipment Policy*. An existing old asset, considered as a possible candidate for replacement, is called the *defender*. The proposed new replacement asset is called the *challenger*.

Some Characteristics of Economy Studies for Retirements and Replacements. This chapter concentrates attention on certain special aspects of studies for retirement and replacement, as follows:

1. Capital recovery costs for extending the services of assets already owned (e.g., defenders in replacement economy studies) are computed differently from capital recovery costs for assets yet to be acquired (e.g., all proposed assets in economy studies discussed in previous chapters, and challengers in replacement economy studies). The reasons for this difference were explained in Chapter 15. Various aspects of this topic are illustrated in all of the examples in the present chapter.
2. There are special difficulties in estimating the effect of a decision regarding retirement or replacement on cash flow for income taxes. Some aspects are illustrated in Examples 17–1 and 17–2.
3. In many replacement studies the appropriate assumption regarding the defender is that, if retained in service at all, it will be kept for a relatively short time, often only one year. In contrast, the appropriate assumption regarding the challenger may be that, if acquired, it will be kept for its full economic life. Although we have already given some consideration (particularly in Chapters 6, 7, and 13) to the interpretation of economy studies in which the alternatives have different services lives, there are special aspects to this problem in replacement economy. Some of these aspects are discussed in connection with Examples 17–3 and 17–4; others are discussed in Appendix D.

In order to start our discussion by concentrating attention solely on points (1) and (2), Examples 17–1 and 17–2 deal with cases where the expected remaining service life of the defender is the same as the expected full service life of the challenger.

These two examples will first be analyzed by an annual cost comparison before income taxes. The effect on prospective disbursements for income taxes of the decision on retirement or replacement will then be computed and an annual cost comparison will then be made after income taxes. Finally, prospective rates of return before and after income taxes will be calculated.

EXAMPLE 17–1. ANALYSIS OF A PROPOSED RETIREMENT

Facts of the Case. A manufacturing company owns a warehouse in a city some distance from its main plant. The warehouse is used by the branch sales office in the area to make delivery of certain products from stock. An equal amount of storage space is available in a new commercial warehouse. As a favorable offer for the old warehouse has been received, consideration is given to its sale and the rental of the needed space.

The property was not new when it was purchased 10 years ago for $100,000. For accounting and income tax purposes, this was divided into $80,000 for the warehouse building and $20,000 for land. Straight-line item depreciation on the building has been used for accounting and tax purposes, assuming a 40-year remaining life and zero salvage value. The warehouse can now be sold for a net $150,000 after payment of selling expenses.

In recent years annual warehouse expenses have averaged $6,440 for operation and maintenance, $2,240 for property taxes on the land and building, $420 for fire insurance on the building, and $1,400 for fire insurance on the stock. It is expected that costs will continue at approximately these figures if the warehouse is not sold.

Equal space in the commercial warehouse can be rented for $31,600 a year. Estimated annual disbursements for operation and upkeep of this space are $2,800. Fire insurance on the stock will be reduced to $900 a year.

If the decision is made not to accept the favorable offer for the warehouse, it is estimated that it will not be sold for another 10 years. The estimated net selling price 10 years hence is $90,000.

In before-tax studies in this company, a minimum attractive rate of return of 20% is used; in after-tax studies, 10%. An effective tax rate of 50% on ordinary income is assumed in all economy studies. It is assumed that a "gain" on the sale of the property either now or later will be taxed at 30%.

Before-Tax Comparison of Annual Costs. Using the stipulated i° of 20%, the comparative annual costs for a 10-year study period are as follows:

Comparative Annual Cost—Continued Ownership of Warehouse

CR = ($150,000 − $90,000)(A/P,20%,10) + $90,000(0.20)	$32,310
Operation and maintenance	6,440
Property taxes	2,240
Fire insurance on building and stock	1,820
Total	$42,810

Comparative Annual Cost—Rental of Equal Space

Rent	$31,600
Operation and upkeep	2,800
Fire insurance on stock	900
Total	$35,300

The foregoing comparison favors disposal of the warehouse and rental of equal space.

After-Tax Comparison of Annual Costs. The decision to sell the warehouse at once will cause an immediate disbursement for the tax on the gain on disposal. As the property has been depreciated for tax purposes at $2,000 a year for the past 10 years, its present book value is $80,000, the difference between the $100,000 original cost and the $20,000 of depreciation charged against the warehouse up to date. There will be a taxable gain of $70,000, the difference between the $150,000 net selling price and the $80,000 book value.

Because this gain will be taxed at 30%, the tax will be $21,000. The effect of this tax will be to reduce the net amount received from the sale from $150,000 to $129,000. In effect, $129,000 is the net realizable salvage value after taxes.

A similar analysis will show that if the warehouse is sold for $90,000 in 10 years, the gain will be $30,000, the tax will be $9,000, and the net amount realized after taxes will be $81,000.

Annual taxes on ordinary income will also be influenced by the decision on retirement. If the warehouse is continued in service, annual deductions from taxable income will be the $2,000 annual depreciation plus current disbursements of $6,440, $2,240, and $1,820, a total of $12,500. If space is rented, annual deductions from taxable income will be $35,300. With continued ownership, annual taxable income will therefore be $22,800 (i.e., $35,300 − $12,500) higher than with rental. Using the effective tax rate of 50%, annual disbursements for income taxes will be $11,400 more with ownership than with rental.

Using the stipulated after-tax i^* of 10%, an after-tax comparison of equivalent annual costs is as follows:

Comparative Annual Cost—Continued Ownership of Warehouse

CR = ($129,000 − $81,000)(A/P,10%,10) + $81,000(0.10)	$15,910
Operation and maintenance	6,440
Property taxes	2,240
Fire insurance on building and stock	1,820
Extra income taxes above those under rental	11,400
Total	$37,810

Comparative Annual Cost—Rental of Equal Space

Rent	$31,600
Operation and upkeep	2,800
Fire insurance on stock	900
Total	$35,300

The margin favoring rental is considerably less in the after-tax analysis than in the before-tax analysis in spite of the added item of $11,400 for extra income taxes. If a 50% tax rate rather than 30% should be applicable to the gain on the present sale, the two alternatives would have approximately equal annual costs.

Calculation of Rates of Return. The prospective differences between cash flows under continued ownership and under rental may be tabulated as follows:

Year	Difference Before Taxes	Difference in Income Taxes	Difference After Taxes
0	−$150,000	+$21,000	−$129,000
1 to 10	+24,800 per year	−11,400 per year	+13,400 per year
10	+90,000	−9,000	+81,000

Trial-and-error calculations of the type that have been illustrated many times in the preceding chapters give the conclusion that the present worth of the before-tax series is zero with an interest rate of approximately 14.4%, and the present worth of the after-tax series is zero with an interest rate of approximately 7.8%.

Interpretation of Analysis in Example 17–1. Most of the economy studies discussed in previous chapters have dealt with proposals to make investments in fixed assets—to convert money into capital goods. In contrast, Example 17–1 might be described as a proposal for a disinvestment; the question at issue is whether it is desirable to convert capital goods into money.

The description of the facts of the example did not tell what would be done with the $129,000 (after taxes) realizable from the sale of the warehouse. However, the statement that the after-tax i^* was 10% implied that this money could be invested in the business in a way that would provide an after-tax yield of at least 10%. Our analysis indicated that a decision to keep the warehouse would be—in effect—a decision to invest $129,000 at a yield of 7.8% after taxes. If, all things considered (including irreducibles not mentioned in the "facts of the case") a 7.8% after-tax rate of return is considered to be unsatisfactory in this instance, the analysis favors the sale of the warehouse.

Just as in our previous analyses by comparative annual costs and by rate of return, the two methods of comparison lead to the same decision between the alternatives as long as the minimum attractive rate of return is used as the interest rate in compound interest conversions in the annual cost method.

Comment on Economy Studies Where Retirements Involve Prospective Purchase of Product or Service of Asset Retired. The general type of situation illustrated in Example 17–1 is a common one. It often is necessary to consider the question "Can we buy this product or this service at a lower figure than our cost of continuing to produce it?" Many such economy studies require determination of increment costs and recognition of sunk costs. The book figure for present costs of production may contain certain allocated costs that would not be eliminated if production were stopped. And the depreciation charges in the books are, of course, based on the original cost, a figure that is irrelevant for purposes of the retirement economy study except for its influence on future income taxes.

The higher the present realizable value of the assets that are being considered for retirement, the more attractive is the proposal to dispose of the assets and purchase the goods or services that they have been producing. This point is generally recognized. If the warehouse in Example 17–1 had only a small resale price, the economy study would favor continued ownership.

Another important element in such comparisons, perhaps not so generally recognized as significant, is the estimated prospective future realizable value. The greater the future resale price, the more attractive is continued ownership, and vice versa. This may be illustrated in Example 17–1 by changing the $90,000 estimate of future net resale price before taxes to a substantially higher and to a substantially lower figure. Of course, the nearer the date of prospective future disposal, the greater the importance of the future resale price.

In many economy studies of this type a third alternative may be to purchase the goods or services in question from the outside source, but to keep the old assets for stand-by and emergency purposes. Conditions favorable to this third alternative are as follows: (1) a low present net realizable value; (2) relatively low annual disbursements required for continuing the ownership of the assets; and (3) the likelihood that continued ownership with its threat of resumption of production will strengthen bargaining power in the establishment of the price for the purchased goods or services.

EXAMPLE 17–2. REVIEWING AN ERROR IN JUDGMENT IN EQUIPMENT SELECTION

Facts of the Case. A year ago, an irrigator purchased a pump and motor which cost him $1,925 installed. He knew nothing of pump selection, and—making his choice on the recommendation of a clerk in a hardware store—selected a pump that was unsuited to the requirements of head and discharge under which it was to operate. As a result, his year's power bill for its operation was $900; this was much higher than if he had purchased a suitable pump.

Just at the start of the current irrigation season, a pump salesman offers him another pump and motor, suited to his requirements. This will cost $1,650 installed and is guaranteed to reduce power requirements to a point where the electric energy for pumping the same amount of water as before will cost only $500. He can sell the original pump and motor to a neighbor for $375.

For purposes of this economy study, we shall assume a 10-year study period with estimated zero salvage value for both pumps at the end of this period. It will be assumed that other expenditures (such as property taxes, insurance, and upkeep) will not be affected by the type of pump being used for this service. The irrigator's effective tax rate on ordinary income is 40%. A minimum attractive rate of return of 10% is to be used in the before-tax analysis and a rate of 6% is to be used in the after-tax analysis.

The irrigator has used years-digits item depreciation for tax purposes on the present pump, assuming a 10-year life and zero salvage value. If the new pump is substituted, the same depreciation method, life, and salvage value will be used.

Before-Tax Comparison of Annual Costs. Using the stipulated 10% minimum attractive rate of return before taxes, the comparative annual costs for a 10-year study period are as follows:

Comparative Annual Cost—Present Pump

CR = $375(A/P,10%,10)	$ 61
Electric energy for pumping	900
Total	$961

Comparative Annual Cost—Proposed New Pump

CR = $1,650(A/P,10%,10)	$269
Electric energy for pumping	500
Total	$769

The foregoing comparison favors the replacement.

After-Tax Comparison of Annual Costs. Under the years-digits method the past year's depreciation charge on the defender was 10/55 of $1,925 = $350. The defender's present book value is therefore $1,925 − $350 = $1,575. If the defender is sold for $375, the books will show a $1,200 "loss" on this sale.

On the assumption that this transaction occurs in the United States (and subject to certain limitations discussed later in this chapter), this $1,200 is viewed for tax purposes as a loss on disposal of depreciable property used in the trade or business. As such, the sale will reduce current taxable income by $1,200; with a 40% tax rate, it will reduce current taxes by $480. Considering the retirement separately from the acquisition of the replacement asset, a consequence of the retirement will be an immediate positive cash flow of $855, the sum of the $375 receipt from the buyer and the $480 reduction in disbursements to the tax collector. The after-tax net realizable salvage value of the defender is therefore $855.

If the defender is kept in service, the next-year deductions from taxable income that are relevant in our economy study will be the depreciation charge of $315 (9/55 of $1,925) and the $900 outlay for electric energy, a total of $1,215. Because years-digits depreciation is being used, this total will decrease by $35 a year to $900 in the 10th year. (For simplicity in this example, we are assuming that the defender can be kept in service for 10 years more, even though the depreciation charge on it will continue for only 9 years more.)

If the challenger is acquired, its relevant next-year tax deductions will be $300 depreciation (10/55 of $1,650) and $500 for electric energy, a total of $800. This total will decrease by $30 a year to $530 in the 10th year.

The next-year difference in taxable income between challenger and defender will therefore be $415 (i.e., $1,215 − $800). This difference will decrease by $5 a year to $370 in the 10th year.

With a tax rate of 40%, the next-year difference in disbursements for income taxes will be $166 (i.e., 40% of $415). This difference will decrease by $2 a year to $148 in the 10th year.

Using the stipulated 6% minimum attractive rate of return after taxes, an after-tax comparison of equivalent annual costs is as follows:

Comparative Annual Cost—Present Pump

CR = $855(A/P,6%,10)	$ 116
Electric energy for pumping	900
Total	$1,016

Comparative Annual Cost—Proposed New Pump

CR = $1,650(A/P,6%,10)	$ 224
Electric energy for pumping	500
Extra income tax = $166 − $2(A/G,6%,10)	158
Total	$ 882

This after-tax comparison also favors replacement.

Calculation of Rates of Return. The prospective differences in cash flow between defender and challenger may be tabulated as follows:

Year	Difference Before Taxes	Difference in Income Taxes	Difference After Taxes
0	−$1,275	+$480	−$795
1	+400	−166	+234
2	+400	−164	+236
3	+400	−162	+238
4	+400	−160	+240
5	+400	−158	+242
6	+400	−156	+244
7	+400	−154	+246
8	+400	−152	+248
9	+400	−150	+250
10	+400	−148	+252
Totals	+$2,725	−$1,090	+$1,635

Trial-and-error calculations indicate that the present worth of the before-tax series is zero with an interest rate of about 29% and the present worth of the after-tax series is zero with an interest rate of a little less than 28%.

The Relationship Between the Past Investment in a Defender and Decision Making About Its Proposed Retirement. Examples 17–1 and 17–2 provide numerical illustrations of a point that has often been emphasized in this book. This point is that in choosing between alternatives, only the differences between the alternatives are relevant. No past occurrences can be changed by a decision between alternatives for the future. Nevertheless, past events may influence the future in different ways, depending on decisions that are made for the future.

In Example 17–1, the prospective difference in cash flow before income taxes between disposal and continued ownership was unaffected by the past investment in the warehouse. And in Example 17–2, the prospective difference in cash flow before income taxes between the defending pump and its challenger was unaffected by the past investment in the defender. In general, in economy studies for retirements and replacements, differences in cash flow *before* taxes will not be influenced by past investments in assets considered as candidates for retirement. Past investments should normally be viewed as irrelevant in before-tax studies.

(As explained in Chapter 15, there may be mental blocks to applying the foregoing rule in particular cases. Thus our irrigator in Example 17–2 might be reluctant to admit to himself his past mistake in judgment in equipment selection; he might reason that he "could not afford" to replace his present pump until he had "got his money out of it.")

In contrast, in economy studies involving proposed retirements, differences in cash flow for income taxes usually will be influenced by past investments. Example 17–1 illustrated prospective taxes on a gain on disposal of an asset. Example 17–2 illustrated how a disposal at less than book value could reduce immediate income taxes. Both the gain and the loss on disposal were influenced by the past investments and by the past method of making depreciation charges for tax purposes. In both examples, the depreciation deductions from taxable income if the existing asset were continued in service depended on the past investment in the asset. Generally speaking, past investments in defenders need to be considered in after-tax studies for retirements and replacements.

In fact, the rational consideration of the income tax aspects of retirements may lead to conclusions exactly opposite from the ones that many people would reach by intuition. Although intuition often favors disposal at an apparent profit, a taxable gain reduces the net cash realized from such a disposal. Although intuition often is opposed to disposal at an apparent loss, a loss deductible from taxable income increases the net cash realized from such a disposal.

Example 17–2 illustrated the tax advantage of such a deductible loss. The prospective rate of return before income taxes on the purchase of the challenger was 29%. Ordinarily, one would expect a 40% tax rate to make a nearly proportionate reduction in the rate of return. However, the after-tax rate of return was nearly 28%, a negligible reduction.

It should be noted that in Example 17–2, the entire $1,925 investment in the defender, less salvage value, was scheduled to be deducted from taxable income at some time regardless of whether the decision favored the challenger or the defender. The selection of the challenger merely changed the *timing* of the deduction in a way that favored the challenger.

Some Comments on Income Tax Aspects of Disposal of Fixed Assets in the United States. The tax aspects of proposed retirements often are more complex than the reader might assume from studying Examples 17–1 and 17–2. As related to retirements in the United States, an adequate discussion of this topic would not be possible without a fairly detailed consideration of various types of multiple-asset depreciation accounting and of income tax regulations. Such a discussion would require more space than would be appropriate in this book.[2]

A number of separate issues arise in finding out whether the retirement of an asset will have an immediate tax consequence, either a favorable one (i.e., a reduction of taxes) such as was assumed in Example 17–2, or an unfavorable one (i.e., an increase in taxes) such as was assumed in Example 17–1. Still other issues arise in finding out whether the "gain" or "loss" will influence taxes at the rate applicable to ordinary income (such as the 50% in Example 17–1 and the 40% in Example 17–2) or whether some lower tax rate should be applied to these special items (such as the 30% in Example 17–1).

Both Examples 17–1 and 17–2 assumed item accounting. However, where there are many assets, multiple-asset accounting is sound in principle and often is used. Ordinary retirements in multiple-asset accounting do not cause the recording of so-called gains or losses in the books of account.

Multiple-asset accounting reflects the existence of mortality dispersion, a topic mentioned in Chapter 10. Figure 10–1 (page 151) showed a representative survivor curve for a group of assets that had an average service life of 20 years; this average resulted from retirements that occurred all the way from age 1 to age 45. In the usual case where it is reasonable to expect mortality dispersion, retirements short of the estimated average life are not "premature" in the sense that they are inconsistent with the estimated average; it is to be expected that there will also be assets that survive considerably longer than the estimated average life. The foregoing viewpoint is recognized in multiple-asset depreciation accounting by the continuation of depreciation charges after the expiration of the estimated average life and by the prohibition, under ordinary circumstances, of entries for loss on disposal when assets are retired before they have reached the estimated average life. Moreover, the policy of the U. S. Treasury Department has been, in effect, to apply the rules of multiple-asset accounting even when item accounting is used, wherever there are a number of assets of a similar type and it is

---

[2] For a statement of the regulations themselves, see *Internal Revenue Service Publication 311—Regulations Relating to Depreciation—Treasury Decision 6182* (Washington, D.C.: Government Printing Office, 1956). See also *Internal Revenue Service Publication 334—Tax Guide for Small Business.*

reasonable to believe that the life estimate applies to the *average* life of the assets. For this reason, a retirement at low salvage value short of the estimated life will not necessarily lead to a tax-deductible loss in the United States even when item accounting is used.

The $1,200 prospective loss on disposal of the defender in Example 17–2 illustrates the conventional treatment in item accounting. Where the taxpayer has only one asset of the type being retired, there is no question of the appropriateness of item accounting for tax purposes.

In the United States, the trade-in of certain assets on new ones leads to "nontaxable exchanges" that transfer to the new asset the remaining tax basis of the old asset that was traded in. In effect, the tax consequences of a retirement are deferred, conceivably for a very long time. Our examples and problems in this book do not illustrate the tax aspects of such exchanges.

The issue of whether the applicable tax rate is the rate on ordinary income or some lower rate depends in part on rather complicated laws and regulations that are different for different classes of assets. These laws and regulations have changed a number of times. The applicable rate also depends in part on the rules for the offsetting of gains and losses. It should be observed that whereas it is favorable to the taxpayer to have a *lower* rate apply to gains, it is also favorable to him to have a *higher* rate apply to losses. Certain aspects of these matters are illustrated in several of the problems at the end of this chapter.

Still another question arising in an after-tax analysis of a proposed retirement is the effect of the retirement on future depreciation deductions from taxable income. This matter is closely related to the topic of entries for gain or loss on disposal. Examples 17–1 and 17–2 illustrated the required calculations under item accounting. In both examples, there were year-by-year depreciation deductions that would occur if the defender remained in service and would be eliminated by its retirement.

In multiple-asset accounting, the rules on this matter differ from those illustrated for item accounting. For example, in declining-balance group accounting using a so-called open end account, a retirement at zero salvage value will have no influence on future depreciation charges. Moreover, different types of multiple-asset accounting have different rules.

The examples in this book that deal with economy studies for retirements and replacements are based on the assumption of item accounting. The chief purpose in using this assumption is to avoid the necessity of devoting considerable space to an explanation of the technical aspects of a number of different types of multiple-asset depreciation accounting. Incidentally, the assumption provides uniformity in the examples and problems. It should go without saying that after-tax studies in industry should be based on the particular type of depreciation accounting that is being used for the assets that are candidates for retirement.

Annual Cost vs. Rate of Return as a Method of Analysis in Replacement Economy. In Examples 17–1 and 17–2, the stipulated minimum attractive rate of return was used as the interest rate in the annual cost comparisons. Where this is done, the alternative favored by an annual cost analysis will be the same as the one favored by an analysis based on rate of return. In this respect economy studies for retirements and replacements are no different from other economy studies.

In Examples 17–1 and 17–2 the assumed remaining service lives were the same for all alternatives. In this characteristic these examples are not typical of the majority of replacement studies. As already pointed out, we have introduced the subject with examples of this type in order to concentrate attention on certain aspects of replacement economy while avoiding the special complications often introduced by the difference between a relatively short assumed remaining service life for the defender and a relatively long one for the challenger.

Where two alternatives have the same service life, as in Examples 17–1 and 17–2, an unknown rate of return can be computed by finding the interest rate that makes the present worth of the difference in cash flow equal to zero. Where the lives are different, this method cannot be used without making specific assumptions about differences in cash flow after the expiration of the life of the shorter-lived alternative.

In Examples 17–3 and 17–4 the assumed remaining service life of the defender is considerably shorter than the assumed service life of the challenger. In these examples our presentation will be simplified by making our comparisons solely on the basis of annual costs.

Where To Introduce Present Defender Net Salvage Value in Annual Cost Comparisons. Chapter 15 presented the concept that in making decisions on whether or not to continue to own an asset, the capital costs of extending its service should be based on its present net salvage value and on its prospective future net salvage value at the end of a study period. (See Example 15–6.) This concept was applied in computing capital recovery costs of existing assets in the annual cost comparisons of Examples 17–1 and 17–2.

An alternate method sometimes advocated for replacement economy studies is to assume zero capital costs for the defender and to subtract the present net defender salvage value from the challenger's first cost before computing capital costs of the challenger. In this method the capital recovery costs of the challenger are based on the new money required rather than on the total investment.

In a certain limited group of cases this alternate method gives a difference in annual costs identical with the difference obtained by the method illustrated in Examples 17–1 and 17–2. For instance, consider the use of this alternate method for the after-tax comparison of annual costs in Example 17–2 as follows:

Comparative Annual Cost—Present Pump

Electric energy for pumping $900

Comparative Annual Cost—Proposed New Pump

CR = ($1,650 − $855)(A/P,6%,10)	$108
Electric energy for pumping	500
Extra income tax	158
Total	$766

The difference in annual costs favors the challenger by $134, just as in our solution in Example 17–2.

Nevertheless, this alternate method has certain weaknesses that lead the authors to recommend against its use in annual cost comparisons. The method clearly is not applicable where the defender has an estimated future salvage value. It is troublesome to interpret in multiple-alternative studies. And it can lead to misleading conclusions in the common case where the remaining life assumed for the defender differs from the assumed service life of the challenger.

An error that sometimes occurs in replacement studies is to base capital costs of the defender on present net salvage value and *also* to subtract this salvage from challenger first cost before computing the capital costs of the challenger. It should be evident that this procedure counts defender salvage value twice—as a basis for a plus item in defender annual costs and as a basis for a minus item in challenger annual costs. Such double counting has the effect of biasing the analysis in favor of the challenger.

EXAMPLE 17–3. ANALYSIS TO DETERMINE WHETHER CERTAIN GAS MAINS SHOULD BE REPLACED

Facts of the Case. A city is engaged in the distribution of natural gas, purchased at a flat rate of 30 cents per MCF (thousand cubic feet). As a result of corrosion, its gas mains eventually develop small leaks which increase as time goes on. The question arises of how much gas should be lost before it is economical to replace any given section of main.

Mains have no salvage value when retired. New mains cost about $8,000 per mile installed. Because of improved protective coatings and better methods of installation, it is believed that new mains will be tight for a longer period than was the case for the mains in the original distribution system. The engineer for the city's gas department estimates that under average conditions, a new main will lose no gas during its first 15 years of service; starting with the 16th year, gas losses will increase by about 200 MCF per mile of main per year. The only operation cost that is variable with the age or condition of the main is the cost of lost gas.

In this municipally owned utility, economy studies are made using an interest rate (minimum attractive rate of return) of 7%.

Calculation of Annual Cost of Challenger. In this comparison any section of main that is losing gas is a possible defender in a replacement economy study. In all cases the challenger is a new main that has an estimated first cost of $8,000, zero salvage value at all times, and operating costs that start at $60 in the 16th year and increase by $60 a year thereafter. Table 17–1 provides a basis for estimating challenger life and equivalent annual cost.

The actual compound interest calculations are not shown in the table. A sample calculation assuming retirement after 25 years is as follows:

$$CR = \$8,000(A/P,7\%,25) = \$8,000(0.08581) \qquad = \$686$$
$$\text{Equivalent annual cost of gas lost}$$
$$= \$60(P/G,7\%,11)(P/F,7\%,14)(A/P,7\%,25)$$
$$= \$60(32.4665)(0.3878)(0.08581) \qquad\qquad = \underline{65}$$
$$\text{Total equivalent annual cost} = \$686 + \$65 \qquad = \$751$$

In this particular case, it is evident that the equivalent annual costs of the challenger are relatively insensitive to differences in assumptions regarding challenger service life over a considerable range of possible lives. Although the lowest equivalent annual cost, $749, is obtained at 27 years, this figure is changed by less than 3% within the range from 21 to 35 years.

Calculation of Annual Cost of Extending Service of Defenders. It has been stated that the gas mains in this example have zero salvage values at all times. Therefore there are no capital costs associated with extending the service of any defenders. It has also been stated that there is no difference in maintenance cost between old and new mains.

It follows that the costs of gas lost are the only defender costs that are relevant in comparison with challenger costs. For any particular section of main that is being considered for replacement, it is necessary to estimate the MCF of gas that will be lost next year, to express this quantity as a rate per mile of main, and to multiply the rate per mile by the unit price of 30 cents per MCF.

For instance, consider section X of main losing gas at 1,000 MCF per mile; this has a next-year cost of $300 per mile. Or consider section Y losing gas at 3,000 MCF per mile; its next-year cost is $900 per mile.

Because gas losses tend to increase from year to year, it may be presumed that the annual costs in subsequent years for any section of main will be greater than those next year. Therefore, it merely is necessary to estimate next-year defender costs for purposes of comparison with challenger annual costs.

Comparison of Defender and Challenger. Consider the economy study relative to section X of main:

Comparative annual cost of defender = $300 per mile (for next year)
Comparative annual cost of challenger = at least $749 per mile (for 27 years, more or less)

It is evident that section X should be continued in service.

It is worth emphasizing that the use of next-year costs for the defender

TABLE 17-1

Equivalent Annual Costs for a Mile of $8,000 Gas Main Retired at Various Ages, Assuming a Minimum Attractive Rate of Return of 7%

Year n	Cost of Gas Lost During Year	Equivalent Uniform Annual Costs if Retired After n Years		
		Capital Recovery of $8,000	Equivalent Uniform Annual Cost of Gas Lost	Total Equivalent Uniform Annual Cost
A	B	C	D	E
3	$ 0	$3,048	$ 0	$3,048
6	0	1,678	0	1,678
9	0	1,228	0	1,228
12	0	1,007	0	1,007
15	0	878	0	878
16	60	847	2	849
17	120	819	6	825
18	180	795	11	806
19	240	774	17	791
20	300	755	24	779
21	300	738	32	770
22	420	723	40	763
23	480	710	48	758
24	540	698	56	754
25	600	686	65	751
26	660	676	74	750
27	720	667	82	749
28	780	659	91	750
29	840	652	99	751
30	900	645	108	753
31	960	638	116	754
32	1,020	633	124	757
33	1,080	627	132	759
34	1,140	623	140	763
35	1,200	618	148	766

carries no implication that, if the decision favors the defender, it will be kept in service *only* one year more. It is merely that, for purposes of comparison, we are using the period most favorable to the defender. The challenger also has the benefit of the period most favorable to it, namely, approximately 27 years.

In contrast to the foregoing study, consider the comparison relative to section Y of main:

Comparative annual cost of defender = $900 per mile (for next year)
Comparative annual cost of challenger = at least $749 per mile (for 27 years, more or less)

This comparison seems to favor the challenger. However, in a case of this type, it is always pertinent to raise the question of what is expected to happen after the expiration of the one-year period assumed as the remaining life of the defender. This question is discussed later in the present chapter. (Because this type of question is a central one in a number of mathematical models developed for replacement economy, it also is discussed in Appendix D, which deals with these mathematical models.)

At the present stage of our discussion, we can say that if the next-year cost of extending the service of an existing main is not at least $750 per mile, it is doubtful whether replacement is justified. In other words, the sections of main where replacement should be considered are those expected to lose at least 2,500 MCF per mile per year (i.e., $750 per mile divided by the price of $0.30 per MCF).

EXAMPLE 17–4. ANALYSIS OF PROPOSED REPLACEMENT OF CERTAIN CONSTRUCTION EQUIPMENT

Facts of the Case. The first cost of a machine used to perform a certain service in construction is $2,000. It is expected that the secondhand value of this machine will be $1,100 after its first year, $750 after 2 years, $500 after 3 years, and will continue to decline as shown in Table 15–1, page 321. It is believed that the first-year disbursements in connection with ownership and operation of this machine will be $1,200, that second-year disbursements will be $1,350, and that disbursements will increase each year as shown in column C of Table 17–2.

The owner of a machine performing this service has a chance to sell it for a favorable price of $1,350. His machine cost $2,200 one year ago. However, the first costs of new machines have declined and the economy of performance has been slightly improved. A decision must be made between continuing this machine (defender) in service and replacing it with a new machine (challenger) that is expected to have costs for various lengths of life as shown in Table 17–2. All studies are made before income taxes with an interest rate of 8%.

The estimated future salvage values of the defender are $775 next year, $525 two years hence, and $275 three years hence. If the defender is continued in service, annual disbursements are estimated as $1,370 next year, $1,570 the following year, and $1,820 the year after that.

Calculation of Annual Cost of Challenger. It is evident from column G of Table 17–2 that there is a considerable range of possible challenger lives for which the equivalent uniform annual cost is very close to $2,000. However, as a 3-year life yields slightly lower annual costs than any other life, this is the assumed life that is most favorable to the challenger.

Comparative Annual Costs of Challenger (3-year life)

CR = ($2,000 − $500)(A/P,8%,3) + $500(0.08) .... $ 622
Equivalent annual disbursements = [$1,200(P/F,8%,1)
     + $1,350(P/F,8%,2) + $1,550(P/F,8%,3)](A/P,8%,3) 1,358
Total $1,980

Calculation of Annual Cost of Defender. The first impulse of anyone making this economy study might be to compare next year's costs for the defender with the foregoing annual costs over the expected life of the challenger.

TABLE 17–2

Equivalent Annual Costs of $2,000 Machine of Table 15–1 for Assumed Lives of 1 to 10 Years with Interest at 8%

Year n	Costs of Extending Service During nth Year			Equivalent Uniform Annual Costs if Retired After n Years		
	Capital Recovery Cost (Column E of Table 15–1)	Disbursements During Year	Total Cost (B + C)	Uniform Equivalent Annual Capital Recovery Cost (Column H of Table 15–1)	Equivalent Uniform Annual Disbursements	Total Equivalent Uniform Annual Cost (E + F)
A	B	C	D	E	F	G
1	$1,060	$1,200	$2,260	$1,060	$1,200	$2,260
2	438	1,350	1,788	761	1,272	2,033
3	310	1,550	1,860	622	1,358	1,980
4	240	1,800	2,040	537	1,456	1,993
5	124	1,950	2,074	467	1,540	2,007
6	116	2,050	2,166	419	1,610	2,029
7	58	2,125	2,183	379	1,667	2,046
8	54	2,200	2,254	348	1,717	2,065
9	0	2,250	2,250	320	1,760	2,080
10	0	2,300	2,300	298	1,797	2,095

Comparative Annual Cost of Defender (1 year more)

$$\text{CR} = (\$1,350 - \$775)(A/P,8\%,1) + \$775(0.08)$$
$$= (\$1,350 - \$775)(1.08) + \$775(0.08) \quad \dots\dots\dots\dots\dots\dots\dots \quad \$\ 683$$
Operating disbursements 1,370

Total $2,053

It is evident that $(\$1,350 - \$775)(1.08) + \$775(0.08)$ may also be written as $(\$1,350 - \$775)(1.00) + \$1,350(0.08)$. In general, where the assumed remaining life of a defender is one year, it is convenient to think of the capital recovery costs as made up of the prospective decline in salvage value (depreciation in the popular sense) and interest on present salvage value. An alternate statement of next-year defender costs is therefore:

Decline in salvage value = $1,350 − $775 .... $ 575
Interest on salvage value = $1,350(0.08) 108
Operating disbursements 1,370

Total $2,053

The challenger is favored by a comparison of this $2,053 next-year defender cost with the $1,980 annual cost for a 3-year challenger life. However, in this case the decline in defender salvage value forecast for next year ($575) is much greater than the decline forecast for the following year ($250). A comparison favorable to the defender by a slight margin will be obtained if defender costs are considered over the next 2 years.

Comparative Annual Cost of Defender (2 years more)

CR = ($1,350 − $525)(A/P,8%,2) + $525(0.08) .... $ 505
Equivalent annual disbursements = [$1,370(P/F,8%,1)
   + $1,570(P/F,8%,2)](A/P,8%,2) 1,466
Total $1,971

A similar calculation assuming 3 years more for the defender yields an equivalent annual cost of $2,014.

One purpose of including this example has been to emphasize the point that in any declining salvage situation, it may be advisable to consider defender costs for several different assumed remaining lives. The practical conclusion of this particular study should be that the comparative cost figures are so close that the decision between challenger and defender ought to be made on so-called irreducibles—that is, on considerations that have not been reduced to money terms in the study.

The $2,200 original cost of the defender is, of course, irrelevant in any before-tax study.

Some Aspects of Tables Such as 17–1 and 17–2. The figures given in column E of Table 17–1 and column G of Table 17–2 are valid equivalent annual costs for the respective challengers, given the assumed interest rate and first cost, and the predictions of the patterns of salvage values and operating costs. Nevertheless, even though the various disbursements turn out exactly as predicted, the tables do not tell us that it will necessarily be economical to replace the challenger of Table 17–1 when it is 27 years old or the challenger of Table 17–2 when it is 3 years old. The economic replacement date may be sooner or later, depending on the costs and prospective performance of challengers that may be available in the future, and on other matters.

Calculations such as those illustrated in Tables 17–1 and 17–2 may be viewed as yielding "economic lives" only under very restrictive assumptions. All future challengers must have the same first cost as the present challenger, the same expected salvage values at each age, and the same expected operating costs for each year. Moreover, it must be assumed that the need for the particular service continues indefinitely and that the minimum attractive rate of return remains unchanged.

In general, replacement decisions should not be based on such assumptions, which obviously are unrealistic in our modern world of changing technology and changing prices. The question in a replacement decision should not be "How old is the defender?" The issue should always be viewed as an economic choice between extending the service of the defender, regardless of its age, and its retirement in favor of the best available challenger. But a temporary view of Tables 17–1 and 17–2 as "economic life" calculations may be helpful as an aid to the exposition of certain theoretical aspects of replacement economy and as a basis for pointing out a useful check on the arithmetic and the analysis in any tables or formulas of this type.

For instance, consider Table 17–1 as applicable to future challengers as well as to the present one. As long as the cost of extending the service of the present challenger is less than $749, the annual cost of a future challenger, it will pay to keep the present challenger in service. Because salvage values are zero at all times, the only cost of extending service is the operating disbursement (cost of lost gas) in column B. Consider the start of the 27th year; as the column B figure is $720, it will not pay to replace. Now consider the start of the 28th year; as the prospective cost of extending service another year is $780 and as $780 exceeds $749, replacement is justified after 27 years. The various elements in the analysis are shown graphically in Figure 17–1. The minimum point on the curve of total equivalent annual cost occurs where the curve is intersected by the dotted line for cost of lost gas during the year.

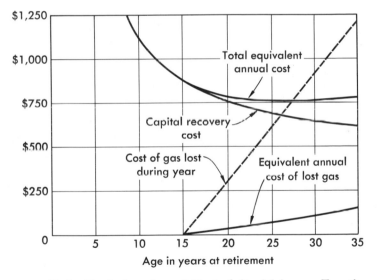

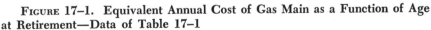

Age in years at retirement

FIGURE 17–1. Equivalent Annual Cost of Gas Main as a Function of Age at Retirement—Data of Table 17–1

Figure 17–2 shows the same type of relationship for the more complicated facts of Table 17–2. Because salvage values are not zero and are declining, the cost of extending service in any year is the sum of operating disbursements, interest on salvage value at the start of the year, and decline in salvage during the year. But the same principle applies

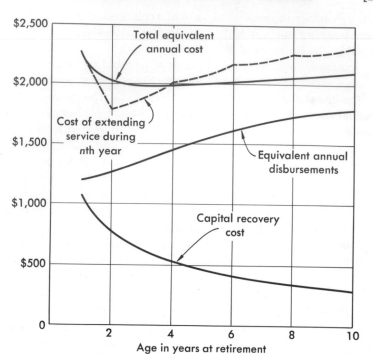

Figure 17–2. Equivalent Annual Cost as a Function of Age at Retirement —Machine of Table 17–2

that the minimum annual cost is reached when the cost of extending service next year is greater than the equivalent annual cost up to date.

If the curves of total equivalent annual cost in Figures 17–1 and 17–2 should be interpreted as the basis for finding the economic life, they would suggest the conclusion that there is a wide range of possible lives of these assets that are almost equally economical. Although there are minimum cost points, these curves are relatively flat through a considerable range. Mathematical models developed in connection with replacement economy often indicate a substantial minimum cost range as well as a minimum cost point.

If one could imagine a static society in which prices and service requirements never changed and in which challengers always repeated the cost history of their defenders, the exact timing of replacement in such a society doubtless would be of little consequence. In our dynamic modern industrial society where challengers often differ greatly from their defenders, the timing of replacements is likely to be much more important than would be suggested by any mathematical model.

What Shall Be Assumed as Remaining Defender Service Life in a Replacement Economy Study? Examples 17–3 and 17–4 are typical of many replacement studies in which the assumed remaining defender life is shorter than the assumed challenger life. In such studies, one problem is to select the defender remaining life that is most favorable to the defender.

When a major outlay for defender alteration or overhaul is needed, the remaining defender life that will yield the least annual cost is likely to be the period that will elapse before the next major alteration or overhaul will be needed.

When there is no defender salvage value now or later (and no outlay for alteration or overhaul), and when defender operating disbursements are expected to increase annually, as in Example 17–3, the remaining life that will yield the least annual cost will be one year (or possibly less).

When salvage values are expected to decline from year to year, as in Example 17–4, it may be necessary to try several remaining service lives before selecting the one to be used in the comparison.

It should be emphasized that the selection of a remaining defender service life for use in a replacement study does not imply a commitment that if the decision favors the defender, it will be retired at the end of this period. The problem is merely to find the period that yields the lowest annual cost of continuing the service of the defender.

How Prospective Occurrences After the Expiration of the Assumed Remaining Life of the Defender Should Influence the Choice Between Defender and Challenger. Consider the comparison of annual costs in Example 17–3 relative to section Y of main:

Defender—$900 per mile for next year
Present Challenger—$749 per mile for 27 years

Such a comparison appears to favor the present challenger. Nevertheless, it does not necessarily follow from such a comparison that a decision in favor of the present challenger will lead to maximum economy in the long run. If the replacement is put off for a while, a better challenger than the present one may be available. If the future challenger is enough better than the present one, a long-run comparison may favor continuing the defender in service for the time being in order to realize the advantages obtainable from the future challenger.

As a simple numerical illustration of this point, assume that it is expected that the first cost of new gas mains will decline a little during the coming year and that protective coatings will be somewhat improved. Let us assume that a monetary allowance for these changes leads to a figure of $720 a year as the annual cost per mile for 26 years of service from next year's challenger. Now our comparison is:

Defender and Next Year's Challenger—$900 next year followed by $720 a year for 26 years

Present Challenger—$749 a year for 27 years

The defender alternative may be converted (at 7%) to an equivalent uniform annual cost of $734 for 27 years. If our assumption about next year's challenger turns out to be correct, it is better to make our present decision in favor of the defender.

More often than not, an analyst is likely to feel that he has no basis for such a specific numerical estimate of the difference in annual cost between a known present challenger and an unknown future one. But coming events may cast their shadows before sufficiently well for the matter to be considered on a qualitative basis. In one instance it may be known that greatly improved designs of certain machines are in the development stage and that new commercial models may be expected in the near future. In another case new models containing drastic improvements may have recently appeared, and it may be thought unlikely that machines with further great improvements will be available soon. Sometimes there may be good reason to believe that future challengers will have higher first costs than the present one (perhaps because of their greater complexity or because of rising prices); sometimes it may be expected that future challengers will be lower priced (perhaps because of economies realizable from their production in greater quantities).

Any forecast about differences between the present challenger and future challengers is relevant in decision making about a proposed replacement—particularly so in borderline cases. A forecast that future challengers will be superior to the present one or that they will have lower first costs is favorable to postponing replacement. A forecast that future challengers will be inferior [3] or that they will have higher first costs is favorable to immediate replacement. If an analyst desires to consider such forecasts quantitatively but is unwilling to make a single monetary estimate, he may test the sensitivity of the replacement decision to forecasts about future challengers by making an analysis of several different estimates.

[3] Of course the normal expectation in modern industry is that technological progress will cause future challengers to be superior. However, it sometimes happens that style change or technological change causes new machines to be less well adapted to certain services. Moreover, periods occur in history when it seems likely that the quality of new assets available in the future will be inferior to those presently available. For example, the period 1939–41 in the United States, prior to the entry of the country into World War II, was a time when an analyst making a replacement study might have forecast that challengers in the near future, if any, would be inferior to present ones.

Since 1949 in the United States there has been a considerable vogue for the use of mathematical models as a guide to decisions on replacements. A first step in the understanding of such models is an understanding of calculations of minimum annual cost such as the ones illustrated in Tables 17–1 and 17–2. A second step is an understanding of the problem of giving weight to the expectation that if replacement is deferred for a while a better challenger will be available. Several of the more popular models, discussed briefly in Appendix D, involve a formal monetary allowance (as a charge against the challenger) for the expectation that if replacement is deferred a better challenger will be available one year hence.

What Shall Be Assumed as Challenger Service Life in a Replacement Economy Study? In Examples 17–3 and 17–4 we assumed the challenger life that would yield the lowest annual cost for the challenger. (We noted that in Examples 17–3 and 17–4, because of consideration of the prospective increase of annual disbursements with age, the challenger annual cost was not sensitive to a moderate change in assumed challenger life.)

In these examples we did not shorten the assumed life of the present challenger because of the expectation that better challengers would be available in the near future. However, decisions on replacements in industry sometimes are made by methods of analysis that in effect make an excessive shortening of challenger service life for this reason.

The use of a very short payout period for a challenger that has a relatively long prospective life should not be regarded as "conservative." Using a one or two or three year payout period for such a challenger has the effect of continuing the service of defenders that are obsolete and uneconomical.[4]

Nevertheless, *some* shortening of assumed challenger service life may be appropriate in lieu of a formalized allowance for the prospect that if replacement is deferred, a superior challenger will be available. It is explained in Appendix D that the use of one of the common formulas containing such a formalized allowance has approximately the same effect on the analysis as cutting the estimated primary service life of the challenger in half before computing its capital recovery cost.

The Problem of Securing Adequate Cost Data for Certain Types of Replacement Economy Studies. It is a common condition for operation and repair costs of machinery and other assets to increase with

---

[4] George Terborgh has written forcefully on this point. See *Dynamic Equipment Policy, op. cit.,* chap. xii. See also his "fable," "The Profits of Procrastination," quoted in Appendix D.

age.[5] For adequate replacement studies, it is not enough to be aware of these matters in a qualitative way; specific quantitative information is needed applicable to each study.

In the frequent case where an organization operates many similar machines of different ages, there is an opportunity to secure such information. Usually the accounting system does not furnish data in the form needed by an analyst studying replacement policy. For example, the accounts may report the total repair costs for all machines of a given type but not give information on individual machines; an analyst may need to examine and classify individual repair work orders. The evaluation of some matters, such as the adverse consequences of breakdowns or other unsatisfactory performance, may require considerable information gathering and analysis that is entirely apart from the accounting system.

Limitation on Uses of "Comparative Annual Costs" Computed for Replacement Studies. It should be emphasized that "costs" such as have been calculated in the examples of replacement studies in this chapter are useful solely for the comparison of the specific alternatives under consideration. Such "comparative annual costs" are properly thought of merely as convenient measure of the differences between the proposed alternatives. Obviously no inferences should be drawn from them except inferences as to the relative merits of the alternatives being compared. This statement applies with particular force to the drawing of inferences about pricing policies.

The Need to Find the Best Challenger. In replacement studies, just as in all other economy studies, it is essential that all promising alternatives be considered. It is not good enough for a particular challenger to be more economical than the defender; it also needs to be more economical than other possible challengers.

Several of the problems at the end of this chapter illustrate the comparison of several possible challengers with one another as well as with a single defender.

Often the Source of a Product or Service Is Replaced Without a Retirement. The examples and problems in this chapter generally imply that if the challenger is acquired the defender will be retired. Often

---

[5] See Terborgh, *Dynamic Equipment Policy, op. cit.*, pp. 70–71, for graphs showing the relation between age and repair cost per unit of service for certain metal working equipment, textile machinery, locomotives, farm implements, light trucks, passenger automobiles, intercity buses, and local buses. In all of these graphs repair costs per unit of service increase with age. In some instances the relationship is linear; in others the increase per year is less in the later years than in the earlier years.

the circumstances of the case make it reasonable that the old asset be retired as soon as the new one is available.

But frequently new assets are acquired for a given service in a way that displaces the old assets but does not involve their retirement. The old assets are simply relegated to a different use—one that might generally be described as an inferior use. Assignment for peak load or stand-by purposes is an example of this. Another familiar example is the assignment of a displaced main-line railroad locomotive to branch-line service. It may be many years before an asset displaced in this way is finally retired; in fact, there may be several successive different inferior uses before retirement.

In periods of expanding demand for a product or service (generally, but not necessarily, corresponding to periods of general business prosperity), the tendency is to acquire new assets of improved design but not to retire the older less economical assets. In periods when there is apparent overcapacity (generally, but not necessarily, in business depressions), the older assets are retired. Much replacement of industrial assets occurs with this type of time lag. Where this takes place, the economy studies in periods of expanding demand involve the displacement of the sources of a service and those in overcapacity periods involve retirements, but there are no replacement economy studies as such.

Common Errors in Replacement Studies. Observation of the practice of industrialists in such studies and of the published literature of the subject indicates four errors which it seems are often made in dealing with replacement economy:

1. Considering the excess of present book value over the net realizable value of the old asset as an addition to the investment in the new asset. This error increases the apparent cost associated with the new asset, and thus tends to prevent replacements that are really economical.
2. Calculating depreciation and interest (i.e., capital recovery) on the old asset on the basis of its original cost rather than its present net realizable value. This usually increases the apparent costs associated with the old asset, and thus tends to favor replacements that are really uneconomical.
3. Where indirect costs (burden) are allotted in the cost accounting system in proportion to direct costs (usually in proportion to direct labor cost), assuming without investigation that a reduction of direct expenditures will effect a corresponding saving in indirect expenditures. This error usually makes the apparent saving from proposed replacements greater than the saving that is actu-

ally possible to realize, and thus tends to favor replacements that
are really uneconomical.

4. In cases where the proposed new asset provides more capacity
than the old asset, comparing calculated unit costs realizable only
with full-capacity operation, rather than comparing the actual
costs realizable with the expected output. Where such excess of
capacity is not likely to be used, this unit cost comparison tends
to favor the asset with the surplus capacity, and is therefore favorable to replacements that are really uneconomical.

The first two of these errors cited result from a failure to recognize
the true nature of depreciation accounting as a time allotment against
future dates of money already spent. The third results from a failure to
understand clearly the nature of cost accounting allocations. The fourth
is merely an unrealistic use of unit costs.

EXAMPLE 17–5. INFLUENCE OF BUDGETARY CONSIDERATIONS ON THE TIMING OF REPLACEMENT EXPENDITURES

Facts of the Case. As a result of a change from the purchase of manufactured gas to natural gas, a city that had its publicly owned gas distribution
system was faced with a great increase in leakage of gas from its mains. (The
moist manufactured gas contains bituminous compounds that tend to plug up
any small holes caused by corrosion of the mains; the dry natural gas dries
these plugs, with the result that the gas escapes through the holes.) An analysis of the cost of lost gas and the cost of main replacement indicated that it
would pay to replace a number of the oldest mains and services. There were
other old mains and services that had not quite reached the point where replacement was economically justified even though considerable gas was being
lost from them.

If all of the gas mains that justified replacement were to be replaced at
once, the only possible source of funds would have been a bond issue; this
would have required an affirmative vote of two-thirds of the voters at a bond
election. As gas main replacement was not considered well adapted to contract, a program of immediate replacement would have necessitated the hiring
of a number of temporary employees for the gas department.

For a number of years this gas department had operated with a pay-as-
you-go policy for financing capital improvements, with all capital expenditures
budgeted out of current earnings from the sale of gas. If this policy were to
be adopted for the replacement program, only enough funds could be budgeted
annually to keep one crew busy on main replacement. As a result it would
take several years to replace all of the mains requiring replacement.

After careful consideration, it was decided to continue this pay-as-you-go
policy. It was believed to be desirable to avoid bond issues except for major
expenditures for plant expansion. Moreover, it was felt that a single crew
working full time on main and service replacement would become more efficient and, therefore, would operate at a lower cost than several temporary
crews working a shorter period on the same type of work. Considerations of
personnel policy were also against the hiring of temporary crews.

After several years, all of the mains that were losing enough gas to justify immediate replacement had been replaced. It was then decided to continue to budget funds for replacement for another year or two. These funds would be used to replace those mains that were losing considerable gas even though the losses had not quite reached the point where replacement was justified strictly on economic grounds. It was clearly possible to finance these replacements at once whereas the possibilities of financing at a later date were less certain.

Thus, because of budgetary considerations and other reasons, some mains were replaced a few years later than the date indicated by economy studies and others were replaced a few years sooner than the apparent economic date. Considerations such as these quite properly enter into decisions on the timing of expenditures for replacements.

Need for a System Viewpoint in Certain Types of Replacement Studies.

Ray I. Reul illustrates a common type of occurrence with the following example: [6]

Suppose we have a plant shutdown because of a burned-out transformer. This plant, when operating, produces an annual profit of $10,000. If a transformer is not immediately purchased and installed at a cost of $8,000, the $10,000 profit will no longer be received. Therefore, we can truthfully say that the investment of $8,000 will "save" $10,000 per year. This sounds like a magnificent return. So we buy and install the transformer.

One year later the steam boiler, which is also an integral part of the plant, breaks down and must be retubed with an investment of another $8,000. Again, we can truthfully state that expenditure of $8,000 will "save" $10,000 per year. (Theoretically, we could repeat the process of "saving" $10,000 per year over and over again with further expenditures.) The catch is that this is the *same* $10,000 per year we "saved" before. Actually, there is only *one* $10,000 per year to be "saved."

Reul classifies investment proposals into "profit-maintaining" and "profit-adding" as follows:

Profit-maintaining

1. Replacement of existing facilities which will no longer function.
2. Improvement of existing facilities to circumvent competition.
3. Provision of new facilities which were accidentally or intentionally omitted when the original facilities were installed but which have now become essential to the continuation of existing activities.

Profit-adding

1. Provision of new facilities that will increase profit by providing new business or by expanding existing operations.
2. Provision of facilities that will improve product quality and permit higher prices and profit margins.
3. Provision of facilities that will reduce the cost of production and result in increased profit through larger profit margins or increased volume of sales.

[6] R. I. Reul, "Profitability Index for Investments," *Harvard Business Review*, XXXV, No. 4 (July–August, 1957), 116–32.

He comments on the viewpoint that should be applied to profit-maintaining proposals, as follows:

To convert a profit-maintaining proposal to a profit-adding basis, we must investigate the future of the particular operations at stake. This investigation must cover the entire life of the proposed new facility. All income during this period must be predicted; all expenditures, including operating costs, replacements of other related facilities, revisions, additions, and so forth, must be anticipated. These data, viewed against the alternative of doing nothing and losing existing income, will permit the proposed investment to be evaluated as a true profit-adding proposal.

By way of illustration, let us return for a moment to the plant requiring replacement of the burned-out transformer. To evaluate this proposal properly we must include all other investments anticipated during the years for which continued profit is predicted. Thus, if savings are claimed in the second year, the investment required for boiler tubes must be included in the evaluation.

Summary. The following points brought out in this chapter may be restated for emphasis as follows:

1. It is helpful to use the word *defender* to apply to an existing asset being considered for replacement and to use the word *challenger* to apply to a proposed new replacement asset.
2. Capital recovery costs for extending the service of a defender should be based on its present net realizable value.
3. In evaluating the effect of a proposed replacement decision on cash flow for income taxes, it is necessary to consider the past investment in the defender as well as the depreciation accounting method that has been used for the defender in past tax returns.
4. As in all comparisons of alternatives, prospective receipts and disbursements that are unaffected by the choice may be omitted from a replacement study.
5. Generally speaking, the annual cost of extending the service of a defender should be based on the number of years of additional service that results in the lowest figure for this annual cost.
6. Where the remaining life assumed for the defender is shorter than the life expected for the challenger, it is appropriate to recognize that if replacement is deferred, a different challenger from the present one is likely to be available. This prospect may be given weight in the economy study in a number of different ways. Mathematical models that make a formalized allowance for better future challengers are discussed in Appendix D.

PROBLEMS

17-1. A corporation engaged in large-scale farming operates a fleet of tractors. Major overhauls generally have been needed when tractors are 4 and 8 years old. In the past most tractors have been retired after 8 years, just before the second major overhaul. However, a few tractors have been retired after 4 years, just before the first overhaul. Some others have been overhauled when 8 years old and kept in service until they were scrapped at the end of 12 years. In reviewing past replacement policy, an analyst estimates typical year-by-year annual disbursements that appear to have been influenced by the age of a tractor (chiefly routine maintenance, fuel, and lubricants) as follows:

Year	Disbursements	Year	Disbursements	Year	Disbursements
1	$4,000	5	$6,500	9	$8,000
2	5,000	6	7,000	10	8,000
3	6,000	7	7,500	11	8,000
4	7,000	8	8,000	12	8,000

The first cost of a tractor is $16,000. A typical salvage value before overhaul at the end of 4 years is $5,600. A typical cost of overhaul at the end of 4 years is $5,000. A typical salvage value before overhaul at the end of 8 years is $1,600. A typical cost of overhaul at the end of 8 years is $7,000. Salvage values at the end of 12 years are negligible.

Depreciation used in accounting and income tax returns has been based on the years-digits method assuming an 8-year life and 10% salvage value.

Assuming a minimum attractive rate of return (interest rate) of 12% before income taxes, compare the before-tax equivalent annual costs of service for lives of 4, 8, and 12 years, using the foregoing "typical" figures for the relevant costs. (*Ans.* = $9,460; $9,800; $10,000.)

17–2. In Problem 17–1, consider the decision whether a typical 4-year-old tractor should be overhauled and kept in service for 4 years more or replaced with a new tractor. Using an i^* of 12%, make a before-tax comparison of equivalent annual costs of (a) extending the service of the old tractor for 4 years or (b) acquiring a new tractor to be retired after 4 years. (*Ans.* = (a) $10,340; (b) $9,460.)

17–3. Make an after-tax comparison of the alternatives in Problem 17–2 by the method of rate of return, assuming an effective tax rate of 50%. Assume that the entire $5,000 overhaul cost of the defender at the end of its 4th year of life may be treated as a current expense for tax purposes in that year (i.e., at zero date for this economy study). What is the prospective rate of return? If the minimum attractive rate of return is 6% after income taxes, does this comparison favor the defender or challenger? (*Ans.* = 11.2%; challenger.)

17–4. In the circumstances described in Problem 17–1, the question arises whether it would not be advantageous to retire tractors considerably earlier than the first overhaul date, say, at the end of 2 years. Obviously, an important element in comparing a policy of retirement after 2 years with retirement after 4 years is the salvage value after 2 years. How great must this salvage value be for the 2-year retirement to be as economical as the 4-year retirement for a typical tractor? Determine this figure by a before-tax analysis using a minimum attractive rate of return of 12%. (*Ans.* = $9,490.)

17–5. An individual owns a rental property in an industrial district of a city. This is rented to a single tenant at an annual rental of $10,000. The present lease is about to expire. The tenant is willing to renew the lease for a long term at the present figure but not at a higher one.

A manufacturing company adjoining the building site has made an offer of $120,000 for this property. Because of the particular needs of this manufacturer for an area to expand, the property owner believes that this is a better offer than can be secured from any other buyer. If the offer is not accepted at once, it is considered likely that the manufacturer will make other plans for plant expansion and that the offer will therefore not be renewed at a later date. A decision must therefore be made at once whether or not to accept this offer.

It is believed that if the property is not sold at once, ownership will be continued for a fairly long time. For purposes of the economy study to guide the decision, assume that ownership will continue for 20 years and that the net resale value before income taxes at the end of that period will be $50,000. The original cost of the property 5 years ago was $80,000, divided for accounting and tax purposes into $20,000 for land and $60,000 for the building. Since purchase, the building has been depreciated for accounting and tax purposes at $1,500 a year based on an estimated remaining life of 40 years from the purchase date and a terminal salvage value of zero.

If ownership is continued, it is estimated that receipts from rental will continue at $10,000 a year. Annual disbursements are estimated to be $1,500 for upkeep, $2,100 for property taxes, and $400 for insurance.

(a) Compute a rate of return before income taxes that provides a basis for comparison between the alternatives of continued ownership and immediate sale. (*Ans.* = 2.8%.)

(b) Compute a rate of return after income taxes that provides a basis for comparison between these two alternatives. Consider both the income taxes on any capital gain and on annual taxable income. Assume a 55% tax rate on ordinary income and a 25% tax rate on capital gains. (*Ans.* = 0.7%.)

17–6. A furniture manufacturer is considering the installation of an automatic machine for boring holes to replace two machines that now provide the same total capacity. The proposed machine will cost $10,000 ready to operate. If acquired, it will be depreciated for accounting and tax purposes by the straight-line item method assuming a 10-year life and zero salvage value. Annual disbursements for its operation are estimated as follows:

Direct labor will be one operator at $110 per week for the entire year.
Labor extras are 30% of direct labor cost.
Power will be 4,000 kw-hr per year at 3 cents per kw-hr.
Annual repairs and supplies are estimated as $240.
Property taxes and insurance total 2% of first cost.

The two present machines cost $2,250 each and are 5 years old. Straight-line item depreciation has been used for accounting and tax purposes assuming a 15-year life and zero terminal salvage value. Their present realizable value is $100 each. Annual expenditures are:

Direct labor is two operators at $90 per week each for the entire year.
Labor extras are 30% of direct labor cost.
Power is 2,500 kw-hr per machine per year at 3 cents.
Annual repairs and supplies are $150 per machine.
Property taxes and insurance total 2% of first cost.

(a) Assuming a 12% minimum attractive rate of return before income taxes, compute the before-tax annual cost of extending service of the defenders for 10 more years. Compare this with the annual cost of the challenger over a 10-year service life. Assume zero salvage values for both defender and challenger at the end of the 10 years. (*Ans.* = defender, $12,749; challenger, $9,766.)

(b) Make an after-tax comparison of annual costs assuming a 6% minimum attractive rate of return. Use a tax rate of 50%. Consider extra annual income taxes as an additional annual cost of the challenger. Assume that any "loss" on disposal of the defender will be fully deductible in the year of retirement; consider the resulting tax saving as an addition to the net salvage value of the defender. (*Ans.* = defender, $12,931; challenger, $11,364.)

(c) Compute the after-tax rate of return on the net investment needed to acquire the challenger, assuming a 10-year remaining life for both challenger and defender. (*Ans.* = 29.9%.)

(d) Disregarding any time value of money, find how long it will take for the difference in cash flow after income taxes to equal zero. (This may be viewed as the crude payout period after taxes.) (*Ans.* = 3.1 years.)

17-7. A 3-year-old machine has the following cost history:

Disbursements for

Year	Operation and Repairs	Delays Due to Breakdowns
1	$ 700	$ 0
2	900	200
3	1,100	400

If the machine is continued in service for the 4th year, it is estimated that the operation and repair costs will be $1,300 and breakdowns will cost $600. The corresponding estimates for the 5th year of service are $1,500 and $800. The machine has a present net realizable value of $1,500; this will probably reduce to $1,200 in another year and to $1,000 in 2 years.

It is suggested that this be replaced by a new machine of improved design costing $6,000. It is believed that this will completely eliminate any breakdowns and the resulting cost of delays, and that it will reduce operation and repair costs to $200 a year less at each age than the corresponding costs with the old machine.

Make a before-tax comparison of annual costs using a minimum attractive rate of return of 12%. Base the annual cost of extending the service of the defender either on 1 or 2 years more of service, whichever gives the lower annual cost. Assume a 5-year life for the challenger with a $1,000 terminal salvage value. (*Ans.* = defender, $2,380; challenger, $2,361.)

17-8. The question arises whether it is more economical to replace a certain motorboat engine with a new one, or to rebore the cylinders of the old engine and thoroughly recondition it. The original cost of the old engine 10 years ago was $700; to rebore and recondition it now will extend its useful life for an estimated 5 years and will cost $280. A new engine will have a first cost of $620 and will have an estimated life of 10 years. It is expected that the annual cost of fuel and lubricants with the reconditioned engine will be about $200 and that this cost will be 15% less with the new engine. It is also believed that repairs will be $25 a year less with the new engine than with the reconditioned one. Assume that neither engine has any net realizable value when retired.

What irreducibles can you think of favorable to each plan? Compute comparative equivalent annual costs assuming an i° of 6%. (*Ans.* = recondition, $291; replace, $254.)

17–9. The butt of a pole in a municipal electric distribution system has decayed to the point where it is necessary either to replace the pole or to "stub" it. A new pole will cost $58 installed and will have an estimated life of 21 years. The pole inspector estimates the remaining life in the upper portion of the present pole as 8 years; this may be realized if the pole is stubbed. Stubbing will cost $17. The stubbed pole will have zero salvage value after 8 years. The upper portion of the present pole has an estimated value for use elsewhere of $8. The terminal salvage value of a new pole after 21 years is estimated to be $12. Maintenance costs will be unaffected by the decision.

Compare equivalent annual costs of these alternatives using an i^* of 6%. (*Ans.* = stub, $4.03; new pole, $4.63.)

17–10. A flood that washed out a section of recently completed canal indicates the need for a larger drainage structure. Three possibilities are considered:

    A. Leave the existing 48-in. corrugated metal culvert in place (it is undamaged) and install another of equal size alongside.
    B. Remove the present 48-in. corrugated metal culvert and replace it with a single pipe 72 in. in diameter.
    C. Remove the present metal culvert and replace it with a reinforced concrete box culvert of adequate cross section.

If the present 48-in pipe is removed, it will have a salvage value of $400. Estimates regarding the new installations are as follows:

	48-in. Pipe	72-in. Pipe	Concrete Culvert
Cost of pipes, delivered	$1,000	$2,000	0
Installation cost	$500	$700	$2,800
Estimated life	25 years	25 years	50 years

With an i^* of 7%, which alternative would you recommend? Explain your analysis. (*Ans.* = Plan A.)

17–11. Black owns his home for which he paid $25,000 5 years ago. This property is free of debt. His employer has transferred him to another city where he has decided to rent an apartment. He has the opportunity to sell his house for $30,000; expenses of the sale would be a 6% broker's commission and $250 for title insurance. He also has the chance to rent the house on a 5-year lease to a desirable tenant for $250 a month. If he rents the property, he estimates his annual disbursements for property taxes, insurance, and upkeep as $600. He anticipates that if he rents the property now he will sell it at the end of the 5-year lease. He estimates the future selling price as $28,000, also subject to 6% broker's commission and $250 title insurance.

If he sells the property, he expects to invest the net proceeds in bonds yielding 6%. His effective tax rate on ordinary income is 30% and on long-term capital gains is 15%.

If he sells the property now, he will be taxed on a long-term capital gain of $2,850, the difference between his selling price (net after deducting selling expenses) and his original cost. (No depreciation on the house has been allowed or allowable on tax returns during the years it has been his personal residence.) If he rents the house, he can deduct $500 a year depreciation in his tax return in addition to his disbursements each year for property taxes, insurance, and upkeep. (This figure is based on a division of his investment into $20,000 for house and $5,000 for land, and on the straight-line method assuming a 40-year life.)

Based on the foregoing estimates, will he have a greater after-tax yield from continued ownership of this property or from the proposed investment in bonds? Explain your analysis, showing an after-tax rate of return on continued ownership.

Discuss the irreducibles that you think might reasonably enter into his decision. Discuss the sensitivity of the computed rate of return to the estimated selling price at the end of 5 years.

17-12. Two years ago a manufacturing company designed, built, and installed a gas-fired drying oven at a total cost of $18,000. A firm manufacturing drying ovens of a new and radically different design now offers a new oven for $30,000. The maker of the new oven guarantees a fuel saving of $6,000 per year compared to the present oven. Repairs and maintenance are estimated at $1,000 per year.

For accounting and income tax purposes, depreciation has been charged on the present oven at $1,500 a year, using the straight-line method with a 12-year life and zero salvage value. This depreciation rate will be continued if the oven is not retired. If the new oven is purchased, its depreciation charges will be based on a 10-year life, zero salvage value, and the straight-line method. Item depreciation accounting is used and is appropriate because only one oven is owned.

Repairs and maintenance costs on the present oven are about $600 a year and it is estimated they will continue at this figure. All other costs except fuel in connection with the drying operation will be unaffected by the type of oven used. Either oven, once installed, has value only as scrap if removed; the scrap value is about equal to the cost of dismantling and removal.

The company's effective tax rate on ordinary income is 50%. If the present oven is retired now, it is believed there will be no offsetting gains during the current year that will prevent securing the full advantage of the tax loss.

Assume that if continued in service the defender will be kept 10 years more, and that the challenger life is 10 years. If the company's minimum attractive rate of return is 12% after income taxes, which oven should be selected? Explain your answer.

Discuss the sensitivity of your conclusion to the assumed remaining defender service life.

17-13. Five years ago, at a cost of $9,600, a film processing concern designed and installed the necessary equipment to develop semiautomatically a certain size of film. A salesman now proposes that this equipment be discarded and that a new machine that his firm has just put on the market should be installed to do this work. His estimate of a $2,000 annual saving in the cost of labor and supplies seems to be reasonable. It is believed that there will be no other difference in annual disbursements between the old and new equipment. The price of the new machine is $15,000. The salesman has found a buyer willing to pay $1,000 for the old equipment.

The present equipment is fully depreciated on the books of account and for tax purposes, as the assumed life was 5 years with zero salvage value. Item accounting has been used. However, this equipment is still serviceable and could be used for several years more at approximately the present level of annual disbursements. Unless sold at once, it is expected to have zero salvage value. If acquired, the new machine will be depreciated by the years-digits method, assuming a 5-year life and zero salvage value; this estimated life and salvage value will also be used in the economy study to guide the decision on this suggested purchase.

The company's effective tax rate is 50% on ordinary income and 30% on capital gains. If the minimum attractive rate of return is 8% after income taxes, would you recommend purchase of the new equipment? Explain any assumptions that you make in your analysis.

17–14. An electrochemical company produces a portion of the electric energy required in its production processes in two hydroelectric power plants A and B. A consists of a dam and short wooden flume leading to a power house. B consists of a longer wooden flume leading from the tailwater of A to a second power house. The two plants use the same amount of water. The flumes are in such bad condition that their repair at once is imperative.

You are called in as engineer to make recommendations, and find the situation to be as follows:

The original investment in the two plants was $900,000. Of this, depreciation of $300,000 has been written off in the company's accounts so that the present book value is $600,000. Annual taxes on the two plants total $12,000.

The estimated cost of flume repair to maintain the power plants in service is $100,000. It is estimated that the repaired flume will have a life of 10 years after which another similar repair will be necessary. The life of the two plants as a whole is estimated to be 20 years. If the flume is repaired and plants A and B are maintained in service, their total operation and maintenance costs are estimated to be $15,000 a year.

However, investigation discloses that both plants are relatively inefficient compared to what is possible in modern hydroelectric design. Plant A is turning out 4,000 kw. at an over-all efficiency of 50%; plant B turns out 3,000 kw. at an over-all efficiency of 60%. (Efficiency is the ratio of energy output to energy input.)

Investigation further discloses that the existing power plants might be immediately scrapped, making use merely of a portion of the diversion dam at A. Repairs to the dam and a new intake would cost $50,000; a long tunnel costing $600,000 would be built leading to a new power house costing with machinery $350,000. The result would be a new modern plant operating at 80% over-all efficiency, with an expected life of 50 years. The net head would be the same as in A plus B, as the losses in the new tunnel equal the grade of the flumes. The same amount of water would be utilized. Plants A and B would become valueless, their scrap value being less than cost of dismantling. Operating costs of the new plant would be about $9,000 a year and taxes would be about $18,000 a year.

The increased power generated in the new plant would reduce the amount of power purchased by the electrochemical company from outside sources. This purchased power is costing $35 per kw. per year.

(a) Compute comparative annual costs before income taxes, assuming a minimum attractive rate of return of 20%.

(b) Compute comparative annual costs after income taxes, assuming a tax rate of 58% and a minimum attractive rate of return of 8%. Assume that the annual straight-line depreciation charge on the old plants has been $30,000 based on an estimated remaining life of 30 years when they were purchased 10 years ago. Assume that item depreciation has been used and that any write-off on the immediate scrapping of the old plants may be treated as a deduction from current taxable income. Assume that straight-line depreciation would be used for accounting and tax purposes if the new plant is built, using a 50-year life and zero salvage value.

17–15. A high-speed, special-purpose, automatic strip-feed punch press costing $25,000 has been proposed to replace 3 hand-fed presses now in use. The life of this automatic press has been estimated to be 5 years, with no salvage value at the end of that time. Expenditures for labor, maintenance, etc. have been estimated to be $5,000 per year.

The general-purpose, hand-fed punch presses cost $3,000 each 10 years ago and were estimated to have a life of 20 years, with a salvage value of $200 each at the end of that time. Their present net realizable value is $750 each. Operating expenditures for labor, etc. will be about $3,850 per year per machine. The net value is expected to decrease at the rate of about $100 per press per year.

It is expected that the required service will continue for only 5 years more and that the salvage value of the challenger will be $5,000 at the end of this period.

(a) Make an analysis before income taxes to provide a basis for the decision on whether or not to make this replacement. Assume a before-tax minimum attractive rate of return of 25%.

(b) Make a similar analysis after income taxes using a minimum attractive rate of return of 12%. Assume a tax rate of 52%. Although the expected service period of the challenger is only 5 years, it will be necessary to use a 15-year life (with zero salvage value) for depreciation used in tax returns; years-digits depreciation will be used. Straight-line depreciation has been used for the defenders. Assume that item depreciation is used in this company and that any "losses" on disposal will be fully deductible from taxable income in the year of disposal.

17–16. A municipal water department has as part of its system of delivery a flume that is 60 years old. Maintenance costs on this flume have averaged $4,200 a year during the last 10 years. Gagings made at both ends of the flume indicate an average loss of water in its length of about 15%.

This water department serves its customers in part with surface water brought in the aqueduct of which this flume is a part; the remainder of its water supply is pumped from wells located in the city. The loss of water in the flume thus requires additional pumping from wells. The average amount of water delivered at the inlet end of the flume is 10 millions of gallons per day. The increment cost of pumping from wells is $16.45 per million gallons.

It is estimated that a standard metal flume to replace the existing one would cost $112,000. It is believed that this would reduce the average loss of water in the flume to not more than 3%, and that the maintenance cost of such a flume would not exceed $1,000 a year. For the purposes of an economy study, the life of such a replacement flume is to be assumed as 20 years, although it would actually be much longer.

Irreducible factors favorable to the change are the lessened danger of breaks in the aqueduct line, and the reduced drain on the underground water supply.

Using an $i°$ of 6%, determine whether you would consider it economical to make the replacement.

17–17. A grain elevator requires additional capacity for the grinding of feed. Two plans for securing this capacity are to be compared.

Plan A. Replace the existing centrifugal bar mill with a patent feed grinding mill manufactured by the XYZ Company. This XYZ mill will provide 3 times the present capacity.

Plan B. Continue the present centrifugal bar mill in service and supplement it by another similar mill of like capacity. This will provide double the present capacity which appears to be adequate for all needs.

The existing centrifugal bar mill cost $1,400 5 years ago. Straight-line depreciation has been charged on the books against it based on an estimated life of 15 years. It has a present net realizable value of $400. A new similar mill will now cost $1,700. The XYZ mill has a first cost installed of $3,300.

It is estimated that the maintenance cost of the existing centrifugal bar mill will average at least $250 a year in the future. A new centrifugal bar mill with somewhat improved design can be maintained for about $175 a year, it is believed. The XYZ mill is expected to have an annual maintenance cost of $150.

Energy requirements for a centrifugal bar mill of this capacity are 23 kw-hr per hour of operation. It is expected that if two such mills are operated each will operate about 1,200 hours per year. Because of its greater capacity the XYZ mill will grind the same total amount of feed as the other two in 800 hours per year. Its energy requirements are 41 kw-hr per hour of operation. Energy is purchased for 3.6 cents per kw-hr. Labor cost and taxes will be practically unaffected by the choice of plan.

Make a before-tax comparison of equivalent annual costs for Plans A and B assuming a 10-year remaining life for the present mill and a 10-year life for both new mills with zero terminal salvage values for all. Use a minimum attractive rate of return of 20%.

17–18. A study of the costs of operating a 4-year-old piece of construction equipment indicates that the only costs variable with age are repairs and losses due to lost time. These have been as follows:

Year	Repair Cost	Cost of Lost Time
1	$ 88	$ 0
2	132	50
3	415	150
4	640	300

The present realizable value of this piece of equipment is $1,100. The first cost of a new one is $3,820. Due to certain improvements in design it is believed that the new one will reduce annual costs for fuel and supplies by $150; however, it is expected that repair costs and lost time will behave about as before. If the old unit is kept in service, it is guessed that repairs and cost of lost time next year will be 20% higher than last year. An estimate of the net realizable value at the end of the 3rd year of life is $1,500; at the end of the 5th year it is $900. Assume these salvage values apply to both old and new assets. Compare the annual cost of extending the service of the old asset one year more with the annual cost over the number of years (3, 4, or 5) that gives the lowest figure for the new asset. Make your comparison before income taxes using a minimum attractive rate of return of 15%.

17–19. A company engaged in the canning of food uses machine filling rather than hand filling for a certain product. The machine filler now in use was purchased 6 years ago at an installed cost of $3,600. Recently this machine has experienced lubrication troubles that have caused frequent breakdowns. The maintenance engineer considers these troubles to be due to a fundamental defect in the design of the machine. However, the machine manufacturer has developed a new design that eliminates this defect. A new machine of this design would cost $5,400 installed. It is believed that such a machine would be much more reliable because of the elimination of the lubrication difficulties.

When the machine filler breaks down, hand filling must be used temporarily until the machine is repaired. It is difficult to determine the exact cost occasioned by a breakdown. A brief shutdown is more costly per hour than a long-continued one; on a shutdown for an entire shift, it is possible to change assignments of workers in the cannery in a way that takes account of the lower filling rate. But a careful analysis of the situation by the plant industrial engineer leads to the conclusion that the extra labor cost created by a shutdown of the machine filler is, on the average, at least $5.50 per hour. In order to meet government specifications on minimum filling weights, it is necessary to overfill somewhat more with hand filling than with machine filling. The plant quality control engineer estimates the cost of this additional overfill as $2 for each hour that hand filling is used.

During last year's pack, the machine filler was shut down for a total of 320 hours. It is estimated that with the greater reliability of the new machine the average hours of breakdown can be reduced to 100 or less, and that annual repair costs, now $850, can be reduced to $200.

Income tax authorities require the use of a 12-year estimated average life for machine fillers for tax accounting purposes. The present machine has been depreciated on the books at 8⅓% a year. It has no secondhand resale value. As its scrap value will not be appreciably more than the cost of removal, its net realizable value is assumed to be zero both now and later.

The required payoff period for the new machine is assumed as 4 years. It is understood that another new design for an improved machine filler suitable for this operation is currently in the development stage. When and if this design is perfected by the manufacturer, it will increase the rated output by about 50%. It seems probable that whenever such an improved machine should become available, it will make possible enough cost reduction so that any machine purchased today would be retired in its favor. For this reason the analysis is to be based on a 4-year challenger life with zero salvage value.

It is believed that property taxes and insurance will not be affected by the change in the machine filler. As the rated output of the new machine is the same as that of the old one, it is assumed that the only savings due to the change will be in the costs incident to breakdowns and in repair costs.

(a) Compute comparative annual costs before income taxes for the next 4 years assuming a minimum attractive rate of return of 25%.

(b) Compute comparative annual costs after income taxes for the next 4 years using a tax rate of 52% and a minimum attractive rate of return of 12%. Assume that the 8⅓% straight-line depreciation rate will also be used for the new filler. Assume that because of the use of group depreciation accounting, no "loss" on disposal will be allowable for tax purposes either on disposal of defender or challenger. The retirement of either will terminate the depreciation charge against it. (The 12-year life is in fact the approximate average service life of machine fillers owned by this particular taxpayer. Retirements at ages of less than 12 years are offset by other retirements at ages greater than 12 years. Under the rules of straight-line group accounting, the 8⅓% rate continues to be charged as long as a machine filler continues in service even though is it more than 12 years old.)

17–20. A manufacturer must double his press brake capacity for making certain sheet metal parts. Two plans are set up for comparison:

A. Continue the present XY–10 press brake in service, and supplement it by an XY–12 (a newer model) of equal capacity. The XY–10 cost $9,000 5 years ago. It has been depreciated for tax purposes by the straight-line item method assuming a 15-year life and zero salvage value. A new XY–12 model will cost $12,000. If purchased, it will be depreciated for tax purposes by the years-digits item method assuming a 15-year life and zero salvage value.

B. Sell the XY–10 for $4,500. Buy an XZ–20 model press brake that has double the capacity of the XY–10. The first cost of the XZ–20 is $24,000. If purchased, it will be depreciated for tax purposes by the years-digits item method assuming a 15-year life and zero salvage value.

It is desired to compare these two plans on the assumption that the need for this particular operation will terminate after 5 years. Expected salvage values 5 years hence are $3,000 for the present XY–10, $5,500 for the XY–12, and $11,000 for the XZ–20. Average annual operating disbursements for the three press brakes are estimated as follows:

	XY–10	XY–12	XZ–20
Direct labor	$6,200	$5,800	$10,000
Labor extras	1,550	1,450	2,500
Maintenance	1,800	1,200	2,000
Power	200	150	250
Taxes and insurance	140	240	480

The XZ–20 has the same space requirements as the total of XY–10 and XY–12. Receipts from the sale of product are not expected to be influenced by the choice between A and B. The manufacturer's effective tax rate is 50% on ordinary income and 30% on capital gains.

(a) For years 0 to 5, both inclusive, tabulate the difference in prospective cash flow before income taxes. What interest rate makes plans A and B equivalent to one another?

(b) For years 0 to 5, both inclusive, tabulate the difference in prospective cash flow after income taxes. Assume that any "loss" on disposal can be treated as a deduction from taxable income in the year of disposal. What interest rate makes plans A and B equivalent to one another?

(c) Discuss the interpretation of your computed interest rates in (a) and (b) as a basis for the choice between the two plans.

17–21. The following problem deals with a decision that it was necessary to make in the RST Company in November of 1967.

Early in 1966, the maintenance department of this company ordered a specially designed machine, Machine X, costing $120,000. Nearly 2 years was needed to secure delivery of Machine X. It was delivered and paid for in mid-November 1967. However, it could not be used until it was installed. The installation period would require another month and the estimated cost of installation was $24,000.

The maintenance department had two objectives in mind when Machine X was originally ordered. The primary objective was to improve the diagnosis of certain types of troubles that had occurred in equipment subject to periodic overhaul. A secondary objective was to effect a moderate reduction in the labor, fuel, and power costs in the testing of overhauled equipment. This secondary objective alone was not sufficient to have justified the purchase of Machine X.

When Machine X was ordered, the management of the RST Company knew that the equipment that Machine X was designed to service would gradually be superseded by a different type of equipment by the end of 1975. It was believed that after 1975, Machine X could no longer be used and that it would have a negligible salvage value at that time.

In the period of nearly 2 years that had elapsed between the order date and the delivery date of Machine X, other methods had been developed for diagnosing the troubles in the equipment Machine X was designed to service. It was believed that these other methods were satisfactory enough that Machine X was not actually needed for purpose of diagnosis.

Mr. A, the controller of the RST Company, was therefore opposed to spending the $24,000 to install Machine X. He said: "We are always short of funds for plant investment. Why send good money after bad?" He favored disposing of Machine X at the best available price. A prospective buyer was found who was willing to pay $36,000 for this machine. The market for specialized machines of this type was quite limited, and it seemed unlikely that Machine X could be sold for more than this figure.

Mr. B, the superintendent of the maintenance department, favored keeping Machine X. He pointed out that there would be substantial savings in disbursements for the testing of overhauled equipment if Machine X was installed. The industrial engineering department made careful estimates of these savings, as follows:

1968	$32,000	1971	$19,000	1974	$10,000
1969	25,000	1972	16,000	1975	7,000
1970	22,000	1973	13,000		

The following questions are to be answered as if it were November of 1967. They deal with various aspects of the choice between the alternatives, I, to sell Machine X at once for $36,000, and II, to install Machine X and operate it for the next 8 years. Where necessary to make assumptions about the timing of receipts and disbursements, assume that money payments near the end of 1967 are made on January 1, 1968 (i.e., at zero date on your time scale). Assume the end-of-year convention with respect to the savings in annual disbursements. In answering questions that involve income taxes, assume an end-of-year convention with regard to tax payments. For example, assume that anything that affects 1967 taxable income influences a tax payment at the end of 1967; anything that affects 1968 taxable income influences a tax payment at the end of 1968, etc.

(a) Assume Alternative II is selected. At what rate of return will the *total* investment in the purchase and installation of Machine X be recovered?

(b) Discuss the relevance of the rate of return computed in your answer to (a) in the decision between Alternatives I and II.

(c) Determine the year-by-year differences between Alternatives I and II in cash flow before income taxes.

(d) Use compound interest calculations to make an analysis of the cash flow series in your answer to (c) in a way that would provide a rational basis for choice between Alternatives I and II if the RST Company were not subject to income taxes.

(e) Analyze the effect of the choice between I and II on cash flow for income taxes. Assume an effective tax rate of 50% throughout the period of the study. Assume that if Machine X is installed, it will be depreciated for tax purposes by the years-digits method using a life of 8 years with zero salvage value. Assume that depreciation charges will start with the year 1968 and that a full-year's depreciation will be charged in 1968. Assume that if Machine X is sold at once, any loss sustained will be deductible from 1967 taxable income. Tabulate the differences between I and II in cash flow after income taxes.

(f) Use compound interest calculations to make an analysis of the final cash flow series in your answer to (e) in a way that provides a rational basis for choice between I and II.

(g) How would you recommend that your analysis in your answer to (f) be used by the management of the RST Company in choosing between Alternatives I and II?

18

The Influence on Economy Studies
of Sources of Investment Funds

The long-run profitability of the enterprise hinges on the solution of two problems of management of corporate capital: (1) sourcing (acquisition) of capital funds and (2) rationing (investment) of that capital. They should be quite separate. Investment proposals should compete for corporate funds on the basis of financial merit (the productivity of capital), independent of the source or cost of funds for that particular project. Investable funds of the corporation should be treated as a common pool, not compartmented puddles. Similarly, the problem of acquiring capital should be solved independent of its rationing and also on the basis of merit (the comparative costs and risks of alternative patterns of sourcing).—JOEL DEAN [1]

Engineering economy impinges on many other fields. We have seen some relationships between engineering economy and accounting and income taxation. In this chapter we shall examine some relationships between engineering economy and certain aspects of business finance and government finance. Some additional aspects of government finance are discussed in the next chapter.

We shall see how certain types of confused reasoning may be introduced into economy studies where calculations appropriate for judging long-run economy of proposed investments in physical assets are combined with calculations related to the financing of these assets. We shall also see how certain techniques of engineering economy, particularly cash flow analysis and rate of return calculations, can be used to help in comparing the merits of alternative financing plans.

Possible Sources of Funds for Financing of Fixed Assets. Plant and equipment may be financed by (1) ownership funds or by (2) borrowed

[1] Joel Dean, Sec. 2, Managerial Economics, in *Handbook of Industrial Engineering and Management*, W. G. Ireson and E. L. Grant, eds. (Englewood Cliffs, N.J.: Prentice-Hall, Inc., 2d ed., copyright 1970).

funds or by a combination of the two. In many cases another possible source of funds is (3) long-term leasing.

As the name implies, ownership funds are those furnished by the owners of an enterprise. In the case of an individual this is limited by his personal resources. A partnership may secure ownership funds from the existing partners, or it may possibly reorganize by taking another partner—a new owner. Similarly, a corporation may secure ownership funds in various ways from its existing stockholders, or it may acquire some more owners by selling stock to new stockholders. The ownership funds of governmental bodies are those supplied by current taxation and other current revenues.

Before we can discuss the relationship between borrowing and economy studies, some general background material is needed.

Borrowing. For funds to be borrowed, some security is usually required by lenders. This may be specific property that is put up as collateral. Thus, an individual may finance the purchase of a home by giving the lender a mortgage—a deed that conveys title to the lender (after appropriate legal action) in case the borrower fails to pay interest or principal on his note in accordance with his promise. Similarly, by means of somewhat more elaborate legal devices, a corporation may give a mortgage on specific physical property as security for a bond issue. Often, however, borrowing takes place without specific collateral, the security being the general credit of the borrower; this is the case with nearly all governmental loans.

Whatever the security, borrowed money must ultimately be repaid. It follows that if a proposed investment is to be financed by borrowing, two questions must be answered regarding it:

1. Is it economical in the long run as compared to other possible alternatives?
2. Do the conditions of repayment make it advisable in the short run?

Various Possible Plans for Repayment of Borrowed Money. Table 3–1 (page 26) described four different ways in which money borrowed for a period of several years or more might be repaid. These are representative of the ways of repaying personal loans, business loans (including corporate borrowings through bond issues), and government loans.

In Plan I, interest was paid each year.[2] No annual payments at all were made on the principal of the debt that was to be repaid in a lump sum at the end of a stipulated number of years. This is a common plan

---

[2] As brought out in Chapter 7, the almost universal practice in bond issues of private corporations is for interest to be payable semiannually. This is also a common practice in other types of long-term loans.

of repayment for corporate bond issues as well as for secured loans for business and personal purposes.

Where money is borrowed to be repaid in a lump sum, some plan is necessary for securing the lump sum to make the repayment. There are two possibilities here: (a) refunding, or (b) the accumulation of the necessary funds through the use of a sinking fund.

Refunding means that the money for repayment is secured through a new borrowing. This is common in corporate bond issues, particularly those of public utilities (including railroads) where the public regulation of rates generally makes it impracticable to accumulate sufficient funds to pay off bonds out of earnings. Although individual bonds carry a definite maturity date and there is an obligation to pay the bondholders on that date, it is merely a case of borrowing from Peter to pay Paul. When the refunding of a bond issue is contemplated, there are no short-run burdensome repayment obligations to influence decisions between engineering alternatives. From the viewpoint of the engineer at the time the money is borrowed, the debt may be thought of as perpetual. Whenever refunding is contemplated, the managerial problem is to maintain the company's assets and earning power so that the company's credit position will permit a new borrowing at the time refunding is necessary.

Plans II and III in Table 3–1 called for annual payments on the principal of the debt. In Plan II the debt repayment was uniform from year to year with a resulting steady decrease in the annual interest payment. In Plan III the debt repayment increased from year to year in a way that permitted the sum of the principal and interest payments to be constant.

Where a bond issue provides for *serial maturities*, repayment plans similar to Plans II and III are used. For example, a $500,000, 20-year bond issue might consist of 500 bonds, each of $1,000 denomination. Of these, 25 might mature at the end of the 1st year, 25 more at the end of the 2nd, and so on until the 20th year when the final 25 bonds would mature. Each separate bond with its definite maturity date would be comparable to Plan I. However, the bond issue as a whole would be comparable to Plan II. This type of uniform serial maturities is characteristic of bond issues by states, counties, cities, school districts, and the many special types of local improvement districts. In such public borrowing, the use of serial maturities often is required by law in order to prevent the diversion of sinking funds to other purposes than debt repayment.

If uniform annual payments of principal plus interest are desired in a bond issue, it is possible to schedule serial maturities so that these payments are roughly uniform, approximating the equivalent uniform annual cost of capital recovery. This is sometimes done in real estate bond issues and in bond issues by local governments. The Plan III type of uniform payment is also characteristic of real estate loans to individuals.

In Plan IV no current interest was paid during the life of the loan and the final lump-sum payment covered both principal and compound interest. The well-known and popular Series E United States Savings Bonds are of this type. However, this scheme of payment is seldom used by business.

The different plans of debt repayment may sometimes be combined. For instance, a bond issue might run "flat" without repayment for 5 years, after which time uniform serial maturities start. Or half the bonds might mature serially, the other half coming due in a lump sum at the end of 20 years, with refunding contemplated.

Serial Maturities vs. Sinking Funds. Where a bond issue is to be paid off in a lump sum and refunding is not contemplated, it is necessary to establish a sinking fund to provide the lump sum. This involves the use of current receipts to amortize the debt just as is necessary when serial maturities are used. A sinking fund to pay off a bond issue might involve uniform annual deposits such as were discussed in the chapters on compound interest. However, it is also possible for the sinking fund deposits to be variable, possibly depending on net earnings each year.

One difficulty with sinking funds is that if they are conservatively invested with a view to maximum safety, the interest rate is likely to be considerably less than that which is being paid on the outstanding debt. For instance, a corporation with 7% bonds outstanding might be able to invest with safety at only 4½%. For this reason the best investment for current revenues intended for ultimate debt repayment is to pay off some of that debt immediately. This means that a borrowing corporation or public body may best invest its sinking fund in its own outstanding bonds, provided they can be purchased without paying too high a premium above par. If a borrower purchases his own bonds at par, this amounts to an investment of his sinking fund at the coupon rate of the bond issue.

The adoption of a plan calling for serial maturities has the same effect as if a regular sinking fund investment were made each year in the borrower's bonds at par. The serial maturities insure that such bonds will be available, and thus avoid all possibility of loss of interest due to the difference between what the borrower pays and what he can get on a conservative sinking fund.

From the standpoint of keeping to a minimum the total disbursements on account of the bond issue, the serial maturity plan would thus seem to

have a definite advantage over the plan of establishing a sinking fund
to provide for lump-sum repayment. In cases where either plan might
be used, the choice between the two plans should depend somewhat on
the prospective relative difficulty of meeting serial repayments and of
maintaining a sinking fund. In the case of an industrial borrower anticipating wide fluctuations in annual earnings, a fixed annual repayment
obligation may be a severe burden in bad years, and a sinking fund plan
in which deposits (if possible in the form of purchases of outstanding
bonds) vary with earnings may be advantageous. On the other hand,
the tax revenues of local governments may be expected to be reasonably stable; here serial maturities on public bond issues prevent the possibility of pressure on public officials to appropriate existing sinking
funds to current needs. Thus, serial maturities are advantageous in
bond issues by cities, counties, states, and special improvement districts.

Many enterprises, if they are to finance at all, must do so on a serial
repayment basis in order to satisfy the lender's requirements that the
margin of security behind the loan be maintained or increased. This is
particularly true if the loan is secured by a single property (such as an
office building subject to depreciation). It is also likely to be true of
hazardous enterprises or relatively small enterprises; in such cases the
required repayment period is likely to be much shorter than the estimated life of the property being financed.

The Relationship Between Debt Repayment and Economy Studies.
Many economy studies relate to the proposed acquisition of fixed assets
that must be financed by borrowing. In such studies, in addition to considering the question "Will it pay in the long run?" it is also necessary
to consider the question "Can the required repayment obligation be
met?" If short-run repayment obligations for a proposed alternative are
such as to prevent ever reaching the "long run," it is impractical to select
that alternative even though it may show theoretical long-run economy.

However, the two questions of long-run economy and practicability
of debt repayment should not be confused. It is only in those rare cases
in which a proposed plant is to be financed entirely by borrowing, with
the debt repayment spread fairly uniformly over its entire estimated life,
that the debt charges may be correctly substituted for the annual cost of
capital recovery (depreciation plus interest) in a study of long-run economy. This situation occurs in connection with some public improvements made by cities and other local governmental units, but seldom
happens in private enterprise.

The mistake is sometimes made of including both debt repayment
and depreciation as "costs" in an economy study. It should be obvious

that the estimator who does this is badly confused in his reasoning, and that his calculations serve to answer neither the question of long-run economy nor the one of practicability of debt repayment.

A General Principle—Debt Charges Are Equal to the Annual Cost of Capital Recovery Where the Life of the Debt Is Equal to the Capital Recovery Period and the Interest Rate on the Debt Is Used as the Minimum Attractive Rate of Return. A city owns its electric distribution system, generating part of the electric energy that it distributes and purchasing the rest. It is proposed to increase the capacity of the generating station to eliminate the necessity of purchasing energy. An economy study is to be made to determine whether or not this will be economical.

The estimated cost of the new generating facilities is $2,000,000. If constructed, they will be financed entirely by long-term borrowing repayable from the revenues of the electric system. The proposed bonds will mature serially, with the entire issue to be paid off at the end of 20 years. Consultation with investment bankers indicates that such a $2,000,000 bond issue will need to have an interest rate of 5½%. Serial maturities are to be scheduled in a way so that the sum of interest and bond repayment will be as nearly uniform as possible throughout the 20-year period. This annual payment of interest plus principal will, of course, be approximately $2,000,000($A/P$,5½%,20) = $2,000,000(0.08368) = $167,400.

If the estimated life of the generating plant is 20 years, with zero terminal salvage value, and if 5½% is used as the minimum attractive rate of return, this annual outlay for debt service is exactly equal to the annual cost of capital recovery that should be used in the economy study. In an engineer's presentation to city officials of his analysis of the proposed investment, it may be more understandable if he shows this annual charge for debt service instead of an annual figure for capital recovery with a 5½% return (or an annual figure for depreciation plus 5½% interest). But it would be double counting to include *both* a figure for bond repayment with interest and a figure for depreciation plus interest. This would be charging the proposed generation of power with the investment costs of two generating stations during the life of one.

However, in this connection we should mention that in Chapter 11 we explained that the minimum attractive rate of return used in economy studies should ordinarily be greater than the bare cost of borrowed money. Further comments on this point, with particular reference to governmental projects, are made in Chapter 19.

Advantages and Hazards of Doing Business on Borrowed Money. Consider a business enterprise financed entirely by ownership funds and earning a 12% return after taxes.   Assume that this business expands by borrowing money at 6% interest and that the after-tax cost of this borrowed money is 3%.   If the new funds are as productive as the old ones, the owners will earn 9% (i.e., 12% − 3%) on the borrowed money without increasing their personal investments in the enterprise.

Using an ownership investment as a basis for borrowing is referred to as "trading on the equity."   In effect, the owners' equity in an enterprise provides a margin of security that makes it possible to secure a loan. It is a general principle that trading on the equity makes good business better and bad business worse.   The owners who succeed in earning more on the borrowed funds than the cost of the borrowed money will, of course, increase the rate of return on their own investments.   On the other hand, if such an enterprise does not continue to be prosperous, all of its earnings may have to go to pay interest and principal on the debt, and the owners will have no return at all; in the absence of sufficient earnings to meet the debt charges, foreclosure on the part of the lenders may result in the owners losing their entire investment.

The foregoing comments about financing by borrowing are also applicable—with some modifications—to financing by long-term leases of fixed assets.   The question of whether any particular business enterprise ought to finance in part by long-term loans and/or long-term leases cannot be analyzed without considering many aspects of business finance that are outside the scope of this book.   However, it should be evident that long-term obligations are less suitable to enterprises of the feast-or-famine type than to enterprises with stable earning power.   An enterprise financed entirely by ownership funds may weather a few bad years that could be fatal to an enterprise that has substantial fixed obligations.

When rate-of-return studies are made assuming financing by borrowing or by leasing, there is danger of an incorrect interpretation of computed rates of return.   However, a rate-of-return-type analysis of alternate possible financing plans is an extremely useful tool to aid decisions on methods of financing.   The foregoing ideas can be explained to best advantage with the help of numerical examples.   Examples 18–1, 18–2, and 18–3 are designed for this purpose.

EXAMPLE 18–1. RATE OF RETURN AFTER INCOME TAXES WITH PART OF THE FINANCING BY BORROWED MONEY

Facts of the Case.   In Examples 8–2 and 16–5 we considered a proposed $12,000 investment in rental machinery.   In Example 8–2 the prospective rate of return before income taxes was found to be 12.0%.   In Example 16–5 a 30% income tax rate was assumed and the prospective rate of return after income taxes was found to be 8.1% using straight-line depreciation and 8.6% using

TABLE 18–1

Calculations To Determine Cash Flow After Income Taxes, Example 8–2, Assuming Half of Initial Financing by a $6,000 8% Loan

Year	Cash Flow Before Debt Service and Taxes	Cash Flow for Debt Repayment	Cash Flow for Interest on Debt	Cash Flow After Debt Service	Depreciation	Taxable Income	Cash Flow for Taxes	Cash Flow After Taxes
	A	B	C	D	E	F	G	H
0	$\left\{\begin{array}{l}-\$12,000\\+6,000\end{array}\right.$			−$6,000				−$6,000
1	+3,700	−$750	−$480	+2,470	−$2,400	+$820	−$246	+2,224
2	+3,000	−750	−420	+1,830	−2,100	+480	−144	+1,686
3	+2,400	−750	−360	+1,290	−1,800	+240	−72	+1,218
4	+2,100	−750	−300	+1,050	−1,500	+300	−90	+960
5	+1,700	−750	−240	+710	−1,200	+260	−78	+632
6	+1,500	−750	−180	+570	−900	+420	−126	+444
7	+1,300	−750	−120	+430	−600	+580	−174	+256
8	+1,150	−750	−60	+340	−300	+790	−237	+103
8 *	+1,200			+1,200				+1,200
	+$12,050	−$6,000	−$2,160	+$3,890	−$10,800	+$3,890	−$1,167	+$2,723

* Salvage value.

years-digits depreciation. In computing cash flow for income taxes, equity financing was assumed.

Now we vary the conditions of the example by assuming that half of the initial financing of the $12,000 machine will come from the borrowing of $6,000. This loan is to be repaid over 8 years at $750 a year with interest each year at 8% of the unpaid balance.

Calculation of Rate of Return After Income Taxes. Table 18–1 shows calculations to find cash flow after income taxes assuming years-digits depreciation and the same 30% effective tax rate used in Example 16–5. A separate calculation, not shown in the table, gives +$33 as the present worth of this cash flow with interest at 12% and −$413 as the present worth with interest at 15%. Interpolation indicates a return of 12.2% after income taxes on the equity capital invested.

The student of engineering economy may note certain aspects of the difference between 100% equity financing and partial financing by borrowing by comparing Table 18–1 with Table 16–6 (in which 100% equity financing was assumed for the same project). Although, as pointed out in earlier chapters, column totals in such tables are not a reliable guide to decision making, certain aspects of the differences between the two methods of financing can be brought out to good advantage merely by comparing column totals.

The figures for years 1 to 8 in column A of Table 18–1 are the same as those in column A of Table 16–6. For year 0, however, Table 18–1 shows separate figures indicating the disbursement of $12,000 for the machine and the receipt of $6,000 from the lender.

The two segments of the annual payments to the lender are shown separately in columns B and C of Table 18–1 because the debt repayment of $750 a year does not affect taxable income, whereas the interest payment is a deduction from taxable income.

Column A of Table 16–6 showed that the total positive cash flow before taxes was $6,050; this was also the total taxable income (column C). The totals of columns D and F in Table 18–1 show this figure to be $3,890; cash flow before taxes and taxable income have been reduced by the total interest payment of $2,160 (shown as the total of column C of Table 18–1).

The depreciation deduction from taxable income in column E of Table 18–1 is unchanged from column B of Table 16–6; the depreciation charged on the books of account and on the tax return is not affected by the fact that part of the financing is by borrowed money.

Each year's taxable income in column F of Table 18–1 is less than the same year's taxable income in column C of Table 16–6 by the amount of the year's interest payment. With our assumed tax rate of 30%, each year's cash flow for taxes in column G of Table 18–1 is less than the corresponding figure in column D of Table 16–6 by 30% of the interest. Where with 100% equity financing, the total income taxes were $1,815, in Table 18–1 they are only $1,167; the difference is $648, 30% of the $2,160 total interest payment.

The total positive cash flow after taxes is $2,723 in Table 18–1 and $4,235 in Table 16–6; the borrowing has diminished this favorable cash flow by $1,512, 70% of the $2,160 interest. But the rate of return to equity capital is greater in Table 18–1 (12.2% as compared to 8.6% in Table 16–6) because only $6,000 of equity capital has been invested in Table 18–1 in contrast to the $12,000 invested in Table 16–6.

EXAMPLE 18–2. ANALYSIS OF BEFORE-TAX AND AFTER-TAX EFFECTS OF EQUIPMENT PURCHASE USING DEBT FINANCING

Facts of the Case. It is proposed to acquire certain equipment having a first cost of $20,000, an estimated life of 8 years, and an estimated zero terminal salvage value. (These estimates of life and salvage value will be used for income tax purposes as well as in the economy study.) It is estimated that this equipment will reduce disbursements for labor and related costs by $6,000 a year. This saving in annual disbursements will be partially offset by increased expenditures of $800 a year for maintenance and property taxes. The net reduction in estimated annual disbursements (disregarding capital costs and income taxes) is therefore $5,200. It is believed this saving will continue throughout the 8-year life.

Straight-line depreciation will be used for accounting and income tax purposes. An effective income tax rate of 50% is to be assumed throughout the 8-year period.

This equipment might be purchased from equity funds. An alternative proposal calls for buying the equipment on time. The initial payment will be $8,000, with the remaining $12,000 to be paid off over the 8-year period. At the end of each year, $1,500 will be paid on the principal of the debt plus 8% interest on the unpaid balance. Thus the payments will decline uniformly from $2,460 at the end of the first year to $1,620 at the end of the 8th year.

Rate of Return Assuming Purchase from Equity Funds. Interpolation indicates a rate of return before income taxes of approximately 19.9% (crf = $5,200 ÷ $20,000 = 0.260).

The investment will increase annual taxable income by $5,200 − $\dfrac{\$20,000}{8}$

    = $2,700.

Annual disbursements for income taxes will therefore be 0.50($2,700) = $1,350.

Annual cash flow after income taxes will be $5,200 − $1,350 = $3,850.

Interpolation indicates a rate of return after taxes of approximately 10.7% (crf = 0.1925).

Rate of Return Assuming Purchase on Time. To compute rate of return before income taxes, the cash flow series (0, −$20,000; 1 to 8, +$5,200) must be combined with the cash flow associated with the $12,000 debt. The resulting cash flow series is 0, −$8,000; 1, +$2,740; 2, +$2,860; and so on, increasing $120 a year to +$3,580 at year 8. A trial-and-error calculation with the aid of the table of gradient present worth factors is:

PW at 30% = −$8,000 + $2,740($P/A$,30%,8) + $120($P/G$,30%,8) = +$792
PW at 35% = −$8,000 + $2,740($P/A$,35%,8) + $120($P/G$,35%,8) = −$239

The approximate before-tax rate of return on equity capital is 33.8%.

To compute rate of return after income taxes, an analysis is needed along the lines of Table 18–1. Such an analysis will indicate cash flow at 0 date of −$8,000. The positive cash flow at date 1 will be $1,870; this will increase by $60 a year to $2,290 at date 8. (In each year from 1 to 8, there will be negative cash flow for debt repayment with interest. This will be partially offset because disbursements for income taxes will be reduced by 50% of the interest. For example, in year 1, the cash flow after income taxes is +$3,850 − $2,460 + 0.50($960) = $1,870.)

Trial-and-error calculations are:

PW at 15% = −$8,000 + $1,870($P/A$,15%,8) + $60($P/G$,15%,8) = +$1,140
PW at 20% = −$8,000 + $1,870($P/A$,20%,8) + $60($P/G$,20%,8) = −$232

The approximate after-tax rate of return on equity capital is 19.2%.

After-Tax Cost of Borrowed Money. It is of interest to compare the after-tax cash flow under complete equity financing with that under partial debt financing, as follows:

Year	After-Tax Cash Flow, Equity Financing	After-Tax Cash Flow, Purchase on Time	Difference in After-Tax Cash Flow
0	−$20,000	−$8,000	+$12,000
1	+3,850	+1,870	−1,980
2	+3,850	+1,930	−1,920
3	+3,850	+1,990	−1,860
4	+3,850	+2,050	−1,800
5	+3,850	+2,110	−1,740
6	+3,850	+2,170	−1,680
7	+3,850	+2,230	−1,620
8	+3,850	+2,290	−1,560

No trial-and-error present worth calculations are needed here to see that 4% is the interest rate that will make the present worth of the final column equal to zero. That is, the series of disbursements from years 1 to 8 would repay $1,500 of principal of a $12,000 debt each year with 4% interest on the unpaid balance, so that the debt would be completely repaid with 4% interest at the end of 8 years.

It should also be obvious that our final column of differences in cash flow is unrelated to the merits of the equipment that it is proposed to finance. The figures in the column depend only on the amount borrowed, the repayment schedule, the interest rate on the loan, and the effective income tax rate.

Our tabulation of difference in after-tax cash flow between equity financing and purchase on time was really unnecessary in this simple case. If we borrow money at 8% and if our effective income tax rate is 50%, the after-tax cost of our borrowed money obviously is 4%. However, we shall see in Example 18–3 that a similar tabulation will be a useful tool in the more complex circumstances that exist in many leasing agreements.

EXAMPLE 18–3. ANALYSIS OF BEFORE-TAX AND AFTER-TAX EFFECTS OF PROPOSED ACQUISITION OF EQUIPMENT BY LEASING

Facts of the Case. The equipment in Example 18–2 can also be acquired under an 8-year lease. The proposed lease contract calls for an initial deposit of $2,000, which will be returned at the end of the period of the lease. Rental charges will be $6,000 at the *beginning* of each of the first 3 years and $2,000 at the *beginning* of each of the remaining 5 years. Under this contract the lessee will pay all maintenance, insurance, and property taxes just as if he owned the equipment.

Rate of Return Before Income Taxes. Table 18–2 shows before-tax cash flow and calculation of present worths at 15% and 20%. Interpolation indicates a rate of return of approximately 17.8%.

Rate of Return After Income Taxes. Table 18–3 develops the year-by-year effect on taxable income of the proposal to lease the equipment. The taxable income each year will be increased by the $5,200 operating saving and decreased by the rental payment applicable to the particular year. It should be noted that because each year's rental is *prepaid,* the effect on taxable income applies to the year following the payment date; the influence on cash flow for income taxes of each item of cash flow for rental occurs one year after the rental payment. (Under our end-of-year convention, we assign cash flow for income taxes to the end of the tax year.) Of course the $2,000 negative cash flow for the deposit of zero date and the $2,000 positive cash flow for the refund at date 8 have no effect on taxable income. As the equipment is not owned, no depreciation is recognized in computing taxable income. (Depreciation will enter into the *lessor's* taxable income but not the lessee's.)

The present worth of the cash flow series in column F of Table 18–3 may be computed to be +$432 at 10% and −$392 at 12%. The approximate after-tax rate of return on equity funds is 11.0%.

Cost of Money Provided by the Lessor. The following tabulation shows the differences in cash flow before and after income taxes between financing by the proposed lease agreement and financing entirely from ownership funds.

Year	Before-Tax Difference in Cash Flow Between Equity Financing and Leasing	After-Tax Difference in Cash Flow Between Equity Financing and Leasing
0	+$12,000	+$12,000
1	−6,000	−4,250
2	−6,000	−4,250
3	−2,000	−250
4	−2,000	−2,250
5	−2,000	−2,250
6	−2,000	−2,250
7	−2,000	−2,250
8	+2,000	+1,750
Totals	−$8,000	−$4,000

The present worth of the before-tax series is −$855 at 20% and +$225 at 25%. In effect, the funds made available by the lessor will cost the owners approximately 23.9% before taxes. The present worth of the after-tax series is −$106 at 10% and +$481 at 12%. Considered after income taxes, the cost of money provided by the lessor is approximately 10.4%.

It will be noted that, although $20,000 worth of equipment is being leased, the effect of the leasing agreement is to make only $12,000 of cash available to the lessor. Because of the requirement of a $2,000 deposit and a prepayment of $6,000 for the first year's rent, an initial outlay of $8,000 of ownership funds is required under the leasing agreement.

TABLE 18–2

Before-Tax Analysis of a Proposal To Lease Certain Equipment

Year	Effect on Cash Flow of Use of Equipment	Cash Flow for Payments Related to Lease	Combined Cash Flow	Present Worth at 15%	Present Worth at 20%
0		−$8,000	−$8,000	−$8,000	−$8,000
1	+$5,200	−6,000	−800	−696	−666
2	+5,200	−6,000	−800	−605	−556
3	+5,200	−2,000	+3,200	+2,104	+1,852
4	+5,200	−2,000	+3,200	+1,830	+1,543
5	+5,200	−2,000	+3,200	+1,591	+1,286
6	+5,200	−2,000	+3,200	+1,383	+1,072
7	+5,200	−2,000	+3,200	+1,203	+893
8	+5,200	+2,000	+7,200	+2,354	+1,675
Totals	+$41,600	−$28,000	+$13,600	+$1,164	−$901

TABLE 18–3

After-Tax Analysis of a Proposal To Lease Certain Equipment

Year	Effect of Proposal on Cash Flow Before Income Taxes	Effect of Use of Equipment on Taxable Income	Effect of Rental Payment on Taxable Income	Combined Effect on Taxable Income $(B + C)$	Effect on Cash Flow for Income Taxes $(-0.5D)$	Effect on Cash Flow After Income Taxes $(A + E)$
	A	B	C	D	E	F
0	−$8,000					−$8,000
1	−800	+$5,200	−$6,000	−$800	+$400	−400
2	−800	+5,200	−6,000	−800	+400	−400
3	+3,200	+5,200	−6,000	−800	+400	+3,600
4	+3,200	+5,200	−2,000	+3,200	−1,600	+1,600
5	+3,200	+5,200	−2,000	+3,200	−1,600	+1,600
6	+3,200	+5,200	−2,000	+3,200	−1,600	+1,600
7	+3,200	+5,200	−2,000	+3,200	−1,600	+1,600
8	+7,200	+5,200	−2,000	+3,200	−1,600	+5,600
Totals	+$13,600	+$41,600	−$28,000	+$13,600	−$6,800	+$6,800

It will also be noted that Example 18–3 is like Example 18–2 in that the difference in cash flow between equity financing and outside financing is unrelated to the merits of the equipment that it is proposed to acquire. The before-tax and after-tax series of cash flow differences can be derived solely from the terms of the leasing agreement, the allowable depreciation if the equipment is to be owned, and the effective tax rate. However, unlike the case of debt financing in Example 18–2, the after-tax cost of money with a 50% tax rate is not exactly half of the before-tax cost. The favorable timing of the tax consequences of this particular leasing agreement is such that the after-tax cost of the money (10.4%) is considerably *less* than half the before-tax cost (23.9%).

Desirability of Separating Decision Making on Physical Plant from Decision Making on Methods of Financing. Throughout this book, the general principle has been stressed that separable decisions should be made separately. Some cases occur where a decision to acquire the use of certain fixed assets is inseparably linked with one particular plan for financing the assets. In such instances it is rational to apply a single analysis to the proposed acquisition and financing. But in the more common case where decisions among alternative fixed assets are clearly separable from decisions regarding policies on methods of financing, both types of decisions are likely to be made more intelligently if the analyses are separated.

Difficulties in Judging Merits of Proposed Plant Investments on the Basis of Prospective Rate of Return to Equity Capital Where It Is Assumed That a Portion of Financing Will Be by Borrowing or Leasing. In Examples 18–1, 18–2, and 18–3 we have computed rates of return to the portion of a proposed investment to be made from ownership funds, 12.2% to the $6,000 equity investment in Example 18–1, and 19.2% and 11.0% to the respective equity investments in Examples 18–2 and 18–3. Calculations such as these are often made in industry. Given the assumptions regarding income taxation and method of financing, these are unquestionably valid as exercises in the mathematics of compound interest.

Nevertheless, the authors recommend against using such computed rates of return on equity investments as guides to decisions about the acquisition of fixed assets. Their objections to such use are as follows:

1. Because such computed rates of return depend on the fraction of equity funds assumed, they are not appropriate to determine the relative merits of types of plant that are to be financed in different ways.
2. In the common case where the cost of outside money (secured by borrowing or leasing) is less than the return earned by the equipment itself (as computed under the assumption of equity financing), a computed rate of return on a fractional equity investment tends to give an unduly favorable impression of the productivity of the equipment.

The foregoing objections apply to studies made either before or after income taxes. A numerical example may help to clarify the reasoning underlying the objections. We shall use the after-tax analysis from Example 18–2.

It will be recalled that with complete equity financing, the after-tax return was 10.7%. With 60% of the cost of the equipment borrowed at an after-tax cost of 4%, the return on the remaining 40% of equity capital was 19.2%.

Now let us change the leverage exerted by the low after-tax cost of borrowed money by assuming that 80% ($16,000) can be borrowed at 8% (before taxes). A calculation similar to that made in Example 18–2 will show that the after-tax return on the 20% ($4,000) of equity capital is approximately 30.6%. If we assume 90% can be borrowed, the return on the remaining 10% of equity capital can be computed to be approximately 49.6%. If we assume that 100% can be borrowed, the absurdity of the rate of return analysis is evident because the computed rate of return is infinite. (That is, there is a money return even though no equity investment is attributed to the proposed equipment.)

Shall Economy Studies Assume a Stipulated Percentage of Debt Financing in the Analysis of *All* Investment Proposals? The quotation from Joel Dean at the start of this chapter stated that in the evaluation of investment proposals "investable funds of the corporation should be treated as a common pool, not compartmented puddles." Our discussion in which we assumed various percentages of debt for the data of Example 18–2 illustrated the rationale of Dean's colorful statement. If proposed alternatives are compared on the basis of prospective rate of return on equity investments, and if it is assumed that each alternative will be financed from its own "compartmented puddle," and if the different puddles involve different percentages of debt or different interest rates on the debt or different types of repayment schedules, the comparison is likely to give a badly distorted view of the actual merits of the different alternatives.

The distortion of relative merits can be avoided if it is assumed that *all* proposals are to be financed from a "common pool" that contains a stipulated percentage of debt financing at some stipulated average interest rate. A number of mathematical models for investment analysis have been developed that have made such an assumption. One of these models is discussed briefly in Appendix D.

Certainly it is better to assume constant percentages of debt and equity financing for all proposals than to distort comparisons by changing the assumed percentages from proposal to proposal. Nevertheless, in economy studies for competitive industry, it is questionable whether any advantage is gained by having all analyses based on the assumption of partial debt financing. And there are some practical disadvantages in departing from the practice of making analyses that assume 100% equity financing. A minor disadvantage is a somewhat greater difficulty in computing the required figures for cash flow, particularly in an after-tax analysis. A more serious disadvantage arises in the danger of misinterpretation of the results of the economy studies, particularly when these results are expressed in terms of rate of return to equity capital. Although, generally speaking, the relative attractiveness of the various investment proposals is not changed by assuming a stipulated percentage of debt financing, all the acceptable proposals seem better because the return is computed on equity rather than on the total investment. Moreover, the leverage exerted by the debt financing has a disproportionate influence on the proposals that have the higher prospective rates of return. Also the assumption of debt financing makes the computed rates of return much more sensitive to moderate changes in estimated cash flows.

For reasons that are explained in Chapter 20, there are special reasons for assuming stipulated percentages of debt and equity financing in calculations to introduce income taxes into economy studies for regulated public utility companies under the rules of regulation that have developed in the United States.

The Usefulness of Computed After-Tax Costs of Money. Throughout this book, we have stressed the point that interest rates are not always what they seem. In this connection we strongly recommend calculation of the after-tax cost of money to be borrowed or secured through leasing agreements, with such costs expressed as an interest rate in the manner illustrated at the ends of Examples 18–2 and 18–3. In these two examples it is evident that leasing at an after-tax cost of 10.4% is unattractive if we can borrow at an after-tax cost of 4.0%. In general such calculations are a great help in comparing the merits of alternate plans of financing. Such calculations employ techniques that are similar to the ones we use in engineering economy, since they start with estimates of differences in cash flow and apply compound interest mathematics to these differences to find unknown interest rates.

The calculation of the after-tax cost of borrowed money is not always as simple as in Example 18–2. Some sources of complications in finding the true cost of borrowed money were illustrated in Chapter 8. These included the difference between a cash price and a price on terms, initial disbursements incident to securing a loan, and required annual disbursements throughout the life of a loan. Although the illustrations in Chapter

8 dealt with the before-tax cost of borrowed money, the same complications arise in computing after-tax costs. Several of the problems at the end of this chapter illustrate after-tax calculations where these complications exist.

Some Aspects of the Analysis of Proposed Leasing Agreements. There is great variety in the types of leasing agreements made in industry. In many cases both the lessor and lessee recognize that the lease may continue only for a relatively short term; such leases are terminable by the lessee on short notice.

The more interesting problems for the student of engineering economy arise where the lease is used as a device for long-term financing. In such cases it often is true that the same assets would be acquired with leasing or outright ownership and that the assets would be continued in service for the same number of years whether leased or owned. From the viewpoint of the lessee, the long-term lease is a fixed obligation not unlike an obligation for debt interest and repayment.

Frequently the analysis of difference in cash flow before income taxes between leasing and ownership is more complicated than in Example 18–3. Certain disbursements necessary if an asset were owned (e.g., major maintenance overhauls, property taxes, insurance) may be made by the lessor—not by the lessee as stipulated in Example 18–3. There may be substantial prospective salvage values, realizable under ownership but not under leasing. These matters are illustrated in some of the problems at the end of this chapter.

An analysis of the difference in cash flow for income taxes requires a tabulation of deductions from taxable income under ownership and leasing. The after-tax analysis made at the end of Example 18–3 could also have been obtained by means of the following tabulation:

Year	Deduction for Depreciation	Deduction for Rental	Difference in Taxable Income	Difference in Cash Flow for Income Taxes
1	$ 2,500	$ 6,000	−$3,500	+$1,750
2	2,500	6,000	−3,500	+1,750
3	2,500	6,000	−3,500	+1,750
4	2,500	2,000	+500	−250
5	2,500	2,000	+500	−250
6	2,500	2,000	+500	−250
7	2,500	2,000	+500	−250
8	2,500	2,000	+500	−250
Totals	$20,000	$28,000	−$8,000	+$4,000

Long-term leases of machinery and equipment generally are like Example 18–3 in requiring the highest rental charges during the early years. As illustrated in the foregoing tabulation, such an arrangement leads to a favorable timing of the tax consequences of leasing. The large difference between the before-tax cost and after-tax cost of money secured by leasing in Example 18–3 was due to the fact that a tax credit in the near future is more valuable than one in the more distant future. The longer the expected life of the equipment to be leased, the more favorable to leasing may be the tax consequences of the difference in timing of tax deductions under leasing and ownership.

When Is an Agreement That Purports To Be a Lease Not Recognized as a Lease for Income Tax Purposes? In order to secure the advantage of larger tax deductions in the early years of life, some agreements that are—in effect—sales on time are drawn in a way that makes them appear to be leases. Such agreements are viewed critically by taxing authorities in the United States. A Treasury publication contained the following advice to taxpayers on this topic: [3]

If you decide to lease equipment, rather than purchase it, you should determine whether the agreement is actually a lease or is, in reality, a conditional sales contract.

If the agreement is a lease, you will be entitled to deduct rental payments for the use of such equipment in your trade or business.

If the agreement is a conditional sales contract and you have acquired, or will acquire, title to or equity in the equipment, the payments under the agreement, to the extent they do not represent interest or other charges, will be considered as payments for the purchase of the equipment. You may not deduct these payments as rentals, but must capitalize them and recover them through deductions for depreciation over the useful life of the equipment.

Look to the agreement, because whatever interest you obtain is acquired under the terms of the agreement. Whether the agreement, which in form is a lease, is in substance a conditional sales contract, depends upon the intent of the parties as shown by the agreement, read in the light of the facts and circumstances existing at the time the agreement was executed.

In determining the intent, no single test, or special combination of tests is absolutely determinative. In the absence of compelling and persuasive factors to the contrary, an agreement is considered a conditional sales contract rather than a lease if one or more of the following conditions are present:

1. Portions of the periodic payments are made specifically applicable to an equity to be acquired by you.
2. Title will be acquired upon payment of a stated amount of rentals that you are required to make under the contract.
3. The total amount which you are required to pay for a relatively short period of use constitutes an excessively large proportion of the total sum required to be paid to secure the transfer of the title.

[3] *Tax Guide for Small Business,* Internal Revenue Service Publication No. 334 (Washington, D. C.: Government Printing Office, 1969).

4. The agreed rental payments materially exceed the current fair rental value. This may be indicative that the payments include an element other than compensation for the use of the property.

5. The property may be acquired under a purchase option at a price that is nominal in relation to the value of the property at the time when you may exercise the option, as determined at the time of entering into the original agreement, or which is a relatively small amount when compared with the total payments you are required to make.

6. Some portion of the periodic payments is specifically designated as interest or is otherwise readily recognizable as the equivalent of interest.

7. Title will be acquired upon payment of an aggregate amount (the total of the rental payments plus the option price, if any) that approximates the price at which you could have purchased the equipment when you entered into the agreement, plus interest and carrying charges.

In the problems at the end of this chapter requiring the after-tax analysis of various leasing agreements, it will be assumed that the agreements described are legitimate leases and not conditional sales contracts.

A Classification of Sources of Equity Funds in Business Enterprise. Although the issues involved in choosing between equity financing, on the one hand, and long-term obligations involving borrowing or leasing, on the other hand, are beyond the scope of this book, it is helpful to classify sources of equity funds as follows:

1. New equity money (e.g., the sale of new stock by a corporation)
2. Profits retained in the business
3. Capital recovered through the depreciation charge

The relationship between depreciation charges and the financing of fixed assets is not always clear to persons who have not studied accounting. Example 18–4 presents this topic in a simplified form.

EXAMPLE 18–4. FINANCING FIXED ASSETS WITH CAPITAL RECOVERED THROUGH THE DEPRECIATION CHARGE [4]

Facts of the Case. The accounting expense of depreciation was discussed in Chapter 10. One of the reasons for recognizing depreciation in the accounts is to include it in the selling price of the product or service. A concern that includes an adequate amount for depreciation in its selling price year after year will at least succeed in recovering the invested capital that is being used up through the decrease in value of its plant and machinery. In such a concern a part (or all) of the excess of income currently received over expenses currently paid out (i.e., expenses not including depreciation) will not be profit but will be recovered capital.

[4] For a more complete version of this same example and a more detailed discussion of this subject, see E. L. Grant and P. T. Norton, Jr., *Depreciation* (rev. prtg., New York: The Ronald Press Co., 1955), Chap. 14.

Assume that on January 1 of some specified year, a manufacturing company has the following balance sheet:

Assets

Current Assets
Cash		$ 300,000	
Accounts Receivable		500,000	
Inventories		600,000	$1,400,000

Fixed Assets
Land		150,000	
Plant and Machinery	$2,000,000		
Less			
Allowance for Depreciation	800,000	1,200,000	1,350,000
			$2,750,000

Liabilities and Owners' Equity

Current Liabilities
Accounts Payable		$ 300,000	
Notes Payable		200,000	$ 500,000

Fixed Liabilities
Mortgage Bonds Outstanding			500,000

Owners' Equity
Capital Stock		1,500,000	
Surplus		250,000	1,750,000
			$2,750,000

Suppose there is no profit or loss for the year, the company just clearing its expenses including estimated depreciation. A condensed form of its profit and loss statement for the year might be as follows:

Sales		$1,200,000
Less		
Cost of Goods Sold (including $100,000 Depreciation Expense) ...		850,000
Gross Profit on Sales		$ 350,000
Less		
Selling, Administrative, and Financial Expense (including Bond Interest)		350,000
Net Profit for Year		—

The cost of goods sold includes $750,000 currently paid out and $100,000 of depreciation expense, prepaid in previous years, which is balanced by a $100,000 increase in allowance for depreciation. Thus total expenses currently paid out are $1,100,000 ($750,000 + $350,000); with revenues of $1,200,000 there remains $100,000 of additional assets in the business to compensate for the estimated decrease in value of plant and machinery.

For the capital invested in the business to be conserved, this $100,000 must be left in the enterprise in some form. Conceivably it might all be an addition to cash. Or it might increase other current assets through financing additional accounts receivable, or financing a larger investment in inventories. Or the cash might be applied to decrease liabilities, reducing accounts or notes payable or paying off some of the mortgage bonds. In certain circumstances one of these uses or some combination of them might be imperative. But it is generally recognized that the primary use for such recovered capital should be the financing of fixed assets. This includes both those assets needed to replace those retired and other fixed assets acquired to reduce operating costs or increase revenues. If $30,000 of the $100,000 should be devoted to the replacement of assets having an original cost of $20,000 that were retired during the year, $50,000 to the acquisition of other new plant and machinery, $15,000 to financing increased inventories, and $5,000 to an increase of cash, and if the receivables and payables should be the same at the year end as at the start of the year, the year-end balance sheet will be as follows:

Assets

Current Assets			
Cash		$ 305,000	
Accounts Receivable		500,000	
Inventories		615,000	$1,420,000
Fixed Assets			
Land		150,000	
Plant and Machinery	$2,060,000		
Less			
Allowance for Depreciation	880,000	1,180,000	1,330,000
			$2,750,000

Liabilities and Owners' Equity

Current Liabilities			
Accounts Payable		$ 300,000	
Notes Payable		200,000	$ 500,000
Fixed Liabilities			
Mortgage Bonds Outstanding			500,000
Owners' Equity			
Capital Stock		1,500,000	
Surplus		250,000	1,750,000
			$2,750,000

This corporation has made no profit during the year. If, as may well be the case, it is impossible to borrow more money or to sell more stock, the capital recovered through the depreciation charge is the only possible source of ownership funds to finance the purchase of plant and machinery. These funds are therefore of great importance in the continuation of the business.

As pointed out in Chapter 17, the factors that make replacements economical do not usually make them imperative. Machines and structures do not collapse like the "one hoss shay"; it is possible to continue them in service for a long time after it has become economical to replace them.

A business cannot continue indefinitely to operate profitably with an uneconomical plant; if its plant is worn out or obsolete, the concern is likely to have difficulty competing with rival concerns that have lower operating costs because their plants are new and modern. A manufacturing company that year after year diverts its recovered capital to uses other than the financing of fixed assets may ultimately find itself in this unfavorable competitive position. The difficulty of securing funds for other capital requirements (such as financing receivables and inventories or reducing debt) and the ease of putting off plant modernization may combine to bring about such diversion of funds.

Deferring replacements beyond the date when they are economical not only results in an uneconomical plant; it also has the hazard of causing depreciation rates that are much too low. Such low rates cause an overstatement of profits; the possible unfortunate consequences of such overstatement are obvious.

Some Ways in Which Proposed Investments May Be Vetoed Because of Considerations of Financing. If it is impossible to finance proposed physical assets in some way—either from equity funds, borrowing, or leasing—it is merely of academic interest that they would earn a good rate of return. And it is not only the proposals that *cannot* be financed that are eliminated due to considerations related to their financing. It often happens that one or more ways exist in which assets might be financed, but that for one reason or another these ways are unattractive from the viewpoint of the decision maker. This point is illustrated in Example 18–5. It also was illustrated in Examples 11–1 and 11–2.

EXAMPLE 18–5. EFFECT ON AN INVESTMENT DECISION OF A REQUIREMENT FOR RAPID DEBT REPAYMENT

Facts of the Case. A family living in a rented house was offered a chance to purchase this house at a favorable price. However, because the house was an old one, only 50% of the purchase price could be borrowed on a long-term first mortgage. The family had funds for only a 10% down payment. The present owner agreed to take a second mortgage for the remaining 40%. But he insisted that one-fifth of the principal of this second mortgage be repaid each year. No better source of money could be found for this 40% of the purchase price.

An analysis of the long-run economy of home ownership and renting was favorable to home ownership. However, because of the high repayment requirements on the second mortgage, the money outlays to finance home ownership would be much higher than rent. These outlays included principal and interest payments on both mortgages, maintenance, property taxes, and insurance. When these outlays were considered with relation to the prospective family income, it was evident that not enough money would be left for the other necessary family living expenses during the next 5 years. Therefore, it was advisable to continue to rent.

The Possible Influence of Project Financing on the Choice of Decision Criteria. There are exceptions to the rule that an investment proposal ought to be evaluated apart from its "compartmented puddle" of financing. An exception sometimes exists when a project must be financed partly or entirely by borrowing, when the borrowed funds must be repaid too rapidly in relation to the useful life of the project, and when there is too great a limitation on the financial resources of the prospective investor. One such case was illustrated in Example 18–5. Another is illustrated in Problems 18–6, 18–7, and 18–8. Although each of these cases refers to an actual occurrence, the types of circumstances described in the two cases are not uncommon.

In effect, where the financial resources of an individual or family or business enterprise are too small in relation to a proposed investment, the requirement for too rapid debt repayment may change the appropriate primary criterion for the investment decision. It may be desirable to give short run cash flow greater weight than long run economy. A similar relationship between repayment requirements and decision criteria may exist with reference to certain types of local governmental works for which 100% debt financing is common. Further comments regarding financial aspects of local governmental projects are made in Chapter 19.

Some Comments on Relationships of Prospective Inflation to Business Finance and to Engineering Economy. Certain aspects of price level change were discussed in Chapter 13. Our discussion there pointed out that in choosing among alternative investment proposals, it is desirable in principle to make analyses in units of constant purchasing power. If *all* prices are expected to rise or fall by the same percentage, a comparison of alternatives based on the assumption of a continuation of present prices will, in effect, be a comparison in monetary units of constant purchasing power. But to the extent that a differential price change can be forecast, such differential change is relevant and needs to be given weight in the choice among proposed investments.

Whenever a series of prospective cash flows is fixed in dollars (or in whatever other monetary units are relevant), any change in the purchasing power of the monetary unit causes a differential price change with respect to the particular set of cash flows. This category of future cash flows fixed in money amounts includes interest and principal payments on nearly all long term borrowings as well as rental payments on many long term leases. Some aspects of the analysis of proposals to incur long term debt under conditions of expected inflation or deflation are brought out in Problems 18–19 to 18–22.

Either inflation or deflation influences the results of a long term loan when results are expressed in terms of purchasing power of the money involved. Of course the effect of price level change is quite different when examined by lenders and by borrowers. The period of generally falling prices in the United States from the mid-1860's to the mid-1890's was unfavorable to borrowers, who found themselves paying interest and repaying principal in dollars that were more and more valuable when viewed in terms of purchasing power. (In the presidential campaign of 1896 in the United States, the losing candidate, William Jennings Bryan, appealed to farmers and other long term borrowers on the issue of "free silver." This was really a plea for cheap money.) In contrast, the period of continuously rising prices that started about 1940 has been unfavorable to lenders, who have received their payments of interest and principal in dollars of lower and lower purchasing power.

The reader may conclude that a forecast of inflation favors financing by long term borrowing. But this matter is not quite as simple as it might seem at first glance. An expectation of inflation by *lenders* naturally tends to increase the general level of interest rates to compensate for the expected decrease in the value of money. When very rapid inflation is expected, it may be impossible to borrow for long terms; even short term loans may carry extremely high interest rates. We do not attempt in this book to give an exposition of the complex subject of business finance; a particularly troublesome segment of this important subject deals with the relationship between business finance and past or prospective price level change.

Some Complications in the Financing of Fixed Assets Created by a Rise in Price Levels. Example 18–4 brought out the point that replacement assets tend to be financed in part through internally generated funds, with the amount of such funds related to the depreciation charge made in the accounts. When inflation occurs, the conventions of accounting and the rules of income taxation create special difficulties in the way of financing replacement assets.

As pointed out in Chapter 10, the depreciation charge in the accounts is a writing off of *cost*. In the years immediately following a price-level rise, the depreciation charges in the accounts apply in large measure to assets acquired before price levels had risen. Hence the funds that appear to have been made available through the depreciation charge tend to remain nearly constant whereas the funds needed to finance the replacement of any asset are greatly increased. At the same time, rising price levels create an increased demand for funds to finance inventories and accounts receivable. In such a period the funds needed for investment in fixed assets often cannot be secured without either a substantial diversion of profits to this purpose or the issuance of new securities or both. The rules of income taxation, which generally use cost as the basis for the depreciation deduction from taxable income, complicate the problem of plowing back "profits" into the business enterprise to finance replacement assets.

Summary. Some of the points brought out in this chapter may be restated for emphasis as follows:

In most instances where it is expected that the major part of the cost of fixed assets will be financed by borrowing or leasing, the prospective rate of return on a small increment of equity capital is not a sound guide to investment decisions.

In comparing different possible schemes of financing through borrowing or leasing, it is desirable to compute an after-tax cost of money for each scheme. A tabulation should be made of prospective differences in cash flow after taxes between equity financing and each other proposed scheme of financing. Appropriate compound interest calculations should then be made to find the unknown interest rate in each case.

Whenever it is proposed to acquire the ownership of property through the borrowing of money, consideration should always be given to the question of whether or not it is practicable to meet the repayment obligations.

The question of the practicability of debt repayment should not be confused with the question of long-run economy; repayment obligations and depreciation should not appear as "costs" in the same study.

The problem of meeting short-run repayment obligations does not arise in connection with a bond issue on which refunding is contemplated; it does arise whenever bonds mature serially.

Doing business on borrowed money has the tendency to make good business better and bad business worse.

Available funds for plant expansion and replacement are often limited; if so, the problem is likely to be to select, from a number of desirable uses for these funds, those which seem likely to yield the highest returns.

Where for some reason it is impossible or undesirable to secure funds by borrowing or to secure new ownership funds, the sources of financing for new fixed assets are limited to profits and to capital recovered through the depreciation charge. It often happens that such funds are practically limited to the latter source by company policies or by income tax considerations influencing the use of profits.

PROBLEMS

18–1. A machine tool builder will rent new machine tools for 3 years under the following rental contract:

The purchase price of a tool is designated as 100N. The lessee must deposit 10N at the start of the rental period; when the tool is returned to the lessor in good condition at the end of 3 years, this deposit is refunded to the lessee. Annual rental payments are 24N, payable at the start of each year. Lessee pays all operation and maintenance costs, including property taxes and insurance.

A user of machine tools has determined that he intends to use a certain machine tool for a 3-year period. He is undecided whether to purchase the machine and sell it in the secondhand market at the end of 3 years or to rent it. Designate purchase as Plan P and rental as Plan R. Show the year-by-year differences in cash flow before income taxes for these two plans. Assume that the machine can be sold for a net figure of 55N after 3 years of use. Find the interest rate that makes the two plans have equal present worths of net cash flow before income taxes. (This rate might be interpreted as a basis for decision making in an organization not subject to income taxes—such as a non-profit organization.) (*Ans.* $= (P - R)$ cash flow; 0, $-66N$; 1, $+24N$; 2, $+24N$; 3, $+45N$; interest rate, 17.2%.)

18–2. (a) In Problem 18–1, assume an effective tax rate of 50%. If Plan P is selected, years-digits depreciation will be used for tax purposes assuming a 3-year life and 55% salvage value. If Plan R is selected, assume that rental paid for a particular year will affect taxes paid at the year end. What is the after-tax cost of the money made available by the lease agreement? (*Ans.* = 9.1%.)

(b) What would be the after-tax cost of the money made available by the lease agreement if straight-line depreciation were to be used? (*Ans.* = 8.6%.)

18–3. (a) It is estimated that a proposed equipment investment of $30,000 to be financed from equity funds will cause an excess of receipts over disbursements of $9,000 a year for 5 years. The equipment will have zero salvage value at the end of 5 years. What is the prospective rate of return before income taxes? (*Ans.* = 15.2%.)

(b) Assume that this equipment can be financed by a $15,000 down payment from equity funds. The remainder will be paid off at $3,000 a year plus 8% interest on the unpaid balance. What is the prospective before-tax rate of return on the equity investment? (*Ans.* = 21.6%.)

(c) Assume that the equipment can be financed by a $5,000 down payment from equity funds. The remainder will be paid off at $5,000 a year plus 8% interest on the unpaid balance. What is the prospective before-tax rate of return on the equity investment? (*Ans.* = 42.0%.)

18–4. Find the after-tax rates of return on equity investment in parts (a), (b), and (c) of Problem 18–3, assuming a 50% effective tax rate and years-digits depreciation based on a 5-year life and zero salvage value. (*Ans.* = (a) 8.8%; (b) 14.0%; (c) 38.7%.)

18–5. A home may be purchased for cash for $20,000. Or it may be purchased by a $6,000 down payment and a $15,000 mortgage loan with interest at 6%. The loan is scheduled to be paid off in 15 years by payments of $1,000 at the end of each year plus interest on the balance that was unpaid at the start of the year. A "gift" of $500 must be made to a "financial consultant" to secure this loan. The homeowner will itemize his nonbusiness deductions and will, therefore, secure a tax deduction for interest paid. No tax deduction will be available for the higher purchase price on time or for the $500 "gift."

(a) Compute the true cost of this borrowed money before income taxes, analyzing the matter along the lines explained in Chapter 8. (*Ans.* = 7.9%.)

(b) Compute the after-tax cost of this borrowed money, assuming an effective tax rate of 25% throughout the 15 years. (*Ans.* = 6.2%.)

18–6. Mrs. Z is a widow, 62 years old, who must live on a modest life annuity supplemented by social security payments, plus the moneys received from investment of the $24,000 proceeds of an insurance policy. She has decided to invest the $24,000 in an apartment rental property. She is giving serious consideration to purchasing either apartment house S or apartment house T.

The asking price of S is $60,000. To finance this project, she will assume an existing $36,000 mortgage on the property and pay the remaining $24,000.

The mortgage must be paid off at $2,400 a year for 15 years with interest at 6% on the unpaid balance. With all apartments rented, the rental income is $7,500 a year. Her financial adviser tells her that it is conservative to assume that in the long run there will be an average occupancy of 90%. In addition to the payments of interest and principal on the debt, estimated annual disbursements are $900 for property taxes, $150 for insurance, and $750 for other operation and maintenance, a total of $1,800.

Since the asking price of T is $24,000, it can be purchased free of debt. With all apartments rented, the rental income is $3,000 a year. An average occupancy of 90% is to be assumed in the following analysis. Property taxes, insurance, and other annual disbursements are estimated to be a total of $720.

Either apartment will have to be depreciated for income tax purposes by the straight-line method, assuming a remaining life of 50 years with zero salvage value. In S, the investment is divisible into $10,000 for the land (nondepreciable) and $50,000 for the building. In T, the division is $4,000 for the land and $20,000 for the building. For the purpose of the following analysis, assume Mrs. Z's effective tax rate to be 20%.

(a) Assume that the criterion for decision making is after-tax rate of return on equity investment. What will this be for each apartment house, based on the assumed 90% occupancy. Base your analysis on the assumption of a 15-year period of ownership (approximately equal to Mrs. Z's life expectancy). Assume that the resale value 15 years hence of each apartment house will be equal to its present purchase price, on the grounds that population growth and price level increases will offset the obsolescence and deterioration of the properties. Neglect any possible taxes (e.g., capital gains taxes or estate taxes) on disposal of the properties at the end of 15 years. (*Ans.* = S, 8.3%; T, 6.9%.)

(b) Compute the cash flow after income taxes for each property for the first year and for the 5th year of ownership, assuming 90% of occupancy in these years. (*Ans.* = first year, S, +$32, T, +$1,664; 5th year, S, +$492.8, T, +$1,664.)

18-7. In order to judge the sensitivity of the conclusions in Problem 18-6 to the assumption of 90% occupancy, compute prospective rates of return on equity capital for S and T assuming average occupancy rates of 100% and 80%. Compute cash flow for the 5th year of ownership on the assumption of 60% of occupancy during this year.

18-8. Discuss the issues involved in Mrs. Z's choice of the major criterion for decision making between investments S and T in Problem 18-6. Under what circumstances would prospective positive cash flow in the next few years be a superior criterion to rate of return? What weight in the choice do you think should be given to the matter of differences in sensitivity to percentage of occupancy, examined in your solution of Problem 18-7?

18-9. Find the after-tax cost of the borrowed money in Problem 8-32 (page 132), assuming the corporation's effective tax rate to be 50%. Assume that the $800,000 difference between the amount received and the face amount of the bonds, and the $400,000 initial outlay in connection with the bond issue will both be prorated equally among the 20 years as a tax deduction. The interest payments themselves and the $150,000 annual disbursements in connection with the interest payments will both be deductible from taxable income in the years they are made.

18-10. A proposal is made for a city-owned public garage to be built in the business district of a certain city. The purchase price of the required land is $500,000 and the estimated first cost of the garage building is $1,000,000. The proponents of this garage project suggest that it be financed by $1,500,000 of general obligation bonds of the city. These bonds would mature at $75,000 a year for 20 years and would pay 5% interest per annum. The estimated life of the garage building is 50 years.

A committee from a local garage owners' association has submitted a report on this project. This report, given to the city council, seems to show that the expenses of the project will exceed its revenues. The tabulated annual expenses include the following items:

Building depreciation ($1,000,000 ÷ 50)	$20,000
Bond repayment	75,000
Bond interest	75,000
Sinking fund at 4% for building replacement	6,550

Comment on the relevance of these items in the economic evaluation of this project. Discuss also the question of the different types of decision criteria that it might be desirable to apply to this project and the relevance of these four items in applying each suggested criterion.

18–11. (a) It is estimated that a proposed equipment investment of $42,000 to be financed from equity funds will cause an excess of receipts over disbursements of $8,000 a year (before income taxes) for 14 years. The equipment will have zero salvage value at the end of the 14 years. What is the prospective rate of return before income taxes?

(b) Assume that this equipment can be financed by a $14,000 down payment from equity funds. The remainder will be paid off at $2,000 a year plus 8% interest on the unpaid balance. What is the prospective before-tax rate of return on the equity investment?

(c) Assume that the equipment can be financed by a $7,000 down payment from equity funds. The remainder will be paid off at $2,500 a year plus 8% interest on the unpaid balance. What is the prospective before-tax rate of return on the equity investment?

18–12. Find the after-tax rates of return on equity investment in parts (a), (b), and (c) of Problem 18–11, assuming a 40% effective tax rate and years-digits depreciation based on a 14-year life and zero salvage value.

18–13. The J & L Trucking Company is engaged in the business of contract hauling of sand, gravel, cement, and other bulk materials for construction companies and manufacturers. At present, the trucking company owns all its tractors and hopper, dump-bottom, trailers. Business is growing rapidly and the company needs to add several tractors and trailers to its fleet, but it does not have equity funds available to purchase all the needed equipment.

The B Leasing Company will supply trailers on a 5-year lease that is not subject to cancellation. The J & L Company must pay $3,760 on delivery of each trailer, $2,960 at the end of the first year, $2,220 at the end of the second, $1,540 at the end of the third, and $920 at the end of the fourth year. The J & L Company will be responsible for all repairs, maintenance, insurance, tires, property taxes, and other current expenses, just as if it owned the trailer. The trailer must be returned to the leasing company in good condition at the end of the 5 years.

Alternately, the trailers can be purchased for $10,500 each. If so, it is estimated that they will be kept for 5 years and that they can be sold for $3,000 each at the end of that period. If the trailers are to be purchased, the J & L

Company will borrow $7,000 per trailer at 10% interest from Mr. A, a local investor, giving him a chattel mortgage. Each loan will be repaid in 5 years. End-of-year payments will be $1,400 plus interest on the unpaid balance.

(a) Make a before-tax economic comparison of the two methods of financing by any method that seems to you to be appropriate. If no income taxes were involved, which method of financing would you recommend? Why?

(b) Make an after-tax economic comparison of the two methods of financing by any method that seems to you to be appropriate. Assume that the trucking company will have an effective tax rate of 50% throughout the 5-year period. If the trailers are owned outright, they will be depreciated for tax purposes by the years-digits method assuming a 5-year life and $3,000 salvage value. The rental payments will be deductible from taxable income computed one year later than the date of each payment. Considering income taxes, which method of financing would you recommend? Why?

(c) Discuss the sensitivity of the choice between these two financing methods to the estimated terminal salvage value of a trailer at the end of the 5-year period.

18–14. The four parts of this problem all deal with different aspects of an agreement under which Company B, the lessee, rents certain machine tools from Company A, the lessor. The particular agreement deals with a 5-year lease of tools that have a first cost of $100,000. Company B pays $25,000 rental at the start of the first year, $24,000 at the start of the second, $23,000 at the start of the third, $22,000 at the start of the fourth, and $21,000 at the start of the fifth year. (The annual figures were computed as if $100,000 had been borrowed to be repaid by 5 annual payments of $20,000 plus 5% interest on the unpaid principal; however, the rental is paid at the start of each year rather than at the end of each year as would be the case if a debt were repaid with interest.) There are many other equipment rental agreements between Companies A and B that are similar to the one cited. Under all of these agreements, Company B pays all insurance, repairs, and property taxes.

(a) On the assumption that the machine tools will be scrapped with a zero net salvage value at the end of the 5-year period, compute the rate of return before income taxes that Company A will earn on its investment.

(b) On the assumption that the machine tools will be removed from the premises of Company B at the end of the 5-year lease and immediately sold in the secondhand market, compute the rate of return before income taxes that Company A will earn on its investment. Assume a net realized value of $25,000. (This figure is based on an estimate that the tools can be sold for $30,000 and that necessary disbursements in connection with their sale will be $5,000.)

(c) For the assumptions of part (b), compute Company A's rate of return after income taxes. Assume an effective tax rate of 50%. Assume that tax payments are made at the end of the year in which taxable income is received. Company A uses years-digits depreciation accounting. Assume that an estimate of a 5-year life and 25% net salvage value will be acceptable to the taxing authorities.

(d) For nearly all of the equipment that it leases from Company A, Company B terminates its use of the equipment at the end of its 5-year rental period. However, for certain equipment, it is probable that Company B will require 20 years of service. It is therefore desired to compare an outright immediate purchase from equity funds for $100,000 with the plan of leasing for 5 years and then purchasing the equipment from Company A at the going secondhand market price. It is estimated that this purchase price 5 years hence will be $30,000. A comparison of estimated cash flow before income taxes for the two plans of financing the 20 years of service is as follows:

Year	Plan I—Lease Now; Purchase in 5 Years	Plan II— Purchase Now
0	−$25,000	−$100,000
1	−24,000	
2	−23,000	
3	−22,000	
4	−21,000	
5	−30,000	

It is desired to compare Plans I and II after income taxes. Assume that Company B will have an effective tax rate of 50% of taxable income for the next 20 years. It uses straight-line depreciation for tax purposes. Assume that if Plan I is adopted, the depreciation write-off from years 6 to 20 will be based on an estimate of a 15-year remaining life and zero salvage value. Assume that if Plan II is adopted, the depreciation write-off from years 1 to 20 will be based on an estimate of a 20-year life and zero salvage value. Compute an interest rate that makes Plans I and II equivalent after income taxes. Give your interpretation of your computed rate as a basis for a choice between the two plans by the management of Company B.

18–15. Company X is a lessor of capital assets. This company holds title to office buildings, hotels, warehouses, stores, machine tools, construction equipment, slot machines, and various other types of assets intended to produce income for their lessees. All of the assets are leased to the respective operators under an agreement that requires the lessee to pay all upkeep, property taxes, and insurance. Mr. A, one of the officials of Company X, is very articulate in pointing out why he believes it is to the advantage of the operators of capital assets to acquire the use of such assets by means of leasing rather than by outright ownership. He states that working capital usually is the most productive capital invested in a business enterprise and that leasing agreements (such as those made by Company X) have the effect of making more working capital available to the lessee. He uses the following example to compare a 10-year lease of a fixed asset with outright ownership of the same asset:

An asset having a first cost of $110,000, a life of 10 years, and zero salvage value may be purchased or leased. If leased, the lessor requires an initial deposit of $10,000 to be refunded at the end of the term of the lease. The rental charge will be $2,500 a month for the first 5 years and $500 a month over the final 5 years. If purchased, the asset will be depreciated for tax purposes by the years-digits method. If leased, the rental charge will be deductible from taxable income for the year in which it is made. For the sake of simplicity in Mr. A's example, an effective tax rate of 50% is used. He assumes that any funds made available by choosing the lease rather than outright purchase will serve to increase working capital. Because Mr. A contends that working capital generally earns at least 20% after income taxes, his example assumes that all funds made available by the choice of the lease agreement will earn a rate of 20%. His conclusion from the following table is that the decision to lease this $110,000 asset rather than to own it outright will yield the company leasing the asset an additional $149,300 after income taxes in 10 years. Therefore, he asserts, it is better to lease than to own.

Year	Difference in Cash Flow Before Income Taxes Between Leasing and Ownership	Difference in Cash Flow for Income Taxes	Difference in Cash Flow After Income Taxes	Cash Accumulation from Differences After Allowing for 20% Return Each Year
0	+$100,000		+$100,000	$100,000
1	−30,000	+$5,000	−25,000	1.2(100,000) − 25,000 = 95,000
2	−30,000	+6,000	−24,000	1.2(95,000) − 24,000 = 90,000
3	−30,000	+7,000	−23,000	1.2(90,000) − 23,000 = 85,000
4	−30,000	+8,000	−22,000	1.2(85,000) − 22,000 = 80,000
5	−30,000	+9,000	−21,000	1.2(80,000) − 21,000 = 75,000
6	−6,000	−2,000	−8,000	1.2(75,000) − 8,000 = 82,000
7	−6,000	−1,000	−7,000	1.2(82,000) − 7,000 = 91,400
8	−6,000	0	−6,000	1.2(91,400) − 6,000 = 103,680
9	−6,000	+1,000	−5,000	1.2(103,680) − 5,000 = 119,416
10	+4,000	+2,000	+6,000	1.2(119,416) + 6,000 = 149,300

(a) Has Mr. A made a correct analysis of the prospective differences in cash flow after income taxes? Given his figures for differences in cash flow, is his figure of a difference of $149,300 in compound amount at the end of 10 years consistent with his assumptions? Explain your answers. (It will be noted that he has used an end-of-year convention with respect to monthly rental payments to be made during a year and with respect to the payment of income taxes on each year's income. In your analysis of this problem, assume that this end-of-year convention is satisfactory.)

(b) The leasing agreement may be viewed as providing a source of investment capital for the lessee. Disregarding the effect of the leasing agreement on income taxes, express the cost of this capital as an interest rate.

(c) Considering the effect on income taxes of the difference between leasing and outright purchase, express the cost of this capital as an interest rate. Accept the assumptions of years-digits depreciation and an effective tax rate of 50% throughout the 10-year period.

(d) Discuss the relevance of Mr. A's analysis and of the two interest rates that you computed in your answers to (b) and (c) as a basis for a decision between leasing and outright ownership to be made by the prospective lessee. Assume that equity funds can be made available for the purchase of this $110,000 asset if it is decided that outright purchase is more advantageous than leasing. What information other than leasing terms, tax rate, and depreciation method, if any, would you need before deciding on your recommendation between leasing and ownership? How would this additional information influence your recommendation?

18–16. A manufacturer of machine tools offers the following plan for the rental of his product. The outright price of a tool is designated as 100C. Upon rental, a deposit of 10C is required, to be returned upon termination of the rental. For the first 4 years, the rental charge, payable at the *start* of each year, is 18C. For the next 3 years, the rental charge, payable at the start of each year, is 14C. Thereafter, the annual prepaid rental is 6C. The lessee may terminate the agreement at the end of the 4th year, at the end of the 7th year, or at the end of any year thereafter.

The GH Company uses many of these tools that have been purchased outright. These have typically been retired when 9 years old with a 10% salvage value. This company's effective tax rate is 50%. Consideration is being given to a change in policy to rental for a 9-year period rather than outright purchase from equity funds. If purchased, tools are depreciated for tax purposes by the years-digits method using the life and salvage value based on the company's experience. On the assumption that tools will be leased, compute the after-tax cost of the money made available by the leasing agreement.

18–17. A municipally owned water plant showed in its report the following figures for January 1, 1969:

A. Total investment in plant now in service $426,415
B. Estimated depreciation to date on plant now in service 151,200
C. Net present value (A − B) 275,215
D. Bonds outstanding against the plant 180,000

The accounts of the plant were kept on a "cash" basis, so that this figure for net present value was merely a statistical figure built up from past records of the cost of plant additions and the city engineer's estimates of the amount of depreciation chargeable each year. The cash receipts and disbursements from the water department fund for the year 1969 were as follows:

Receipts		Disbursements	
Sale of water to private customers	$68,300	Labor	$ 7,800
		Miscellaneous operating supplies	1,500
Sale of water to city departments including hydrant rental ..	5,600	New well	5,000
		Power for pumping	10,240
		Pump house and pump at new well ...	3,200
		Repairs to pumps	1,870
		Maintenance of distribution system ...	4,100
		Cost of new water mains	1,580
		Interest on bonds	9,000
		Repayment of bonds	10,000
		Transfers to other city departments (used for general city offices, police department, and street lighting)	19,610
	$73,900		$73,900

The city engineer's figure for depreciation chargeable in 1969 was $20,120.

A committee of citizens, criticizing the financial policy of the city in running the water department, point out that since no sinking fund has ever been maintained, there has been no financial provision made to take care of the depreciation of the plant. Discuss the topic of whether this criticism is sound, giving specific answers to the following questions:

(a) What outlays, if any, during 1969, do you think should be viewed as financial provision for depreciation? If the city engineer's figure for 1969 depreciation is accepted, do you think this financial provision has been adequate? Why or why not?

(b) It is known that the original construction of this plant was financed entirely by a bond issue. If operation and maintenance, debt service, and plant additions have been financed solely from the sale of water, and if the city engineer's over-all depreciation figure is accepted as reasonable, what can you say about the over-all financial provision for depreciation up to the end of 1969?

18–18. A writer on the subject of the determination of the costs of public hydroelectric power projects included the following items as costs: (1) interest on the first cost of the project; (2) depreciation by the straight-line method based on the estimated life of the project; (3) an annual deposit in an amortization sinking fund sufficient to amount to the first cost of the project at the end of 50 years (or at the end of the life of the project if that should be less than 50 years); (4) where money is borrowed, the annual disbursements for bond interest and bond repayment; (5) all actual annual disbursements for operation and maintenance of the project.

Do you believe that annual cost should properly be considered as the sum of these items? Explain your answer.

18–19. Consider Plan I of Table 3–1 (page 26). Assume that throughout the 10-year period covered by this table, the purchasing power of the dollar was gradually declining. Considering the purchasing power at zero date to be $1.00, it declined to $0.98 at date 1, $0.96 at date 2, and continued to decline at 2 cents per year to $0.80 at date 10. (Note that such purchasing power figures are not price indexes but would be calculated by dividing the selected price index at zero date by the corresponding price index at each subsequent date.) If all before-tax receipts by the lender should be expressed in dollars having the purchasing power of the dollars loaned at zero date, what was the lender's before-tax rate of return on his $10,000 investment? (*Ans.* = 3.7%.)

18–20. Assume that the lender in Problem 18–19 was subject to a 50% income tax on the interest payment that he received each year. If all his after-tax receipts should be expressed in dollars having the purchasing power of the dollars loaned at zero date, what was his after-tax rate of return on his $10,000 investment? (*Ans.* = 0.75%.)

18–21. Consider the loan described in Plan II of Table 3–1 (page 26). Assume the same decline in purchasing power of the dollar stipulated in Problem 18–19. If all before-tax receipts by the lender should be expressed in dollars with the purchasing power of the dollars loaned at zero date, what was the lender's before-tax rate of return on his $10,000 investment?

18–22. Assume that the lender in Problem 18–21 was subject to a 50% income tax on the interest payment that he received each year. If all his after-tax receipts should be expressed in dollars having the same purchasing power as the dollars loaned at zero date, what was his after-tax rate of return on his $10,000 investment?

19

Some Aspects of Economy Studies for Governmental Activities

> ... a government can determine its policies most effectively if it chooses rationally among alternative courses of action, with as full knowledge as possible of the implications of those alternatives. The requirement of choice is imposed on it by the fact that any government is limited by the scarcity of resources. It is fundamental to our culture that rational choice is better than irrational choice. The government must choose not only among various courses of government action, but also between the government's total program and the private sector of the economy. The task of choice is not rendered easier by the fact that a substantial part of the government's program is designed to affect the future performance of the private economy.—ARTHUR SMITHIES [1]

The words *benefits* and *costs* as applied to the economic evaluation of proposed public works projects were introduced in Chapter 9. It was pointed out that benefit-cost analysis generally requires calculations of present worths or equivalent uniform annual money amounts, and that such calculations need to be preceded by the choice of a minimum attractive rate of return. Certain pitfalls in the use of the *ratio* of benefits to costs (which we abbreviated to **B/C**) were noted both in Chapters 9 and 12.

Chapter 9 pointed out that conceptually the evaluation of proposed government projects often is more complex than the evaluation of projects in private enterprise. Moreover, it was stated that the application of concepts generally is more difficult when an analyst deals with government projects. The present chapter expands the foregoing statements.

The Case for Economy Studies in Public Works. Sometimes it is contended that because governments are not organized to make a profit,

[1] From page 26 of Chapter 2, "Conceptual Framework for the Program Budget," *Program Budgeting: Program Analysis and the Federal Budget,* David Novick, ed., Cambridge, Mass.: Harvard University Press, 1965. Reproduced here by courtesy of the RAND Corporation.

there is no need to make any economic analysis of proposed government projects. In the opinion of the authors of this book, such a contention is unsound. Two factors that make economy studies particularly desirable for proposed public works are the limitation of available resources and the diversity of citizen viewpoints regarding any given project.

Whether one looks at national governments, state and regional governments, or local governments, he is likely to find that the government has limited resources and that citizens are making many demands on these resources that it is not practicable to meet.

Let us contrast private business with public works. In private business there is a unified owner interest—the interest in the securing of profits—and ownership control of decisions on technical matters, at least in the case of large corporations, is comparatively remote. (That is, the individual stockholder is not likely to be greatly concerned about technical decisions under the jurisdiction of the chief engineer; even if concerned, he is not in a position to do much about it.) In public works there may be a wide variety of owner interests (assuming that the citizens of a community bear a relation to its government similar to the relation of the stockholders to their corporation) that often are in conflict with one another, individual owners frequently are much more articulate about decisions on technical matters, and their influence on such decisions can be fairly direct, particularly in local government.

Moreover, the customers of a private business are generally in the position of making a voluntary purchase of goods or services for which they make payment in the form of a price that is presumably less than their valuations of the benefits they receive. The beneficiaries of public works, on the other hand, generally receive their services without any specific voluntary purchase; payment that is made for these services in the form of taxes does not bear any necessary relation to benefits received by the individual taxpayer. This tends to intensify the diversity of owner interests that we have noted. Because the beneficiaries of public works do not pay for their benefits directly in the form of a price, there is a constant pressure on public officials to undertake projects and activities that are decidedly uneconomical from any common-sense viewpoint. This pressure for an unreasonably high standard of service is much less likely to exist from the customers of a private enterprise. On the other hand, because there are nearly always a number of taxpayers who do not receive benefits that are in excess of their payments for particular public works projects, there is frequently determined opposition by influential taxpaying groups to projects that are sound and economical.

It sometimes is stated that an economy study with reference to proposed public works makes it possible to examine alternatives from the viewpoint of the silent majority rather than from the viewpoints of various vocal minorities.

A Classification of Consequences to Whomsoever They May Accrue. The famous passage from the United States Flood Control Act of 1936, which we quoted at the start of Chapter 9, used the words "if the benefits to whomsoever they may accrue are in excess of the estimated costs . . ."

A reasonable interpretation of what Congress presumably had in mind in 1936 is that the favorable consequences deemed to be relevant ought to be greater than the unfavorable consequences deemed to be relevant. The classification of possible consequences that we shall adopt for purposes of our discussion in this chapter is as follows:

1. Favorable consequences to the general public apart from consequences to any governmental organization. We illustrated such consequences in Chapter 9 by savings in costs to highway users and by reductions in expected damages due to floods.

2. Unfavorable consequences to the general public apart from consequences to any governmental organization. We illustrated such consequences in Example 9–2 by damages to anadromous fisheries and by a loss of land for agricultural purposes.

3. Consequences to governmental organizations. Usually consequences of this type can be estimated as net disbursements by governments over a period of years. And usually, such disbursements must ultimately be financed by taxation. Thus, once removed, these may be viewed as unfavorable consequences to the taxpayers, i.e., to the general public.

In our examples in Chapters 9 and 12, we described the first two of these categories as *benefits* (which we summarized algebraically in Example 9–2 when we viewed category 2 as "disbenefits"). The consequences to governments we described as *costs*. But we noted in Chapter 9 that our classification there was entirely arbitrary and that some analysts classify certain adverse consequences to the general public as costs, whereas other analysts classify certain maintenance costs paid by government as disbenefits. We also noted that the excess of favorable over unfavorable consequences (i.e., $B - C$) was not changed by decisions on classification, whereas the ratio B/C sometimes was greatly influenced by arbitrary decisions on classification.

Estimating "Costs" for Purposes of Comparing Alternatives in Public Works. Within the foregoing classification of possible consequences, our third category is the simplest to identify conceptually and the easiest to evaluate practically. If it were necessary only to estimate consequences to governmental organizations, we could eliminate many of the troublesome and controversial aspects of making economy studies for public works. Nevertheless, certain controversial matters would remain.

One of these matters is the selection of the i^* to be used. This is a basic and critical question even though (as will be illustrated in Example 19–1) the alternatives involve no differences to the general public except those in connection with governmental disbursements.

Another matter is the consideration, if any, to be given to taxes foregone. Although this question does not arise as an issue in most governmental economy studies, it may be critical in certain types of studies.

The Controversial Question of the Treatment of Interest in Economy Studies for Public Works. Engineers do not agree on the point of view that should be taken toward the treatment of interest in judging the soundness of proposed public works expenditures. Some different viewpoints on this subject are as follows:

1. Costs should, in effect, be computed at zero interest rate. The advocates of this viewpoint generally limit its application to those public works that are financed out of current taxation rather than by borrowing.
2. Costs should be computed, using an interest rate equal to the rate paid on borrowings by the particular unit of government in question. If the proposed public works are to be financed by borrowing, the probable cost of the borrowed money should be used. Otherwise the average cost of money for long-term borrowings should be used.
3. Just as in private enterprise, the question of the interest rate to be used in an economy study is essentially the question of what is a minimum attractive rate of return under the circumstances. Although the cost of borrowed money is one appropriate element in determining the minimum attractive rate of return, it is not the sole element to be considered. In most instances the appropriate minimum attractive rate of return should be somewhat higher than the cost of borrowed money

Our discussions in Chapters 9 and 11 made it clear that the authors of this book favor the view stated under heading 3. Some further aspects of the case supporting this view are developed following Example 19–1.

EXAMPLE 19–1. THE EFFECT OF THE SELECTION OF THE MINIMUM ATTRACTIVE RATE OF RETURN ON A COMPARISON OF HIGHWAY BRIDGE TYPES

Facts of the Case. In a certain location near the Pacific Ocean, two alternative types of highway bridge are under consideration for the replacement of an existing timber trestle bridge on a state highway in a rural area. The first cost of a steel bridge will be $340,000; the first cost of a concrete arch bridge will be $390,000. Maintenance costs for the steel bridge consist chiefly of painting; the average annual figure is estimated to be $3,000. Maintenance costs on the concrete arch bridge are assumed to be negligible over the life of the bridge. Either bridge has an estimated life of 50 years. The two bridges have no differences in their prospective services to the highway users.

It is evident that in this instance the choice between the two types depends on the assumed interest rate or minimum attractive rate of return. A tabulation of annual costs with various interest rates is as follows:

Interest Rate	Annual Cost		Difference in Annual Cost	
	Steel	Concrete	Favoring Steel	Favoring Concrete
0%	$ 9,800	$ 7,800		$2,000
2%	13,820	12,410		1,410
4%	18,830	18,150		680
5%	21,630	21,360		270
6%	24,570	24,740	$ 170	
8%	30,790	31,880	1,090	
10%	37,290	39,340	2,050	
12%	43,940	46,960	3,020	

If i^* is below 5.6%, the concrete bridge is more economical for this location. If above 5.6%, the steel bridge is more economical.

The Need for Some Minimum Attractive Rate of Return in Economy Studies for Public Works. Examples 9–1 and 19–1 both dealt with economy studies for state highway projects. In general, such projects in the United States are financed entirely by current highway user taxes and involve no public borrowing. This is the field in which the advocates of 0% interest rate in public works projects have been most articulate. It is also a field in which the funds available in any year are limited by current tax collections, and in which the typical situation is that at any given time there are many desirable projects that cannot be constructed because of the limitation on current funds.

Example 19–1 represents a type of decision that usually is made on the level of engineering design rather than on the policy level of determining the order of priority of projects competing for funds. If each authorized project is to be designed to best advantage, it is essential that economy studies be made to compare the various alternative features in the design. If such studies were made at 0% interest, and if the conclusions of the studies were accepted in determining the design, many extra investments would be made that would yield relatively small returns (such as 1% or 2%). These extra investments in the projects actually undertaken would absorb funds that might otherwise have been used for additional highway projects. If the additional projects put off by a shortage of funds should be ones where the benefits to highway users represented a return of, say, 15%, on the highway investment, it is clearly not in the over-all interest of highway users to have invested funds earning a return of only 2%. In other words, where available funds are limited, the selection of an appropriate minimum attractive rate of return calls for consideration of the prospective returns obtainable from alternative investments. This is as sound a principle in public works as it is in private enterprise.

If the time should ever be reached when economy studies indicate that all the highway funds currently available cannot be used without undertaking a number of highway investments yielding very low returns (such as 2%), a fair conclusion would be that highway user taxes should be lowered. In such a case the alternative investments would be those that might be made by individual taxpayers if taxes should be reduced. Money has a time value to the taxpayers; this is a fact that should be recognized in the use of funds collected from taxpayers.

Opportunity Cost Versus Cost of Borrowed Money in Selecting i^* for Economy Studies for Public Works.[2] Chapter 9 emphasized the point that the question of what ought to be the minimum attractive rate of return, all things considered, is still present when decision making is based on comparisons of annual costs, comparisons of present worths, or on an analysis of benefits and costs. These methods all require the use of an interest rate for conversion of nonuniform money series to equivalent uniform annual figures or to present worths. The operational effect of using a particular interest rate in calculations of annual costs, present worths, or benefits and costs, is to adopt that interest rate as the minimum attractive rate of return. Moreover, the foregoing statement is true regardless of what the interest rate may be called; various names such as discount rate, vestcharge, or imputed interest rate sometimes are used.

Historically, government agencies in the United States that have made economy studies to evaluate proposed public works have inclined toward the selection of interest rates based on costs of borrowed money. But whenever i^* is chosen to reflect the costs of borrowing by a particular unit of government, the question arises whether the rate ought to represent an average interest cost on long-term debt already outstanding (sometimes called the *imbedded cost* of borrowed money) or the pro-

[2] For an expansion of the ideas presented here followed by a discussion that reflects a variety of opinions held by government engineers and economists, see "Interest and the Rate of Return on Investments" by E. L. Grant in *Highway Research Board Special Report 56, Economic Analysis in Highway Programming, Location and Design*, pp. 82–90. Special Report 56 contains the proceedings of a "workshop conference" held in September 1959 and is published by the Highway Research Board, Washington, D.C.

spective cost of new borrowings.[3] Under the rules stipulated in the early 1950's by the Bureau of the Budget for the economic evaluation of federal water projects in the United States, the interest rate was based on the average rate that was being paid on long-term bonds of the United States. Under these rules, rates in the range from 2½% to 3¼% were used for a number of years when outstanding long-term U. S. bonds were selling to yield 4½% to 5% and *no* new long-term federal borrowing was possible because of a legal limitation that placed an interest ceiling of 4¼% on debt maturing in more than 5 years. In the late 1960's, the stipulated interest rates for benefit–cost studies on proposed new federal water projects were raised, first to 4⅝% and later to 4⅞%.

Two analyses made in 1962 gave a good picture of the practices of highway agencies in the United States at that time with respect to the choice of interest rate in economy studies.[4] Under the chairmanship of Evan Gardner, a subcommittee of the Committee on Highway Engineering Economy of the Highway Research Board used a mailed questionnaire to survey the practices of the highway agencies of the 50 states plus the District of Columbia and Puerto Rico with respect to various aspects of their use of engineering economic analysis. Replies were received from 50 of the 52 agencies. One of the questions dealt with the interest rate used in economy studies by the various organizational units in each agency. The answers to this question showed that different organizational units in any one agency often used quite different interest rates. On the average, 45% of the organizational units that made economy studies used an interest rate of 0%, 22% used rates from 2% to 3¾%, and 33% used rates from 4% to 7%.

In the same year, Charles Dale, Research Engineer of the U. S. Bureau of Public Roads, analyzed 130 economy studies prepared by state highway departments or their consultants. Projects examined in these studies included (a) alternate highway locations, (b) alternate river crossing schemes, (c) grade–separation studies, and (d) surface-type determinations. Of those reports that stated the interest rate used in the analysis, 20% used 0%, 22% used rates from 0.1% to 3.9%, 45% used rates from 4% to 5.9%, and 13% used rates from 6% to 7%.

The diverse practices of federal government agencies in the United

[3] Over the years, there seems to have been a tendency always to select the *lower* of these two figures. When new public borrowings were at very low interest rates, these low rates were used even though outstanding debt had a considerably higher interest cost. When the cost of new borrowing rose above the cost of outstanding debt, the imbedded cost of debt was used.

[4] See the paper by David Glancy entitled "Utilization of Economic Analysis by State Highway Departments" included in *Highway Research Record Number 77, Engineering Economy 1963*, pp. 121–132. This is publication 1262 of the Highway Research Board, Washington, D.C. The results of the analysis by Charles Dale were reported in C. H. Oglesby's discussion of the Glancy paper.

States in 1968 are described and criticized in published testimony before a congressional committee.[5] As might have been expected, the hearings brought out considerable difference of opinion regarding the appropriate concept that should govern the selection of an interest rate for benefit–cost studies. However, Otto Eckstein and Arnold C. Harberger, the two distinguished economists who testified, favored the concept of opportunity cost; under 1968 conditions, this concept led them to suggest, respectively, rates of about 8% and about 12%.

In the opinion of the authors of this book, there are a number of reasons why the i^* used in economy studies for government projects usually ought to be greater than the bare cost of borrowed money. These reasons may be summarized as follows:

1. The opportunity cost within the particular government agency may be quite high in the sense that there are many good investment projects that the agency cannot finance because of the limited amount of funds available to it.[6] The acceptance of a proposed investment that has a low prospective rate of return will inevitably cause the rejection or postponement of some other proposed investment with a much higher rate of return.

2. The opportunity cost outside the government agency may be high in relation to the cost of borrowed money to the government. This may be because of desirable investment opportunities that are being foregone either by other government agencies or in the private sector of the economy.[7]

3. Whenever an analyst attempts the difficult task of placing money valuations on consequences to whomsoever they may accrue, there are

---

[5] *Economic Analysis of Public Investment Decisions: Interest Rate Policy and Discounting Analysis,* Hearings before the Subcommittee on Economy in Government of the Joint Economic Committee, Congress of the United States, Ninetieth Congress, Second Session. Washington, D.C.: U.S. Government Printing Office, 1968.

[6] A noteworthy illustration of this point was given in a Highway Research Board paper entitled "Sufficiency Rating by Investment Opportunity" by E. H. Gardner and J. B. Chiles. This paper described a computerized method for determining the order of priority over a period of years for proposed highway improvements over an entire state highway system. For the particular state in question, the computer derived a minimum attractive rate of return of 20%. This high rate, in effect, was a cutoff rate similar to the 15% in our Table 11–1, and reflected the opportunity cost of capital within the state highway system, considering the limitation of highway funds and the many productive projects competing for these limited funds.

[7] Consider, for instance, certain investment opportunities that are being foregone by the highway users who pay the taxes that finance highway improvements. For the many taxpayers who have to borrow money for one purpose or another, a gilt-edge risk-free investment is to borrow less money or to reduce the amount of an outstanding loan. For those taxpayers who borrow to finance homes, this risk-free investment will yield, say, 7% or thereabouts. For those numerous taxpayers (all of them highway users) who borrow to finance automobiles, such a risk-free investment might yield from 12% to 18%.

obvious risks that his estimates will turn out to be incorrect. If risk has not been allowed for in his estimates of benefits and costs, risk can be allowed for by increasing i^* just as decision makers often do in private enterprise.

4. When an economic analysis of proposed public works is made on the basis of relevant consequences to whomsoever they may accrue, it often is evident that such consequences are distributed quite unevenly among the population. Certain persons may be affected extremely favorably. Other persons will not be affected at all. Still other persons will be adversely affected. This uneven distribution of consequences of certain public works is a reason why such works should not be deemed to be justified unless their prospective rate of return is appreciably higher than the bare cost of money to the government.

5. Interest rates at which governmental units can borrow money do not always fully reflect the adverse consequences of borrowing. For example, increased federal borrowing may contribute to inflation. State and municipal borrowings in the United States have had a concealed subsidy because of the exemption of the interest on the debt from federal income taxes and from certain state income taxes. A large issue of general obligation bonds of a state may have the effect of increasing future interest rates to be paid by cities, school districts, and other civil subdivisions of the state.

It is easier to accept the general proposition that the value of i^* used in governmental economy studies ought to be greater than the bare cost of borrowed money, either imbedded or current, than to defend any single value for i^* against all possible challengers. One of the co-authors of this book has suggested a value of 7% for highway economy studies.[8] In the examples and problems in this book for which it has been necessary to stipulate i^* for economy studies for public works, we have generally used values in the range from 5% to 8%. However, higher and lower values of i^* have sometimes been introduced to illustrate sensitivity.

In a 1968 report of a United States Congressional subcommittee that had held extensive hearings on this matter, the general conclusions seem to be summarized in the titles of the final five chapters, as follows: [9]

III. The discounting procedure must be used if good public investment decisions are to be made.

IV. Current discounting practices in the Federal agencies are neither adequate nor consistent.

[8] In *Highway Research Board Special Report 56*, op. cit., p. 86.
[9] *Economic Analysis of Public Investment Decisions: Interest Rate Policy and Discounting Analysis*, A Report of the Subcommittee on Economy in Government of the Joint Economic Committee, Congress of the United States, together with Separate and Supplementary Views. Washington, D.C.: U.S. Government Printing Office, 1968.

V. The appropriate interest rate concept is the opportunity cost of displaced private spending.

VI. The current risk-free interest rate which should be used for evaluating public investments is at least 5%.

VII. All Federal agencies should establish consistent and appropriate discounting procedures utilizing an appropriate base interest rate computed and published on a continuing basis.

Taxes Foregone as a "Cost" in Certain Types of Economic Comparisons for Governments. Taxes are levied to meet the costs of government. When a governmental decision cuts off some sources of taxes without a corresponding reduction in the cost of conducting government, presumably one of the long-run consequences of the decision will be higher tax rates than would otherwise have been required. Such a consequence ought to be recognized in an economy study that examines all relevant consequences "to whomsoever they may accrue."

The foregoing statement bears on any economy study to evaluate a proposal that a government produce goods or services that it would normally buy from private industry. Part of the purchase price of the goods or services acquired from private industry ordinarily will be returned to government in the form of taxes. These particular taxes will be denied to government if the decision is made in favor of government production of the goods or services. In principle, the comparison of the two alternatives should be somewhat as follows:

I. Cost of purchase from private industry:
   Purchase price of goods or services . . . . . . A
   Less: Portion of purchase price returned as taxes . . B
   Net cost to government . . . . $A - B$
II. Cost of production by government C

The foregoing indicates that $(A - B)$ should be compared with C. However, the same difference between the alternatives will be obtained if the taxes foregone are viewed as one of the "costs" of production by government, and A is compared with $(C + B)$.

This problem of considering taxes foregone does not arise in the usual economy studies relative to public works alternatives, either for project formulation or project evaluation.

Some Aspects of Estimating Benefits of Public Works Expenditures. A number of the problems at the end of this chapter illustrate the monetary evaluation of benefits and disbenefits. The reader will observe that some types of data that are desirable for the economic planning of public works cannot be secured on the spur of the moment when the decision is made to consider the merits of some proposed expenditure. Systematic fact finding on a continuing basis is needed to permit valid economy studies to be made for many types of projects.

For example, one of the objectives in many highway investments is the improvement of highway safety. The influence of alternative proposals on highway accidents cannot be judged without a complete and accurate system of reporting highway accidents whenever they occur. Regular traffic counts carried out on a routine basis throughout a highway system are essential for this purpose as well as for other aspects of the economic planning of highways.

Another good example is the recognized need for systematic collection for information regarding flood damages. This information is difficult to secure with reasonable accuracy except immediately following a flood; memories of specific aspects of a flood become dimmed after a very few years.

Double-Counting in Economy Studies for Public Works. Without careful reasoning there is danger that the same benefits from a public works project may be measured in different ways and added together.

For example, the common approach to estimating the benefits of flood protection works lies in making estimates of the flood damages that they will eliminate. An alternative approach, possible only in those circumstances where an extreme flood has followed a long period without any floods, is to determine the reduction in property values that has taken place as a result of the flood. In this approach it is reasoned that property values before the flood were based on the assumption that no destructive flood would ever occur; property values shortly after the flood (assuming reconstruction has restored property to something like its preflood condition) discount the expected damages from future floods.

It should be clear that these two approaches are alternative ways of trying to measure the same thing. Because both are imperfect measures they will not agree; nevertheless, the reduction in property values represents a collective estimate of the present worth of the costs of future flood damages. However, in some studies of flood protection economy these two measures were added together to determine the prospective benefits of flood protection!

A Classification of Consequences of Highway Improvements. Some of the difficulties of placing money valuations on benefits and disbenefits to whomsoever they may accrue can be illustrated by a brief look at the field of highway economy.[10] One suggested classification of data for a highway economy study is as follows: [11]

I. *Expenditures of the highway agency*

    A. Capital outlay, including the costs of rights-of-way, final design, construction, and field engineering

    B. Annual expense for maintenance, operation, etc.

II. *Consequences to highway users*

    A. Market consequences (*i.e.*, those where the market provides a basis for money valuations). These include:

        (a) Motor vehicle operating costs

        (b) Time costs to commercial vehicles

        (c) Direct costs of motor vehicle accidents (including the overhead costs of insurance that can be demonstrably influenced by highway improvements)

    B. Extra-market consequences (*i.e.*, those where the market does not provide a basis for money valuations)

        1. Consequences where a basis may be found for a somewhat arbitrary assignment of money valuations. These include:

           (a) Deaths and permanently disabling injuries from highway accidents

           (b) Time saving to non-commercial vehicles

           (c) Increase or decrease in the value of parks, recreational facilities, and cultural and historical areas where the principal gain or loss is to highway users

        2. Consequences to which (at least at present) money values cannot be assigned

           (a) Sightseeing and driving for pleasure

III. *Consequences to other than highway users*

    A. Market consequences

        (a) Costs or cost reductions to public services (*i.e.*, public transit, police and fire departments, school bus operation, etc.)

        (b) Damages or savings from increased or decreased hazards created by the improvement (*e.g.*, flooding of property)

        (c) Increases in land values or in the value of crops or natural resources (but not both) where areas are made more readily accessible

        (d) Changes in the value of land and improvements or changes in business activity (but not both) where these changes can be clearly attributed to the highway improvements

---

[10] For an excellent and comprehensive discussion of this subject, see Robley Winfrey's *Economic Analysis for Highways* (Scranton, Pa.: International Textbook Co., 1969).

[11] This is quoted from a paper by C. H. Oglesby and E. L. Grant, "Economic Analysis—The Fundamental Approach to Decisions in Highway Planning and Design," *Highway Research Board Proceedings 37th Annual Meeting* (Washington, D.C.: Highway Research Board, 1958), pp. 45–57.

B. Extra-market consequences
  (a) Over-all impact of motor vehicle use, highway expenditures, and the character and location of the highways themselves on the economic and social well being
  (b) Increase or decrease in the value of parks, recreational facilities, and cultural and historical areas where the principal gain or loss is to other than highway users

Some of the troublesome aspects of placing money values on a number of the foregoing types of consequences will be discussed following Example 19–2.

EXAMPLE 19–2. AN ECONOMY STUDY COMPARING ALTERNATE HIGHWAY LOCATIONS

Facts and Estimates. A certain rural highway is to be relocated. Two locations are under consideration.

Location A involves a distance of 8.6 miles with a first cost for right-of-way, grading, and structures of $610,000. The surface will cost $280,000 and will require renewal after 15 years. Annual maintenance cost is estimated as $1,000 per mile.

Location B involves a distance of 7.1 miles. Because of the much heavier grading required to shorten the distance, the first cost of right-of-way, grading, and structures will be $920,000. The surface will cost $240,000 and will require renewal after 15 years. Annual maintenance cost is estimated as $2,000 per mile; this is higher than the estimate for location A because of deeper cuts and the consequent possibility of earth slides.

In comparing the economy of the two locations, an i^* of 7% is to be used. Considering the likelihood of obsolescence of location, the assumed life for either location is 30 years with zero terminal salvage value.

The present average daily traffic is 1,120 vehicles per day, made up of 960 passenger cars, 110 light trucks (under 2 tons), and 50 heavy trucks. It is estimated that this volume of traffic will remain fairly constant throughout the 30-year analysis period. Average figures for the increment costs of operation of these three types of vehicles are estimated to be 4.5 cents, 8.6 cents, and 28.3 cents, respectively; these figures will be the same at both locations. Therefore the difference of 1.5 miles in distance between Locations A and B involves an annual difference in cost of vehicle operation of:

Passenger cars—960(365)(1.5)($0.045) $23,650
Light trucks—110(365)(1.5)($0.086) 5,180
Heavy trucks—50(365)(1.5)($0.283) 7,750
Total annual difference $36,580

Because of the shorter distance there will be a time saving to all traffic. The average value of this saving is estimated as 5 cents per vehicle minute for all commercial traffic. It is estimated that 20% of the passenger cars are commercial. Passenger cars and light trucks are estimated to travel on this road at an average speed of 40 miles per hour, and will thus save 2.25 minutes each if Location B is selected. Heavy trucks are estimated to travel at an average speed of 30 miles per hour and will thus save 3 minutes each with

Location B. The total money value of the annual time saving by commercial vehicles is:

Passenger cars—960(0.20)(365)(2.25)($0.05)	$ 7,880
Light trucks—110(365)(2.25)($0.05)	4,520
Heavy trucks—50(365)(3.0) $0.05)	2,740
Total annual value	$15,140

It is estimated that costs influenced by grades, curvature, and stops will be approximately equal for the two locations and that there will be no difference in accident hazard.

Comparison of Alternatives. With an i^* of 7% and a 30-year life with zero terminal salvage values, annual highway costs at the two locations are:

Location A

CR—Right-of-way, grading, and structures = $610,000($A/P$,7%,30)	$ 49,160
CR—Surface = $280,000($A/P$,7%,15)	30,740
Maintenance cost = 8.6($1,000)	8,600
Total	$ 88,500

Location B

CR—Right-of-way, grading, and structures = $920,000($A/P$,7%,30)	$ 74,140
CR—Surface = $240,000($A/P$,7%,15)	26,350
Maintenance cost = 7.1($2,000)	14,200
Total	$114,690

A comparison of the relevant annual costs of the two locations considering the total highway costs and the differences in highway user costs is as follows:

	Location A	Location B
Highway costs	$ 88,500	$114,690
Extra user costs due to differences in vehicle operating costs	36,580	
Extra user costs due to difference in time	15,140	
Totals	$140,220	$114,690

If comparison by the incremental **B/C** ratio is desired, the annual benefits from the shorter location would be the savings in highway user costs of $36,580 + $15,140 = $51,720. This figure is to be compared with the extra highway costs of location B, namely, $114,690 − $88,500 = $26,190.

The incremental **B/C** ratio therefore is $51,720 ÷ $26,190 = 1.97.

One element omitted from the preceding analysis is the saving in time by non-commercial traffic. If this time saving is evaluated at a figure of, say, 1.5 cents per vehicle minute, the resulting annual figure is 960(0.80)(365)(2.25) ($0.015) = $9,460. By adding this to the benefits, the **B/C** ratio is increased from 1.97 to 2.34.

Comments on Example 19–2. In our examples that compared highway alternatives in earlier chapters (Examples 9–1 and 12–6), the prospective annual benefits due to savings in road user costs were given in total dollars without any indication as to how they were derived. Example 19–2 brings out the point that to find road user benefits it is necessary to estimate the amount and character of the motor vehicle traffic throughout the study period. To find relevant motor vehicle operating costs for alternative designs, it is necessary to estimate how much the incremental costs of operation will be affected by differences in design. To secure a monetary figure for the benefit of a prospective saving in time to road users, it is necessary to estimate average speeds for various classes of vehicles and to assign a value per unit of time saved by each class.

Certain common complications that were illustrated in the earlier highway examples were omitted from Example 19–2. Example 9–1 illustrated estimated growth of traffic during the initial years of the study period; Example 19–2 assumes constant traffic. Example 9–1 illustrated the use of estimated residual values at the end of the study period whereas Example 19–2 assumes zero terminal salvage values. Both Examples 9–1 and 12–6 illustrated the common problems arising in the analysis of more than two alternatives.

Consider the 4.5 cents per hour used as the increment cost of operation for passenger cars. Presumably this is an estimated average figure that is deemed to apply to the mixture of many makes and models of cars that will use this highway. Presumably, also, this average cost of vehicle operation has been built up from an analysis of such components as fuel, lubricants, tires, repairs and maintenance, and depreciation. And presumably it is deemed to be applicable to the particular conditions of speed, surface, grade, curvature, and other conditions of operation applicable to the particular highway.[12]

Obviously a fair amount of fact finding by someone is required to find an appropriate unit value to be placed on prospective time saving by commercial vehicles. The assignment of an average value of 5 cents per vehicle mile in Example 19–2 implies that such fact finding has taken place.[13]

[12] Tables and diagrams for highway users costs based on 1959 prices and available data were given in the so-called highway "Red Book"—*Informational Report by Committee on Planning and Design Policies on Road User Benefit Analyses for Highway Improvements* (Washington, D.C.: American Association of State Highway Officials, 1960). Later and more comprehensive tables are given in writings by Winfrey and Claffey. See *Economic Analysis for Highways, op. cit.* See also Paul Claffey, *Running Cost of Motor Vehicles as Affected by Highway Design—Interim Report,* National Cooperative Highway Research Program Report 13 (Washington, D.C.: Highway Research Board, 1965).

[13] See W. G. Adkins, A. W. Ward, and W. F. McFarland, *Values of Time Savings of Commercial Vehicles,* National Cooperative Highway Research Program Report 33 (Washington, D.C.: Highway Research Board, 1967). This report concluded that at 1962 prices in the United States, the average value of a saving of time to a commercial vehicle was approximately 8 cents per vehicle minute, with variations above or below this figure depending on the region of the United States. See also G. A. Fleischer, "Effect of Highway Improvement on Travel Time of Commercial Vehicles: A Twenty-five Year Case Study," *Highway Research Record No. 12* (Washington, D.C.: Highway Research Board, 1963), pp. 19–47. The Fleischer research

Although prospective time to be saved by pleasure traffic is an extra-market consequence of a proposed highway improvement, analysts often wish to place a money valuation on such a time saving. Usually the unit figure per vehicle minute, such as the 1.5 cents in Example 19–2, is chosen quite arbitrarily. However, some researchers have studied the division of traffic between free roads and competing toll roads to obtain a figure for the value that pleasure motorists seem to be placing on their time.[14] Because many factors other than time savings can enter into motorists' choices in such cases, research studies of this type tend to be somewhat inconclusive.

If monetary values are assigned to extra-market benefits, it always is desirable to follow the policy illustrated in Example 19–2 of stating the relationship between benefits and costs both without and with such benefits included. When **B − C** or **B/C** is stated only *with* the extra-market benefits included, decision makers often are unaware of the extent to which the conclusions of the economic analysis depend on values that were somewhat arbitrarily assigned to the extra-market benefits.

Where no monetary valuations are assigned to certain extra-market consequences (such as time savings to pleasure traffic), such consequences should be considered as part of the irreducible data of the economy study.

Irreducibles in Economy Studies for Public Works. Although measurements of benefits of public works in money terms make it possible to take many decisions out of the "hunch" class, such measurements have obvious limitations. These limitations lie not only in the difficulties of measurement, but also in the much greater importance of irreducibles in public works than in private enterprise.

In many respects the irreducibles in public works projects create problems of judgment similar to those that arise in personal economy studies. The best that an individual can do in dealing with his personal problems of economy may be to note the satisfactions that will come from particular expenditures, and to consider them in the light of their long-run costs and in the light of his capacity to pay.

A similar analysis may be applied to such a public works project as one for park improvement. Even though the services provided by

---

indicated that a substantial time lag may exist before successive small increments of time savings actually have any commercial value.

[14] For instance, see P. J. Claffey, "Characteristics of Passenger Car Travel on Toll Roads and Comparable Free Roads," *Studies in Highway Engineering Economy, Highway Research Board Bulletin 306* (Washington, D.C.: Highway Research Board, 1961), pp. 1–22.

the park are not expressible in money terms, it is pertinent to estimate how many people will use the proposed facilities, and in what ways. It is also pertinent to estimate the long-run cost of the park improvement, considering not only the immediate investment (translated into annual cost in the conventional manner) but also the necessary annual expenditures for upkeep. The annual cost of the service of the proposed park improvement may even be expressed as so much money per unit of use in order to permit its comparison with other similar improvement proposals. Finally, any such proposed expenditure must always be considered in relation to the capacity of the community to pay for it, particularly in the light of other possible uses for available public funds.

Use of a Money-Based Index Where Major Consequences Are Not Reducible to Money Amounts. Assume that the expected favorable consequences from proposed governmental expenditures that are competing for limited funds can be stated in some units that are deemed appropriate in relation to the objectives of the expenditures. Assume also that there is no satisfactory way to convert these units into money units. Therefore, an analysis cannot be made to determine whether benefits exceed costs.

In such cases, it still is possible to secure a money-based index that is helpful in comparing alternatives that are intended to reach the same general type of objective. Such an index might be computed as follows:

$$\text{Cost Effectiveness Index} = \frac{\text{Units that somehow measure net favorable consequences}}{\text{Costs to government}}$$

If the outlays by government are for public works that will be used over a period of years, it is desirable in principle that the denominator of the index fraction be an equivalent uniform annual cost that includes operation and maintenance costs and uses an appropriate value of i^* in finding the capital costs. But in cases where the annual costs for all the alternatives that are being compared will be approximately the same percentage of first cost, it is good enough for practical purposes to use first cost as the denominator.

Using a Cost Effectiveness Index to Establish Priorities on Rural Road Construction in a "Developing" Country. Problems 19–11 and 19–12 illustrate two such indexes of cost effectiveness as used in Mexico and as described in a research paper by Henry M. Steiner.[15]

---

[15] These problems are adapted from H. M. Steiner's *Criteria for Planning Rural Roads in a Developing Country: the Case of Mexico, Report EEP-17* (Stanford, Calif.: Program in Engineering-Economic Planning, Stanford University, 1965). At the time of the Steiner study, Mexico had 0.024 miles of rural road per square mile of area whereas the United States had 0.868 miles of rural road per square mile. The United States therefore had approximately 37 times as dense a rural road net-

One index applied to proposed "social roads" and the other applied to proposed "economic penetration roads."

Social roads are those that will reach isolated population groups where there are no natural resources that are likely to make possible substantial new production as a consequence of better transportation. Steiner comments about such roads in part as follows:

A social road undoubtedly will bring about a decisive change in the way of life of the inhabitants of the affected region. It will facilitate the establishment of schools, both for the children and for adults (over one million Mexicans speak no other language than their own tribal dialect; thus some Mexicans need interpreters to speak to other Mexicans). Sanitary and welfare services will be established. There will be an opportunity to engage in commerce with the rest of the country, that is, a market economy will replace barter.

The priority criterion for proposed social roads is the ratio of investment cost to number of inhabitants served. In effect, this is an inverse index of cost effectiveness; the lower the value of the index, the higher the priority. The denominator of this index, inhabitants served, is a rough measure of the expected favorable consequences. The numerator, the first cost of the project to the government, is money-based.

Economic penetration roads also serve isolated population groups but in areas where it is believed that natural resources exist to make possible a considerable increase in economic activity, particularly in agriculture. In these areas, economic development has been held back because of the absence of satisfactory roads. However, it would not be possible to show an excess of benefits over costs for proposed roads classified as economic penetration roads.

The numerator of an index used to compare proposed economic penetration roads is the estimated gross value of the agricultural output from the area served in the fifth year of service of the road. The denominator is the estimated first cost of the project to the government. This ratio is a direct index of cost effectiveness, so that projects with higher ratios have higher priorities.

A Limitation on the Use of Economic Measures to Guide Governmental Decisions. At the time of the Steiner research, proposals for improvement in the existing highway network in Mexico were analyzed by conventional benefit-cost comparisons. These were carried out along the lines of the better studies of this type made by highway agencies in the

---

work as Mexico in spite of having almost the same population density, 50.6 persons/ sq. mile in U.S. as compared to 46.2 in Mexico. Thus, where the rural road problem in the United States was how best to use limited resources in the *improvement* of existing roads, the comparable Mexican problem was how best to use limited resources to construct *new* rural roads.

United States; the chief difference was that in Mexico a minimum attractive rate of return of 12% was used. Such benefit-cost studies could give decision makers guidance about the best use of the limited funds available to improve existing highways.

Similarly, the inverse cost effectiveness index chosen for social roads could be used to compare projects competing for the limited funds available to build such roads. And the direct cost effectiveness index adopted could be used to compare competing proposals for economic penetration roads.

Nevertheless, it is evident that none of these three economic measures could provide a basis for dividing the total highway funds among the three general categories of social roads, economic penetration roads, and improvements to the existing highway network. This division had to be made on the basis of other criteria, some of which would be hard to quantify.

We have mentioned earlier the importance of irreducibles in many government decisions and the similarity of a number of resource allocation decisions in government to resource allocation decisions in a family. The decision in Mexico to allocate certain highway funds to social roads and economic penetration roads is similar to many other decisions by governments and by families that are not made primarily on economic grounds. But once such over-all decisions on resource allocation are made, it is a desirable objective to make the best possible use of the resources to be devoted to each major purpose. The use of some measure of cost effectiveness to compare competing proposals for the use of the limited resources allotted to each major purpose can help in achieving this desirable objective.

Some Economic Aspects of Standards for Low-Volume Rural Roads in the United States. Several of the problems at the end of this chapter make use of data from a research study made by C. H. Oglesby and M. J. Altenhofen as part of the National Cooperative Highway Research Program (NCHRP).[16] This research program is sponsored by the American Association of State Highway Offiicals (AASHO) in cooperation with the U. S. Bureau of Public Roads and is administered by the Highway Research Board. (All NCHRP reports carry a standard disclaimer that the opinions and conclusions expressed or implied are those of the research agencies and are not necessarily those of any of the sponsoring agencies.)

---

[16] The report on the Oglesby-Altenhofen research is entitled *Economics of Design Standards for Low-Volume Rural Roads* and was issued in 1969 by the Highway Research Board, Washington, D.C., as *National Cooperative Highway Research Program Report 63*.

The total rural road mileage in the United States at the time of the study was 3.1 million miles. For various reasons, some of them related to AASHO standards, low-volume roads for purposes of this study were defined as those carrying 400 or fewer vehicles per day. With this definition, the study applied to about three-fourths of the rural road mileage of the United States. (In 1962, the 2.3 million miles of rural roads under the control of county, township, or other local road agencies had an average traffic of 85 vehicles per day. This contrasted with an average of 2,800 vehicles per day on the rural portion of the Interstate and Federal-aid primary system, and with an average of 500 vehicles per day on the Federal-aid secondary system.)

A general theme that appeared in a number of different parts of this research study was that many of the standards of design that were being applied to low-volume rural roads were higher than desirable. The authors commented regarding this point in part as follows:

1. Most of those who set the standards are from the state highway departments and the Bureau of Public Roads. Their primary concern usually is with the design and operation of high volume roads where wide lanes and shoulders have become accepted almost without question. Little recognition has been given to the fact that the situation is very different on low-volume facilities. For example, at peak hours on a road carrying 400 vehicles per day, there will be, on the average, only one or two vehicles in a mile of road at one time. At peak hours on roads where the traffic totals only 50 vehicles per day, a mile of road will be completely free of vehicles three-fourths of the time. Thus, there is reason to suspect that the standards may have grown out of impressions gained under entirely different conditions of vehicle operation and conflict. . . .

2. There is a widespread impression that narrow roads or those without shoulders are extremely dangerous. No factual support for this notion could be found in the literature, but it pervades the thinking of highway engineers. In actuality, it may sometimes be that because a situation seems dangerous, drivers are more alert and accidents do not happen. . . .

3. Engineers tend to have a "quality bias" which often leads to overdesign. This is understandable because the things that civil engineers design and build remain in use for a long time. In particular, state and federal highway engineers are haunted by underdesigns based on low estimates of future traffic. It is, therefore, natural to "build in" another factor of safety. However, this experience may not be transferable to the low-volume rural roads where the increase in traffic has been, and probably will continue to be, less spectacular.

4. There is no "countervailing force" tending to hold the standards down. It was mentioned that, at the county engineer level, the political and financial facts of life are brought home through the elected officials and the public. This force did not seem to exist in the setting where the AASHO standards were developed. Rather, the standards represented a consensus among engineers at the state and federal level whose function it was to see that local agencies make proper use of state and federal funds. These men were not under day-by-day pressures to stretch the dollars over a large mileage of poor roads.

One of the authors' general recommendations was as follows:

. . . it is recommended . . . that highway engineers and administrators alike recognize that:

a. Low-volume roads and major highways serve different functions and that the demands on them in serving these functions are not the same. To require that low-volume rural roads fit the needs associated with major highways is to overdesign them and make them far more costly than need be.

b. Accidents on low-volume rural roads are rare events so that, even if all accidents could be eliminated, the economic gain is extremely small. Furthermore, since accident records show that higher standards do not seem to reduce non-intersection accidents, to adopt high standards with this aim in view is pointless.

c. That, since high standards are not economical and do not reduce accidents, adopting them is taking up scarce resources that might be used to better advantage elsewhere.

The Oglesby-Altenhofen study illustrates an important point in the public works field, namely, that many decisions that are of an economic character are, in effect, made by default through the establishment of standards. Certain general standards that may lead to economic decisions in one type of setting may lead to extremely uneconomic decisions when they are applied in another type of setting.

Whose Point of View? It is possible to consider the economy of a public works proposal from several viewpoints:

1. That of the particular governmental body (or governmental department) concerned
2. That of all of the people of a particular area (such as a state, county, city, or special district)
3. That of all of the people in the country

It is necessary to have clearly in mind whose viewpoint is being taken, before it is possible to proceed with such an economy study.

In many cases the first impulse of the engineer will be to take viewpoint 1, considering only the prospective receipts and disbursements by the governmental body—or, in some cases, merely the particular governmental department—concerned. This appears to be comparable to an economy study for a private corporation in which the relevant matters are the prospective receipts and disbursements of that corporation. It should be clear that this viewpoint is a sound one in public works economy studies only when the alternatives being compared provide identical services to the people whom the government is organized to serve. For instance, this viewpoint might be correct in the choice between centrifugal pumps and reciprocating pumps for a municipal water works if it appeared that the service received by the water users would be equally satisfactory with either; the differences between the alternatives would then merely be differences in costs to the city's water department.

But where there are differences in the service provided by two alternatives, it is necessary to recognize the broader viewpoint that what the government does is simply something done collectively by all the people. If the ideal of democratic government that it is the objective of government to "promote the general welfare" is to be followed, it is necessary to consider the probable effects of alternative governmental policies on all of the people, not merely on the income and expenditures of a particular governmental unit.

Ideally, perhaps, it should be viewpoint 3 rather than 2 that should be considered in the public works policies of cities, counties, and states. For example, in comparing alternative plans for sewage treatment and disposal, a city should give consideration to the differences in their effects on downstream communities that take their water supply from the stream into which the sewage is discharged. Practically, however, experience indicates that the public officials and people of a community look at matters from the standpoint of what they consider to be the self-interest of their own community. Usually, the most that can be hoped for in economy studies for local governmental units is viewpoint 2 rather than viewpoint 1. If the broader question of the effect of one community's action on other communities is to be considered, it must be by the governmental authority of an area that includes both. Thus, a state board of health may regulate the sewage treatment policies of individual communities from the standpoint of the interests of all of the people of a state.

Viewpoint 3 definitely seems to be the correct one in all federally financed public works. Nevertheless, because the direct effects of most works of this character (e.g., navigation, flood control, reclamation), seem to be concentrated in a particular locality, there may be difficulty in applying this broad viewpoint even here. All of the effects on the people of a nation of a particular public improvement may be hard to trace, and doubly hard to evaluate quantitatively, even though the prospective local effects are fairly clear.

Analyses that are unsound from the broad viewpoint of the best use of limited national or state resources are fairly common when a national or state government has a policy of paying a substantial part of the cost of certain types of projects for which the chief benefits are local. Although Example 19–3 describes an actual case (with certain data changed a bit to disguise the source), the authors have observed many cases where the same type of reasoning was used. Too often, local governments take the attitude that money to be obtained from a higher level of government will be costless.

EXAMPLE 19–3. AN UNSOUND ANALYSIS OF A PUBLIC WORKS PROPOSAL

Facts of the Case. A certain consultant was employed to make a benefit-cost analysis of a proposed county expressway project. His conclusion that annual benefits would be $400,000 and annual costs would be $1,000,000 led to a B/C ratio of 0.4. On this basis, the project did not appear to be justified.

However, the consultant had what seemed to him to be a bright idea to suggest to the county supervisors. He proposed that they make an effort to have this expressway incorporated into the Interstate highway system. If this could be done, 90% of the cost would be paid by the federal government. He advised the supervisors that this would reduce the local annual costs to $100,000 and that **B/C** would then be $400,000 ÷ $100,000 = 4.0.

Who Gets the Benefits and Who Is Responsible for the Costs? As has been suggested, certain public works may be a benefit to some people, a matter of indifference to others, and possibly a detriment to others. This raises the question not only of what are the benefits, but who gets them.

The effort is frequently made in public works to allocate taxes or other charges according to a price principle that recognizes benefits and responsibility for costs. This is likely to involve somewhat arbitrary allocations of joint benefits and joint costs; in some instances, however, it is necessary to recognize increment costs in such studies.

Consider, for example, the case of a trunk-line sewer that, in addition to collecting the sewage of the buildings on its own street, also carries the sewage from a large tributary area. Here, the only charge that may be made legitimately in the form of a special assessment against the abutting property is a charge sufficient to build a sewer of the size necessary to serve that property. The difference between the actual cost of the trunk sewer and the estimated cost of a sewer adequate to serve the local needs should be financed in some other way, perhaps by considering it as a general benefit to the entire community and paying for it out of general taxation, or perhaps by considering it as a special benefit to the entire area tributary to the trunk sewer and distributing it over the property in that area in the form of a special assessment.

Some General Aspects of Cost Allocations. Because cost allocation problems arise so often in connection with public works, it is desirable to make certain general observations about all kinds of cost allocations, as follows:

1. A proposal that certain costs should be "allocated" suggests that there is no unique "correct" method of dividing the costs among the various purposes involved. This fundamentally indeterminate nature of

most cost allocations tends to make many such allocations extremely controversial. (However, it is rare for persons who make cost allocations to concede—at least, in public—that they believe their allocation problem has no correct answer.)

2. In spite of the somewhat arbitrary aspect of many cost allocations, the allocations can often be extremely important because of their consequences. Therefore, in making a cost allocation or in judging the merits of cost allocations made by someone else, it is desirable to consider what types of decisions (if any) are likely to be influenced by the particular allocation. Here it may be necessary to look beyond the stated purpose of a particular allocation. (In public utilities and public works, the stated purpose may be to make or to influence—or possibly to justify— some sort of pricing decision.) In this connection, one also should look at the possible consequences of making no allocations at all.

3. An important matter in any cost allocation is the choice of the "purposes" among which costs are to be allocated. This choice needs to be related to the intended uses of the allocation. In some cases, it may be desirable to have two or more classifications of "purposes" among which certain costs are to be allocated; for example, a manufacturer with a variety of products might allocate distribution costs among products, among geographical areas, and among different marketing channels.

4. Wherever it is proposed to make any use of a cost allocation, there are usually different groups of persons with conflicting interests in the results of the allocations. This is particularly true where an allocation influences budgets, pricing decisions, taxes, or the evaluation of the performance of persons or organizations.

5. The word "cost" is capable of many different definitions. It, therefore, is important to start any allocation with a set of rules for establishing the "costs" that are to be allocated. In considering the interests of various persons and organizations in certain allocations, the choice of a definition of cost often is of greater importance than the choice of a method to make the particular allocation.

6. A first step in any cost allocation ought to be to identify all costs that are separable (or incremental) among the various chosen purposes. By so doing, the size of the job of allocation is reduced by limiting it only to the fraction of the total cost that is residual, i.e., nonseparable. Nevertheless, the identification of separable costs is not necessarily a straightforward and noncontroversial matter. (Consider, for example, the troublesome problem of allocating highway costs among different classes of motor vehicles.) In judging the merits of any particular allocation, existing or proposed, one matter to examine is the method used for identifying the separable costs.

7. One cannot judge the merits of any plan for allocating nonsepa-

TABLE 19-1

Summary of Cost Allocation by Separable Costs—Remaining Benefits Method

(Unit: thousands of dollars)

Item	Flood Control	Irrigation	Power	Domestic and Industrial Water	Fisheries	Navigation	Totals
1. Costs to be allocated							46,853
a. Construction costs							(39,500)
b. Op., maint., and repl. costs (capitalized)							(7,353)
2. Benefits (capitalized)	10,975	54,875	12,622	16,462	1,975	2,195	99,104
3. Alternative costs	20,000	28,800	12,622	15,600	—	—	
4. Justifiable expenditure	10,975	28,800	12,622	15,600	1,975	2,195	72,167
5. Separable costs	8,110	9,434	9,992	1,929	—	—	29,465
a. Construction costs	(8,000)	(6,800)	(6,700)	(1,600)	—	—	(23,100)
b. Op., maint., repl. costs (capitalized)	(110)	(2,634)	(3,292)	(329)	—	—	(6,365)
6. Remaining justifiable expenditure	2,865	19,366	2,630	13,671	1,975	2,195	42,702
7. Per cent distribution	6.7	45.4	6.2	32.0	4.6	5.1	100.0
8. Remaining joint costs	1,165	7,894	1,078	5,564	800	887	17,388
a. Construction costs	(1,099)	(7,446)	(1,017)	(5,248)	(754)	(838)	(16,400)
b. Op., maint., repl. costs (capitalized)	(66)	(448)	(61)	(316)	(46)	(51)	(988)
9. Total allocated cost	9,275	17,328	11,070	7,493	800	887	46,853
a. Construction cost	(9,099)	(14,246)	(7,717)	(6,848)	(754)	(836)	(39,500)
b. Op., maint., repl. costs (capitalized)	(176)	(3,082)	(3,353)	(645)	(46)	(51)	(7,353)
10. Annual operation, maintenance and replacement costs	8	141	153	29	2	2	335

rable costs without some criterion—or, preferably, some set of criteria—for judging merit. (The rather awkward word *nonseparable* is used here because of special meanings that have been attached to *joint costs, common costs,* and *residual costs.*)

8. The concept of sensitivity, so useful in engineering economy, also is useful in any study of cost allocation. It is of interest to note the sensitivity of the results of various cost allocations to the definition of cost, to the method used to identify separable costs, and to the method used for allocating nonseparable costs.

9. Because, as stressed throughout this book and as emphasized particularly in Chapter 15, the analysis of problems in engineering economy calls for examining *differences* between alternatives, cost allocation is not a useful tool for solving problems in engineering economy.

An important field of cost allocation of public works has been in connection with multiple-purpose water projects. The importance has arisen out of the common practice of having the costs allocated to certain purposes repaid by the beneficiaries and having the costs allocated to other purposes paid for out of general taxation. Example 19–4 illustrates a method of making such allocations that has been favored by many writers and government agencies.

EXAMPLE 19–4. AN ILLUSTRATION OF COST ALLOCATION FOR A MULTI-PURPOSE WATER RESOURCE PROJECT

The Separable Costs–Remaining Benefits Method of Cost Allocation. Table 19–1 is reproduced from a United Nations manual on water resource projects.[17] It illustrates the use of the separable costs—remaining benefits method of allocating costs as applied to a project that serves six purposes, namely, flood control, irrigation, hydro-power, domestic and industrial water supply, fisheries, and navigation. The project includes a dam and reservoir, irrigation canals and distribution works, a power plant and transmission facilities, and a domestic-industrial pipe line. The total first cost is $39,500,000. For purposes of the cost allocation, the project life is assumed to be 100 years with no terminal salvage value. The capitalized figures in Table 19–1 (in lines 1b, 2, 5b, 8b, and 9b) are present worths of estimated annual figures for a 100-year period computed with an i of $4\frac{1}{2}\%$.

This method of cost allocation requires estimates of costs for single-purpose alternates that would produce equivalent single-purpose benefits. Such estimates, shown in line 3, involved a single purpose reservoir for flood control, irrigation, and domestic and industrial water. For power, the alternate was a thermal plant with the same capability and production as the project hydro plant. Because the power benefits from the water project were measured by the cost of power from the most economical alternate source (thermal power),

[17] DIVISION OF WATER RESOURCES DEVELOPMENT of ECONOMIC COMMISSION FOR ASIA AND THE FAR EAST, *Manual of Standards and Criteria for Planning Water Resource Projects,* Water Resources Series N. 26, United Nations Publications Sales Number: 64, II, F. 12 (New York: United Nations, 1964), p. 53.

lines 2 and 3 under "Power" contain identical figures. No alternates were deemed possible for fisheries or for navigation.

The justifiable expenditure given in line 4 for each purpose is the lesser of the figures in lines 2 and 3. That is, the justifiable expenditure clearly should not exceed the benefits; neither should it exceed the costs of a single-purpose project that will have the same consequences.

To obtain the separable costs given in line 4 for each purpose, it is necessary to estimate the construction costs and the annual operation, maintenance, and replacement costs for a multi-purpose project from which the particular purpose is excluded. The excess of the total project costs over the costs with the purpose excluded gives the separable costs. For instance, if flood control were omitted, the construction cost of the project would be $31,500,000 as contrasted with $39,500,000 with flood control included; the difference of $8,000,000 is the separable construction cost of flood control. Without flood control, the annual cost for operation, etc., would be $330,000 as contrasted with $335,000 with flood control included; the separable annual cost of flood control for operation, etc., is $5,000.

The separable costs do not need to be allocated; the allocation procedure applies only to the excess of total costs over the sum of the separable costs. Thus, since total construction cost is $39,500,000 and the sum of separable costs of construction is $23,100,000, only $16,400,000 of construction cost needs to be allocated.

The annual separable operation, maintenance, and replacements costs are $5,000 for flood control; $120,000 for irrigation, $150,000 for power; and $15,000 for domestic and industrial water. As the sum of these separable costs is $290,000, only $45,000 out of the annual total of $335,000 needs to be allocated.

The allocation of nonseparable costs is in proportion to the ratio of the remaining justifiable expenditure (line 6) for each purpose to the sum of the remaining justifiable expenditures for all purposes. For example, for flood control $2,865,000 ÷ $42,702,000 = 0.067 or 6.7%.

Special Problems of Public Borrowing. When cities, counties, or special improvement districts (such as water districts, sanitary districts, irrigation and drainage districts, and bridge districts) wish to construct public works of any substantial magnitude, it is often necessary to finance such works by borrowing 100% of their cost. In many instances only minor works can be financed out of current taxes and revenues.

In order to prevent excessive borrowing and assure systematic repayment, the states of the United States, either through constitutional provisions or legislative enactments, have put various restrictions on borrowing by local governments. These restrictions are commonly of three types:

1. The total borrowing power of a local government is limited to a specified percentage of the assessed valuation of the property within its area.
2. No bonds may be issued without the approval of the voters at an election; with the exception of "revenue bonds" in certain jurisdic-

tions, it often is specified that this approval must be by a two-thirds affirmative vote.

3. Repayment must be within a specified number of years, and must be in accordance with a specified plan. This plan often requires uniform serial maturities over the life of a bond issue.

In considering any proposal for local public works to be financed by bond issues, the effect of these legal restrictions must be considered. Will borrowing power, considering probable future needs, be impaired by the proposed issue? Are the chances good for a two-thirds favorable vote? Can required obligations for interest and repayment be met, particularly in the earlier years when they are the greatest?

The necessity for 100% borrowing to finance many local public works, and the requirement that the bonds be completely paid off within a limited period, usually 40 years or less, makes the financial background quite different from that found in private enterprise. Private enterprises seldom have the opportunity for 100% borrowing; on the other hand, they are not confronted with the necessity for retiring all of their capital obligations within a limited period.

Borrowing by states are generally subject to restrictions similar to those enforced on cities, counties, and special districts. However, state highway improvements, which are the major state-financed public works, are now generally financed on a pay-as-you-go plan through the proceeds of gasoline taxes and other forms of motor vehicle taxation. Thus the problems of debt limit, bond elections, and debt repayment, which are so common in connection with municipal public works, arise less frequently in connection with state works.

The situation with respect to borrowing by the federal government is entirely different from that existing in other governmental units. Whereas each bond issue by a state, city, county, or special district is for a definitely specified purpose, borrowings by the federal government are for the general purpose of supplying funds to take care of the excess of current disbursements over current receipts.

The relationship between the financing of federal deficits, the banking and credit mechanism, and the general price structure, is much too complex for discussion here. Let it suffice to point out that federal borrowing (except that engaged in for purposes of debt refunding) serves to create purchasing power and is thus a stimulant to business activity that may be used for the purpose of promoting recovery from periods of business recession. Federal borrowing also, if carried on in large amounts, has the tendency to cause a great rise in price levels with all of the ills that the experience of the world has demonstrated to be attendant upon inflation. Both of these effects—one good, the other bad—

are decidedly relevant in connection with any federal public works proposal made when the federal government is operating at or near a deficit. They are, however, a long way removed from matters of engineering technology.

Shadow Pricing in Economy Studies for Proposed Public Works. Sometimes it may be felt that market prices do not provide a suitable measure of the opportunity costs associated with certain elements of project input and output when such costs are looked at from the national viewpoint. If there is substantial unemployment of unskilled labor that would be likely to be used in a proposed project, or if a proposed project will make appreciable demands on limited resources of foreign exchange, it may be a good idea to make a supplementary economic analysis that substitutes "shadow prices" for market prices. For example, in one research study, W. W. Shaner assumed that opportunity costs were reflected by shadow prices for unskilled labor, skilled labor and domestic materials, and foreign exchange which were 50%, 100%, and 120% of their respective market values.[18] The need for such a supplementary analysis arises chiefly in developing countries.

A Proposed Technique for Improving Decision Making Procedures Where Many Irreducibles Are Present. In any economy study that involves irreducible data, a first step should be to identify those consequences that are to be given consideration as irreducibles in the final choice among the alternatives. By definition, what we have called "irreducibles" are expected consequences of a decision that it is not practicable to express in units of money for purposes of the particular economy study. Nevertheless, even though these matters are not to be quantified in monetary units, a desirable step is to quantify each irreducible in some manner; this involves finding an appropriate unit to measure the favorable or unfavorable consequences that are deemed to be relevant. Finally, as we pointed out in Chapter 12, whenever there are multiple alternatives and multiple irreducibles, it is helpful to compare alternatives in pairs.

Oglesby, Bishop, and Willeke have proposed a systematic procedure for dealing with multiple irreducibles in one particularly troublesome field of public works decision making.[19] The choice among several proposals

[18] W. W. Shaner, *Economic Evaluation of Investments in Agricultural Penetration Roads in Developing Countries: A Case Study of the Tingo Maria-Tocache Project in Peru, Report EEP-22.* Stanford, Calif.: Program in Engineering-Economic Planning, Stanford University, 1966.

[19] C. H. Oglesby, A. B. Bishop, and G. E. Willeke, "A Method for Decisions Among Freeway Location Alternatives Based on User and Community Consequences." This paper was presented at the annual meeting of the Highway Research Board in January 1970 and was scheduled to be published by the Board during 1970.

for a location of an urban freeway often is a controversial matter. Different locations have different expected impacts on the community. Generally speaking, it is not practicable to express the various community impacts in money terms so that they can be counted as benefits or disbenefits in a benefit–cost analysis. A common complication is that different community impacts favor different locations, and that the locations that look best if only irreducibles are considered are not the same locations that look best if only estimated benefits and costs are considered.

These writers list many different possible types of community impacts and suggest one or more different possible units that might be applied to each type. For example, under the general category *Neighborhood Impact*, one community impact is *family units displaced;* this unfavorable consequence can be measured in numbers of living units. Under the general category *Community Planning*, one community impact is *developable land to which freeway provides excellent access;* this favorable consequence could be measured in acres.

Oglesby, Bishop, and Willeke make the following pertinent remarks about each measured community consequence:

The time period over which the consequences of the various factors are evaluated is also important. Otherwise short run consequences might be given more weight in the decision as compared to the long run effects, or vice versa. An example might be the community concern that elderly people would be displaced from their homes in a given area. At the same time, the community master plan may indicate that the area is suitable for high-density apartments and a survey show that the transition is already under way. In this instance, an appreciation of the time factor is extremely important to a rational appraisal of the possible alternatives.

They suggest plotting the various quantified irreducibles for all of the alternative proposed freeway locations on a "community factor profile," which they illustrate. They describe this "profile" in part as follows:

The community factor profile is a graphical description . . . of the effects of each proposed freeway location alternative. . . . On this figure, each profile scale is on a percentage base, ranging from a negative to a positive 100%. One hundred either negative or positive is the maximum absolute value of the measure that is adopted for each factor. Reduction to the percentage base simplifies scaling and plotting the profiles. The maximum positive or negative value of the measure, the units, and the time span are indicated on the right-hand side of the profile for reference. For each alternative, the positive or negative value for any factor is calculated as a percent of the maximum absolute value over all alternatives, and is plotted on the appropriate abscissa.

An important aspect of the system of analysis proposed by these writers is the use of paired comparisons of multiple alternatives, somewhat along the lines that we mentioned in Chapter 12. They comment on this point in part as follows.

A highly simplified example to illustrate the paired comparison approach is given by the question: "Is it preferable to save $50,000 per year to local residents in vehicle operating costs by adopting a shorter route or to retain a commercial enterprise employing ten people and paying $20,000 per year in property taxes? It is estimated that a substitute enterprise will develop in five years." It is admitted that this example is far simpler than those of the real world where the factor profile would include several elements. Even so, such comparisons make clear the actual points at issue and may greatly reduce the number of irrational arguments that accompany most controversial decisions.

PROBLEMS

19-1. Two alternate locations for a new rural highway are to be compared.

Location X involves a distance of 11.3 miles. Total first cost is estimated to be $1,694,000. The location and grading are assumed to be permanent. Resurfacing and reconstruction of the base will be required every 15 years at an estimated cost of $40,000 per mile. In addition, annual maintenance cost will be $1,000 per mile.

Location Y involves a distance of 13.5 miles. Total first cost is estimated to be $1,160,000. Costs per mile for resurfacing and annual maintenance are the same as for X. Location and grading are assumed to be permanent.

The estimated average traffic over this highway is 700 vehicles per day, of which about 15% will be trucks and an additional 10% will be commercial passenger cars. The increment cost per mile of vehicle operation is assumed as 5.4 cents for passenger cars and 20 cents for trucks. Traffic will travel at an average speed of 40 miles per hour. The money value of time saving to commercial traffic is estimated as 6 cents per vehicle minute.

Assuming an i° of 8%, compute a **B/C** ratio applicable to the extra investment in Location X. (*Ans.* = 1.46.)

19-2. For the data of Problem 19-1, find the approximate value of i° above which the incremental **B/C** for the extra investment required by Location X will be less than unity. (*Ans.* = 11.1%.)

19-3. For the multi-purpose water project of Example 19-4, what is the over-all **B/C** ratio assuming an i° of 4½% (i.e., assuming the same i that was used in computing all the capitalized values in Table 19-1)? What are the respective incremental values of **B/C** for flood control, irrigation, power, and domestic and industrial water? (*Ans.* = 2.12; 1.35; 5.82; 1.26; 8.53.)

19-4. Using the data of Example 19-4 and an i° of 4½%, what would have been the respective values of **B/C** for single purpose projects for flood control, irrigation, and domestic-industrial water? Assume that the costs of alternates given in line 3 of Table 19-1 include capitalized operation, maintenance, and replacement costs as well as construction costs. (*Ans.* = 0.55; 1.91; 1.06.)

19-5. In the cost allocation in Table 19-1, 77.4% of the nonseparable costs were allocated to two of the six purposes of the water project, namely, irrigation and domestic-industrial water. None of the other four purposes had an allocation of more than 6.7% of the nonseparable costs.

In the solution to Problem 19-3, the incremental **B/C** ratios for irrigation (5.82) and for domestic-industrial water (8.53) were much higher than for flood control (1.35) or power (1.26). Does it seem likely to you that the separable costs-remaining benefits method of cost allocation will ordinarily allocate higher percentages of the nonseparable costs to the purposes that have the highest incremental **B/C** ratios? Use your answer to this question as a starting point for a general discussion of what seems to you to be the rational foundation that underlies the separable costs-remaining benefits method.

19–6. Annual benefits in Example 19–4 (which were used to compute the present worth figures in line 2 of Table 19–1 but which were not explicitly stated in the text of the example) are as follows:

Flood control	$ 500,000
Irrigation	2,500,000
Power	575,000
Domestic-industrial water	750,000
Fisheries	90,000
Navigation	100,000
Total	$4,515,000

Compute the various values of **B/C** asked for in Problem 19–3 assuming an i^* of 6% instead of the 4½% used in that problem.

19–7. Recompute the cost allocation of Table 19–1 using an i of 6%. (Annual figures for benefits are given in Problem 19–6, and the required annual figures for the separable costs of operation, etc., are given in the text of Example 19–4. Because the source of the example does not break down the figures for alternate costs in line 3 into the components of construction costs and operation costs, etc., it will be necessary to assume that these figures are also appropriate for an i of 6%.)

Discuss the sensitivity of the results of this cost allocation to this change in the chosen value of i.

19–8. What is the break-even value of i^* above which it would not have paid to include flood control as one of the purposes of the water project of Example 19–4? Answer the same question for the hydro-power features of the project. (See Problem 19–6 for certain necessary data not given in the example.)

19–9. In Example 19–4 it was assumed that the water project would have a life of 100 years with a zero terminal salvage value. In Problem 19–3, the value of **B/C** was computed to be 2.12 with an i^* of 4½%. To examine the sensitivity of **B/C** to certain assumptions, compute this ratio assuming a perpetual life. Compute **B/C** assuming a life of 50 years with zero terminal salvage. Using the life and salvage of Example 19–4, compute **B/C** first with an i^* of 4% and then with an i^* of 5%.

19–10. The monetary figures in Table 19–1 are present worths computed for a 100-year period with an i of 4½%. How would the allocation have differed if equivalent uniform annual figures rather than present worths had been used for the various benefits and costs shown in the table?

19–11. Rank the following proposed Mexican social roads according to the criterion of cost per inhabitant served.

Proposed Road	Length in Kilometers	Cost per Kilometer in Pesos	Population Served
1. Las Norias–Cruillas	32	110,000	1,999
2. El Capulin–Bustamente	32	109,000	1,692
3. Palmillas–Miquihana	43	112,000	2,853
4. Mendez–Entronque	45	119,000	3,037

19–12. Rank the following proposed Mexican economic penetration roads according to the criterion of the ratio of the estimated gross value of agricultural product in the 5th year of operation to the construction cost of the road.

Proposed Road	Principal Crops	Estimated Hectares of Area in Production, 5th Year	Estimated 5th Year Average Value of Output per Hectare in Pesos	Construction Cost of Road in Pesos
1. Hidalgo–La Mesa	corn	1,600	1,400	2,500,000
2. Altamira–Aldama	tomatoes	4,500	2,100	6,000,000
3. El Barretal–Santa Engracia	corn	1,300	1,400	1,000,000
4. Casas–Soto La Marina–La Pesca	corn, cotton	15,500	1,400	10,300,000
5. Limon–Ocampo	citrus, fruit, cane	3,400	1,800	5,500,000
6. Llera–Gonzalez	cane, corn	8,900	1,500	6,600,000
7. Ebano–Manuel	corn, cane	4,700	1,900	7,400,000
8. El Barretal–Padilla	corn, cotton, fruit	3,400	2,300	3,900,000
9. Jimenez–Abasolo	cotton, fruit, corn	2,100	2,500	3,500,000
10. Mendez–Burgos	corn, beans, cotton	5,300	1,400	3,720,000

19–13. A city of 40,000 population uses an average of 150 gallons of water per capita per day. Its water supply has a total hardness of 320 parts per million (p.p.m.). A municipal water softening plant is proposed to reduce this to 70 p.p.m.

The plant capacity must be double the average daily consumption; the plant will cost $25,000 per millions of gallons per day (m.g.d.) of capacity. The plant would be financed by 20-year 5½% serial bonds, with a uniform number of bonds maturing each year. Chemicals are estimated to cost 12 cents per m.g. per p.p.m. of hardness removed. Plant labor costs at the water treatment plant will be increased by $6,000 a year. Pumping in the softening plant will cost $1.60 per m.g. pumped. Average annual maintenance cost is estimated as 3% of investment. The life of the plant is estimated as 20 years with a negligible salvage value. The city will raise water rates sufficiently to cover the extra operating costs for water softening plus first year's bond interest and repayment.

Assume a saving in annual per capita soap consumption from 38.5 lb. to 30.8 lb. as a result of the water softening, with an average retail soap price of 20 cents per lb. Assume a saving in cost of chemicals to customers already softening their water of 18 cents per m.g. per p.p.m. of hardness removed; this applies to 110 m.g. per year. It is estimated that the life will be doubled for 4,000 storage water heaters having an average life of 8 years under present conditions; the average investment per heater is $65.

Estimate the required increase in water rate per 1,000 gallons. Make an analysis to determine whether the foregoing estimated monetary savings are sufficient to justify water softening.

19–14. The following question is adapted from one used a number of years ago in a state examination for registration as a professional engineer:

Estimates are made for the first costs of various elements of a new highway assuming designs for different numbers of lanes, as follows:

	4 Lanes	6 Lanes
Right of way	$ 240,000	$ 320,000
Pavement	960,000	1,440,000
All other elements of first cost	1,200,000	1,440,000
Total	$2,400,000	$3,200,000

It is estimated that 4 traffic lanes will be sufficient for the next 10 years; after that, 6 lanes will be required. The interest rate is 4%. How much money, in addition to the cost of a 4-lane highway, can be spent economically at once? How should your recommended total be divided among the foregoing elements of first cost? Explain your answers.

Give the solution that you think was expected by the examiner.

Assume that you are confronted by this type of problem in an actual case. What additional data and estimates, if any, would you want before arriving at your recommendations? How would you use the additional data in your analysis?

19–15. A steel bridge on a county highway near the ocean cost $230,000 12 years ago. Although the average annual maintenance costs of $7,200 a year have seemed excessive to the county supervisors, these costs, mostly for painting, have been necessary to prevent severe corrosion in this particular location.

A consulting structural engineer proposes to the county supervisors that he be employed to design and to supervise the construction of a reinforced concrete bridge to replace this steel bridge. He estimates the total first cost of the concrete bridge to be $420,000 and the net salvage from the steel bridge to be $20,000. The required net outlay is therefore $400,000. Since the county receives $500,000 a year from state gas tax funds to be used for county highway improvement, the engineer points out that this bridge could be financed without borrowing. His economic comparison is as follows:

Annual Cost of Proposed Bridge

Depreciation (based on 100-year life) — $400,000 ÷ 100 = $ 4,000
Annual maintenance cost .... =   200
        Total annual cost .... = $ 4,200

Annual Cost of Present Bridge

Depreciation (based on 50-year life) = $230,000 ÷ 50 = $ 4,600
Annual maintenance cost .... =   7,200
        Total annual cost .... = $11,800

Comment on the engineer's analysis. Explain how you would approach this problem.

19–16. The elimination of a certain level crossing of a highway and railway is under consideration. The total cost of this grade crossing elimination is estimated as $479,000. Although the improvement is assumed to be permanent, it involves estimated pump renewal expenditures of $35,000 every 20 years, and an annual cost for energy for pumping drainage water and for maintenance of $700.

The highway traffic is 2,800 vehicles per day, and the railway carries 50 trains per day. Time studies indicate that on the average a train stops 11 vehicles with an average delay per vehicle of 2.5 minutes. The cost of a vehicle stop (applicable to all cars stopped) is estimated as 0.18 cent. The

cost of lost time (applicable to the 30% of commercial vehicles only) is estimated as 7 cents per vehicle minute.

Based on past accident statistics at this and other similar locations, it is
estimated that if this grade crossing is continued, it will be responsible for one
fatal accident every 4 years and 3 nonfatal accidents per year. Assume a
benefit of $50,000 for eliminating a fatal accident and $800 for eliminating a
nonfatal one.

The railway company has maintained a watchman at this crossing for 14
hours per day at an annual cost of $6,800.

In order to decide which of a number of proposed grade-crossing elimination projects are to receive limited available funds, it is desired to compare
annual benefits with annual costs for each. Compute **B/C** for this project assuming an i^* of 7%. Also compute a revised value of **B/C** including an extra-
market benefit of 2 cents per vehicle minute for reducing the lost time to noncommercial traffic.

19–17. Discuss the sensitivity of the value of **B/C** in Problem 19–16 to
the various estimates and assumptions used in the analysis. Discuss the irreducible elements in the choice of the grade-crossing elmination projects that
are to receive the limited funds.

19–18. A state highway department is considering the installation of an
overpass and cloverleaves to eliminate a grade crossing at the intersection of
two main highways. The installation will cost $700,000. An economy study
to evaluate this project will use a life of 25 years with zero terminal value because it is likely that one of these highways will ultimately be relocated. An
i^* of 7% is to be used.

The average traffic is 3,000 vehicles per day on one of the highways and
2,000 vehicles per day on the other. Traffic is made up of 20% trucks, 20%
light commercial, and 60% private passenger vehicles. Increment costs of
operation are assumed to be 20 cents per mile for the trucks and 5 cents per
mile for all others. Time is valued at an average of 6 cents per minute for
the trucks and light commercial vehicles and 1.5 cents per minute for private
passenger vehicles. It is estimated that the cloverleaf arrangement will increase the mileage traveled by 0.3 mile for 25% of the vehicles. The average
time saving per vehicle is estimated to be 1.5 minute. The installation will
eliminate an annual expense by the state of $7,200 now spent for patroling
the intersection. Annual highway maintenance costs will be increased by
$3,000. It is forecast that the installation will effect a 75% reduction in the
accident rate at the intersection. During the past 5 years, there have been
two fatal accidents and 31 nonfatal accidents at this intersection. Assume
a benefit of $50,000 for eliminating a fatal accident and $800 for eliminating
a nonfatal one.

Determine the **B/C** ratio for this proposed installation.

19–19. The flood plain in the lower reaches of the Rattlesnake River is
subject to occasional severe floods. A flood control district has been organized
that includes all of the area subject to flood damages. Engineers for the district have found four feasible sites for dams and detention reservoirs. Site A
is on the main river just below the junction of the three forks of the river.
Sites B and C are on the North Fork and Middle Fork respectively, not far
above the junction point. Neither B nor C can be used if A is used, because
the reservoir area from A will extend above these two sites. Site D is some
distance upstream on the South Fork and can be combined with A, B, or C.

The first cost at each site (including interest during construction) has been estimated, and annual operation and maintenance (O & M) costs also estimated, as follows:

	First Cost	Annual O & M
Site A	$20,000,000	$50,000
Site B	4,700,000	20,000
Site C	4,400,000	20,000
Site D	4,200,000	20,000

For any practicable combination of sites (such as A and D, or B and C), the total first cost will be the sum of the first costs at the respective sites, and the total O & M will be the sum of the respective O & M costs. For purposes of an economic analysis, the life of each dam and reservoir is assumed to be 50 years with zero salvage value. The funds to provide the needed first costs will be secured entirely from general obligation bonds to be voted by the flood control district. It is believed that the district can borrow at 5½% interest. Bonds will mature serially over a 50-year period, with a maturity schedule that will result in a fairly uniform annual total of principal repayment plus interest. Bond interest, repayments of principal, and payment of O & M costs, will all come from ad valorem taxes levied on the property in the flood control district.

The consulting hydrologist for the district has estimated the probabilities of floods of various magnitudes with no flood control and with each reservoir and combination of reservoirs. Estimates have been made of the relationship between flood stages and the monetary cost of damage caused by floods. The district's engineers have analyzed these figures and have estimated average annual flood damages within the district under each of the feasible plans, as follows:

Plan Number	Plan	Average Annual Flood Damages
1	No flood control	$1,600,000
2	A alone	300,000
3	B alone	800,000
4	C alone	900,000
5	D alone	850,000
6	A and D	250,000
7	B and D	580,000
8	C and D	700,000
9	B and C	640,000
10	B, C, and D	450,000

Make an economic analysis to determine which of these 10 plans you would recommend. Use an i^* of 5½%, the bare cost of money to the flood control district.

19–20. Our examples and problems related to highway engineering economy have not broken down incremental highway user costs per mile of vehicle operation into such components as fuel, lubricants, tires, maintenance and repairs, and depreciation. However, it is obvious that each component needs to be analyzed and priced in order to determine relevant highway user costs in any actual case.

Assume that the average retail price of gasoline is 35 cents per gallon, and that this 35-cent figure is made up of 11 cents of state and federal highway-user taxes and 24 cents paid for the gasoline. Some analysts would use the

35-cent figure and others would use the 24-cent figure in computing the benefits to highway users from a reduction in vehicle operating costs. Which would
you use? Explain your answer.

19–21. A critic of highway economy studies such as the one illustrated in
Example 19–2 points out that savings to highway users because of lower vehicle operating costs are offset by lost revenues to service stations, oil companies, tire dealers, repair shops, and others. If consequences "to whomsoever
they may accrue" are to be examined, the critic contends that the favorable
consequences to highway users are counterbalanced by unfavorable consequences to others and therefore should be given no weight in the economic
evaluation of proposed highway improvements. Discuss this contention, explaining whether or not you agree with this critic. If so, why? If not, why
not?

19–22. (Problems 19–22 through 19–24 are adapted from the Oglesby-
Altenhofen research report cited in footnote 16.)

Sometimes very sharp horizontal curves are used in the location of low-
volume rural roads in order to avoid the extra construction costs that would
be associated with flatter curves. (An example of such extra costs would be
earthwork costs associated with deeper cuts and higher fills.) Of course the
influence of the radius of curvature on construction costs will vary greatly
with differences in topography. In evaluating the economic aspects of sharp-
ness of curvature, it is helpful to consider the extra construction cost that will
be justified by the savings to road users when flatter curves are used.

For example, consider a curve with a central angle of 30 degrees. If a
curve having a radius of 133 feet is used, the curve length will be 70 feet.
The design speed for such a curve is 20 miles per hour. If a curve with a
radius of 535 feet is used, the curve length will be 280 feet and the design
speed will be 40 miles per hour. The sharper curve will involve 216 more
feet of tangent than the flatter curve.

For an average passenger car that operates at the design speed of 40 miles
per hour before and after the curve and that slows to the design speed of 20
miles per hour for the sharper curve, there is an estimated extra vehicle
operating cost of 0.953 cents per vehicle if the sharper curve is used; the difference is chiefly due to costs caused by the required deceleration and accelera-
tion. There will also be a time saving of 0.073 minutes per vehicle with the
flatter curve.

Assuming a traffic of 400 passenger vehicles per day and assuming that all
vehicles operate at design speeds, what will be the total annual saving in
vehicle operating cost caused by the choice of the flatter rather than the
sharper curve? Using an i^* of 7% and a life of 30 years with no terminal
salvage value, what extra construction cost for the flatter curve is justified
by the saving in vehicle operating costs? If time is valued at 2.5 cents per
vehicle minute, what further increase in construction cost is justified? How
would your answers to the last two questions be changed by a change of the
estimated traffic to 100 vehicles per day?

The student of highway engineering economy will recognize that the foregoing calculations do not give any weight to differences in tire wear (which
will be greater with the sharper curve) or to differences in highway maintenance costs (which may be greater with the flatter curve if deeper cuts and
higher fills are involved). Neither does the analysis reflect differences, if any,
in the probabilities of accidents.

19–23. The vehicle operating costs on a straight level rural highway for a given volume of traffic will be influenced by the distribution of traffic among different classes of motor vehicles, by the average vehicle speed and the dispersion about this average, and by the type of pavement. An important matter affecting speed changes will be the number of interactions (meetings and passings) between vehicles in relation to the width of roadbed. For a relatively narrow roadbed width such as 16 feet, the speed changes per interaction can have a considerable influence on vehicle operating costs. The wider the roadbed, the less the speed change caused by interactions.

Consider a mile of straight level rural highway that will carry 400 vehicles per day. Assume a gravel surface with a 16-foot width of roadbed. Under certain assumptions about the type of traffic, it is assumed that the desired speed will be 35 miles per hour and the interaction speed will be 19 miles per hour. An analysis of vehicle operating costs and of numbers of expected interactions leads to an estimate that the total of incremental vehicle operating costs per year for this mile of road will be $9,231 and that the vehicle hours per year will be 4,307.

For a roadbed width of 24 feet with gravel surface and the same volume and type of traffic, a corresponding desired speed is 39 miles per hour. With this wider roadbed, the interaction speed also is 39 miles per hour. Assuming these speeds, the total of incremental vehicle operating costs per year per mile of road will be $8,180 and the vehicle hours per year will be 3,744.

Compare the sum of the relevant annual highway user costs and highway costs for these two stated widths of gravel road. The investment per mile for embankment and drainage is estimated as $10,300 for a 16-foot width and $11,900 for a 24-foot width. The life is estimated as 28 years with zero terminal salvage value. The initial cost of the gravel surface will be $5,800 for 16 feet and $7,750 for 24 feet; the estimated life of the surface is 7 years. Incremental annual cost of maintenance per mile is $168 for the 16-foot width and $200 for the 24-foot width. Assume an i^s of 7% and assume the average value of time is 3 cents per vehicle minute.

19–24. The preceding problem compared 16-foot and 24-foot widths of roadbed for an average traffic of 400 vehicles per day. In this problem you are asked to make the same comparison for 100 vehicles per day. Initial costs for embankment and drainage and for gravel surface will be unchanged. Also there will be no change in estimated life. Incremental annual maintenance costs per mile will be $56 for the 16-foot width and $80 for the 24-foot width.

Although desired speeds and interaction speeds will be the same as with the larger volume of traffic, there now will be relatively few interactions. The total of incremental vehicle operating costs per mile of road will be $2,053 with the 16-foot width and $2,045 with the 24-foot width. The respective vehicle hours per year will be 1,051 and 936.

20

Some Aspects of Economy Studies for Public Utilities

Since utility systems must be in place before their external economies can be available, their development must precede or lead the development of other industries. A growing economy requires expansion of its transportation and communications, for example, in two dimensions: first, they must be made more *extensive*, to carry heavier loads imposed by the growing populations and output; and second, they must be made more *intensive* by the development and assimilation of technology in order to lower costs and maintain and improve the quality of service under heavier loads. The extensive development is shown in the large and continuous increase in capital invested in these industries, and the intensive development by the long-term increase in output per unit of capital. Think, for example, what resources of capital and manpower would be consumed, at what cost, if the electric power system or the telephone system tried to carry 1966 loads with the technology of 1930, or even of 1950!—R. R. NATHAN [1]

In the United States and elsewhere, certain types of privately owned business enterprises are subject to regulation as public utilities. These include suppliers of electricity, gas, water, telephone service, and other communications services, and various types of transportation services. Regulation is conducted by various state and federal commissions, with certain decisions by regulatory commissions subject to review by the courts. Matters regulated include the general level of rates, specific rate structures, certain standards of service, the issuance of securities, and classifications of accounts.

With certain exceptions in the case of transportation utilities, regulated utilities tend to be monopolistic in character with their monopoly protected by public regulation. There are a number of good reasons why the public both restricts and to some extent protects the activity

[1] R. R. Nathan, *Testimony of Robert R. Nathan,* Federal Communications Commission Docket No. 16258, Bell Exhibit 16, May 23, 1966.

of public utilities. Many utilities require a franchise from the community to put their pipes or poles or conduits or tracks in the streets and require the exercise of the state's privilege of eminent domain to secure certain needed rights of way. All public utilities clearly perform a service that is of great importance to the community. Moreover, most utilities require a very high investment in plant and equipment in comparison to their annual revenues and annual operating costs.

Perhaps this relatively high plant investment is the most distinguishing characteristic of the public utility field. A large proportion of public utility costs are so-called fixed costs such as taxes, depreciation, and cost of capital. For this reason, a monopoly in the public utility field is highly economical. For example, if we have two competing electric light and power companies in a community, they must duplicate each other's distribution systems with a resulting higher total investment than would exist if there were but one system. If both had enough revenues to earn a fair return on their respective investments, the aggregate revenues of the two would be much more than the revenues of a single company that earned a fair return on the investment in only one distribution system. In certain types of utilities particularly telephone utilities and urban transportation utilities, the service available from either of two competing utilities is less satisfactory than that obtainable from a monopolistic company covering the entire area. Moreover, there is often a nuisance factor to having an extra set of poles or an extra pipe line in a given street that makes monopoly desirable.

In most industries competition tends to regulate rates and service in the public interest. Before the days of public utility regulation in the United States, experience indicated that competition was not an adequate regulator in the utility field. What is likely to happen where competing utilities exist with no regulation is cut-throat competition with a tendency to cut rates down to increment costs of production. This is likely to be followed by a consolidation and unregulated monopoly with a price that is set on a monopoly price basis.

Relationship Between Regulatory Policies and the Rapid Growth of the Need for Public Utility Service. The general experience in the United States and other industrialized countries has been one of continuous increase in demand for utility service. Since 1900 this has been particularly true of electric, gas, water, and telephone utilities. There are high social costs caused by inadequate capacity of utility plant. The public interest therefore requires that utility companies be in a position to finance necessary expansion and modernization of plant. If new capital to finance expansion is to be secured, a utility must have the prospect of earnings sufficient to attract such capital.

Rates, therefore, should be high enough to attract capital. At the same time they should be low enough so that the charges to the public are reasonable, all things considered. A common method used by commissions to accomplish these two ends has been to set rates at a level so that the prospective total revenues received by a utility from the sale of its public utility services will equal its prospective operating expenses including an allowance for depreciation, plus income taxes, plus a "fair return" on the investment in the property employed in the utility service.[2]

The appropriate rate of return to be allowed in any given instance should reflect the over-all cost of money to the utility being regulated, considering both the interest that must be paid for borrowed money and the dividend rate needed to attract new equity capital. The return will properly be higher for a relatively risky utility enterprise (such as an urban transportation company) than for a relatively secure one (such as a large electric light and power company). The rate of return necessary to attract capital will also be influenced by the size of the utility and the extent to which it is well known to investors. The appropriate fair return will change from time to time with changes in the general level of interest rates. In recent years regulatory commissions have generally allowed rates of return somewhere in the range from 6% to 8%.

Occasionally one hears the statement that public utilities are *guaranteed* a return on their investments. Any such statement is incorrect. The most that a regulatory commission can do is to allow a rate schedule that gives the utility a chance to earn a fair return *if it can get it*. Certain utilities (such as some urban transportation companies) find it impossible to earn an adequate return with any schedule of rates.

Authority of Regulatory Commissions. In the United States, any public utility company engaging in interstate commerce is regulated by two or more commissions. Interstate activities are regulated by a federal commission, such as the Federal Power Commission, Federal Communications Commission, or the Interstate Commerce Commission. The intrastate activities usually are regulated by a state public utility commission. Although federal and state commissions consult with one another, there is still the possibility that their decisions on certain matters will not be consistent.

The complexities of the actual regulation of utility rates and services are beyond the scope of this book; we shall not attempt to examine all

[2] The rules governing rate regulation have been laid down in a series of decisions by the United States Supreme Court and other courts. These decisions have taken place over a period of years. The viewpoint of the Supreme Court on underlying principles has changed from time to time. Later court decisions permitted regulatory bodies to exercise much more latitude than was allowed in earlier years. See particularly *Federal Power Commission v. Hope Natural Gas Co.*, 320 U.S. 591 (1944).

the numerous controversial issues involved in this interesting and important subject. Nevertheless, it is desirable to examine certain aspects of the authority of regulatory commissions and to note the possible effects of commissions' decisions on a regulated utility's engineering economy studies.

Commissions generally have the authority to:

1. Set the "fair rate of return" that the company may earn on its rate base.
2. Determine what the rate base includes and how it is to be computed.
3. Determine what expenditures are allowed to be recovered as allowable expenses.
4. Prescribe the permissible ways of applying depreciation, tax credits, and tax incentives.
5. Approve or disapprove the rate schedules presented by the company.
6. Prescribe a uniform classification of accounts and stipulate certain accounting methods to be used by the company.
7. Require periodic reports on all matters under commission jurisdiction.

As already noted, the "fair return" should reflect the over-all cost of money to the utility. However, because the money market is changeable, interest rates for borrowed money (bonds) may vary a good deal over relatively short periods of time. Prices of utility stocks also rise and fall irregularly. Many utility companies must obtain new, external capital each year regardless of the conditions of the money market. The "fair return" rate is not always adjusted by the regulatory commission to reflect the current money market; companies may find it necessary to adjust expansion and improvement plans in order to delay the need for new capital during times of high cost of money.

It also is possible that the "fair return" may be adjusted downward on the initiative of the regulatory commission as a means of penalizing a company for inadequate or poor service. Such action may occur because of complaints by customers. On the other hand, if a utility's earnings are higher than the stipulated "fair return," the commission either can ignore the matter, or it can require that new rate schedules be presented that will bring the net earnings down to the specified level. Because correct predictions of the exact growth of demand for utility service are difficult, there has been a trend to specify a range of acceptable returns rather than a single rate, or at least not to take commission action unless earnings exceed the stipulated rate of return by some given amount.

The rate base presents many special problems. Many commissions in the United States define the rate base as the depreciated book value of the assets used in providing service. They include working capital as well as fixed assets (land and plant). But assets acquired in advance of immediate needs, such as land on which a utility expects to build new facilities ten years hence, sometimes are excluded from the rate base. Under certain circumstances, some plant may be included in the rate base but at a lower price than actually paid by the utility.

Plans to issue new stock or to sell bonds must be approved by the state commission. Generally, such plans are accompanied by a statement of the intended use of the funds. Commissions are interested in these matters for two major reasons. First, the plan for raising new capital will affect the cost of money to the utility, and the commission wants to see that capital is obtained in the most advantageous way. Second, although part of the new capital may be to refund maturing bonds, some of it doubtless will be used to acquire assets that will increase the rate base. The commission wants to know what development, improvement, or service extension plans are to be funded so that it can judge the appropriateness of the plans.

The foregoing discussion indicates some of the complexities of the regulatory problem. Utility managements have the responsibility of maximizing the long run value of the stockholders' investments, and commissions have the responsibility of protecting the public, collectively, from monopolistic pricing. At the same time, commissions need to encourage the development of the desired services at the lowest possible cost to the consumer. This latter objective provides a basis for judging the attractiveness of competing plans for the provision of a service. Generally both commissions and utilities should make decisions among alternative plans on the basis of minimizing revenue requirements (minimizing the long-run cost to the customers).

For the purposes of our present discussion, it is sufficient to note that in the United States the usual condition has been for utilities to expand rapidly and to be able to raise new capital when needed. This has been particularly true of electric, gas, water, and telephone utilities.

Some Differences Between Economy Studies in Regulated Public Utilities and in Competitive Industry. Some contrasts between public utilities and competitive industry that bear on the central theme of this chapter are as follows:

1. As already pointed out, the funds available for investment in new fixed assets are often limited in enterprises engaged in competitive industry. In contrast, a public utility is likely to be raising new capital for expansion at frequent intervals and decisions made by the utility management ordinarily are not controlled by a limitation on funds that can

be made available for plant investment. For this reason, the considerations of capital rationing that often are so important in competitive industry do not usually enter into the selection of a minimum attractive return in public utilities. (Exceptions to this statement occur in certain utilities where it is difficult or impossible to raise new capital, for example, the urban transportation utilities already mentioned.) It follows that justifiable figures for minimum attractive return in public utilities are generally lower than in competitive industry; figures such as 15% or more after income taxes that are common in competitive industry are rarely appropriate in public utilities.

2. Just as in competitive industry, the over-all cost of money to a public utility, considering both borrowed money and equity capital, tends to establish an appropriate *lower limit* for the minimum attractive return to be used in economy studies. However, unlike competitive industry, the *upper limit* for minimum attractive return in a public utility should rarely be much greater than this cost of money. When the return that the regulatory authorities allow on a utility's investment is used as the minimum attractive return in the utility's economy studies, these studies are—in effect—being made from the viewpoint of the utility's customers. That is, decisions between alternative types of plant are being made in a way that will minimize the rates that will be charged for the utility's service.

A policy of making engineering economy studies to minimize a utility's revenue requirements not only takes the viewpoint of the customers but also implies that the interests of the customers and stockholders are identical. This may be true in the long run in many utilities, but it is not true in some and may not be true in the short run in many cases, particularly when the major consequences of a decision will occur between rate cases. The answer to the question of whether customers' and stockholders' interests are really identical depends on a number of factors, foremost of which is the matter of how the regulating commission treats investments for rate base purposes and what expenditures it allows as operating expenses. It also depends on whether or not the "fair return" is realistic relative to the cost of capital at the time of a decision on rates. As already mentioned, cost of capital may fluctuate more rapidly than regulatory commissions change the "fair return." If the permitted rate of return is too low, this tends to cause utility companies to put off investments in new facilities to provide better service. Some of the social costs of inferior or inadequate utility service are discussed later on in this chapter.

Thus it can be argued that the principle of basing engineering decisions on minimizing revenue requirements, while promoted as the best policy from the customers' viewpoint, may occasionally be inappropriate either for customers or for stockholders.

3. It has been pointed out that the common rate-making formula for utilities is designed to permit the utility to earn a "fair return" *after* income taxes. In effect the rate-making authorities view prospective income taxes as an element of expense to be included in the rates charged for utility service.

It is shown later that under certain assumptions regarding rate making, the income taxes resulting from any plant investment may be expressed as a percentage of that investment. The appropriate percentage will depend on the income tax rate, on the life and per cent salvage value of the fixed assets, on the depreciation accounting method being used, and on the average interest rate being paid on long-term-borrowing and the proportion of capital raised by borrowing. A common minimum attractive rate of return used in utility economy studies is 7%. Common annual income tax percentages for utility economy studies in the United States are from 2% to 6% of first cost depending on matters that we shall explain.

Special Aspects of Treatment of Income Taxes in Economy Studies for Regulated Public Utilities in the United States. Under common rules of regulation in many parts of the United States, a utility's revenue requirements are made up of current operating disbursements (not including interest on debt), an allowance for depreciation, income taxes, and a "fair return" on a rate base that usually is approximately equal to depreciated book value. The income taxes paid, of course, depend on the taxable income; as explained in Chapters 16 and 18, interest on debt is a deductible expense in computing taxable income. The income subject to taxation will depend on the interest rate paid on borrowed money, on the debt/equity ratio, on the "fair return," and on the rate base. The following three equations show the relationship between the permitted revenues and the income taxes:

I. Permitted revenue − (Current operating disbursements + Depreciation + Interest paid on debt) = Taxable income
II. Taxable income × Effective tax rate = Income taxes
III. Permitted revenue = Current operating disbursements + Depreciation + Income taxes + (Fair return × Rate base)

We have noted that economy studies for regulated utilities usually aim to minimize a utility's revenue requirements. Given the rules under which utility rates are to be regulated, it usually is possible to express the income tax element in revenue requirements as a percentage of the first cost of the plant under consideration. The appropriate formulas for this percentage will be dependent on the expected rules of rate regulation.

Examples of Formulas for the Ratio of Income Tax Requirements to First Cost of Plant for Regulated Utilities. The following formulas assume that straight-line depreciation is used in the determination of regulated rates and also in the calculation of taxable income. They assume that each year the "fair return" is allowed on a rate base equal to the depreciated book value. They assume that the "fair return" is used as the interest rate to convert a diminishing series of income tax requirements into an equivalent uniform annual series. They assume that the borrowed money applicable to any particular physical assets may be considered to be a stated fraction of the depreciated book value of the assets, and that this fraction will remain constant throughout the life of the assets. They assume that the "fair return" and the interest rate on borrowed money will remain constant throughout the life of any assets.

The presentation of the formulas is simplified by using the functional representation of the gradient factor rather than the algebraic symbols for this factor.

Let a = rate of return ("fair return") on depreciated investment
b = interest rate paid on borrowed funds
c = fraction of plant investment financed by borrowing
e — effective income tax rate
n = life of plant
s = ratio of terminal salvage value to first cost of plant
t = ratio of equivalent annual income taxes to first cost of plant
(with equivalence calculated at rate a)

The general formula for t is

$$t = \frac{e}{1-e}(a - bc)\left[s + (1-s)\left(1 - \frac{(A/G, a\%, n)}{n}\right)\right] \qquad (1)$$

For the special case where the salvage value is zero, the formula becomes

$$t = \frac{e}{1-e}(a - bc)\left(1 - \frac{(A/G, a\%, n)}{n}\right) \qquad (2)$$

For the special case of 100% salvage value, the formula becomes

$$t = \frac{e}{1-e}(a - bc) \qquad (3)$$

For the special case of 100% salvage value and 100% equity financing, it is

$$t = \frac{e}{1-e}a \qquad (4)$$

Explanation of the Basis of the Foregoing Formulas. In explaining the assumptions on which these formulas are based, it is helpful to use several numerical examples and to start with the simplest case, gradually adding various complicating factors to the examples. In all of the following examples, the effective income tax rate e is 0.51 (i.e., 51%), and the permitted rate of return a is 0.07 (i.e., 7%).

First assume $1,000 of investment in an asset assumed to have 100% salvage value (such as land) and assume that the utility is financed entirely from equity funds. The utility will be permitted to earn $70 after income taxes on this investment, i.e., 7% of $1,000. The before-tax earnings, subject to 51% income tax, must be high enough to cover the tax and leave $70 remaining after taxes. Let T represent the income tax. Then

$$T = 0.51(\$70 + T)$$

$$T - 0.51T = 0.51(\$70)$$

$$T = \frac{0.51}{0.49}(\$70) = \$72.86 \text{ or } 7.29\% \text{ of the investment}$$

The foregoing reasoning is the basis of formula (4), which we may apply as follows:

$$t = \frac{e}{1-e}a = \frac{0.51}{1-0.51}(0.07) = 0.0729$$

Now change the conditions of the example by assuming that this $1,000 asset is financed half by equity funds and half by money borrowed at 4% interest. In the terminology of our formulas, $b = 0.04$ and $c = 0.50$. The permitted earnings, before interest but after income taxes, will still be $70. However, $20 of this will go for interest on debt (4% of the $500 borrowed), and this $20 will be a deduction from taxable income. Thus

$$T = 0.51(\$70 + T - \$20)$$

$$T - 0.51T = 0.51(\$70 - \$20)$$

$$T = \$52.04 \text{ or } 5.20\% \text{ of the investment}$$

The foregoing reasoning is the basis of formula (3), which we may apply as follows:

$$t = \frac{e}{1-e}(a - bc) = \frac{0.51}{0.49}[0.07 - 0.04(0.5)] = 0.0520$$

Now make a further change in the conditions of the example by assuming that the $1,000 asset has an estimated life of 10 years with zero salvage value. In the first year of life of the asset the 7% earnings permitted will apply to the full $1,000 of investment, and the tax deduction for interest will apply to 4% of $500, just as in the previous example; it follows that the income tax will be $52.04, just as before. But in the second year, the 7% will apply to the depreciated book value of $900, and the 4% interest is applicable to a debt of $450. And so on. Year-by-year figures are shown in Table 20–1.

The income tax made necessary by the $1,000 investment starts at $52.04 in the first year and reduces each year by $5.204. At 7% interest, the equivalent uniform annual figure is $52.04 − $5.204($A/G$,7%,10) = $52.04 − $5.204(3.95) = $31.48 or 3.15% of the investment.

TABLE 20–1

Year-by-Year Income Tax Payments Caused by $1,000 Investment in Utility Plant Having 10-Year Life and Zero Salvage Value

Effective tax rate assumed as 51%. "Fair return" on depreciated book value assumed as 7%. Straight-line depreciation assumed for both rate regulation and income tax purposes. Half of utility financing by debt with interest at 4%.

Year	Required Earnings To Cover Depreciation, "Fair Return," and Income Taxes	Depreciation Deduction from Taxable Income	Interest Deduction from Taxable Income	Taxable Income	Income Tax	
1	$170 + T_1	$100	$20	$50 + T_1	T_1	= $52.04
2	163 + T_2	100	18	45 + T_2	T_2	— 46.84
3	156 + T_3	100	16	40 + T_3	T_3	= 41.63
4	149 + T_4	100	14	35 + T_4	T_4	= 36.43
5	142 + T_5	100	12	30 + T_5	T_5	= 31.22
6	135 + T_6	100	10	25 + T_6	T_6	= 26.02
7	128 + T_7	100	8	20 + T_7	T_7	= 20.82
8	121 + T_8	100	6	15 + T_8	T_8	= 15.61
9	114 + T_9	100	4	10 + T_9	T_9	= 10.41
10	107 + T_{10}	100	2	5 + T_{10}	T_{10}	= 5.20

The foregoing reasoning is the basis of formula (2), which we may apply as follows:

$$t = \frac{e}{1-e}(a - bc)\left(1 - \frac{(A/G,a\%,n)}{n}\right)$$

$$= \frac{0.51}{0.49}[0.07 - 0.04(0.5)]\left(1 - \frac{3.95}{10}\right) = 0.0315$$

Now make a still further change in the conditions of the example by assuming that the $1,000 asset has a 10-year life with a prospective 50% salvage value at the end of the life. This may be thought of as a $500 asset with 100% salvage value, responsible for a tax of half of $52.04 or $26.02, and another $500 asset with a zero salvage value, responsible for a tax of half of $31.48 or $15.74. The total tax will be the sum of these two figures, $41.76, midway between the figure for zero and 100% salvage values. In general, the income tax percentage for any salvage value above zero and less than 100% can be found by a linear interpolation between the figures for salvage percentages of 0 and 100. Formula (1), our general formula, may be viewed as giving a linear interpolation between the results computed from formulas (2) and (3).

Contrast Between Regulated Public Utilities and Competitive Industry with Respect to Economy Studies and Income Taxes. Our discussion has assumed that, in a regulated utility, income taxes will be allowed by the regulatory authority as one of the components of the price of the utility's product or service, and that economy studies comparing alternative types of plant should—in effect—be made from the viewpoint of the utility's customers. In contrast, our discussion in Chapter 16 implied that the price of a competitive product or service will be established by market conditions unrelated to an individual producer's decision on alternative types of plant and that economy studies for a competitive enterprise should be made from the viewpoint of the owners of the enterprise.

Some important aspects of this difference in viewpoint may be clearer if we examine a specific numerical example. Consider Example 16–1 in which an outlay of $50,000 for materials handling equipment having a 10-year life was expected to decrease net annual operating disbursements by $12,000. If it were to be installed by a manufacturer in competitive industry, the price of the manufactured product presumably would be unaffected by the method of materials handling used by this one manufacturer. The influence of the investment on the manufacturer's income taxes would arise as a result of the change in taxable income caused by the $12,000 annual saving in net operating disbursements partially offset by the $5,000 annual increase in his depreciation charge. If the annual saving in net operating disbursements should be $18,000 instead of $12,000, taxable income would be increased by $6,000 and annual income taxes would be increased by $3,060, 51% of $6,000.

In contrast, if the materials handling equipment had been proposed for a regulated public utility, an additional saving of $6,000 in annual operating disbursements would have no influence on taxable income because this saving would be accompanied by an equal decrease in revenues from the sale of the utility's product or service. The influence of the investment on income taxes would depend on the size of the investment itself and on the company's over-all cost of money, reflected in its permitted rate of "fair return." The higher the after-tax return permitted on the $50,000, the greater the before-tax return must be and the greater the element in income taxes caused by this $50,000 investment.

A Further Comment on Income Tax Considerations in Economy Studies for Regulated Utilities. The formulas given in this chapter for ratio of equivalent annual income taxes to first cost of plant in a regulated utility were based on certain stated assumptions about the rules of regulation and the method of depreciation used in computing taxable income. They have been presented here to illustrate how formulas may be developed to fit a particular set of assumptions on these matters. It is not intended to suggest that these are the only such formulas that are appropriate. In many public utilities other assumptions regarding the rules of rate regulation and methods of tax depreciation may be closer to the facts. Various other formulas have been published based on a number of different assumptions.[3] Even though the different formulas naturally give somewhat different results from one another as well as from the formulas in this chapter, the ratios of income tax to first cost for given tax rates and rates of return on investment all seem to be of the same general order of magnitude.

Two Approaches to a Special Utility Engineering Economy Problem. A common problem in public utilities is caused by the need to add service capability at frequent intervals to meet the growing demand of an area. Expected service lives of units added at different dates may be approximately the same. Moreover, some units may be retired to be replaced by larger units. Often there is no "natural" study period for an economy study to compare different plans to meet expected growth in demand.

This type of problem was first introduced in Examples 7-1 and 7-2. The question arises how best to formulate such a problem in regulated public utilities. Two methods are commonly used. One is called the "coterminated plant" plan; the other is the "repeated plant" plan.

In the coterminated plant plan, the assumption is made that there is some terminal date at which all the units then in service will end their lives. This arbitrary assumption is made only for convenience of calculation, and requires that a "residual value" be estimated to reflect the remaining service life of the units that actually will remain in place and in use at the end of the arbitrarily chosen study period. A simple way to implement this assumption is to calculate the present worth of the costs for the portion of the life that will take place up to the end of the study period. Another way is to compute the present worth of the unre-

[3] American Telephone and Telegraph Co., *Engineering Economy* (2d ed.; New York: A. T. & T. Co., 1963).

covered investment at the end of the study period. A third way is simply to use the book value at the end of the study period.

The repeated plant type of analysis was first discussed in Chapter 7 in connection with present worth comparisons. This method makes the assumption that each replacement of an asset will repeat the cost history of the first one. If a unit added to a system to expand capacity is identical with the first unit, then its equivalent annual cost, once it has been installed, is assumed to be the same as for the first unit. The economy study needs to reflect the fact of the deferment of an investment and its related costs until the need actually arises. The equivalent annual cost of each added unit starts at a different time and the assumption is made that this specific annual cost will be repeated indefinitely. Consequently, the capitalized cost of infinite service can be computed for the date of installation. This capitalized cost can be brought back to zero date by using the appropriate single payment present worth factor.

The Effect of the Coterminated Assumption Depends on the Method Used in the Analysis. The three methods of dealing with the coterminated plant assumption give slightly different results and opinions differ as to their relative merits. The differences are illustrated in the following example.

EXAMPLE 20–1. COMPARISON OF TWO PROPOSED DEVELOPMENT PLANS FOR UTILITY SERVICE TO A NEW RESIDENTIAL COMMUNITY

Facts of the Case. A real estate development company owns a tract of land that it has held for several years in order to develop it for middle income type homes. Available housing in the adjacent city has become scarce and the prices for apartments and private homes have been increasing rapidly. The company has decided that it is time to start the actual development. Since the company does its own contracting the management is well aware of the necessity to build homes at a rate that will enable it to sell all the houses as they become available and still not depress the housing market. Therefore, it has reached a final plan that will require about eight or more years for completion. These plans have been presented to the local electric utility company in order that the utility company can start its engineering designs and be ready to install underground conduits, etc., as the streets are being built, and to be able to supply energy to the early home buyers.

The electric company's engineers have arrived at two different plans to meet the demand, based on the projected number of homes to be occupied each year and the gradual growth in the utilization of electrical energy by the home owners. The first plan, called A, will provide full capacity for twenty years with the initial installation. The second plan, called B, will be a two step development, with the second step being supplied in eight years.

The "fair return" allowed by the state public utility commission is 7%, but the company is now borrowing money at 5%. It is the company's policy to maintain about a 50/50 ratio between debt and equity capital at all times. The effective tax rate for both federal and state income taxes is 54%.

Plan A calls for an initial investment of $200,000 now with a prospective salvage value of 20% of first cost twenty years hence. The operation and maintenance disbursements are estimated to be $15,000 a year and ad valorem taxes will be 2% of first cost.

Plan B calls for an immediate investment of $140,000 and a second investment of $160,000 eight years later. The O & M disbursements will be $9,000 a year for the initial installation, and $8,000 a year for the second installation, making a total of $17,000 a year after eight years. It is believed that each installation will have an economic life of 20 years, with a prospective salvage of 20% of the initial investments. Ad valorem taxes will be 2% of the first cost of all plant in place at any time.

The utility company needs to determine which plan is better, based upon the concept of minimization of revenue requirements.

Comparison of Revenue Requirements. Using the methods described earlier in the chapter,

$$t = \frac{0.54}{1-0.54}(0.07 - 0.05 \times 0.50)\left[0.20 + (1-0.20)\left(1 - \frac{(A/G,7\%,20)}{20}\right)\right]$$

and substituting 7.32 for $(A/G,7\%,20)$, we find that

$$t = 0.038$$

Plan A:

Capital recovery = $160,000(A/P,7%,20) + $40,000(0.07)	$17,902
O & M Disbursements	15,000
Ad valorem taxes = 0.02($200,000)	4,000
Equivalent annual income tax disbursement = 0.038($200,000)	7,600
Total equivalent annual revenue required	$44,502

Plan B:

First installation:

Capital recovery = $112,000(A/P,7%,20) + $28,000(0.07)	$12,532
O & M Disbursements	9,000
Ad valorem taxes = 0.02($140,000)	2,800
Equivalent annual disbursement for income taxes = 0.038($140,000) . .	5,320
Total equivalent annual revenue required	$29,652

Second installation:

Capital recovery = $128,000(A/P,7%,20) + $32,000(0.07)	$14,322
O & M Disbursements	8,000
Ad valorem taxes = 0.02($160,000)	3,200
Equivalent annual disbursement for income taxes = 0.038($160,000) . . .	6,080
Total equivalent annual revenue required	$31,602

The second installation is made at year 8, so only 12 years of that service is "chargeable" to the first twenty years of service. Therefore, the equivalent annual revenue required by Plan B is:

$$AR = \$29,652 + \$31,602(P/A,7\%,12)(P/F,7\%,8)(A/P,7\%,20)$$
$$= \$29,652 + \$31,602(7.943)(0.5820)(0.09439)$$
$$= \$43,441$$

This calculation indicates that Plan B requires slightly less annual revenue than Plan A.

The previous method of analysis is the one that is preferred by the authors because it clearly "charges" to the twenty-year study period the prorated share of the revenue requirements incurred by the second installation, and spreads that increment of revenue requirements over the entire twenty years by a logical method.

Another method proposes that any unrecovered initial investment in plant that is to be retained in service after the study period be used to compute its "salvage value" at the end of the study period. In the foregoing example, the depreciable amount with 7% interest requires an annual capital recovery of $12,082 a year for twenty years, and at that time the installation will still have an estimated salvage value of $32,000. Therefore, the unrecovered investment at the end of the study period (after 12 years of service for the second installation) will be:

$$\$12,082(P/A,7\%,8) + \$32,000 = \$104,144$$

If that value is taken as the prospective salvage value for the second installation at the end of the twenty-year study period, a new t must be calculated for the second installation. The salvage value as a percentage of original investment will be

$$(\$104,144/\$160,000)(100) = 65.1\%$$

$$t = \frac{0.54}{1 - 0.54}(0.07 - 0.05 \times 0.50)\left[0.651 + 3.349\left(1 - \frac{(A/G,7\%,12)}{12}\right)\right]$$

Substituting 4.70 for $(A/G,7\%,12)$, we find $t = 0.0464$ and we can recalculate the revenue requirement for the second installation based upon a 12 year life with a salvage value of $104,144.

Second installation:

Capital recovery = ($160,000 − $104,144)($A/P,7\%,12$)
+ $104,144(0.07) $14,321
O & M Disbursements 8,000
Ad valorem taxes = 0.02($160,000) 3,200
Equivalent annual disbursement for income taxes
= 0.0464($160,000) 7,424
Total equivalent annual revenue required by second installation $32,945

Using this method of evaluating the residual value of the second installation, the equivalent annual revenue required by Plan B becomes:

$$AR = \$29,652 + \$32,945(7.943)(0.5820)(0.09439)$$
$$= \$44,027$$

This calculation shows that Plan B is only slightly more desirable than Plan A, and it is obvious that the higher revenue requirement stems from the fact that only 35% of the total amount to be depreciated in twenty years is actually depreciated in the first twelve years of the installation's life. Therefore, the investment on which the utility company is allowed to earn its "fair return" is higher throughout the twelve year period by this method than by the previous method.

A third method of dealing with the coterminated plant assumption is to assume that the salvage value of the asset at the end of the study period is equal to the book value of the asset at that time. Thus, for the second installation, the original estimate was that the asset would have an economic life of 20 years and would be depreciated to 20% of the original value in twenty years. The study period was set so that only twelve years of that twenty-year life would be applicable to the study period. Using straight line depreciation, 4% of the original value will be charged to depreciation expense each year. Therefore, the book value at the end of twelve years is $(1- 0.04 \times 12)\$160,000 = .52(\$160,000)$. Now a third value for t must be calculated due to the change in the salvage value expressed as a percentage of the first cost. By using 52% of the first cost as the salvage value, the new t will be found to be 0.0394, and the equivalent annual revenue required for the second installation during the last twelve years of the study period will be $32,997. The total equivalent annual revenue required for Plan B by this method is:

$$AR = \$29,652 + \$32,997(7.943)(0.5820)(0.09439)$$
$$= \$44,050$$

This result is not seriously different from that obtained in the previous calculation, but it shows that the increased capital recovery due to the smaller salvage value is greater than the increase obtained in the previous calculation due to the larger rate base times the "fair return."

Three methods of computing the revenue required by a unit of investment that is to be retained in service after the end of the study period have given us revenue requirements for Plan B from $43,441 to $44,027 to $44,050, and the only differences involved were the results of different methods of appraising the residual value of the asset at the end of the study period.

The Reason for Using Debt/Equity Ratio and Cost of Debt in Computing Public Utility Revenue Requirements. In Chapter 18 we gave a number of reasons why, generally speaking, it is undesirable to make comparisons of alternatives on the basis of return to equity capital. The reader should note that we are not disregarding our own advice when we explain the use of the revenue requirements approach in economy studies for public utilities. The "fair return" adopted as i^* applies to total capital, not merely to equity capital. The debt/equity ratio and the cost of borrowed money are used in the economy study *only* as data that are required to calculate the income tax portion of revenue requirements.

To compute the income tax element in revenue requirements, we must first estimate the extent to which a proposed investment will influence taxable income. In making this estimate in regulated utilities, we—in effect—assume that all items of new plant will be financed by the same proportion of debt and equity capital with all debt carrying the same interest rate. With respect to the debt/equity ratio, this simplifying assumption is a reasonable one for the many regulated utility companies in the United States that endeavor to maintain a fairly constant ratio of debt to equity capital in spite of the need for frequent new financing.

"Fair Return" Is Not Guaranteed for Regulated Public Utilities. We have noted that a "fair return" authorized by a regulatory body for a utility company merely grants permission to earn that rate of return on the rate base *if it can.* When utilities experience steadily rising costs over a long period of time, there may be no reason to believe that the costs of materials, labor, services, and supplies will decrease in the future. After a rate schedule has been approved by the regulatory commission, a company is likely to be under pressure to effect economies in order to continue to earn something near the stipulated "fair return." The rate schedule usually is based on the company's performance in a given "test year." With rising costs, the test year is likely to be more favorable to the company than any future year. Once a rate schedule has been approved, commissions are reluctant to grant rate increases until a utility can show that it is being badly penalized by the existing schedule.

Many economy studies are made by engineers for regulated utilities to find the least costly method of meeting the service demand over a long period of time. Frequently these studies are, in effect, cost reduction studies involving the selection of equipment, the design of service extension programs (full capacity now vs. stepped development), adoption of new technology vs. continuing existing technology, and mechanization or automation to eliminate or reduce labor expenses. A company that does not engage in such cost improvement programs is doomed to find itself with actual earnings substantially below the "fair return."

If the cost reduction should be accomplished by these studies, and if ordinary operating costs do not rise, the utility can expect that the commission will eventually initiate a new rate case and require a new schedule with lower rates. If customers' utilization of the utility's services increases to the point where economies of scale result in earnings above the "fair return" under the existing rate schedule, the commission is also likely to initiate a rate case. Both of these results have been observed in the 1960's in the United States. Thus success in providing more or better service at lower costs may force a utility to redouble its efforts to reduce costs.

Social Costs of Short-sighted Regulatory Policies May Actually Defeat the Objectives of the Regulatory Agency. Anyone who has lived or traveled in some of the developing nations can testify to the frustrations that result from inadequate, inefficient, unreliable, or inferior utility service. If the water supply system operates only a few hours a day, or if the pressure is so low that little or no flow occurs when a tap is opened, the home owners and the industrial firms will compensate by installing their own storage tanks and booster pumps. The actual monetary cost of providing, individually, the difference between an inadequate system and a satisfactory (but perhaps still inferior) system usually is much greater than the cost would have been to have provided an adequate system from the beginning.

Inadequate, unreliable, or inferior electrical service normally results in each industrial firm installing its own generation plant, with higher investment cost per unit of capacity and the loss of economies of scale inherent in large generation plants. Consumers of the products or services of these firms pay higher prices for the products or services as a result of the inferior central station electrical system.

Lack of transportation facilities deprives communities of industry and the resulting payment of spendable income in the community. Raw materials go unused, labor goes unemployed, and the area becomes an economic drain on the national or state budget to provide some semblance of relief for the population there.

Even where existing telephone service is relatively good for those fortunate enough to have an instrument, new customers may have to wait months or years to obtain service because the expansion of the service facilities lags behind the demand for service.

But such social costs are not exclusive characteristics of developing nations. Regulatory policies in industrialized nations can cause similar (although perhaps not as extensive) adverse effects. Certain rate reductions may seem to provide short run benefits for the existing customers but may also result in higher costs in the long run because investments to provide for future growth may not be allowed in the rate base until the facilities actually are being used. Consequently, construction of service facilities may be undertaken on a piecemeal basis at a higher total cost.

Imposing an artificially low "fair return" in times of high capital costs increases the difficulty of raising new funds that are needed to take advantage of new technology. Thus plant is kept in service beyond its economic life with resultant higher costs for maintenance and repair, and customers are deprived of more modern and more effective services. Both the customers and the utility stockholders suffer from such a policy. The good intentions underlying the regulatory commission's policies may lead to over-all higher costs to the customers for somewhat inferior services.

Some Differences Between "Monopolistic" and "Competitive" Public Utilities. Earlier in this chapter, attention was called to the fact that most telephone, gas, water, and electric systems occupy a monopolistic position in an area. One company is granted exclusive rights to serve a certain area, and regulation under the laws of the states or nation substitutes for the effects of competition in forcing a company to render satisfactory service at a reasonable cost. Some public utilities, however, are not granted such exclusive service areas. Notable in this list is the transportation industry. Two or more airlines will be granted the same routes, and consequently compete with each other for the available business. Dozens or hundreds of trucking and bus lines may serve a certain area. Railroad and steamship lines often have duplicate, or almost duplicate, routes.

Thus in the transportation business, not only do similar companies compete with each other, but also must compete with other modes of transportation. Truck lines, railroads, steamship lines, and airlines may all be competing for the same business. The Interstate Commerce Commission and the various state regulatory agencies have the responsibility to establish commodity freight rates between cities for the various modes of transport, and slight differences in rates for the different modes can almost eliminate competition from other modes. Then the commissions find themselves playing the role of enforcers to assure that one transportation company does not undercut the established rates in order to take business away from another company.

The principle of minimization of revenue requirements ordinarily does not enter into the establishment of commodity rates for transportation companies. The rates are usually set high enough that the less efficient operators can expect to be able to stay in business if they provide reasonably good service and practice good management. The transportation companies normally try to out-do each other in service in order to obtain a larger share of the available business. Thus air lines promote their food service, comfort of the airplanes, speed, convenient times of departure and arrival, and such as a means of gaining public acceptance. Truck lines and bus lines try to compete on the basis of door-to-door, or downtown- to downtown service, speed in total service time from point of origin to final destination, and lower cost.

Thus, in the monopolistic utilities, the engineering economy studies are usually made to find the least expensive way to provide a given service to the customer because the regulatory bodies require that approach, but the competitive utility companies perform engineering economy studies primarily for cost cutting purposes accompanied by improved service since their rates are fixed for all the competitors. In that respect, economy studies for competing utility companies are exactly analagous to studies for any privately owned competitive business organization. The methods shown in Example 20–1 are not necessary, because the regulatory body is not really controlling the rate of return earned by the company relative to some rate base.

Transportation companies cannot either raise or lower their rates without commission approval, and when such changes are made, they apply to all the competing companies equally. Thus the normal forces of competition are not allowed to work, and the result is that probably many commodity rates are higher than they need be. It is important, however, to note the public is protected from one of the older evils of non-regulated common carriers: lower rates for preferred customers. One effect of this kind of regulation that protects the relatively in-efficient carrier is that there is less incentive for the better carriers to exert much effort and capital toward innovation and modernization of their systems. Progress tends to be inhibited and new ideas or concepts are not accepted and implemented as quickly under these conditions as when the firms are not protected from competition.

PROBLEMS

20–1. A utility company is considering the following two plans to provide a certain service required by present demand and the prospective growth of demand for the coming 18 years:

Plan R requires an immediate investment of $500,000 in property that has an estimated life of 18 years with 20% terminal salvage value. Annual dis bursements for operation and maintenance will be $50,000. Annual property taxes will be 2% of first cost.

Plan S requires an immediate investment of $300,000 in property that has an estimated life of 18 years with 20% terminal salvage value. Annual dis-bursements for its operation and maintenance during the first 6 years will be $40,000. After 6 years, an additional investment of $400,000 will be required in property having an estimated life of 12 years with 40% terminal salvage value. After this additional property is installed, annual disbursements (for years 7 to 18) for operation and maintenance of the combined properties will be $60,000. Annual property taxes will be 2% of the first cost of property in service at any time.

Make your recommendation for a choice between the two plans on the basis of minimum equivalent annual revenue requirements for the coming 18 years. The regulatory commission is allowing a 6% "fair return" on depreciated book value to cover the cost of money to the utility. Assume that this rate of return will continue throughout the 18 years. The utility company's effective income tax rate is 50%. Straight-line depreciation is to be used for both rate regulation and income tax purposes. Half of the utility's financing is by debt with interest at 3½%. (*Ans.* = Plan R, $117,630; Plan S, $123,780.)

20–2. Solve Problem 20–1 changing the "fair return" to 7%, the tax rate to 48%, and the debt financing to 60% of the capital furnished by debt with interest at 4%. (*Ans.* = Plan R, $121,650; Plan S, $126,340.)

20–3. To provide service for an area that is rapidly being changed from farming to residential developments, a telephone company has estimated the prospective demands for a twenty-year period, and has drawn up several alter-native plans for providing the service. Two plans appear to justify detailed economy studies. The first plan will provide underground conduits and exchange facilities immediately to take care of the entire demand for 20 years. Cables will be installed in three steps, one set now, a second set 8 years hence and a third set 14 years hence. This plan will require an initial investment of $250,000, and each addition of cable will require an investment of $60,000. The annual O and M disbursements for the first unit will be $30,000, and each addition of cable will add $8,000 to the annual O and M disbursements.

Of the initial investment, $10,000 is for land on which to build the exchange. The land will not depreciate. $200,000 is for the exchange building and the underground conduit, both of which are assumed to have a 40-year life with zero salvage value. The remaining initial investment is for the first cable installation. Cable is assumed to have a 20-year life with a 20% salvage value.

The second plan calls for full development of the service capacity needed for 20 years at once. The total investment will be made up of $10,000 for land, $200,000 for building and conduit, and $100,000 for cable. Lives and salvage values are the same as for the stepped development program. The O and M disbursements for the full program will be $38,000 a year for the full 20 years.

Assume that the company maintains a 40/60 debt/equity ratio and that it pays 5% for the borrowed capital. The state utility commission allows the company a "fair return" of 7%. The company's effective income tax rate is 52% and the ad valorem taxes average about 3% of the first cost of plant. Straight line depreciation is used for all depreciable assets.

Assuming that these conditions will continue for the twenty year study period, determine the equivalent annual revenue requirements for each plan.

20–4. Determine what effects the following changes in the parameters of Problem 20–3 will have individually on the revenue requirements for the full capacity development plan:
  a. Change the debt/equity ratio to 55/45.
  b. Change the cost of debt capital to 6%.
  c. Change the "fair return" to 8%.

20–5. "Imbedded cost of debt capital" is a term frequently used to describe the average cost of the outstanding debt that a public utility has at any time. This is a weighted average. Suppose that in 1970, a public utility company has the following outstanding bonds:

Date of Issue	Amount Outstanding	Maturity Date	Interest Rate Payable
July 1950	$20,000,000	1970	3.2%
July 1956	20,000,000	1976	3.8%
July 1960	20,000,000	1980	4.5%
July 1965	30,000,000	1985	5.0%

  a. Compute the "imbedded cost of debt capital" as of June 1970, before the first issue is redeemed.

  b. Now asume that the company will borrow $20,000,000 in 1970 to redeem the first issue, and also borrow $20,000,000 to invest in service capability expansion, all at 5.8%. After this has occurred and the first issue has been redeemed, what is the "imbedded cost of debt capital"?

20–6. Using the method of analysis illustrated in Table 20–1, compute the equivalent annual revenue requirement for the following set of conditions, first assuming straight line depreciation, and then assuming sum-of-years-digits method of depreciation. Comment on the effects of the depreciation method on the cost of service to the customer. Comment on the effects of the depreciation method on the earnings on equity for the stockholders of the company. Comment on the effect of the depreciation method on the figure for equivalent uniform annual income taxes. Assume that the depreciation method selected is used not only for book and tax purposes but also is used by the regulatory commission in establishing the permitted level of rates.

Investment:	$13,750
Salvage value	20% of first cost.
Effective income tax rate	52%
Debt/equity ratio	40/60 and held constant over life.
Cost of debt capital	4%
"Fair return" allowed	7%
Life	10 years

20–7. The question often arises as to whether or not a regulated public utility company should lease equipment or buildings rather than own them. It is quite obvious that leasing is a form of borrowing and the interest rate for debt capital compared with the effective interest rate paid for the capital investment avoided by leasing is relevant to any such decision. Furthermore, the stockholders' incentive for leasing is affected by the regulatory agency's decision as to the inclusion of the value of the leased asset in the rate base.

For an example, assume that a service truck that could be purchased by a utility company for $3,500, which the company would probably keep for four years and then sell for about $350, can be leased on a four-year lease contract on the basis of $70 per month (beginning of each month) for the first 24 months and $50 a month for the last 24 months. License, maintenance, repairs, etc., will be paid by the utility company in either case.

Compute the equivalent annual revenue required if the truck is purchased, when the debt/equity ratio is 50/50, cost of debt is 6% and "fair return" is 7%. Assume 52% effective income tax rate. No ad valorem taxes except as included in the license fee.

Compute the equivalent annual revenue required if the truck is leased and not included in the rate base, and then compute the equivalent annual revenue required if it is included in the rate base as though financed by 100% debt, depreciated on a straight line, and included in the rate base.

Discuss the results of your computations from the customers' viewpoint and the stockholders' viewpoint.

20–8. In a certain area that has become very popular as a recreational area and the site for "second," or vacation, homes, about 50 private homes have been built over an area of about 100 acres of land. Most of the homes have one-half acre, and some of the land owners expect to sell off additional homesites in the future. Some of the owners have estimated that in 10 years there will be about 100 homes.

At the present time each home owner has a private well with an electric pump and pressure tank to supply water. The average cost for a well is $300 and for a pump is $500. The well probably will last about 40 years and the pump will last about 10 years. Average annual maintenance, repair and electrical energy for each home is about $60.

A large natural spring with a flow of about 50,000 gallons a day is located on the tract of land and is owned by one of the land owners. He has suggested to the other land owners that they form a water company to provide water not only for present owners but for the future home owners. He has had an engineer draw up a preliminary plan that requires the following expenditures and operating costs:

Item	Cost	Life	Salvage Value
Fencing the spring	$ 600	40 yr.	0
Concrete Reservoir	10,000	40 yr.	0
Chlorinator	1,000	10 yr.	$200
Pipe system with capacity for 100 homes	18,000	50 yr.	0
Annual operation and maintenance	1,500		
Ad valorem taxes		2% of first cost/year.	

Since this proposed company will come under the jurisdiction of the state public utility commission, the company will be limited to a fair return of about 8%. The promoter proposes that the landowners provide about 50% of the initial capital and borrow the additional amount. He thinks he can borrow the required amount at 6%. He estimates that about five new homes will be built each year for the next ten years, and he proposes to charge $100 as a connection charge and a flat rate per year per home (thus avoiding the cost of installing water meters.)

Compute the equivalent annual revenue requirement to provide the 8% "fair return," and determine the flat rate that he will have to charge so that by the end of ten years the water company will have realized the 8% "fair return." Assume that the assets will be depreciated on the straight line basis and that the bonds will be retired serially from income so that the 50/50 debt equity ratio is maintained.

Compare the equivalent annual cost of the water service to each customer with the costs of owning and operating a well and pump.

How should the $100 connection charge be handled in the problem? Is there any justification for it? Should it only be levied against future connections for new homes?

21

Capital Budgeting

> Capital budgeting is one of the most important areas of management decision making. This is because the conception, continuing existence and growth of a successful business enterprise is entirely dependent upon the selection and implementation of sound, productive investments. The almost universal reluctance, often complete refusal of top echelon management to delegate authority to make investment decisions amply demonstrates the widespread recognition of this importance.—R. I. REUL [1]

The two related aspects of capital budgeting are the sourcing of investment funds and the choice among investment proposals. We have considered certain aspects of the sourcing of investment funds in Chapters 11 and 18. However, this entire book has dealt with various aspects of the evaluation of proposed investments. In this chapter we take a further look at certain troublesome issues that arise in relating sourcing of funds to investment evaluation. We also examine certain organizational aspects of investment decisions, both at the level of top management and at the level of design.

Cost of Capital. A favorite topic for writers on business finance is the over-all "cost of capital" to a business enterprise.[2] It is generally agreed that the objective should be to find a weighted average of the costs of all the various kinds of capital raised by the enterprise.

There is no particular difficulty in using compound interest methods of analysis to find the cost of money acquired by obligations to make fixed payments. Methods of making such analysis were discussed and illustrated in Chapters 8 and 18, with particular reference to capital

---

[1] R. I. Reul, Sec. 4, Capital Budgeting, in *Handbook of Industrial Engineering and Management*, W. G. Ireson and E. L. Grant, eds. (Englewood Cliffs, N.J.: Prentice-Hall, Inc., 2d ed., copyright 1970).

[2] For a critical view of the literature on this subject, see a paper by David Durand, "The Cost of Capital to the TK Corporation is 00.0%; or Much Ado About Very Little." This paper is included in *Decision Making Criteria for Capital Expenditures, Papers and Discussions of the Fourth Summer Symposium, Engineering Economy Division, A.S.E.E.* (Hoboken, N.J.: The Engineering Economist, Stevens Institute of Technology, 1965).

raised by borrowing and long term leases. However, in those chapters we noted that there sometimes are concealed costs associated with such raising of funds; an uncritical analysis may give a figure for cost of money that is really too low.

But there is great difficulty in finding a numerical figure for the over-all cost of equity capital in a business enterprise. In a corporation, such capital includes retained earnings, if any, as well as the capital raised by the sale of stock. Dozens of different formulas have been proposed by different writers to find the cost of equity capital expressed as an interest rate. When applied to specific cases, the different formulas often give quite different answers. Sometimes the answers clearly are ridiculous.

Even when a particular formula for cost of equity capital is adopted, various possible sources of difficulty remain. Figures taken from the books of account, such as book values and annual profits, are used in many of the formulas. But such accounting figures depend upon a number of arbitrary decisions made by management, including the choice of a depreciation accounting method for book purposes, the choice of a depreciation method for income tax purposes, and—in the frequent cases where different depreciation methods are used for book and tax purposes —the choice of whether or not to recognize the deferment of income taxes in the calculation of profits. Even though the accounting figures are not subject to question, the particular span of years chosen for analysis will greatly influence the computed cost of equity capital in many instances.

Some formulas for cost of equity capital also use market prices of a company's common stock. The fluctuation of stock prices makes the choice of the initial and terminal dates a critical matter in the application of any such formula.

For the foregoing reasons, we do not here propose any method for assigning a figure to the cost of equity capital or for finding the derived figure for the weighted average cost of capital.

Relationship of the Availability of Attractive Investment Proposals to the Sourcing of Investment Funds. The quotation from Joel Dean at the start of Chapter 18 emphasized the point that investment proposals should compete with one another on the basis of merit unrelated to the source of funds that might be deemed to apply to any particular project. Moreover, alternate sources of funds should compete on the basis of merit and the pattern of sourcing should not be determined by the specific investment proposals that are approved. Not only in the quotation from Dean but throughout this entire book, we have stressed the concept that separable decisions should be made separately. Generally speaking, decisions about investment proposals are separable from decisions about financing, although we noted certain types of exceptions in Chapter 18.

The issues involved in choosing a pattern for sourcing of capital funds are quite complex and are outside the scope of this book. An adequate discussion of these issues would call for a treatise on business finance— or perhaps several such treatises.

But clearly there is no point in raising new funds or in retaining funds that might legally be distributed to the owners unless such funds can be invested in a way that is expected to benefit the present owners of an enterprise. Therefore, broad policy questions regarding the amount of investment funds to be made available are related to the existence of attractive investment proposals. It is only because there are good opportunities for investment that the acquisition of new capital funds is desirable.

The cost and the availability of money that can be obtained by borrowing and long-term leasing will vary greatly from time to time and from one enterprise to another. Also, the possibility of new equity financing and the terms on which new equity funds can be secured will change from time to time and differ from enterprise to enterprise.

We have noted certain difficulties in finding a firm figure for the weighted average cost of capital to a business enterprise. If there were one agreed-on and unimpeachable figure for such a cost of capital in any particular case, if this cost did not change, and if there were no obstacles to the raising of new funds at any time, one might argue that the minimum attractive rate of return should be equal to the cost of capital. Actually, the matter is not so simple as this even under idealized assumptions. Further comments on this point are made following our discussion of the review of investment proposals at the capital budgeting level.

An Example of Forms for Presentation of Investment Proposals. A number of facets of the review of investment proposals on the capital budgeting level can be illustrated by a brief description of certain forms and methods of analysis developed for the Chemical Divisions of FMC Corporation. The forms (Figures 21–1 to 21–3) and the descriptive material are reproduced by permission from an article by Ray I. Reul.[3]

Discussion of Figures 21–1 to 21–3. These three forms contain a worked-out example of a hypothetical proposal for facilities to produce a new product. In this example the proposed investment starts in 1956 with the purchase of a site, and the plant construction occurs in 1957 and 1958. Sales of the product start in 1958 at 600 tons and reach a

[3] R. I. Reul, "Profitability Index for Investments," *Harvard Business Review*, XXXV, No. 4 (July–August, 1957), 116–32.

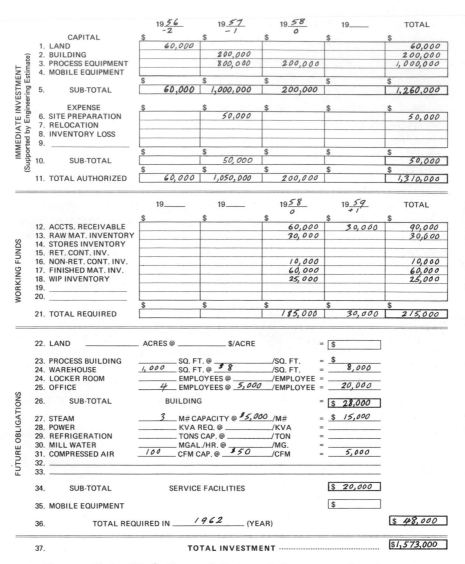

FIGURE 21–1. Work Sheet of Estimated Investment Requirements

SOURCE: R. I. Reul, "Profitability Index for Investments," *Harvard Business Review*, XXXV, No. 4 (July–August, 1957), 123.

INVESTMENT

CAL. YEAR	PERIOD		CAPITAL		EXPENSED	WORKING FUND	TOTAL
			LAND	FACILITIES			
	3rd YR.	AT START					
		DURING					
56	2nd YR.	AT START	$60,000				$60,000
		DURING					
57	1st YR.	AT START					
		DURING		$1,000,000	$50,000		1,050,000
58	1st YR.	AT START					
		DURING		200,000		$185,000	385,000
59	2nd YEAR DURING					30,000	30,000
60	3rd YEAR DURING						
61	4th YEAR DURING						
62	5th YEAR DURING			48,000			48,000
	6th YEAR DURING						
	7th YEAR DURING						
	8th YEAR DURING						
	9th YEAR DURING						
	10th YEAR DURING						
TOTALS			$60,000	$1,248,000	$50,000	$215,000	$1,573,000

RECEIPTS

CAL. YEAR	ANNUAL PERIOD	ANNUAL VOLUME IN TONS	PLANT NET INCOME	PLANT COST BEFORE DEPRECIATION	PROFIT BEFORE DEPRECIATION	DEPRECIATION & DEPLETION DEDUCTION	CASH FLOW BACK AFTER 50% INCOME TAX — ON INCOME	ON DEDUCTION
						$50,000		$25,000
	1st	600	$1,200,000	$1,000,000	$200,000	136,800	$100,000	68,400
	2nd	800	1,600,000	1,200,000	400,000	126,600	200,000	63,300
	3rd	1,000	2,000,000	1,600,000	400,000	114,300	200,000	57,200
	4th	1,000	2,000,000	1,600,000	400,000	110,200	200,000	55,100
	5th	1,000	2,000,000	1,600,000	400,000	105,400	200,000	52,700
	6th	1,200	2,400,000	1,800,000	600,000	95,900	300,000	48,000
	7th	1,200	2,400,000	1,800,000	600,000	87,400	300,000	43,000
	8th	1,200	2,400,000	1,800,000	600,000	79,000	300,000	39,500
	9th	1,200	2,400,000	1,800,000	600,000	69,500	300,000	34,800
	10th	1,200	2,400,000	1,800,000	600,000	61,000	300,000	30,500
	11th	1,200	2,400,000	1,800,000	600,000	52,500	300,000	26,300
	12th	1,200	2,400,000	1,800,000	600,000	43,100	300,000	21,600
	13th	1,200	2,400,000	1,800,000	600,000	34,600	300,000	17,300
	14th	1,200	2,400,000	1,800,000	600,000	26,100	300,000	13,100
	15th	1,200	2,400,000	1,800,000	600,000	16,700	300,000	8,300
	16th	1,200	2,400,000	1,800,000	600,000	8,700	300,000	4,100
	17th	1,200	2,400,000	1,800,000	600,000	7,700	300,000	3,800
	18th	1,200	2,400,000	1,800,000	600,000	7,200	300,000	3,600
	19th	1,200	2,400,000	1,800,000	600,000	6,800	300,000	3,200
	20th	1,200	2,615,000	1,800,000	600,000	6,100	515,000	3,000
	21st					5,800		2,900
	22nd					5,300		2,700
	23rd					5,000		2,500
	24th					4,400		2,200
	25th					3,900		2,000
	26th					3,700		1,800
	27th					3,400		1,700
	28th					3,200		1,600
	29th					2,900		1,500
	30th					2,700		1,400

* NOTE: INCLUDES $215,000 WORKING FUNDS RECOVERED - NOT SUBJECT TO INCOME TAX

FIGURE 21–2. Time Schedule of Expenditures and Receipts

SOURCE: R. I. Reul, "Profitability Index for Investments," *Harvard Business Review*, XXXV, No. 4 (July–August, 1957), 126.

Upper section — Disbursements (before / after zero point)

CAL. YEAR	PERIOD	TRIAL #1 0% — Actual Amount of Disbursements	TRIAL #2 10% — Factor	TRIAL #2 — Present Worth	TRIAL #3 15% — Factor	TRIAL #3 — Present Worth	TRIAL #4 25% — Factor	TRIAL #4 — Present Worth	TRIAL #5 40% — Factor	TRIAL #5 — Present Worth
	3rd YR. AT ST.									
	3rd YR. DURING		1.350		1.588		2.117		3.320	
56	2nd YR. AT ST.	$ 60,000	1.285	$ 73,300	1.466	$ 81,000	1.873	$ 98,000	2.736	$ 133,500
	2nd YR. DURING		1.221		1.350		1.649		2.225	
57	1st YR. AT ST.		1.162		1.253		1.459		1.834	
57	1st YR. DURING	$ 1,050,000	1.052	$ 1,104,600	1.079	$ 1,133,000	1.136	$ 1,192,800	1.230	$ 1,291,500
58	1st YEAR DURING	385,000	.952	366,500	.929	357,700	.885	340,700	.824	317,200
59	2nd YEAR DURING	30,000	.861	25,800	.799	24,000	.689	20,700	.553	16,600
60	3rd YEAR DURING		.779		.688		.537		.370	
61	4th YEAR DURING		.705		.592		.418		.248	
62	5th YEAR DURING	48,000	.638	30,600	.510	24,500	.326	15,600	.166	8,000
	6th YEAR DURING		.577		.439		.254		.112	
	7th YEAR DURING		.522		.378		.197		.075	
	8th YEAR DURING		.473		.325		.154		.050	
	9th YEAR DURING		.428		.280		.120		.034	
	10th YEAR DURING		.387		.241		.093		.023	
	TOTALS (A)	**$ 1,573,000**		**$ 1,600,800**		**$ 1,620,200**		**$ 1,668,700**		**$ 1,766,800**

Lower section — Receipts (after zero point)

CAL. YEAR	PERIOD	TRIAL #1 — Actual Amount of Receipts	TRIAL #2 — Factor	TRIAL #2 — Present Worth	TRIAL #3 — Factor	TRIAL #3 — Present Worth	TRIAL #4 — Factor	TRIAL #4 — Present Worth	TRIAL #5 — Factor	TRIAL #5 — Present Worth
57	1st YR. (Became Outflow)	25,000	1.052	26,300	1.079	27,000	1.136	28,400	1.230	30,800
58	2nd YEAR DURING	168,400	.952	160,300	.929	156,400	.885	149,000	.824	138,800
59	3rd YEAR DURING	263,300	.861	226,700	.799	210,400	.689	181,400	.553	145,600
60	4th YEAR DURING	257,200	.779	205,500	.688	177,000	.537	138,100	.370	95,200
61	5th YEAR DURING	255,700	.705	179,100	.592	151,000	.418	106,600	.248	63,300
62	6th YEAR DURING	252,700	.638	161,200	.510	128,900	.326	82,400	.166	41,900
63	7th YEAR DURING	343,400	.577	198,000	.439	152,800	.254	78,800	.112	39,000
64	8th YEAR DURING	347,700	.522	181,500	.378	129,900	.197	67,700	.075	25,800
65	9th YEAR DURING	339,500	.473	160,500	.325	118,500	.154	52,300	.050	17,000
66	10th YEAR DURING	334,800	.428	143,300	.280	93,700	.119	39,800	.034	11,400
67	11th YEAR DURING	330,500	.387	127,900	.241	79,700	.093	30,700	.023	7,000
68	12th YEAR DURING	326,300	.350	114,200	.207	67,500	.073	23,800	.015	4,900
69	13th YEAR DURING	321,600	.317	101,900	.178	57,200	.057	18,300	.010	3,200
70	14th YEAR DURING	317,300	.287	91,100	.154	48,900	.044	14,000	.007	2,200
71	15th YEAR DURING	313,100	.259	81,100	.132	41,300	.034	10,600	.005	1,600
72	16th YEAR DURING	308,300	.235	72,500	.114	35,100	.027	8,300	.003	900
73	17th YEAR DURING	304,800	.212	64,600	.098	29,500	.021	6,400	.002	600
74	18th YEAR DURING	303,000	.192	58,200	.084	25,500	.016	4,900	.001	300
75	19th YEAR DURING	203,200	.174	35,400	.073	14,800	.013	2,600	.001	300
76	20th YEAR DURING	57,800	.157	9,100	.062	3,600	.010	600	.001	300
77	21st YEAR DURING	51,900	.142	7,400	.054	2,800	.008	400	.001	100
78	22nd YEAR DURING	2,700	.129	300	.046	100	.006			
79	23rd YEAR DURING	2,500	.117	300	.040	100	.005			
80	24th YEAR DURING	2,200	.105	200	.034		.004			
81	25th YEAR DURING	2,000	.095	200	.029		.003			
82	26th YEAR DURING	1,800	.086	100	.025		.002			
83	27th YEAR DURING	1,700	.078		.022		.002			
84	28th YEAR DURING	1,600	.071		.019		.001			
85	29th YEAR DURING	1,500	.064		.016		.001			
86	30th YEAR DURING	1,400	.058		.014		.001			
87			.052		.012		.001			
	TOTALS (B)	**6,257,700**		**2,530,800**		**1,796,500**		**1,062,100**		**630,700**
	RATIO A/B	**.25**		**.63**		**.90**		**1.57**		**2.80**

FIGURE 21–3. Calculation of the Profitability Index

SOURCE: R. I. Reul, "Profitability Index for Investments," *Harvard Business Review*, XXXV, No. 4 (July–August, 1957), 127.

plateau of 1,200 tons per year in the sixth year. Although the analysis assumes sales for only 20 years, the tax consequences of the depreciation deductions are shown for 30 years.

In Figure 21–1, the estimated investment requirements are classified by years and by various categories. The reader will note that different categories have different income tax consequences. Thus "land" and "working funds" have no income tax effects. Items listed as "expense" can be charged off for tax purposes in the year in which the expenditure is made. Mr. Reul's suggested treatment of "future obligations" was discussed in Chapter 15. In this instance the project will employ existing unused warehouse and office space and existing surplus steam and compressed air capacity; the analysis assumes that, in this expanding enterprise, the commitment of these presently unused facilities to this proposed project will result in construction of new similar facilities in 1962.

The *Harvard Business Review* article reproduced a "depreciation and depletion work sheet" not shown here. On this sheet the income tax deductions for depreciation (and depletion, where applicable) are shown on a year-by-year basis. Any investment-type outlay chargeable as a current expense for tax purposes (such as the $50,000 for site preparation in this example) is tabulated on this work sheet in the year of its occurrence. In this example years-digits depreciation is assumed for all depreciable assets. Assumed lives are 40 years for buildings, 15 years for process equipment, and 20 years for future requirements.

Figure 21–2 is a general summary of expected cash flow resulting from the proposal, including investment type disbursements, receipts from the sale of the product, operating disbursements (referred to as "plant cost before depreciation"), and income taxes. The end product of the tabulation and calculation in this form is a year-by-year listing of certain disbursements in the right-hand column under "investment" and of certain net receipts in the two right-hand columns under "receipts."

Although the information and calculations in Figure 21–2 are organized differently from the tables in Chapter 16 that showed calculation of cash flow after income taxes, the end product of the two different types of analysis is identical. This point may be illustrated by computing the net cash flow for 1961 (the fourth year) by the method used in Chapter 16, as follows:

A.	Receipts	$2,000,000
B.	Operating disbursements	1,600,000
C.	Cash flow before income taxes $(A - B)$	$ 400,000
D.	Depreciation write-off for tax purposes	110,200
E.	Taxable income $(C - D)$	$ 289,800
F.	Cash flow for income taxes (50% of E)	144,900
G.	Cash flow after income taxes $(C - F)$	$ 255,100

In Figure 21–2, the same $255,100 is shown in two parts, $200,000 and $55,100. In effect the $400,000 cash flow before depreciation is assumed to be cut in half by the 50% tax, and then half of the $110,200 depreciation tax deduction is restored as positive cash flow.

Figure 21–3 contains the necessary present worth calculations to convert cash flow after income taxes into rate of return. (The phrase "profitability index" is used here to mean rate of return computed by compound interest methods.) The tabulation of cash flow itself, transferred from Figure 21–2, provides the basis for computing present worth at zero interest rate. Present worth factors for interest rates of 10%, 15%, 25%, and 40% are printed on the forms; the necessary multiplications and additions to compute present worths are obvious.

Certain points of difference should be noted from the many calculations of unknown rates of return that have been illustrated throughout this book. One point, a minor one, relates to the method of interpolation used. The unknown rate of return is, of course, the interest rate that makes the algebraic sum of the present worths of all cash flows equal to zero. We have ordinarily computed present worths for one interest rate giving a positive sum and another interest rate giving a negative sum and interpolated between these two present worth figures to find the unknown rate of return.

Another way to state that the algebraic sum of present worths of all cash flows is equal to zero is to say that the present worth of receipts is equal to the present worth of disbursements. In the analysis illustrated in Figure 21–3, the ratio is computed of present worth of investment-type disbursements to present worth of net operating receipts for each of the five interest rates used. These ratios, designated as A/B at the bottom of Figure 21–3, are plotted against interest rate on a sheet of graph paper. This graph is shown in the *Harvard Business Review* article but is not reproduced here. The rate of return (profitability index) is the interest rate for which the ratio A/B is 1.0. This graphical interpolation gives 16.5% as the rate of return for the data of Figure 21–3. A linear interpolation between the ratios 0.90 for 15% and 1.57 for 25% will also give 16.5% as the rate of return.

A more important difference from the methods illustrated throughout this book is that Figure 21–3 does not use the end-of-year convention. For all of the receipts and most of the investments, the assumption is made that the cash flow occurs uniformly throughout the year in question. To use this uniform-flow convention, it is necessary to use present worth factors computed on the assumption of continuous compounding of interest. The continuous-compounding present worth factors shown in Figure 21–3 differ from the factors for the same interest rates shown in Table E–28 of this book because the interest rates in Figure 21–3 are *nominal* rates whereas those in Table E–28 are *effective* rates. This particular aspect of Figure 21–3 is discussed in Appendix A.

Supplementary Criteria for Decisions at the Capital Budgeting Level. Figures 21–1, 21–2, and 21–3 make use of forms that appear in "Authorization for Expenditures," a standard practice manual of the FMC Corporation, Chemical Divisions. Although several other forms from this manual were included in Reul's 1957 *Harvard Business Review* article, not all the forms from the manual were included in the article.

Two interesting forms in the FMC Manual deal with the calculation of numbers useful in applying supplementary decision criteria.[4] One set of calculations gives the number of years for the crude payout after taxes. (We illustrated such calculations in Chapter 16.) This figure is a rough measure of the dependence of the merits of a project on the estimated duration of its favorable consequences.

Another set of calculations gives year-by-year calculations for the expected effect of the project on profit before income taxes at the division level, as profit will be shown on the books of account. A third set of calculations gives several figures that relate to the sensitivity of the success or failure of a project to departures from estimated volume of sales; these calculations apply only to completely new products and facilities or expansion of existing facilities. Results of this analysis give per cent margin, and volume of sales required to break even on new products or added sales required to break even on expansion of existing products.

The Concept of an Investment Portfolio. In the mid-1960's a certain educational endowment fund was invested as follows:

Class of Investments	Estimated Market Value as Percentage of Total
Cash	0.8
Bonds:	
Maturing within 5 years	9.3
Maturing in from 6 to 10 years	13.7
Maturing in from 11 to 20 years	8.1
Maturing after 20 years	8.6
Common stocks	50.4
Real estate and related investments	9.1
	100.0

---

[4] These two forms were reproduced by Reul as Exhibits X and XI in his section on capital budgeting in *Handbook of Industrial Engineering and Management*, 2d ed., *op. cit.*

The common stock investments were widely diversified among industries and among companies. The bond investments were similarly diversified and also diversified among years to maturity.

The managers of this fund chose their investments to strike a balance among objectives of safety of principal, present or near-term income, and more distant future income. The various kinds of diversities in investments were related to balancing these objectives.

In a somewhat similar way, it is reasonable for decision makers at the capital budgeting level in competitive industry to view their choices among a group of competing proposals as an attempt to secure a balanced investment portfolio. The use of various other measures of performance that supplement the primary criterion of prospective rate of return can be helpful in reaching this objective.

Further Comment on the Minimum Attractive Rate of Return in Competitive Industry. In our discussion in Chapter 11 of representative values of the minimum attractive rate of return (page 202), reference was made to conversations between the authors and investment analysts who worked at the capital budgeting level. When an analyst was asked the question "What minimum attractive rate of return is used in your company?" a typical answer was "It all depends." Further questioning disclosed that the point that the analysts seemed to have in mind was that it was fairly common for some accepted projects to have lower estimated rates of return than some rejected projects.

They felt that there were various good reasons for not operating with a fixed cutoff point. Often certain important irreducibles favored some of the projects with the lower rates of return. The concept of a balanced investment portfolio might lead to choosing a mixture of higher return projects that were believed to involve relatively high risks with lower return projects that were believed to involve relatively low risks. Various supplementary or secondary decision criteria might be more favorable to some of the lower return projects; often such criteria were based on the concept of sensitivity.

In spite of there not having been a definite cutoff value of estimated rate of return that separated the accepted projects from the rejected ones, it appeared that there always had been some minimum figure for prospective rate of return below which no projects had been accepted. When we quoted representative values of the after-tax i^* in competitive industry (on page 203), we had reference to this minimum figure.

Although decision making among major investment proposals at the capital budgeting level need not be based on any cutoff value for prospective rate of return, it is practically necessary to choose a value of i^* if economy studies are to be made to compare investment alternatives in cases where decisions are to take place below the capital budgeting level in an organization. For the sake of brevity in the following discussion, we shall refer to such decisions as being made at the *design level*. To use some of the special language that has developed in connection with government projects, these are decisions at the level of "project formulation" as contrasted with "project justification."

Implementing Policies for Economic Analysis at the Design Level. There are likely to be a great many decisions between alternatives at the design level for each investment proposal submitted in the capital budget. Every project submitted doubtless has had its subalternatives; many of the subalternatives have had their own subalternatives; and so on. The majority of the examples and problems in this book relate to economic decisions on the level of engineering design rather than on the level of capital budgeting.

Usually it is a physical impossibility for most of the economic decisions on the design level to be reviewed at the level of capital budgeting. Moreover, in a large organization, hundreds of persons are likely to be involved in design level decisions regarding physical plant. What is needed is a feedback to these persons of the criteria for decision making established at the capital budgeting level. The quotation from Robert F. Barrell in Chapter 11 (page 201) stressed the importance of consistency of criteria throughout an organization. It is the authors' observation that Mr. Barrell is correct in his view that a sound and uniform basis for decision making on the capital budgeting level is much more common than on the design level.

If engineers are left to their own inclinations on design alternatives regarding physical plant, some may greatly overdesign in the sense of making large uneconomic increases in first costs and others may greatly underdesign in the sense of keeping first costs uneconomically low. To offset these extreme tendencies, some written material is needed stating the rules to govern economic design in the particular organization and giving some typical examples of economic comparisons of alternate designs. In some cases this material may take the form of a company manual on engineering economy. Such a manual may well be supplemented by short courses on company time for engineers and other persons concerned with decisions among investment alternatives.

Generally speaking, it is impossible to compare all subalternatives and sub-subalternatives within an organization in the way that was first illustrated in Table 11–1. For this reason the case for making economy studies by the rate of return method is not nearly as strong on the design level as on the capital budgeting level. As a practical matter, to secure rough consistency in the criteria for decision making at the two levels, some figure for i^* should be established by management to be used in economy studies made at the design level. Conceivably, this figure may be different for different divisions of an organization, or for different design problems, but it should be definite for any particular case.

Once the minimum attractive rate of return is stipulated, there may be an advantage in using the annual cost method (occasionally supplemented by the present worth method) to make economy studies at the design level. This advantage is that the annual cost and present worth methods are somewhat easier to apply because of the absence of the trial-and-error calculations needed in computing rates of return. Designers may offer less resistance to the making of economy studies based on annual cost than they would offer to studies based on rate of return.

Designers may also be resistant to requirements that they make studies involving specific consideration of the income tax consequences of design decisions. Moreover, they are not always competent to judge the effect on income taxes of different alternatives. For these reasons, and because of greater simplicity, it may be desirable that many economy studies at the design level be based on a minimum attractive rate of return *before* income taxes. In general, someone who understands the income tax aspects of the subject should make a sufficient review of such studies to be sure that they are made in circumstances where the before-tax and after-tax analysis will lead to the same design decisions.

The foregoing comments regarding differences in methods for economy studies at the two levels are not applicable to regulated public utilities that make economy studies based on minimizing revenue requirements. Generally speaking, the same "fair return" should be used as the interest rate in economy studies at all levels; income taxes can be introduced in a simple manner as a percentage of first cost of plant by the type of formula explained in Chapter 20.

Comment on Weakness of the Payout Period as the Primary Criterion for Investment Decisions. In small enterprises it is common to use some variant of the payout (or payback) period as the primary criterion to compare the merits of proposed investments, particularly when the comparisons are made at the level of capital budgeting. Some large enterprises also base decisions on comparisons of payout periods.

Except for the special case where funds are so limited that *no* outlay can be made unless the money can be recovered in an extremely short time (as in Example 11–2), the payout period is *never* an appropriate way to compare a group of proposed investments. The objection is that the payout period fails to give weight to the difference in consequences of different investment proposals after the date of the payout. Thus a proposal for an investment in jigs and fixtures might pay out in

2 years but have no useful results after the end of the two years. Such a proposal would provide recovery of capital with no return whatsoever. Clearly it would not be superior to a proposal for a new production machine having a longer payout period, say 4 years, but favorable enough consequences for many years thereafter to give it an over-all rate of return of 20%. Some numerical examples involving payout calculations and illustrating this deficiency are given at the end of this chapter (Problems 21–1 to 21–4).

Some analysts, attempting to correct the foregoing bias of crude payout in favor of short-lived alternatives, modify the payout calculation by computing so-called payout after depreciation, or, sometimes after both depreciation and interest. Such modified payout figures are meaningless as they involve a double counting of the first cost of plant. There are, in fact, many variants of the payout method in use in industry, none of them providing a sound basis for comparing investment proposals.

We have already noted that there may be merit in using crude payout after income taxes as a supplementary criterion related to the cash budget and to judgments on the sensitivity of proposals to the estimates of the duration of their favorable consequences.

Use of Unreasonably Short Payout Periods. Sometimes the payout technique is combined with the stipulation that no proposal will be accepted unless it has an extremely short payout period, such as one year or two years. Such a stipulation, if rigidly adhered to, tends to block the approval of projects that would earn excellent returns. As applied to replacement decisions, this type of stipulation tends to perpetuate the use of obsolete and uneconomical plant. George Terborgh's forceful writings on this subject are discussed in Appendix D.

Personal Bias as a Factor in Some Decisions on Plant Investment. Where decisions among investment alternatives are made on intuitive grounds, or where the pros and cons of the various alternatives are stated only in words rather than in monetary figures, personal bias often plays a large part in the decision making. Many psychological and personal interest factors, often unconscious, are likely to weigh against a choice for greatest long-run economy.

Particularly insidious among such factors is the desire for personal importance on the part of someone who has the responsibility for an investment decision. Such a desire may lead an individual to make the decision that increases the size of the activities under his own control regardless of considerations of economy.

For example, a mechanical engineer for a municipal water works was responsible for the design of a new pumping station. He had to choose between installation of boiler equipment with steam-driven pumps, and motor-driven pumps with electricity supplied by the local electric light and power company. The power company offered the city a rate for electrical energy that made the operating cost of motor-driven pumps about half that of the steam-driven pumps. Nevertheless, the engineer selected the steam-driven equipment, giving the excuse that it had the advantage of greater reliability of service. This excuse was made despite the fact that the city had pumping plants of both sorts, and breakdowns were as frequent in the steam stations as were interruptions of electrical service in the electrically operated stations. It was quite clear to observers that this steam engineer's desire for more activities under his own control was the chief factor in the decision.

Managers with a purely financial outlook sometimes think in terms of immediate least cost. Occasionally the engineer may go to the opposite extreme. He may think in terms of the most permanent structure, the latest and most mechanically efficient machine; he wants the thing that is the best mechanical job or the most monumental engineering achievement. To be sure, this choice may result in long-run economy in some instances. But there are also cases where the economical thing to do is to choose the temporary installation, or the installation with a low mechanical efficiency and a correspondingly low first cost.

The managerial requirement that decisions among investment alternatives be based on formal economy studies may prevent many bad decisions that would otherwise be based on personal bias. This desirable influence of economy studies may be greatest where they are subject to the possibility of post-audit.

Post-Audit of Decisions on Plant Investment. Two useful purposes may be served by an organized program for an audit of past investment decisions:

1. The expectation that audits will be undertaken may cause more careful estimates to be made for all economy studies. That is, estimators will take more care if they anticipate that their estimates will be checked against performance. This influence may apply to many different kinds of estimates—first costs, savings in annual operating costs, sales, prices at which products can be sold, and so on.
2. The information gained in auditing past decisions may be fed back to estimators and analysts and persons reviewing capital budgets in a way that makes it possible to prepare better estimates in the future and to do a better job of reviewing future investment proposals.

Nevertheless, a systematic program for auditing past economy studies should not be undertaken by management without a clear idea regarding the limitations of post-audits. An economy study deals with prospective differences among alternative courses of action. In principle an audit should aim to analyze the difference between what happened with the decision as actually made and what would have happened if some other different decision had been made. But it is rarely possible to be *sure* what would have happened with the other decision. Therefore, a past *decision* is not really subject to audit. Moreover, an uncritical use of accounting allocations—among activities or among different periods of time—can be as misleading in an audit as in any economy study.

Generally speaking, where audit procedures are used, they should be applied to various elements of a group of economy studies rather than to each study as a whole. For example, it is useful to know that particular individuals consistently over- or underestimate on certain items.

Only in a limited number of cases is it possible to make a valid audit of a past estimate of a rate of return. This may be done only for projects that are clearly separable from the other activities of an enterprise and where it is possible to carry the analysis to the date of termination of consequences of an investment. Of course, short of the terminal date, it frequently may be evident that a project is turning out approximately as estimated, or much better, or much worse.

Post-audit procedures are most readily applied to projects for which estimates have been submitted at the level of capital budgeting. In some cases they might be applied on a sampling basis to certain aspects of economy studies made on the design level.

Summary. This chapter has given a brief introduction to the topic of the steps that may be taken by management to ensure that sound decisions are made regarding proposed plant investments. The basic criteria for decision making should be consistent throughout an organization. Nevertheless, it is helpful to make a distinction between decision making at the level of capital budgeting and at the level of engineering design. It often is advantageous to use different methods of implementing decision making criteria at different levels in an organization.

PROBLEMS

21–1. Three proposals, each for the immediate disbursement of $10,000, are to be compared in crude payout before income taxes and in rate of return before income taxes. Proposal A has a net positive cash flow of $3,500 a year for 3 years. Proposal B has a net positive cash flow of $2,000 a year for 6 years. Proposal C has a net positive cash flow of $1,200 a year for 20 years.

All three proposals have zero salvage values. (*Ans.* = A, 2.9 years, 2.5%; B, 5.0 years, 5.5%; C, 8.3 years, 10.3%.)

21–2. Compare the proposals in Problem 21–1 by crude payout after income taxes and rate of return after income taxes. Assume an effective tax rate of 50%. Assume straight-line depreciation and that the lives and salvage values used in the economy study are also used for tax purposes. (*Ans.* = A, 2.9 years, 1.2%; B, 5.5 years, 2.8%; C, 11.8 years, 5.7%.)

21–3. Two proposals, each for the immediate disbursement of $20,000, are to be compared in crude payout before income taxes and in rate of return before income taxes. Both proposals have a 5-year life. Proposal D has a net positive cash flow of $6,000 a year for 5 years and zero salvage value. Proposal E has a net positive cash flow of $4,200 a year for 5 years and a $20,000 salvage value. (*Ans.* = D, 3.3 years, 15.2%; E, 4.8 years, 21.0%.)

21–4. Compare the proposals in Problem 21–3 by crude payout after income taxes and rate of return after income taxes. Assume an effective tax rate of 50%. Assume straight-line depreciation and that the lives and salvage values used in the economy study are also used for tax purposes. (*Ans.* = D, 4.0 years, 7.9%; E, 5.0 years, 10.5%.)

21–5. For each proposal of Problem 21–1, subtract annual straight-line depreciation from annual cash flow before income taxes. Divide the resulting figure into the investment to obtain a so-called payoff period after depreciation. (*Ans.:* In A and B, the respective answers of 60 years and 30 years obviously are meaningless as they are much longer than the estimated lives of the projects. As the answer in C is 14.3 years, the double counting of the depreciation is not so obvious.)

21–6. Two investment proposals are to be compared. Each requires the immediate disbursement of $30,000. Both proposals have a 5-year life. Proposal J has a net positive cash flow of $9,600 a year and a zero salvage value. Proposal K has a net positive cash flow of $4,500 a year and a $30,000 salvage value. It may be shown by simple calculation that J will yield a rate of return of 17.6% as compared to 15.0% for K. However, in this organization proposals are compared on the basis of payout period (so-called) after straight-line depreciation. Compute for each proposal the number of years required for the excess of positive cash flow above straight-line depreciation to equal the original investment. Which proposal appears superior by this distorted criterion? (*Ans.:* K, as its payout is computed to be 6.7 years as compared to 8.3 years for J.)

21–7. A certain project has a first cost of $100,000, a 5-year life with zero salvage value, and estimated excess of receipts over disbursements of $42,000 a year throughout the life. In computing "payout," it is proposed to subtract straight-line depreciation and 6% interest on the depreciated book value from the positive cash flow each year. The payout period is defined as the number of years needed for the results of these annual subtractions to add up to the original investment. With this definition, what is the prospective payout period? Also compute the prospective rate of return by correct compound interest methods. (*Ans.:* According to this definition, the investment will never pay out; the double counting of the depreciation leaves an apparent shortage of $8,000 at the end of the 5 years. However, the rate of return is 31.2%.)

21–8. In Figure 21–3, the interpolation between the ratios of A/B for 15% and 25% indicated a rate of return of 16.5%. Compute the ratios of B/A for

15% and 25% and make a linear interpolation to find the rate of return. Add algebraically the present worths of investments and receipts at 15% and 25% in the manner illustrated throughout this book and make a linear interpolation to find rate of return. Discuss your results.

21-9. The computed rate of return (profitability index) was 16.5% in the example developed in Figures 21-1 to 21-3. Discuss the sensitivity of this index to changes made in the estimates of occurrences during the later years of this study. For example, Figure 21-2 shows $215,000 of positive cash flow in 1977 (year 20) due to recovery of "working funds." How would the index have been changed if this estimated recovery had been omitted? How would it have been changed if the forecast had been made that the land and building would be sold for their book value (about $110,000) at the end of 20 years? How could it have been changed if the residual depreciation tax credits in years 21 to 30 had been omitted? How would it have been changed if the study had assumed that sales of this product would terminate after 15 years rather than after 20 years?

21-10. (This is suggested as a possible term report problem for a course in engineering economy.)

An economy study requires a clear definition either of some proposal for action that is to be considered, or of alternative proposals that are to be compared. It then requires estimates to translate such proposals as far as possible into terms of future money receipts and disbursements, accompanied by estimates of other relevant matters (so-called irreducibles) not so translated. Financial calculations are then necessary to provide a basis for judgment. Finally there must be a decision or recommendation as to action that gives weight both to the financial calculations and to the irreducibles. In preliminary studies to determine whether or not any proposal is really promising, the result of a study may be a recommendation for or against the expenditure of time and money for a more detailed study. This problem is intended as a brief exercise in the carrying out of all of these steps.

Selection of Subject. Choose some proposal or set of alternatives for consideration. Two general types of study are possible:

1. A rough preliminary study of some proposed project or set of alternatives. The result of such a study should generally be a recommendation that the project is or is not worthy of more detailed investigation, or a recommendation that certain alternatives be selected for detailed study.
   Example: Proposal for a group of small furnished apartments as housing for married students, research assistants, instructors, etc., at your college or university.
2. A complete study of some fairly simple problem of engineering alternatives.
   Example: Selection of an electric motor for a given service.

Because the time available for this report is necessarily limited, you are likely to be better satisfied with your results if you do not undertake too complicated a problem. Wherever practicable, it is a good plan to select a problem dealing with some actual situation of which you have personal knowledge. If you wish to make an economy study in some field in which you do not have access to data on an actual situation, it is necessary to set up a hypothetical case for study.

Collection of Data. Investigation of an actual case may require you to do some legwork collecting information. Any problem may involve some library work. The best sources of reference on technical papers and articles are the *Engineering Index* and the *Industrial Arts Index*. Books on cost estimating give general guidance on methods of making preliminary and detailed cost estimates. Some up-to-date price information may be found in the current issues of a number of technical and trade journals.

Report. The report should start with a clear statement of your problem. It should give your analysis of the problem and should state your definite recommendation for action. The sources of all of your estimates should be given.

APPENDIXES

A

Continuous Compounding of Interest and the Uniform-Flow Convention

Throughout this book, we have used the end-of-year convention, making compound interest conversions as if cash flow occurring throughout a year were concentrated at the year end. An alternate convention was mentioned in Chapter 6—namely, that certain cash flow taking place during a year occurs uniformly throughout the year. To use this alternate convention in trial-and-error calculations of unknown rates of return, it is necessary to assume continuous compounding of interest. Tables E–28 and E–29, based on continuous compounding, may be used for calculations employing this uniform-flow convention.

A Present Worth Formula That Assumes Continuous Compounding. To explain Tables E–28 and E–29, it is necessary to develop the formula for present worth of $1 flowing uniformly throughout one year.

The concept of the present worth at zero date of money flowing uniformly throughout a year may be introduced by a numerical example assuming money flowing at different specified intervals during a year. Certain aspects of the subject are illustrated to better advantage if a high interest rate is used and if the rate is specified as a nominal (rather than an effective) rate per annum. The following example assumes a nominal rate of 30% per annum and assumes a total cash flow of $1 during the year.

If the entire $1 flows at year end, the present worth at zero date is $1(P/A,30%,1) = $1(0.769) = $0.769. If there are payments of $½ at the ends of half-year intervals and if interest is compounded semiannually, the present worth at zero date is ($½)(P/A,15%,2) = ($0.50)(1.626) = $0.813. If there are payments of $⅙ at the ends of 2-month intervals and interest is compounded every 2 months, the present worth is ($⅙)(P/A,5%,6) = ($0.1667)(5.076) = $0.846. If there are monthly pay-

537

ments of $1/12 and interest is compounded monthly, the present worth is $($1/12$)(P/A,2.5\%,12) = ($0.0833)(10.258) = 0.855. If payments of $1/24 are made at half-month intervals and interest is compounded 24 times a year, the present worth is $($1/24$)(P/A,1.25\%,24) = ($0.04167)(20.624) = 0.859. It may be shown that as the frequency of payments and compounding periods increases indefinitely, this present worth approaches a limit of $0.864. The formula for this present worth is $\dfrac{e^r - 1}{re^r}$ where r is the *nominal* interest rate per annum.

Derivations in Chapter 4 showed that with continuous compounding, the single payment compound amount factor is e^{rn} and the single payment present worth factor is e^{-rn}. The formula for the present worth of $1 flowing uniformly throughout a year may be derived along lines similar to the derivations in Chapter 4, as follows:

With regular end-of-period payments A and an interest rate of i per period:

$$P = A \frac{(1+i)^n - 1}{i(1+i)^n}$$

If $1 is divided into m end-of-period payments a year, each payment A is $\dfrac{$1}{m}$. If the nominal interest rate per annum is r, the interest rate i per compounding period is $\dfrac{r}{m}$. Therefore:

$$P = \frac{$1}{m} \frac{\left(1 + \dfrac{r}{m}\right)^m - 1}{\dfrac{r}{m}\left(1 + \dfrac{r}{m}\right)^m}$$

Now designate $\dfrac{m}{r}$ by the symbol k as we did in the derivation in Chapter 4.

$$P = $1 \frac{\left[\left(1 + \dfrac{1}{k}\right)^k\right]^r - 1}{r\left[\left(1 + \dfrac{1}{k}\right)^k\right]^r}$$

As the number of compounding periods per year, m, increases without limit, so also must k. It follows that the bracketed quantities in the numerator and denominator approach the limit e. Therefore the limiting value of P is

$$P = $1 \frac{e^r - 1}{re^r}$$

Relationship Between Nominal and Effective Rates Per Annum Assuming Continuous Compounding. It was pointed out in Chapter 4 that the more frequent the number of compoundings during the year, the greater the difference between the values of nominal and effective rate per annum. This difference is greatest in continuous compounding, where an infinite number of compoundings is assumed. In the language of the mathematics of finance, the nominal rate r used in continuous compounding is referred to as the *force of interest*.

For high interest rates the effective rate per annum is considerably higher than the force of interest. For example, assume $1 at zero date accumulating interest for one year at a force of interest of 30%. At the end of the year the compound amount will be $1($e^{0.30}$) = $1.3498. The effective rate is 34.98%, nearly 5% more than the nominal rate.

Table A–1 shows the values of force of interest to yield various integral values of effective interest rates from 1% to 50%. These values of r were used in computing Tables E–28 and E–29.

TABLE A–1

Force of Interest, r, To Be Used in Interest Formulas Involving Continuous Compounding in Order To Yield Various Effective Interest Rates per Annum

Effective Rate per Annum	Force of Interest (i.e., nominal rate compounded continuously to yield the stated effective rate)	Effective Rate per Annum	Force of Interest (i.e., nominal rate compounded continuously to yield the stated effective rate)
1%	0.995033%	15%	13.976194%
2%	1.980263%	20%	18.232156%
3%	2.955880%	25%	22.314355%
4%	3.922071%	30%	26.236426%
5%	4.879016%	35%	30.010459%
6%	5.826891%	40%	33.647224%
7%	6.765865%	45%	37.156356%
8%	7.696104%	50%	40.546511%
10%	9.531018%		
12%	11.332869%		

Explanation of Tables E–28 and E–29. Table E–28 (in Appendix E) converts $1 flowing uniformly throughout stated one-year periods to the corresponding present worth at zero date, with continuous compounding at effective rates from 1% to 50%.

For example, the first figure in the 30% column is 0.8796, the present worth at the start of a year of $1 flowing uniformly throughout the year. This was computed by the formula we have just derived, using an r of 0.26236426. (It will be recalled that when we used an r of 0.30, the present worth was 0.864.) All subsequent figures in the 30% column are the product of 0.8796 and the appropriate single payment present worth factor. For instance, the figure of 0.4004 for the period 3 to 4 is $0.8796(P/F,30\%,3) = 0.8796(0.4552)$.

Table E–29 gives the present worth at zero date of $1 per year flowing uniformly through various stated periods, all starting with zero date and terminating at various dates from 1 to 100. The figures in E–29 may be obtained by adding the appropriate figures in the corresponding column of E–28. For instance, the figure 2.477 for 30% and the period 0 to 4 is the sum of figures 0.8796, 0.6766, 0.5205, and 0.4004 from E–28.

Application of Uniform-Flow Convention in Computing Rate of Return. Consider a cost-reduction proposal to purchase certain machinery for $50,000. This proposal is to be analyzed before income taxes. It is estimated that this machinery will reduce disbursements in connection with certain operations by $10,000 a year for the next 4 years. The re-

TABLE A–2

Present Worth Calculations Applying Uniform-Flow Convention

Time Period	Cash Flow	Assuming 12% Present Worth Factor	Assuming 12% Present Worth	Assuming 15% Present Worth Factor	Assuming 15% Present Worth
0	−$50,000	1.000	−$50,000	1.000	−$50,000
0 to 4	+10,000 per year	3.216	+32,160	3.064	+30,640
4 to 5	+8,000	0.6008	+4,810	0.5336	+4,270
5 to 6	+6,000	0.5365	+3,220	0.4640	+2,780
6 to 7	+4,000	0.4790	+1,920	0.4035	+1,610
7 to 8	+2,000	0.4277	+860	0.3508	+700
8	+25,000	0.4039	+10,100	0.3269	+8,070
Totals	+$35,000		+$3,070		−$1,930

duction in disbursements is estimated as $8,000 for the 5th year, $6,000 for the 6th, $4,000 for the 7th, and $2,000 for the 8th. The estimated salvage value at the end of 8 years is $25,000. Table A–2 shows calculations to determine rate of return before income taxes with the uniform-flow convention applied to each year's reduction in disbursements.

The present worth factors for the 4-year period 0 to 4 are taken from Table E–29. The present worth factors for the one-year periods 4 to 5, 5 to 6, etc. are taken from Table E–28. The present worth factors applied to the salvage value at date 8 are taken from the regular 12% and 15% tables, E–17 and E–18.

Interpolation between the present worth of +$3,070 at 12% and −$1,930 at 15% indicates a before-tax rate of return of approximately 13.8%. If the same cash flow series had been analyzed using an end-of-year convention, the computed rate of return would have been 12.4%. In general, rates of return computed with the uniform-flow convention tend to be slightly higher than with the end-of-year convention.

Application of the Uniform-Flow Convention to Proposed Investments. Table A–2 assumes that all the $50,000 investment was made at zero date on the time scale. As it was stipulated that the machinery was to be purchased, this assumption presumably was reasonably close to the facts.

However, if proposed fixed assets are to be constructed or otherwise acquired over a period of time, it often is reasonable to apply a uniform-flow convention to the investment as well as to the cash flow subsequent to the investment. For example, assume that the machinery in Table A–2 will be built over the one-year period prior to zero date on our time scale. The compound amount of $1 flowing uniformly throughout a year is, of course, the reciprocal of the present worth of $1 so flowing. Table A–2 might therefore be modified to show a cash flow of −$50,000 for the period −1 to 0 rather than for date 0. By dividing $50,000 by the appropriate 0-to-1 present worth factors from Table E–28, the equivalent figure at date 0 may be computed to be −$52,890 at 12% and −$53,570 at 15%. The resulting figures for total present worth are +$180 at 12% and −$5,500 at 15%. Interpolation now indicates a rate of return of 12.1%.

The concept of uniform flow as applicable to proposed investments (as well as to the consequences of investments) was illustrated in Chapter 21 by Figures 21–1, 21–2, and 21–3 taken from the article by R. I. Reul in *Harvard Business Review.*

Choosing Between the End-of-Year Convention and the Uniform-Flow Convention. In most compound interest conversions in economy studies, the year is adopted as a unit of time that is not to be subdivided. Therefore *some* convention is necessary regarding receipts and disbursements that occur each year. For many items in economy studies (e.g., receipts from the sale of a product or service, routine operating disbursements), the uniform-flow convention is somewhat closer to the facts than the end-of-year convention. But there may be other items where the end-of-year convention may be a better approximation to the facts (e.g., property taxes, semiannual interest). Moreover, in many economy studies there are many receipts and disbursements that clearly apply to a point in time rather than to a period of time.

All things considered, the uniform-flow convention probably comes somewhat closer to describing the way most cash flow occurs than does the end-of-year convention. Nevertheless, it is desirable to recognize that either is merely a *convention* to facilitate compound interest conversions; neither is a completely accurate reflection of the way in which cash flow is expected to take place.

The authors have observed a number of instances in which the uniform-flow convention is used. But it is their impression that there are a great many organizations using the end-of-year convention for every one that uses uniform-flow.

The greater use of the end-of-year convention doubtless is based largely on grounds of its greater convenience. Standard interest tables and formulas may be used with this convention. In the numerous cases where annual cost comparisons are made, this convention has the advantage of being better adapted to such comparisons. Where compound interest methods require explanation in presenting the results of economy studies, it is easier to explain periodic compounding of interest than to explain continuous compounding.

Compound interest conversions in economy studies constitute one of the steps in providing a rational basis for decisions among alternatives. In most cases the *decisions* will be the same regardless of the convention used. That is, both conventions will normally array a series of investment proposals in the same order.

However, there are certain cases where the two conventions might lead to different recommendations for a decision between alternative investments and where the recommendation based on the uniform-flow convention will be sounder than the one based on the end-of-year convention. These cases occur particularly where an investment leading to positive cash flow concentrated in the near future is being compared with one leading to positive cash flow spread over a considerably longer period. Several examples of such cases are illustrated in the problems at the end of this appendix.

Comparison of Continuous Compounding Tables Based on Nominal and Effective Rates of Interest. The present worth factors in Tables E–28 and E–29 are given for various effective rates. In contrast, the present worth factors in one of the forms shown in Chapter 21 (Figure

21–3) were based on nominal rates. Both sets of factors are based on continuous compounding and the uniform-flow convention.

Certain differences between uniform-flow analyses using nominal and effective rates and between these analyses and the end-of-year analyses are brought out in Table A–3.

TABLE A–3

Comparison of Certain Present Worth Factors

Period	Present Worth Factors with Nominal 25% Interest (from Figure 21–3) A	Present Worth Factors with Effective 25% Interest (from Table E–28) B	End of Year	Present Worth Factors with Effective 25% Interest (from Table E–20) C
0 to 1	0.885	0.896	1	0.800
1 to 2	0.689	0.717	2	0.640
2 to 3	0.537	0.574	3	0.512
3 to 4	0.418	0.459	4	0.410
4 to 5	0.326	0.367	5	0.328
9 to 10	0.093	0.120	10	0.107
14 to 15	0.027	0.039	15	0.035
19 to 20	0.008	0.013	20	0.012
24 to 25	0.002	0.004	25	0.004

It will be observed that the figures in column A of Table A–3 are always less than the corresponding figures in column B and that the proportionate difference increases as the period becomes more distant from zero date. The differences here are due entirely to difference in interest rate. Column A, based on a nominal rate of 25%, used an effective rate of approximately 28.4%. The lower effective rate used in column B of course gives higher present worths, particularly at more distant dates.

The ratio of each figure in column B to the corresponding figure in column C is constant (0.896 to 0.800). Both columns are computed at the same interest rate, an effective 25%. The present worths in column B are higher than those in C because the cash flow is sooner—uniformly during a year rather than at year end.

The most striking comparison is between the corresponding figures in columns A and C. The present worth factors in A are greater in the first few lines of the table, approximately equal at the 5th year, and less thereafter. As time goes on, the assumption in A that cash flow occurs sooner is more than offset by the use of a higher effective interest rate.

Reasons for Using Effective Interest Rates Rather Than Nominal Rates When the Uniform-Flow Convention Is Adopted. Wherever the decision is made to use the uniform-flow convention in economy studies, there are two advantages in using continuous compounding tables such as E–28 and E–29 rather than similar tables based on nominal rates.

One advantage is that the reporting of prospective rates of return in terms of effective rates gives a more realistic picture of the productivity of an investment than the reporting of a nominal rate that assumes continuous compounding. For instance, it will be recalled that with continuous compounding a nominal 30% yields an effective 35% per annum. For a proposed business investment with this prospective yield, management will have a better basis for decision making if the yield is reported as 35% rather than as a nominal 30% compounded continuously.

(This desirability of identifying effective rates applies to personal loans as well as to business investments. Both lenders and borrowers should be aware of effective rates. The officials of a bank that establishes a credit card plan calling for the payment of interest at 1½% per month are doubtless aware that the effective rate is 19.6% per annum; borrowers under this plan should also know that they are paying an effective 19.6%.)

Another advantage of using such tables as E–28 and E–29 is that these tables can be used in combination with conventional interest tables such as are found in standard handbooks and textbooks on the mathematics of finance (or in Appendix E of this book). That is, the conventional tables can be used for all conversions that do not assume uniform flow of funds. If an analysis is to be based on continuous compounding at nominal rates it is necessary to substitute for the conventional tables a complete set of continuous compounding tables applicable to all types of conversions. All factors in such specialized tables will differ from the corresponding factors in conventional tables.

The authors' observation has been that a certain amount of confusion may arise in organizations where special tables are prepared based on continuous compounding at nominal rates. Some persons in the organization will use the special tables and others will use conventional tables. Difficulties may arise in checking the analysis of investment proposals and in discussion or other communications among persons using the different types of tables.

PROBLEMS

A–1. Proposal X involves an investment of $10,000 at zero date. The expected excess of receipts over disbursements is $6,200 a year for 2 years. The expected life is 2 years with zero salvage value. Proposition Y also involves an investment of $10,000 at zero date. Its expected excess of receipts over disbursements is $2,050 a year for 20 years; the life is 20 years with zero salvage value. Compute the prospective before-tax rates of return for each proposal, using (a) the uniform-flow convention and (b) the end-of-year convention. (*Ans.* = (a) X, 25%; Y, 22.5%; (b) X, 15.6%; Y, 20%.)

A–2. Proposal V involves an investment of $100,000 at zero date. The expected excess of receipts over disbursements is $15,780 a year for 5 years. The expected life is 5 years with a $60,000 terminal salvage value at the end of the 5-year period. Proposal W involves an investment of $100,000 at zero date. The expected excess of receipts over disbursements is $10,000 a year for 25 years with a $40,000 terminal salvage value at the end of the 25-year period. Compute the before-tax rate of return for each proposal, (a) using the uniform-flow convention for annual excess of receipts over disbursements and (b) using the end-of-year convention throughout. (*Ans.* = (a) V, 10%; W, 9.9%; (b) V, 9.1%; W, 9.4%.)

A–3. Compute the prospective before-tax rates of return in Problem A–2 assuming that the $100,000 investment is made uniformly throughout the year prior to zero date. Apply the uniform-flow convention to annual excess of receipts over disbursements (but, of course, not to terminal salvage values). (*Ans.* = V, 8.0%; W, 9.4%.)

A–4. The answers to Problems A–1, A–2, and A–3 illustrate certain differences between rates of return computed using the two conventions. Discuss the points that seem to you to be illustrated by these examples.

A–5. Solve Problem 8–3 (page 130), assuming a uniform-flow convention for annual receipts and disbursements and an end-of-year convention for salvage value.

A–6. Solve Problem 8–21 (page 131), assuming a uniform-flow convention for annual receipts and disbursements.

A–7. Solve Problem 8–27 (page 132), assuming a uniform-flow convention for annual receipts and disbursements and an end-of-year convention for the receipts from resale of the property after 20 years.

A–8. Solve Problem 8–29 (page 132), assuming a uniform-flow convention for the dividends (which presumably were paid quarterly) and an end-of-year convention for the receipts from the sale of the stock at the end of the 9 years.

A–9. Solve Problem 8–37 (page 134), assuming a uniform-flow convention for the dividends and an end-of-year convention for the receipts from the sale of the stock at the end of the 15 years.

B

The Analysis of Prospective Cash Flow Series That Have Two or More Reversals of Sign

Our first discussion of compound interest in Chapter 3 dealt with loan transactions. Although we examined a number of different possible cash flow patterns that occur in various types of loans, all the patterns had one characteristic in common. From the lender's viewpoint, there was an initial negative cash flow and all subsequent cash flows were positive. And, of course, from the borrower's viewpoint, an initial positive cash flow was followed by one or more negative cash flows.

Chapter 8 dealt with the calculation of approximate values of unknown interest rates. Like the initial examples in Chapter 3, all of the cash flows in the examples and problems in Chapter 8 involved only one reversal of sign of cash flow. For borrowings, positive cash flows were followed by negative cash flows. For investments, negative cash flows were followed by positive cash flows. Other things being equal, low interest rates on prospective borrowings were more attractive than high ones. And, other things being equal, high rates of return on prospective investments were more attractive than low ones.

This appendix deals with the analysis and evaluation of proposals that involve two or more reversals of the sign of prospective cash flow. Such proposals, in effect, involve a "borrowing" during one period and an "investment" during another period even though this mixed aspect may not always be recognized or described by these words. A practical difficulty in analysis arises because criteria of attractiveness for proposed borrowings differ from criteria of attractiveness for proposed investments.

The following discussion points out that in the evaluation of such proposals, it often is desirable to use an auxiliary interest rate. For a proposal that is primarily an investment project, the auxiliary rate should be applied during the borrowing period. For a proposal that is primarily a borrowing project, the auxiliary rate should be applied during the investment period. Before examining the use of such auxiliary rates, it is helpful to observe the troubles that may arise when one makes a conventional trial-and-error solution to find the unknown interest rate in cases that have two reversals of the sign of cash flow.

EXAMPLE B–1. COMPUTING "SOLVING RATE OF RETURN" FROM A PROPOSAL INVOLVING A DELAYED INVESTMENT

Facts of the Case. An oil company is offered a lease of a group of oil wells on which the primary reserves are close to exhaustion. A major condition of the contract is that the oil company agrees to undertake the injection of water into the underground reservoir in order to make possible a secondary recovery at such time as the primary reserves are exhausted. The lessor will receive a standard royalty from all oil produced from the property whether from primary or secondary reserves. No immediate payment by the oil company is required.

The production department of the oil company estimates the year-by-year after-tax net cash flow from this project as shown in Table B–1. The net negative cash flow in year 5 is caused by the investment in the water flooding project. The positive cash flows in years 1 to 4 reflect the declining net receipts from primary recovery; the positive cash flows in years 6 to 11 reflect the declining net receipts from secondary recovery.[1]

Conventional Trial-and-Error Calculations to Find an Unknown Interest Rate. Table B–1 shows the present worths of the cash flows computed at various interest rates. The sum of the present worths starts with a positive value (+\$590,000) at 0% interest. It declines to zero at an interest rate of about 28%, is negative at 30% and 35%, rises to zero at about 37% and continues to increase at all rates above 37%. The curve of total present worth as a function of i is shown in Fig. B–1.

EXAMPLE B–2. COMPUTING "SOLVING INTEREST RATES" FOR A PROPOSAL THAT, IN EFFECT, INVOLVES A DELAYED BORROWING

Facts of the Case. A company is offered a contract permitting the use of a piece of land for a limited period. A major condition of the contract is that at the end of the 21st year, the property must be returned to the owner accompanied by a specified payment toward the cost of a new building. A smaller outlay must be made at once for modification of the building now on the land. During the intervening years (1 to 20, both inclusive), the company will be in a position to receive a positive net cash flow from rental of the property. The company's real estate department makes estimates of year-by-year after-tax cash flows that will result from the acceptance of this proposal.

These estimates are shown in Table B–2. The reader will note that the sum of the cash flows is negative. Moreover, a negative cash flow of \$3,000,-000 takes place in the 21st year, the terminal year of the contract. It is evi-

---

[1] This example was suggested by an example of a similar water flooding project described in J. G. McLean's article "How to Evaluate New Capital Investments," *Harvard Business Review*, vol. 36, no. 6 (November–December, 1958), 67–68. However, the project evaluation analysis suggested in this appendix differs from that given in the McLean article.

TABLE B-1

Present Worth of Estimated Cash Flow from Agreement To Undertake Proposed Water Flooding Project, Assuming Various Interest Rates

(000 omitted)

Year	Net Cash Flow (and PW at 0%)	Present Worth								
		at 5%	at 10%	at 15%	at 20%	at 25%	at 30%	at 35%	at 40%	at 50%
1	+$120	+$114	+$109	+$104	+$100	+$96	+$92	+$89	+$86	+$80
2	+90	+82	+74	+68	+62	+58	+53	+49	+46	+40
3	+60	+52	+45	+39	+35	+31	+27	+24	+22	+18
4	+30	+25	+20	+17	+14	+12	+11	+9	+8	+6
5	−1,810	−1,418	−1,124	−900	−727	−593	−487	−404	−336	−238
6	+600	+448	+339	+259	+201	+157	+124	+99	+80	+53
7	+500	+355	+257	+188	+140	+105	+80	+61	+47	+29
8	+400	+271	+187	+131	+93	+67	+49	+36	+27	+16
9	+300	+193	+127	+85	+58	+40	+28	+20	+15	+8
10	+200	+123	+77	+49	+32	+21	+15	+10	+7	+3
11	+100	+58	+35	+21	+13	+9	+6	+4	+2	+1
ΣPW	+$590	+$303	+$146	+$61	+$21	+$3	−$2	−$3	+$4	+$16

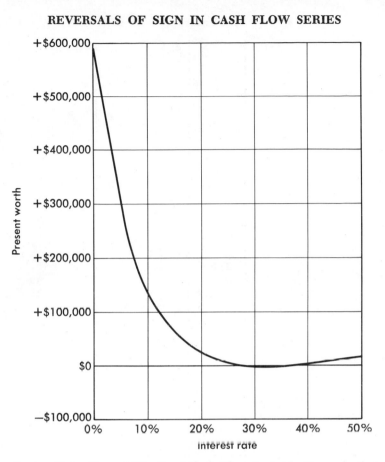

FIGURE B–1. Present Worth of Cash Flow Series in Example B–1

dent that even though this proposal might not be described in legal language as a borrowing, it needs to be analyzed as a borrowing or financing project. This is true in spite of the required initial investment of $700,000.

Conventional Trial-and-Error Calculations to Find an Unknown Interest Rate. Table B–2 shows the present worths of the cash flows computed at various interest rates. The sum of the present worths starts with a negative value (i.e., –$700,000) at 0% interest. It increases to zero at an interest rate of about 2.8%, reaches a maximum at about 10%, after which it declines continuously, passing through zero at about 26.3%. The curve of total present worth is shown in Fig. B–2.

Some General Points Illustrated by Examples B–1 and B–2. The curves in Figs. B–1 and B–2 are typical of curves of sums of present worths of cash flow in cases where there are exactly two reversals of sign of cash flow. With ΣPW plotted as the ordinate and i as the abscissa, the curve will be concave upwards, as in Fig. B–1, when the signs

TABLE B-2

Present Worth of Estimated Cash Flow
from Proposed Agreement Regarding Use of Certain Land,
Assuming Various Interest Rates

(000 omitted)

Year	Net Cash Flow (and PW at 0%)	Present Worth							
		at 2%	at 3%	at 7%	at 10%	at 15%	at 20%	at 25%	at 30%
0	−$700	−$700	−$700	−$700	−$700	−$700	−$700	−$700	−$700
1 to 10	+$200 per year	+1,797	+1,706	+1,405	+1,229	+1,004	+838	+714	+618
11 to 20	+$100 per year	+737	+635	+357	+237	+124	+68	+38	+22
21	−$3,000	−1,979	−1,612	−724	−405	−159	−65	−27	−12
ΣPW	−$700	−$145	+$29	+$338	+$361	+$269	+$141	+$25	−$72

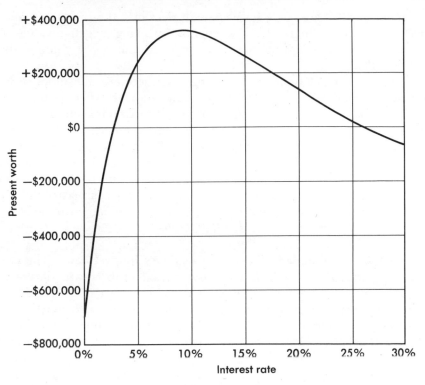

Figure B-2. Present Worth of Cash Flow Series in Example B-2

of cash flows are in the sequence +, −, +. The curve will be convex upwards, as in Fig. B-2, when the signs of cash flows are in the sequence −, +, −.

Such curves will intersect the i axis either in two places or none. For example, consider a slight change in the data of Example B-1; add a positive cash flow of $5,000 at year 0. With such a change, all values of ΣPW in Table B-1 would be increased enough so that the curve would never intersect the i axis; there would be no "solving rate of return" at all.

In both examples, the two places where the curve intersects the i axis are at positive values of i. However, with different figures for cash flow, one or both of the intersections could be at negative values of i. For example, change the data of Example B-2 so that the required outlay at year 21 is $2,000,000 rather than $3,000,000. With this change, ΣPW will be +$300,000 at $i = 0$, and there will be only one positive value of i (about 26.7%) where ΣPW = 0. Nevertheless, the general form of the curve will be similar to the one shown in Fig. B-2. If calculations of ΣPW are made for negative values of i, the curve will intersect the i axis at about -1.3%. (Generally speaking, negative values of solving interest rates do not have any useful meaning as a guide to decision making.)

It seems evident from the foregoing that there are difficulties in interpreting conventional compound interest analyses when prospective cash flow has two reversals of sign. Although in Examples B–1 and B–2 these difficulties arose in our attempt to find an unknown interest rate by trial-and-error calculations, we shall see that difficulties also arise in interpretation of any net present worth calculations in these and similar cases. The key to an evaluation of such proposals lies in the use of an auxiliary interest rate. We shall also see that an important aspect of the matter is the sensitivity of the conclusions of an evaluation to moderate changes in the auxiliary interest rate selected.

Analysis of Example B–1 Using an Auxiliary Interest Rate. The proposed contract in Example B–1 has two periods, a borrowing-financing period in years 1 to 5 and an investment period in years 5 to 11. However, the amount of money involved in years 5 to 11 is so much more than in the earlier years that it is clear that this proposal should be evaluated as an *investment* project. It is helpful to look at the prospective cash flows as follows:

Year	Cash Flow Series A (Borrowing–Financing)	Cash Flow Series B (Investment)
1	+$120,000	
2	+90,000	
3	+60,000	
4	+30,000	
5	$-\ x$	$-\$1,810,000 + x$
6		+600,000
7		+500,000
8		+400,000
9		+300,000
10		+200,000
11		+100,000

Each of these series is a conventional one with only a single reversal of the sign of cash flow. If we assign an interest rate to Series A, we can determine x; we shall then be able to solve for the unknown rate of return in Series B. The auxiliary rate assigned to the borrowing-financing period should be a rate that the enterprise would deem it reasonable to pay for the funds made available during that period and should be selected with consideration given to the need for financing and to the costs of money from various possible alternate sources. Auxiliary rates of 0%, 5%, and 10% give the following results (with 000 omitted from the dollar figures):

Auxiliary Rate	x	$-\$1,810 + x$	Rate of Return on Investment
0%	$300	$-\$1,510$	14.0%
5%	348	$-1,462$	15.5%
10%	401	$-1,409$	17.4%

The foregoing figures for rate of return can be interpreted somewhat as follows:

1. Even though it is believed there is no advantage in the earlier timing of the $300,000 of cash receipts in years 1 to 4, the water-flooding investment should be viewed as earning a 14.0% return.

2. If 0% and 10% are believed to be limiting values for the appropriate auxiliary rate, the corresponding limiting values for the prospective rate of return on the water-flooding investment are 14.0% and 17.4%.

3. The figure for rate of return is somewhat less sensitive to the chosen auxiliary rate in the lower range of values of the auxiliary rate. (An increase in the auxiliary rate from 0% to 5% increases the rate of return by 1.5%, whereas an equal increase from 5% to 10% increases the rate of return by 1.9%.

Table B–1 gave 28% and 37% as the two figures for the solving rate of return for the water flooding proposal. It should be evident that neither of these figures is useful in judging the merits of this proposal as an investment project. Unless an auxiliary rate of 28% is applied to our Cash Flow Series A, Series B will not show a yield of 28%. And unless an auxiliary rate of 37% is applied to Series A, Series B will not yield 37%!

Analysis of Example B–2 Using an Auxiliary Interest Rate. In Example B–2 there were positive cash flows of $200,000 a year for the first 10 years and $100,000 a year for the second 10 years. If the only offsetting negative cash flow had been the $3,000,000 at year 21, this would clearly have been an attractive financing scheme in which money was available for an extended period at a cost of 0%.

However, Example B–2 also had a negative cash flow of $700,000 at zero date. Clearly, the greater the negative cash flow at zero date, the less attractive the proposal is as a financing scheme. An analyst can evaluate this combined proposal by viewing it primarily as a financing scheme and assuming that the positive cash flows of the first few years are applied to the recovery of a $700,000 investment at some stipulated rate of return. It is helpful to look at the prospective cash flows as follows.

Year	Cash Flow Series A (Investment)	Cash Flow Series B (Borrowing–Financing)
0	−$700,000	
1 to $(y-1)$	+200,000 per year	
y	$+\quad x$	+$200,000 − x$
$(y+1)$ to 10		+200,000 per year
11 to 20		+100,000 per year
21		−3,000,000

Each of these series is a conventional one with only a single reversal of the sign of cash flow. If we assign an interest rate to Series A, we can determine x and y; we shall then be in a position to solve for the unknown cost of money in Series B. The auxiliary rate assigned to the investment period should be the estimated rate of return that is believed to be foregone by devoting this $700,000 to a financing project rather than to a normal investment-type project. Auxiliary rates of 0%, 5%, 10%, 15%, and 20% give the following results (with 000 omitted from the dollar figures):

Auxiliary Rate	y	x	$200 − x$	Cost of Money During Borrowing–Financing Period
0%	4	$100.0	$100.0	2.6%
5%	4	188.8	11.2	3.0%
10%	5	106.3	93.7	3.7%
15%	6	68.4	131.6	4.8%
20%	7	125.0	75.0	6.9%

Because all of our cash flow figures were after income taxes, the costs of money are after-tax costs. The reader may recall from Chapter 18 that after-tax costs of money obtained in certain other ways (borrowing or leasing) tend to be considerably less than before-tax costs. It is evident that the attractiveness of this particular project will depend on the auxiliary rate that is deemed to be appropriate.

The computed costs of money are relatively insensitive to the chosen auxiliary interest rate at low values of the auxiliary rate. An increase of the auxiliary rate from 0% to 5% increased the cost of money by only 0.4%. In contrast, the answer is much more sensitive at high values of the auxiliary rate. A 5% increase in the auxiliary rate from 15% to 20% caused a 2.1% increase in the computed cost of money.

Table B–2 gave 2.8% and 26.3% as the two interest rates that made the present worth of the entire cash flow series equal to zero. Neither of these figures is appropriate for judging the merits of this project as a borrowing-financing proposal except under quite unrealistic restrictions. The low cost of money implied by the 2.8% answer implies that the auxiliary rate also is 2.8%; in other words, no alternate investment can be found for $700,000 that will yield more than 2.8%. And the high cost of money implied by the 26.3% answer implies that the auxiliary rate also is 26.3%; in other words, the immediate commitment of $700,000 to this project requires the foregoing of a conventional investment with an after-tax yield of 26.3%.

Special Aspects of Certain Proposals Such as Example B–2. We evaluated the proposal in Example B–2 as a borrowing-financing proposal. The final negative cash flow of $3,000,000 made such an evaluation appropriate in spite of the negative cash flow of $700,000 at zero date.

However, a difficulty may arise in analysis for capital budgeting whenever a proposal that has a −,+,− cash flow sequence calls for evaluation as a borrowing-financing project rather than as an investment project. A *low* value of the cost of money is attractive for a financing project, whereas a *high* rate of return is attractive for an investment project. Nevertheless, the acceptance of a proposal that requires a substantial cash flow at the start may well cause the loss of a good rate of return by taking funds that otherwise could be used for a normal investment project.

In a borrowing-financing proposal that has the cash flow sequence −, +, −, it is not practicable to find a valid rate of return on the first negative cash flows that can be compared with prospective rates of return on normal investment proposals. The best that can be done is to recognize that the opportunity costs associated with the first negative cash flows are relevant in selecting the auxiliary interest rate to be used in the analysis.

Of course, not all proposals that have two reversals of the sign of cash flow are borrowing-financing proposals when the cash flow sequence is −, +, −. The classification of a project as an investment project or a borrowing-financing project should depend on the magnitudes of the negative cash flows at the end of the cash flow series in relation to the magnitudes of the preceding cash flows.

Some Mathematical Aspects of Analysis of Cash Flow Series That Have Two or More Reversals of Sign. If $\dfrac{1}{1+i}$ is designated as x, the usual analysis to find an unknown rate of return on a proposed investment C_0 may be thought of as a trial-and-error solution of the present worth equation:

$$-C_0 + C_1x + C_2x^2 + \ldots + C_{n-1}x^{n-1} + C_nx^n = 0 \qquad (A)$$

where the values of C are the estimated cash flows for the investor at dates 0 to n and all signs after $+ C_1x$ also are plus. Similarly, the usual analysis to find an unknown interest rate associated with the borrowing of C_0 may be viewed as a trial-and-error solution of the present worth equation:

$$+C_0 - C_1x - C_2x^2 - \ldots - C_{n-1}x^{n-1} - C_nx^n = 0 \qquad (B)$$

where the values of C are the stipulated cash flows for the borrower at dates 0 to n and all signs after $-C_1x$ also are minus.

Anyone familiar with the principles of algebra will recognize that such an equation has n different roots. However, some of these roots may be imaginary numbers (that is, they involve $\sqrt{-1}$) and others may be negative.

Descartes's rule of signs tells us that equations such as (A) and (B) which have only one sign change will have one positive real root. Equations with exactly two sign changes, such as those that might have been written for Examples B–1 and B–2, will either have two positive real roots or none. Equations with exactly three sign changes will have either three or one positive real root. Equations with exactly four sign changes will have either four, two, or no positive real roots. And so on.

The reader should note that Descartes's rule applies to positive real roots of an unknown that we have chosen here to represent by x. But our x is an expression for $\dfrac{1}{1+i}$. A positive value of x may correspond either to a positive or negative value of i. However, a negative value of x will always give a negative value of i. It follows that the number of positive values of i that will make $\Sigma PW = 0$ may be *less* than the number of positive real roots given by Descartes's rule but may never be *more*.

Equations in which the sequence of cash flows starting with zero date begins with one or more positive cash flows followed by one or more negative cash flows, and concludes with one or more positive cash flows (the $+,-,+$ sequence) will give a present worth curve that is concave upward, such as the one in Figure B–1. Equations with the $-,+,-$ sequence will give a curve that is convex upward, such as the one in Figure B–2. In our discussion of Examples B–1 and B–2, we noted that moderate changes in the data of the examples could shift the curves up or down so that there would be *no* value of i for which the sum of the present worths would be zero. It also was possible to change the data to shift the curves to the left so that one or both of the solving values of i would be negative (even though the x in our equation would continue to be positive).

Cash Flow Series with More Than Two Reversals of Sign. The greater the number of reversals of sign of cash flow, the greater the possible numbers of values of i for which the sum of the present worth of cash flow is equal to zero. We have seen that in the case of exactly two sign reversals, it may be true that *neither* of the solving interest rates may be a useful guide to any decision making. A similar statement applies to *all* the solving rates obtained when there are three or more reversals of sign.

The difficulties of analysis using auxiliary interest rates may be increased by an increase in the number of reversals of sign in the cash flow series. It may be harder to make the initial decision identifying a proposal as primarily an investment proposal or primarily a borrowing-financing proposal. Moreover, with only two reversals of sign, it is necessary to apply the auxiliary rate during only one time sequence. Extra sign reversals may increase the number of time sequences that require auxiliary rates and may raise the question of whether or not the same auxiliary rate is appropriate for all the different time sequences. Some of these matters are illustrated in our discussion that follows Example B–3; other are brought out in some of the problems at the end of this appendix.

EXAMPLE B–3. COMPUTING "SOLVING RATES OF RETURN" FOR A PROPOSAL THAT INVOLVES THREE REVERSALS OF SIGN IN THE SEQUENCE OF ESTIMATED CASH FLOWS

Facts of the Case. In an extractive industry, it is proposed to make an initial outlay of $180,000 to speed up the recovery of certain ore. It is estimated that one consequence of this outlay will be an increase in after-tax receipts of $100,000 for each of the next 5 years. However, the additional ore recovered in earlier years will not be available for later years. It is estimated that after-tax receipts will be decreased by $100,000 for each year from 6 to 10, both inclusive. Another estimated consequence of the acceptance of this proposal will be an increase in the after-tax receipts from the sale of this property of $200,000 at the end of an estimated 20-year period of ownership.

The prospective influence on cash flow of accepting this proposal is therefore:

Year	Cash Flow
0	−$180,000
1 to 5	+100,000 per year
6 to 10	−100,000 per year
20	+200,000

Conventional Trial-and-Error Calculations to Find an Unknown Interest Rate. Figure B–3 shows the sum of the present worths of the foregoing cash flows computed at various interest rates from 0% to 50%. This curve passes through zero at approximately 1.9%, 14%, and 29%.

It will be observed that the present worth declines from +$20,000 at 0% to a low point of about −$11,200 at 6%, then rises to a high point of about +$4,200 at 20%, and then declines continuously thereafter. Such a curve with two changes of direction is characteristic of present worth curves for cash flow series that have exactly three reversals of the sign of cash flow.

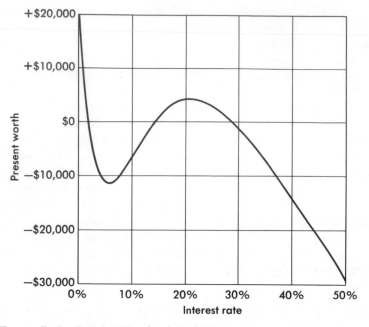

FIGURE B-3. Present Worth of Cash Flow Series in Example B-3

Moderate changes in the estimated cash flow at zero date will make great changes in the points of intersection with the i axis even though they make no change in the shape of the curve. For instance, a change from −$180,000 to −$185,000 will lower the curve so that it has only one intersection with the i axis (at about 1.2%). A further change to −$205,000 will lower the curve so that there will be *no* positive value of i that makes the sum of the present worths equal to zero. (The curve would intersect the i axis at a value of i of about −0.3%.)

It seems apparent that in this case our conventional calculations are not adequate to give us satisfactory guidance on the acceptance or rejection of a proposal.

Analysis of Example B-3 Using an Auxiliary Interest Rate. The first question to be answered in our analysis is whether we want to solve for a cost of money in a proposed borrowing-financing transaction or to solve for a rate of return on a proposed investment. In Example B-3, we should aim to find a cost of money. The purpose of the project is to speed up certain receipts and the dominant cash flows are those in years 1 to 10:

Years	Cash Flow
1 to 5	+$100,000 per year, a total of $500,000
6 to 10	−$100,000 per year, a total of $500,000

If the smaller cash flows at dates 0 and 20 had not been part of this project, it would have been evident that this project would provide financing at a 0% cost. Such financing would obviously have been desirable.

When we apply an auxiliary interest rate to the $-$180,000 at date 0, it is as if we viewed the first $180,000 as an investment to be recovered at the stated auxiliary rate by part of the first positive cash flows during the years 1 to 5. When we apply an auxiliary rate to the final $+$200,000, it is as if we viewed this positive cash flow as the recovery with interest of an investment made by part of the last negative cash flows of the period 6 to 10. Table B–3 illustrates the application of the foregoing concepts with auxiliary rates of 0% and 10%.

TABLE B–3

Application of Auxiliary Interest Rates of 0% and 10% to Analysis of the Cash Flow Series of Example B–3 as a Borrowing–Financing Proposal

Year	Cash Flow Series	Auxiliary Rate at 0%		Auxiliary Rate at 10%	
		Assumed Investments	Borrowing–Financing Series for Analysis	Assumed Investments	Borrowing–Financing Series for Analysis
0	−$180,000	−$180,000		−$180,000	
1	+100,000	+100,000		+100,000	
2	+100,000	+80,000	+$20,000	+100,000	
3	+100,000		+100,000	+8,580	+$91,420
4	+100,000		+100,000		+100,000
5	+100,000		+100,000		+100,000
6	−100,000		−100,000		−100,000
7	−100,000		−100,000		−100,000
8	−100,000		−100,000		−100,000
9	−100,000	−100,000			−100,000
10	−100,000	−100,000		−77,100	−22,900
20	+200,000	+200,000		+200,000	

An inspection of the derived borrowing-financing series obtained with the auxiliary rate of 0% shows that the after-tax cost of this money is negative. However, an auxiliary rate of 0% clearly is not a reasonable one to assume under any normal circumstances.

A trial-and-error solution for the borrowing-financing series that was obtained with the more reasonable auxiliary rate of 10% indicates an after-tax cost of money of approximately 11%. This would seem much too high to be attractive under ordinary conditions.

We have used the same auxiliary rate for the initial period and the terminal period in both analyses. However, it is evident from inspection of Table B–3 that the conclusions of this analysis are much more sensitive to the choice of the auxiliary rate for the final period, which involves a span of at least 10 years, than to the auxiliary rate chosen for the initial period, which involves a much shorter period of time.

The Cult of "Net Present Value." Some writers on economics, finance, and operations research have taken the position that present worth (or *net present value*, as they usually call it) is the only valid method for evaluation of investment proposals. One of several arguments advanced against evaluation by prospective rate of return is that under certain circumstances two or more answers can be obtained for a "solving rate of return."

Our position in this book has been that when the methods are properly applied, sound conclusions can be obtained with a variety of methods, including equivalent uniform annual cash flow, present worth, rate of return, and analyses comparing benefits with costs either with or without the calculation of **B/C** ratios. More specifically, in the ordinary type of investment proposals in which one or more negative cash flows are followed by a sequence of positive cash flows, all of the methods will give the same conclusion on the question of whether or not a stipulated minimum attractive rate of return i^* will be obtained.

When we are confronted with the less common type of proposal in which the prospective cash flow series has two or more reversals of the sign of cash flow, the contention is unsound that the present worth method is superior to the conventional rate of return method. *Neither* method can be counted on to give a sound evaluation. In cases such as Examples B–1, B–2, and B–3, if an analyst should elect to use the rate of return method, there is a fair chance that he will observe that there are multiple solutions and therefore see that some source of difficulty exists. In contrast, if he makes a present worth analysis using only one value of i^*, the existence of the difficulty doubtless will be concealed from him.

For instance, suppose the water flooding proposal of Example B–1 is analyzed by the present worth method using an i^* of 25%. Because the prospective cash flow series has a positive net present value at 25%, such analysis will indicate that this is an acceptable proposal. But our discussion of the application of an auxiliary interest rate to this example brought out the point that the conclusion that this investment will yield 25% is not a valid one unless it would have been appropriate for the enterprise to contract to receive the positive cash flows during the initial borrowing-financing period at an after-tax cost of 25%. Presumably such an after-tax cost of money would be deemed excessive in nearly all circumstances. Therefore, the analysis based on net present value would lead to an incorrect evaluation.

A special difficulty arises with certain prospective cash flow series that have the sequence $-$, $+$, $-$, as in Example B–2, or $-$, $+$, $-$, $+$, as in Example B–3, whenever the timing and magnitudes of the cash flows are such that the proposals ought to be evaluated as borrowing-financing rather than as investments. Because the initial cash flow is negative, there may be a tendency to evaluate such proposals as investments. Such evaluations using net present value with a stipulated value of i^* can be extremely misleading as guides to decision making. This point is illustrated in several of the problems at the end of this appendix.

In Chapter 18 we illustrated calculations to determine before-tax and after-tax costs of money from financing schemes that involved obligations to make future negative cash flows. Although our illustrations there involved either borrowing or the acquiring of the use of assets by long-term leases, the same techniques can be used to find the cost of money whenever certain positive cash flow is to be obtained by an obligation to make stipulated subsequent negative cash flow.

Presumably, in any given case there is some after-tax cost of money above which an enterprise will be unwilling to raise money from sources that involve fixed obligations to make future payments (in other words, from other than equity sources). Let us designate this maximum acceptable after-tax cost of nonequity money as i_0. Usually i_0 will be considerably less than i^*, the minimum rate of return that is deemed sufficient to justify a proposed investment.

When a single value of i is used in computing the present worth of a cash flow series that involves two or more reversals of sign, the implication is that $i_0 = i^*$. This is the implication either in trial-and-error present worth calculations to find the value of i that makes the sum of the present worths equal to zero or in project evaluations by the method of net present value using a stipulated or assigned figure for i^*.

Applying Conventional Methods of Analysis to Slightly Unconventional Cash Flow Series. Nevertheless, there fortunately are many cases where it is good enough for practical purposes to use conventional methods of analysis—such as equivalent uniform annual cash flow, present worth, rate of return, excess of benefits over costs—even though a cash flow series has two or more reversals of sign. Conventional methods are satisfactory for analysis of any such proposals that clearly should be evaluated as investment projects provided the conclusions of the analysis are sufficiently insensitive to the choice of an auxiliary rate during any borrowing-financing period.

Sometimes this lack of sensitivity may be apparent merely from an inspection of the cash flow series. For instance, consider a proposal that starts with a negative cash flow followed by a series of positive cash flows that are in total considerably more than the starting negative flow. At the end there is a relatively small negative cash flow, possibly because of a negative salvage value. The small size of the final cash flow and its distance in time from zero date may make it evident that an analyst should treat this $-$, $+$, $-$ cash flow series in the same manner that he treats any conventional investment proposals that have only the $-$, $+$ sequence. Several problems at the end of this appendix deal with the analysis of $-$,$+$,$-$ proposals with and without the use of auxiliary interest rates.

In some regulated public utility companies in the United States, i^* may be small enough (often about 7%) and i_o may be close enough to i^* for it to be reasonable to make present worth comparisons at the stipulated i^* even though there may be several reversals of sign in a cash flow series that describes the differences between two alternatives. We made such a comparison in Example 7–1 (page 90) where the column of differences in cash flow between Plans G and F showed four reversals of sign. Problem B–11 deals with a further analysis of this example.

Accounting and Income Tax Aspects of Some Proposals Where the Cash Flow Series Has Two or More Reversals of Sign. The accounting aspects of projects of the type discussed in this appendix sometimes are fairly complex and controversial. In some instances, proposals that might be deemed attractive on the basis of the type of analysis explained in this appendix may be vetoed because of the accounting treatment that will be required; there may be too great an adverse short-run influence on reported profits.

Proposals of the type discussed in this appendix are more common in the extractive industries than in other types of business enterprise. In the United States, where the mineral and petroleum industries have the option of using percentage depletion, the income tax aspects of such proposals may be even more complex than the accounting aspects.

In this appendix we have deliberately avoided any discussion of these complexities by assuming after-tax cash flows in all our examples and problems.

Frequency of Occurrence of Cash Flow Series of the Types Discussed in This Appendix. It cannot be emphasized too strongly that cases such as those illustrated in Examples B–1 to B–3 are the exception rather than the rule. They occur chiefly in the mineral industries and the petroleum industry; even there they arise only in rather specialized circumstances.

PROBLEMS

B–1. Our discussion of the analysis of the proposal in Example B–1 using several auxiliary interest rates gave rates of return of 14.0%, 15.5%, and 17.4% corresponding respectively to the auxiliary interest rates of 0%, 5%, and 10%. Make the necessary compound interest calculations to check these stated rates of return.

B–2. Our discussion of the analysis of the proposal in Example B–2 using several auxiliary interest rates gave costs of the money made available by the proposal as 2.6%, 3.7%, and 6.9% corresponding respectively to the auxiliary rates of 0%, 10%, and 20%. Make the necessary compound interest calculations to check these stated costs of money.

B–3. Figure B–3 showed the sum of the present worths of the cash flows associated with the proposal in Example B–3. Make the necessary calculations to check present worth totals for values of i of 0%, 2%, 6%, 10%, 15%, 20%, and 30%.

B–4. Alter the data of Example B–1 in two ways. Assume that an immediate payment of $150,000 is required to secure the lease on the oil wells. Assume that the purchase of the lease does not require any agreement to undertake the water flooding project to secure the secondary recovery; the oil company can make its own decision about whether or not to undertake the water flooding at such time as the primary reserves are exhausted. Make no change in the estimates of the after-tax positive cash flows from primary recovery or from secondary recovery (if undertaken) or in the estimate of the cost of water flooding at date 5. Discuss the question of how to analyze this altered proposal, making any calculations that you consider to be relevant.

B–5. Alter the data of Example B–1 by assuming that an immediate payment of $150,000 is required to secure the lease. Assume that the oil company must agree to undertake the water flooding at date 5, just as stipulated in Example B–1. Discuss the question of how this analysis should differ from the one appropriate for Problem B–4. Make any calculations that you believe are called for to guide the oil company's decision in this case.

B–6. In the discussion of the application of Descartes's rule of signs on page 556, these statements appear:

"A positive value of x may correspond either to a positive or negative value of i. However, a negative value of x will always give a negative value of i."

Show that the foregoing two statements are correct.

B–7. The estimated after-tax cash flow series associated with speeding up the recovery of certain minerals is as follows:

Year	Cash Flow
0	−$22,000
1	+100,000
2	−100,000
10	+40,000

Plot the sum of the present worths of cash flow for interest rates from 0% to 220%. (You will need to compute your own present worth factors above 50%.) At what approximate values of i is the sum of the present worths equal to zero? (*Ans.* = 13%; 42%; 206%.)

B–8. Evaluate the project in Problem B–7 as a borrowing-financing proposal, making use of an auxiliary interest rate of 8%.

B–9. The estimated after-tax cash flow series associated with speeding up the recovery of certain minerals is as follows:

Year	Cash Flow
0	−$16,000
1	+100,000
2	−100,000

Plot the sum of the present worths of cash flow for values of i of 0%, 25%, 50%, 100%, 200%, 300%, 400%, and 500%. (You will need to compute your own present worth factors above 50%.) At what values of i is the sum of the present worths equal to zero? (*Ans.* = 25%; 400%.)

B–10. Evaluate the project in Problem B–9 as a borrowing-financing proposal, making use of auxiliary interest rates of 0% and 10%.

B–11. Examine the cash flow series $(G - F)$ in Table 7–1 (page 91). This cash flow series has four reversals of sign. Example 7–1 gives the sum of the present worths of this series at 0% and 7% as +$22,500 and +$2,610 respectively. Compute ΣPW at 10%. At what approximate value of i will $\Sigma PW = 0$?

Why is it evident that ΣPW will continue to decline for values of i greater than 10%?

In spite of the four reversals of sign, the ΣPW curve seems to have the same form that one would expect from a conventional investment proposal that has only one reversal of sign. Nevertheless, Descartes's rule tells us that there must be at least one more value of i that will make ΣPW equal to zero. Where will this value be? Explain your answer.

B–12. In Problem 13–7 (page 274), the estimated disbursements for two structures are compared for a 50-year service. The estimated difference between cash flows for the longer and shorter-lived structures is:

Year	Cash Flow Difference
0	−$50,000
25	+75,000
26 to 50	−500 each year

The answer given to Problem 13–7 says, in effect, that the after-tax rate of return on the extra investment in the longer-lived structure is a little less than 1%. This answer indicates that the shorter-lived structure is the better economic choice.

This analysis in Problem 13–7 gave no recognition to the fact that the estimated cash flow series has two reversals of sign. Discuss the question of whether there is a second "solving rate of return" that is relevant in this comparison. What would your conclusion be if you assumed an auxiliary interest rate in this comparison?

B–13. A proposed outlay of $10,000 at zero date will lead to a positive after-tax cash flow of $2,500 a year for 11 years. However, there will be a negative terminal salvage value that will be responsible for an after-tax disbursement of $5,000 at the end of the 11th year. At what positive value or values of i will $\Sigma PW = 0$? Determine the prospective after-tax rate of return applying auxiliary interest rates of 0% and 10% to the final negative cash flow.

B–14. Smith offers to give Jones $150 at once and $1,000 at the end of 3 years if Jones will agree to give Smith $800 at the end of 1 year. Assuming that both individuals will honor their agreements and that there will be no income-tax consequences of the three cash payments, evaluate this proposal from Jones's viewpoint. Evaluate it from Smith's viewpoint.

C

The Reinvestment Fallacy in
Project Evaluation

In Appendix B we used an auxiliary interest rate in addition to the unknown or solving rate. However, the two interest rates were not used during the same time period. The proposals being analyzed all combined investment during one or more periods with borrowing or financing during one or more other periods. For proposals that were primarily investment projects, the auxiliary interest rate was applied during the borrowing or financing period or periods. For proposals that were primarily borrowing or financing, the auxiliary interest rate was applied during the investment period or periods.

In this appendix, it is emphasized that it is quite a different matter to use two or more interest rates for equivalence conversions during the same time period. Conclusions regarding the attractiveness of proposed investments can be badly distorted by applying two or more interest rates simultaneously. It also is possible to distort the analysis of proposed borrowing or financing schemes by using two or more rates at the same time. (An actual case of such distortion of the analysis of a financing scheme was described in Problem 18–15, page 452.)

Some Reasons Why Two or More Interest Rates Are Used for Compound Interest Conversions During the Same Time Period. Sometimes an analyst uses two or more interest rates because this method of analysis is required by company policy. Or he may mistakenly believe that this technique will give him useful conclusions. In either case, one aspect of his computational procedure will be the assumption of reinvestment at some stipulated interest rate. Various weaknesses in the reinvestment assumption are brought out in Example C–1 and in several of the problems at the end of this appendix.

Sometimes an analyst unintentionally uses two interest rates during the same time period as a result of substituting accounting charges for cash flows. In such cases, the auxiliary interest rate used unintentionally

566

generally is 0%. Some possible distortions caused by making equivalence conversions at 0% are illustrated in Example C–2.

The authors have also observed cases where it seemed to them that sophisticated analysts were intentionally distorting the conclusions of an evaluation by making compound interest conversions that used two or more interest rates during the same time period. For some reason, it was desired to make a particular investment proposal appear to be better or worse than it would have seemed to be if it had been evaluated on its own merits. The analysis seemed to have been manipulated to support the predetermined conclusions.

EXAMPLE C–1. MISUSE OF AN AUXILIARY INTEREST RATE IN COMPUTING PROSPECTIVE RATES OF RETURN

Misleading Analysis of Two Investment Proposals. The discussion of Hoskold's method in Chapter 8 explained how a proposed investment sometimes is judged by calculating a rate of return that combines the consequences of two investments, the proposed one under review and an investment in an imaginary sinking fund. It was pointed out that, in general, the return from an unrelated investment—either real or imaginary—is irrelevant in judging the merits of a proposed investment under review. The basic error of the Hoskold-type analysis appears in many settings.

For instance, consider an investment proposal that has the following estimates of after-tax cash flow: [1]

Year	Cash Flow for Investment	Cash Flow from Excess of Operating Receipts over Disbursements
0	−$450,000	
1		+$270,000
2		+220,000
3		+170,000
4		+120,000
5		+70,000
Totals (PW at 0%)	−$450,000	+$850,000

A conventional analysis along the lines used in Chapter 8 and thereafter in this book indicates that the prospective rate of return is 33.8%. That is, if the funds indicated in the investment column were loaned and if the borrower made the payments shown in the right-hand column, he would pay back the loan with interest at 33.8%.

However, a proposed method of computing rate of return uses as an auxiliary interest rate "the average rate of return which the company is making on its investment." Assume this rate is 10%. The investment outlays are then discounted to zero date at this rate and the cash flow from the project is compounded to the final date of the study period at the same rate. At date zero

[1] Example C–1 was suggested by a method of analysis proposed in an article by R. H. Baldwin, "How To Assess Investment Proposals," *Harvard Business Review*, XXXVII, No. 3 (May–June, 1959), 98–104.

the present worth of the investment obviously is $450,000. At date 5, the compound amount at 10% interest of the positive cash flows may be computed to be $1,095,900. A single payment compound amount factor for 5 years is then computed as $1,095,900 ÷ $450,000 = 2.435. Interpolation between the 15% and 20% factors indicates a return of 19.4%.

The foregoing proposed method of analysis underestimates the rate of return from the proposed investment by more than 14%. The error in principle here is the same one discussed in Chapter 8 in connection with the Hoskold formula; the computed 19.4% is, in effect, the result of two separable investments, the proposed $450,000 investment yielding 33.8% and an investment of varying amount elsewhere in the business enterprise assumed to yield 10%.

The fallacy in this type of analysis may be even more evident if we apply the method to the following estimates for another investment proposal:

Year	Cash Flow for Investment	Cash Flow from Excess of Operating Receipts over Disbursements
0	−$200,000	
1	−250,000	+$130,000
2		+110,000
3		+90,000
4		+70,000
5		+50,000
Totals	−$450,000	+$450,000
(PW at 0%)		

A simple inspection of the figures shows that the prospective rate of return is 0%; the $450,000 investment will be recovered with nothing left over. But if we use the 10% rate that the company is expected to make on other investments, the present worth of the investments at date zero is $427,300 and the compound amount of the positive cash flows at the end of 5 years is $572,600. If $(F/P,i\%,5)$ is computed as $572,600 ÷ $427,300 = 1.340, interpolation in our interest tables indicates a prospective rate of return of 6.0%. In effect, the investment proposal yielding 0% has been combined with the 10% assumed to be earned elsewhere in the enterprise to give the misleading conclusion that the proposal will yield 6%.

EXAMPLE C–2. DISTORTION INTRODUCED BY EQUIVALENCE CONVERSION AT 0% INTEREST PRIOR TO A PRESENT WORTH CALCULATION

Misuse of Accounting Figures in Economy Studies. Chapter 15 explained that although allocations of expenditures among activities often are necessary for accounting purposes, such allocations occasionally are misused in analyses made to guide decisions among alternatives. It also is true that allocations among time periods that are needed in the accounts sometimes are misused in compound interest calculations made to judge whether a proposed investment will yield a stipulated rate of return.

As an example, consider a proposed investment of $100,000 in a property expected to have a life of 20 years, zero salvage value, and annual disbursements of $5,000 throughout the life. It is desired to compute the present worth of all costs, using an i^* of 8%. The correct total is figured as follows:

$$PW = \$100,000 + \$5,000(P/A,8\%,20)$$
$$= \$100,000 + \$5,000(9.818) = \$149,090$$

However, assume that straight-line depreciation of $5,000 a year is to be used in the accounts. The annual costs shown in the accounts will be $100,000/20 + $5,000 = $10,000. The present worth of this annual figure might conceivably be computed as

$$PW = \$10,000(P/A,8\%,20)$$
$$= \$10,000(9.818) = \$98,180$$

It should be obvious at a glance that this $98,180 figure that purports to be the present worth of the costs is incorrect and misleading; it makes the present worth of investment and operating costs appear to be less than the investment itself. The difficulty, of course, is that the $100,000 outlay at zero date was, in effect, converted to $5,000 a year from years 1 to 20, using an interest rate of 0%. When an 8% interest rate was used in converting the $5,000 a year back to zero date, the original $100,000 at zero date was, in a roundabout way, converted to $49,090 at zero date.

In this particular case the numerical value of the present worth made it evident that some type of error had been made. But the authors have seen conversions of this type made in analyses for industry and government where the existence of an error in principle could not have been discovered merely by looking at the results of the analyst's calculations.

Sensitivity in Relation to Matters Discussed in this Appendix. When a computed rate of return applies to the combined result of two investments, one in a project being evaluated and the other in an actual or hypothetical reinvestment fund, the computed rate will be between the rate of return on the project itself and the assumed rate of return on the reinvestment fund. In the special case where these two rates are close together, the computed rate will be almost the same as if no assumption of reinvestment had been made.

But when the two rates are far apart, their respective influences on the combined rate will be greatly affected by the cash flow pattern of the project being evaluated in relation to the assumed terminal date of the project. In certain types of cash flow patterns, the combined rate of return may depend largely on the assumed rate of return on the reinvestment fund and may be relatively insensitive to the productivity of the project that the analyst is supposed to be evaluating. The foregoing point is illustrated in Problems C–3, C–4, and C–5 at the end of this appendix.

Comparing Investment Proposals When Future Rates of Return Are Expected To Differ Substantially from Present Rates. Chapter 11 introduced the problem of choosing among investment proposals in circumstances where available funds are limited. Table 11–1 (page 194) described an assumed situation in which 8 proposals requiring a total investment of $207,000 were under consideration and in which the available funds were limited to $90,000. The prospective after-tax rates of return had been computed for each proposal and were arrayed in order of descending magnitude. It was evident that the available funds would be exhausted by proposals U, Y, Z, and S, which had prospective rates of return of 15% or more. Our discussion in Chapter 11 indicated that if the maximum possible return should be desired from the available funds, it would be necessary to reject proposals X, T, U, and W, all of which had prospective rates of return of 12% or less.

The cutoff point in Table 11–1 was 15%; this was the minimum attractive rate of return because the selection of any project yielding less than 15% would force the elimination of some project having a prospective yield of 15% or more. However, our discussion in Chapter 11 gave no consideration to one aspect of capital rationing that sometimes is important. When we selected certain projects and rejected others, we gave no consideration to the duration of the favorable consequences of each project except as this duration influenced the computed rate of return. (Although our array in Table 11–1 did not show the expected pattern of future cash flow from each project, such supporting information would necessarily be available in any actual case as the source of the calculation of the respective rates of return.)

Assume that it is expected that the typical rate of return available from future investment proposals will be considerably higher or considerably lower than the rate obtainable from present proposals. To maximize the long-run rate of return on available investment funds, it is necessary to consider the duration of the expected consequences of each present proposal. In general, the prospect of lower future rates of return favors the longer-lived of the projects under present consideration; the prospect of higher future rates of return favors the shorter-lived projects (or sometimes the approval of no present projects at all).

For example, suppose that Project S in Table 11–1, yielding 15%, has a life of 2 years whereas Project X, yielding 12%, had a life of 12 years. Assume that it is believed that rates of return from projects that will be proposed in the next few years will not exceed 8%. The combination of S with its 15% and a subsequent investment yielding 8% may result in a lower over-all rate of return over the next 12 years than the 12% obtainable from X.

Or—in contrast—suppose it is expected that if sufficient funds are available in a year or two, a large project can be undertaken that will yield a 25% rate of return. The acceptance of too many long-lived proposals now may make it impracticable to finance this desirable future project. A present capital rationing analysis may therefore favor projects with short capital recovery periods even though they have relatively low rates of return in order to make funds available for this attractive future project.

Occasionally circumstances arise where such forecasts of future rates of return are deemed appropriate in making decisions about present proposals for investment. If the forecasts are specific enough, it is possible to make the necessary calculations to find an over-all rate of return from a proposed present investment and its successors. Such calculations would, in effect, make use of two or more interest rates. However, in most cases the best thing to do with forecasts about upward or downward trends in rates of return is to consider these forecasts on a qualitative basis, using them as irreducibles to influence capital rationing decisions in borderline cases.

PROBLEMS

C-1. An investment of $75,700 proposed to be made at zero date is expected to cause a net positive after-tax cash flow of $20,000 in the first year of the 20-year life of the asset. This positive cash flow is expected to decrease by $1,000 a year to $1,000 in the 20th year. There is no estimated terminal salvage value.

(a) At what interest rate will the positive cash flow repay the investment? (*Ans.* = 20%.)

(b) Compute the prospective rate of return by the proposed method illustrated in Example C-1, assuming reinvestment at 3% interest of all positive cash flows until the end of the 20-year study period. (*Ans.* = 7.3%.)

(c) Explain the reason for the difference in the answers in (a) and (b).

C-2. An investment of $170,750 proposed to be made at zero date is expected to cause the same series of net positive after-tax cash flows described in Problem C-1. The estimated life of this asset is also 20 years with zero terminal salvage value.

(a) At what interest rate will the positive cash flow repay this investment? (*Ans.* = 3%.)

(b) Compute the prospective rate of return by the proposed method illustrated in Example C-1, assuming reinvestment throughout the 20-year period of all positive cash flows at the 12% average rate of return that is being earned by this business enterprise. (*Ans.* = 9.2%.)

(c) Explain the reason for the difference in the answers in (a) and (b).

C-3. Project A involves negative cash flow of $100,000 at zero date and positive cash flow of $65,500 at dates 1 and 2. Its consequences terminate at the end of 2 years. Project B involves the same cash flows at dates 0, 1, and 2 and also involves positive cash flows of $10,000 on dates 3, 4, 5, 6, 7, 8, 9, and 10. Its consequences terminate at the end of 10 years.

(a) For each project, find the interest rate that makes the present worth of all cash flows equal to zero. (*Ans.* = A, 20%; B, 34%.)

(b) In the WXY Company, rates of return on investment proposals are computed by the method illustrated in Example C-1, assuming that all positive cash flows will be reinvested at 4% interest until the terminal date of the project. With this method of evaluation, what are the computed rates of return on these two projects? (*Ans.* = A, 15.6%; B, 10.6%.)

(c) Project B is clearly superior to A because it involves the same cash flows at dates 0, 1, and 2, and in addition has positive cash flows of $10,000 a year from years 3 to 10. Explain what features of the evaluation method used by the WXY Company are responsible for the conclusion that B has a considerably lower rate of return than A.

C-4. Project E involves a negative cash flow of $100,000 at zero date followed by positive cash flows of $20,000 each year from years 1 to 5 and positive cash flows of $1,000 each year from 6 to 20. The consequences of this investment will terminate at the end of 20 years.

(a) What is the interest rate that makes the present worth of all cash flows equal to zero? (*Ans.* = 3.5%.)

(b) In the YWX Company, rates of return on proposed investments are computed by the method illustrated in Example C-1. It is assumed that all positive cash flows will be reinvested at 15% (the average rate expected to be earned by *all* investments in the company) until the terminal date of the project. A proposal will not be accepted unless its prospective rate of return calculated in this manner is at least 10%. With this method of evaluation, what is the computed rate of return on Project E? (*Ans.* = 12.8%.)

C-5. Project H involves a negative cash flow of $100,000 at zero date followed by a positive cash flow of $170,000 at date 5. The consequences of this investment will terminate at the end of 5 years.

(a) What is the interest rate that makes the present worth of all cash flows equal to zero? (*Ans.* = 11.2%.)

(b) This project is to be evaluated in the YWX Company by the method described in Problem C-4(b). With this method of evaluation, what is the computed rate of return on Project H? (*Ans.* = 11.2%.)

(c) The answers obtained in Problems C-4(b) and C-5(b) make it appear that Project E is preferable to Project H. Do you agree? If not, why not?

C-6. The President of the XYW Company wishes to analyze investment proposals by a method that assumes reinvestment along the lines illustrated in Example C-1. However, he recognizes a point brought out by the three preceding problems, namely, that any such method will not give a satisfactory comparison of competing projects that have substantially different terminal dates. He therefore stipulates that *all* investment proposals shall be analyzed assuming a terminal date 20 years from zero date even though the estimated cash flows directly resulting from the investment do not extend for the full 20 years.

If this rule had been followed by the WXY Company in Problem C-3(b), Project B would have shown a higher computed rate of return than Project A. And if it had been followed by the YWX Company in Problems C-4(b) and C-5(b), Project H would have shown a higher computed rate of return than Project E.

But compare Projects Q and R with the terminal date for all analysis as date 20 assuming reinvestment of all positive cash flows at 4%. Project Q involves a negative cash flow of $100,000 at zero date and a positive cash flow of $150,000 at date 1. Project R involves a negative cash flow of $100,000 at zero date and a positive cash flow of $350,000 at date 20.

Or compare Projects S and T with the terminal date for all analysis as date 20 assuming reinvestment of all positive cash flows at 15%. Project S involves a negative cash flow of $100,000 at zero date and a positive cash flow of $50,000 at date 1. Project T involves a negative cash flow of $100,000 at zero date and a positive cash flow of $680,000 at date 20.

Do you believe that the president's assumption of a common terminal date for all projects that are competing for limited funds meets all objections that can be raised to an analysis based on reinvestment of all positive cash flows at some stipulated rate? Explain your answer.

Some Aspects of the Various
MAPI Systems

This appendix contains a brief discussion of certain features of several related mathematical models for investment analysis developed and modified over a period of nearly twenty years. These models were described and their applications were illustrated in a number of publications written by George Terborgh, Research Director for the Machinery and Allied Products Institute (MAPI), a trade association of producers of capital goods.

Terborgh's four major books that deal with the various "MAPI systems" for investment analysis are:

Dynamic Equipment Policy (1949)
MAPI Replacement Manual (1950)
Business Investment Policy (1958)
Business Investment Management (1967)

All are now published by Machinery and Allied Products Institute, Washington, D.C. (*Dynamic Equipment Policy* was originally published by McGraw-Hill Book Company, Inc.)

The first two books deal chiefly with decisions about the *replacement* of machinery and equipment. Although the mathematical models used in the two later volumes were greatly influenced by certain aspects of the problem of making replacement decisions, these books deal more broadly with matters related to all kinds of investment in physical plant. However, we shall discuss them here with particular reference to the MAPI approach to the replacement problem.

The Fable of Old Frank. A viewpoint about replacement decisions that runs through all of the Terborgh volumes is illustrated by the following "fable:" [1]

[1] This appeared first in *Business Investment Policy*, pp. 43–44, and was later repeated in *Business Investment Management*, pp. 57–58. It is reproduced here by permission of the Machinery and Allied Products Institute.

Once there was a manufacturer with a pension plan calling for retirement at 65, subject to deferment for annual periods by mutual agreement of the company and the employee. One day the personnel manager had lunch with the equipment analyst.

"Henry," said the personnel man, "you remember old Frank in the shipping department? He'll be 65 next June and we have to decide whether to invite him to stay on. The foreman tells me his health is not too good and he has slowed up lately. He's getting the top rate because of seniority, and we could save something by letting him go."

"What is the estimated annual saving?" inquired the analyst.

"Well, we haven't made an estimate, but suppose we say $1,000."

"In that case, we'll make a profit of $1,000 a year by acting now," the analyst replied. "But have you stopped to consider that old Frank is getting feebler and more senile all the time? If we wait until he's 70, we may make $3,000 a year by getting rid of him. If we wait until he's 80, we may make $5,000. Why pass up these additional profits from his replacement?"

"Henry, that's cockeyed," replied the personnel man. "You sound like the guy who slept on a spike bed to enjoy the relief of getting up in the morning."

"Not so fast," protested Henry. "That is the way we do it in equipment analysis. If a machine doesn't show enough savings today, we wait a few years and get more. You'd be surprised how they increase as time goes on. Eventually we get the profit from replacement that we want."

"But how much do you want?"

"That's determined by the head office," answered Henry. "We take their figure."

"Well," rejoined the personnel manager," "I don't see why you should ever *stop* waiting. If it is a good thing to make 20 percent profit on the replacement investment, why isn't 50 percent better and 100 percent better yet? You can get anything you want if you wait long enough. The sky's the limit.

"It seems to me," he continued, "that you are confusing loss-extinguishment with profit. The joker is that you have to incur the losses first before you can realize the profit from ending them. The bigger the losses, the more you make."

"I never thought of it that way," replied Henry. "Maybe you've got something. But you'll have to take it up with the president. We do as we're told."

Old Frank and Equipment Replacement. The words *challenger* and *defender*, coined by George Terborgh for discussion of replacement economy, were defined and used in Chapter 17. These words also are used throughout this appendix.

Some readers of the 1958 or 1967 Terborgh volumes have commented that it might have been even more impressive if Frank had been, say, the plant manager rather than an employee in the shipping department. But whether a defender is a shipping clerk or a plant manager or a piece of equipment, there are certain similarities between the appropriate types of reasoning in a decision between (a) continuing the defender in service for another year, and (b) retiring the defender at once in favor of a present challenger. There are also some points of difference between the retirement of people and the retirement of equipment.

In Frank's case, the discussion between the personnel man and the equipment analyst dealt only with possible defender deterioration. In Examples 17–3 and 17–4, which dealt respectively with a gas main and with a piece of construction equipment, defender deterioration also was expected. In both of these examples, the expected remaining service life of the defender was shorter than the expected economic life of the challenger.

Our discussion in Chapter 17 pointed out that a possible consideration in such cases is the likelihood that if replacement is deferred, a better challenger than the present one will be available. (This apparently was not a consideration in the discussion of whether or not old Frank should be retired immediately.) However, no general rules for making a monetary allowance for this matter were developed in Chapter 17. We shall see that an important aspect of the MAPI models discussed in this appendix is that they contain a formalized allowance for the superiority of future challengers to present ones.

The Concept of an Annual Gradient That Describes the Operating Advantage of Future Challengers as Compared to the Present One. A present challenger may have various advantages over a defender that will influence prospective year-by-year cash flow. These advantages may lead to lower disbursements to provide a given service, higher receipts from the sale of that service, or both. Similarly, future challengers may have such advantages over the present challenger. For simplicity, the following example assumes that defender, present challenger, and future challengers will all have the same receipts and that the year-by-year differences in cash flow are caused solely by differences in disbursements. However, the analysis is entirely general and may be applied to differences in receipts as well as to various differences in disbursements.

Assume that the present challenger for a given service has estimated first-year disbursements of $3,500. Assume that each year these disbursements are expected to increase by $20 so that they will be $3,520 in the second year of service, $3,540 in the third year, etc. Assume that a steady improvement in future challengers is anticipated so that the first-year disbursements will be $3,470 for next-year's challenger, $3,440 for the challenger available 2 years hence, and will continue to decrease by $30 a year. Assume that disbursements for all future challengers, like those for the present one, will increase at $20 a year. Assume that the first cost of the present challenger is $1,000 and that this will be the first cost of all future challengers. Assume that all challengers will have zero salvage values at all times. Assume that decisions on plant investments are to be made by before-tax analyses using a minimum attractive rate of return (interest rate) of 15%.

In the foregoing assumptions it will be noted that the present challenger accumulates inferiority to future challengers at a rate of $50 per year. The expected behavior of annual disbursements for the present challenger is shown by line ABC in Figure D–1. Line JK, for the next-

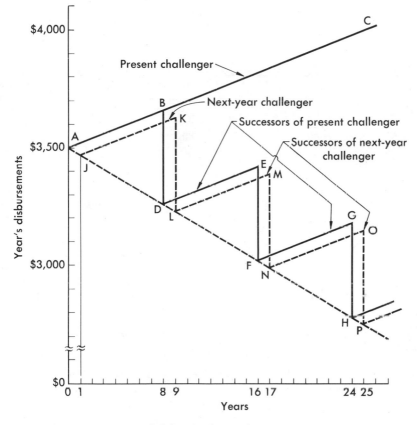

FIGURE D–1. A Model for Analysis of a Proposed Replacement

SOURCE: Adapted from A. A. Alchian, *Economic Replacement Policy*, Publication R-224 (Santa Monica, Calif.: The RAND Corporation, 1952), Fig. 2.1, p. 8.

year challenger, is always $50 below line ABC. Line DE, for the challenger 8 years hence, is always $400 below line ABC. And so on. In Terborgh's *Dynamic Equipment Policy*, such a $50 figure is referred to as an *inferiority gradient*.

Calculation of Economic Life. If all challengers have the same first cost ($1,000 in our example) and zero salvage at all times, the economic

TABLE D–1

Determination of Economic Life of a $1,000 Asset with a $50 Gradient Assuming Zero Salvage Value at All Times and Interest at 15%

Year n	Excess of Disbursements for Year Indicated Over First Year's Disbursements for New Asset	Equivalent Annual Cost—n Year Life		
		Capital Recovery Cost	Excess of Annual Disbursements	Total
A	B	C	D	E
1	$ 0	$1,150	$ 0	$1,150
2	50	615	24	639
3	100	438	46	484
4	150	350	67	417
5	200	298	86	384
6	250	264	105	369
7	300	240	123	363
8	350	223	139	362
9	400	210	155	365
10	450	199	169	368
11	500	191	183	374
12	550	184	196	380
13	600	179	207	386
14	650	175	218	393
15	700	171	228	399
16	750	168	238	406
17	800	165	247	412
18	850	163	254	417
19	900	161	262	423
20	950	160	269	429

life may be shown to depend on the ratio of inferiority gradient to first cost. In our example the gradient-cost ratio is 5% (i.e., $50 ÷ $1,000). Table D–1 shows the economic life to be 8 years.[2]

Line C in this table is simply the product of $1,000 and the capital recovery factor for n years. Line D is the product of $50 and the gradient factor for n years. Line E is the sum of lines C and D. The minimum value in line E, $362, occurs for a life of 8 years. In *Dynamic Equipment Policy*, such a minimum value is referred to as the challenger's *adverse minimum*.

In our discussion of the gas main example in Chapter 17, we noted that as long as the cost of extending the service another year (column B

[2] Table D–1 is computed along the same lines as Table 1 in Terborgh, *Dynamic Equipment Policy, op. cit.*, p. 78.

of Table 17–1, page 397) was less than the equivalent uniform cost up to date (column E), the equivalent uniform annual cost would continue to decrease; once the figure in column B was greater than the column E figure on the preceding line, the figures in column E started to increase. Columns B and E in Table D–1 are, in this respect, comparable to the corresponding figures in Table 17–1. Thus the adverse minimum is reached at the end of 8 years when the 9th-year inferiority in column B, $400, exceeds $362, the 8th-year figure in column E.

An Independent Check on the Comparative Cost Figures Given in Table D–1. The figure in any line of column B of Table D–1 does not represent the current year's operating cost of any particular asset; it is, as stated in the column heading, the excess of disbursements for the year indicated over the first year's disbursements for the best new asset expected to be available in that year. It follows that the total figure in column E does not represent equivalent annual cost for any particular asset. At first glance it may be hard to see why these figures, which depend on the shifting standard of the first year's performance of a different new asset every year, can give a correct comparison of the relative economy of different service lives. Nevertheless, the differences between the figures in column E for different assumed lives are the long-run differences in equivalent annual costs for these lives that would exist if costs should behave as assumed.

For example, let us compare the equivalent annual costs to be realized over a 16-year period on the assumption that the present challenger is continued in service for 16 years, that it is replaced after 8 years, and that there is a replacement every 4 years. By appropriate manipulations of compound interest factors, such costs may be computed to be as follows:

Life in Years	Capital Recovery	Equivalent Annual Disbursements	Total Equivalent Annual Cost	Excess Over Annual Cost for 8-Yr. Life
4	$350	$3,424	$3,774	$55
8	223	3,496	3,719	
16	168	3,595	3,763	44

The excesses over the equivalent annual cost for the economic life of 8 years are exactly the same as the excesses over the $362 adverse minimum as they may be observed in column E of Table D–1.

Use of the Challenger's Adverse Minimum in a Replacement Study. Assume that a certain defender has estimated next-year disbursements of $3,800, that subsequent years' disbursements will be higher than this, and that there is no salvage value now or later. If this defender is to be compared with the present challenger of Figure D–1 and Table D–1 by the method of analysis developed in *Dynamic Equipment Policy*, the comparison is:

Defender

Next-year capital costs (zero because of zero salvage values now and next year) .... $ 0

Next-year operating inferiority to present challenger = $3,800 − $3,500 300

Total is *defender's adverse minimum* $300

Challenger

Challenger's adverse minimum (from Table D–1) $362

This comparison favors the defender by $62. It may be contrasted with the following comparison of next-year costs along conventional lines, assuming an 8-year life and zero salvage value for the $1,000 challenger.

Defender

CR .... $ 0

Next-year disbursements 3,800

$3,800

Challenger

CR = $1,000(A/P,15%,8) = $1,000(0.22285) .... $ 223

Next-year disbursements 3,500

$3,723

This next-year comparison favors the challenger by $77.

The algebraic difference between these two results, $139, consists of a formalized allowance for the prospect that if the defender is kept another year, it will be followed by the next-year challenger and its successors and that the next-year challenger and its successsors will, on balance, be superior to the present challenger and its successors.

Figure D–1 shows a graphical comparison of year-by-year disbursements for the present challenger and its successors (solid line ABDEF-GH, etc.) and the next-year challenger and its successors (dash line JKLMNOP, etc.). Although the graph only goes for 25 years or so, this difference is a perpetual series that may be tabulated as follows:

Years	Advantage of Next-Year Challenger and Its Successors as Compared to Present Challenger and Its Successors
2 to 8	+$50 a year
9	−350
10 to 16	+50 a year
17	−350
18 to 24	+50 a year
25	−350
26 to 32	+50 a year
33	−350

and so on, ad infinitum

If we assume that all future challengers will have first costs of $1,000, 8-year lives, and zero salvage values, and if we accept the other implications of the mathematical model illustrated in Figure D–1, we may modify the next-year comparison of $3,800 for defender and $3,723 for challenger by charging the present challenger with the present worth (one year from zero date) of the infinite series of subsequent differences between the present challenger and its successors and the next-year challenger and its successors. To simplify calculations of present worth, the infinite series may be viewed as +$50 a year forever and −$400 at the end of every 8th year. The present worth at 15% may then be computed as follows:

$$PW = \frac{\$50}{0.15} - \frac{\$400(A/F,15\%,8)}{0.15}$$

$$= \$333 - \frac{\$400(0.07285)}{0.15} = \$333 - \$194 = \$139$$

Adding this $139 to the challenger's next-year costs of $3,723 in order to equalize matters over all subsequent years, we now have a next-year $3,800 figure for the defender to compare with a $3,862 figure for the challenger. If we subtract the common element in next year's disbursements, $3,500, we have the MAPI-type comparison of $300 for defender's adverse minimum with $362 for challenger's adverse minimum.

If instead of our specific figures of $50 for inferiority gradient, 0.15 for interest rate, and 8 years for life, we use the symbols G, i, and n, we note that

$$PW = \frac{G}{i} - \frac{nG(A/F,i,n)}{i}$$

This expression happens to be identical with the expression for the factor to convert a gradient to an equivalent uniform annual series developed in Chapter 4. It follows that under certain circumstances our table of gradient factors, Table E–26, could be used in computing a challenger's adverse minimum.

The total challenger's adverse minimum is the sum of challenger's capital recovery cost and a figure for the present worth of the advantage gained by having the next-year challenger and its successors rather than the present challenger and its successors. To use Table E–26 in computing the latter figure, we need the interest rate, the inferiority gradient, and the challenger's economic life. For instance, in our example the adverse minimum is $1,000(A/P,15\%,8) + \$50(A/G,15\%,8) = \$1,000-(0.22285) + \$50(2.78) = \$223 + \$139 = \$362$.

Usually the foregoing scheme for computing challenger's adverse minimum is not feasible because it assumes that both the inferiority gradient and the economic life are known. But these are not independent figures. Under the conditions of the mathematical model, the gradient determines the economic life, as brought out in Table D–1. Conversely, an assumed economic life implies a particular value of gradient. *Dynamic Equipment Policy* and *MAPI Replacement Manual* contain various formulas and diagrams for calculation of a challenger's adverse minimum without the detailed arithmetic of a table such as D–1.

An Approximate Formula for Challenger's Adverse Minimum as a Function of the Gradient. The recommendation in *Dynamic Equipment Policy* was that, wherever practicable in a replacement economy study, the challenger's adverse minimum should be based on its estimated gradient. Often the data of a study will supply a basis for computing the past gradient. Sometimes there may be reasons for expecting that the future gradient will be greater or smaller than the past one; sometimes it will be reasonable to assume that the past gradient will continue in the future.

For a first cost c, a gradient G, and an interest rate i, *Dynamic Equipment Policy* gave the following approximate formula:

$$\text{Challenger's adverse minimum} = \sqrt{2cG} + \frac{ic - G}{2}$$

This formula was based on average (rather than equivalent) annual disbursements with capital recovery costs computed by straight-line depreciation plus average interest. It assumed a zero salvage value at the end of the challenger's economic life.

Applied to our example of Table D–1, this gives

$$\text{Adverse minimum} = \sqrt{2(\$1,000)(\$50)} + \frac{0.15(\$1,000) - \$50}{2}$$
$$= \$316 + \$50 = \$366$$

Derivation of an Expression for the Relationship Between Adverse Minimum and Economic Life. In contrast to *Dynamic Equipment Policy*, no estimate of the gradient was needed to apply the methods of analysis advocated in *MAPI Replacement Manual;* a challenger's adverse minimum was computed from its estimated life and terminal salvage value. The formula used for adverse minimum in the zero-salvage case may be derived fairly simply, as follows:

The total equivalent annual figure, U, for n years in a calculation such as the one illustrated in Table D–1 is the sum of the annual cost of capital recovery and the equivalent annual operating inferiority.

$$U = c\,\frac{i(1+i)^n}{(1+i)^n - 1} + \frac{G}{i} - \frac{nG}{i}\left[\frac{i}{(1+i)^n - 1}\right]$$

The operating inferiority for any year, n, is $(n-1)G$. The operating inferiority for the year following the nth year is nG. As long as the next-year operating inferiority, nG, is less than U, the value of U for the year $(n+1)$ will obviously be less than for year n. The first year for which the next-year operating inferiority is equal to or greater than U is the year corresponding to the minimum value of U. For a specified first cost, c, with any specified economic life there will be a possible range of values of U_{min} corresponding to the range of values of G that will result in the particular economic life. The lowest possible value of G that will result in the particular economic life will be that for which $U = nG$.

To find the value of U corresponding to this particular value of G, $\dfrac{U}{n}$ may be substituted for G in the general expression for U, as follows:

$$U = \frac{ci(1+i)^n}{(1+i)^n - 1} + \frac{U}{in} - \frac{U}{i}\left[\frac{i}{(1+i)^n - 1}\right]$$

$$U + \frac{U}{(1+i)^n - 1} - \frac{U}{in} = \frac{ci(1+i)^n}{(1+i)^n - 1}$$

Multiply both sides of this equation by $in[(1+i)^n - 1]$,
$$Uin(1+i)^n - Uin + Uin - U(1+i)^n + U = cni^2(1+i)^n$$
Divide by $(1+i)^n$

$$U\left(in + \frac{1}{(1+i)^n} - 1\right) = cni^2$$

$$U = \frac{cni^2}{in + \dfrac{1}{(1+i)^n} - 1}$$

A minor limitation on the use of this formula for challenger's adverse minimum as a function of estimated economic life may be brought out by the following example. Assume $c = \$1,000$, $n = 8$, and $i = 0.15$.

$$U_{min} = \frac{\$1,000(8)(0.15)^2}{(0.15)(8) + 0.3269 - 1} = \frac{\$180}{0.5269} = \$342$$

It will be observed that, although the economic life is 8 years as in Table D–1 and the values of first cost and interest rate are the same ones used in that table, this adverse minimum of $342 is somewhat less than the figure of $362 computed for a gradient of $50 in Table D–1. The $342 adverse minimum corresponds to a gradient of $342 \div 8 = \$43$, the lowest possible gradient that will give an 8-year economic life with a first cost of $1,000 and an interest rate of 15%.

With any given first cost and interest rate there will be a range of values of gradient that will result in any designated economic life. This formula for adverse minimum as a function of economic life always im-

plies the lowest possible gradient within this range. The upper end of
the range may be determined in any case by using the formula to compute adverse minimum for a life of one year less.

For instance if $c = \$1{,}000$, $n = 7$, and $i = 0.15$, $U_{min} = \$370$. The
corresponding gradient is $\$370 \div 7 = \$53$. It follows that any gradient
above $\$43$ and below $\$53$ will give an economic life of 8 years.

**Salvage Values in the Methods of *Dynamic Equipment Policy* and
MAPI Replacement Manual.** The schemes of analysis presented in these
two volumes were identical in their method of calculation of the defender's adverse minimum. This consisted of two parts, the defender's
next-year operating inferiority to the challenger and the defender's next-
year capital cost. This next-year capital cost was a conventional capital
recovery cost made up of one year's interest on present salvage value
plus the prospective decline in salvage value during the next year.
(See the discussion in Example 17–4 under the heading "Calculation of
Annual Cost of Defender.") This use of defender's present and next-
year salvage values in computing defender's adverse minimum is illustrated in Example D–1.

Where challenger's adverse minimum was computed from the prospective gradient by the formula we have quoted from *Dynamic Equipment Policy*, a zero challenger salvage value was assumed. It will be recalled that this adverse minimum is, in principle, made up of two parts,
the challenger's capital recovery cost and a figure that can be computed
from the gradient. With relatively high interest rates (say 10% or more),
the influence of a moderate terminal salvage value on capital recovery
cost was relatively small and a negligible error was introduced by the
arbitrary assumption of zero terminal salvage value (particularly so for
the longer-lived challengers).

In contrast, *MAPI Replacement Manual* used the challenger's estimated life and terminal salvage value to determine its adverse minimum; in effect, as we have seen in the derivation of the no-salvage
formula, the gradient was inferred from the life and salvage value. The
following formula for adverse minimum with a positive salvage value was
derived on the assumption that challengers' salvage values would decline at a uniform rate (i.e., according to a declining-balance curve):

$$U_{min} = \frac{in\left[ci + rs\dfrac{1}{(1+i)^n}\right] - s(i+r)\left[1 - \dfrac{1}{(1+i)^n}\right]}{in + \dfrac{1}{(1+i)^n} - 1}$$

where c is challenger's first cost, n is estimated service life, s is estimated
terminal salvage value, i is interest rate expressed as a decimal, and r

is a symbol for $\dfrac{2.30259}{n} (\log c - \log s)$.

In the formulas used in *MAPI Replacement Manual*, both the challenger's adverse minimum and its implied gradient were quite sensitive to differences in estimated terminal salvage percentages. For example, consider three $10,000 challengers each with an 8-year estimated life and with respective estimated terminal salvage values of 0%, 20%, and 40%. Values of adverse minimum using an interest rate of 15% may be computed and broken down into their elements as follows:

Estimated Terminal Salvage	Total Adverse Minimum	Portion of Adverse Minimum Due to Capital Recovery Cost	Portion of Adverse Minimum Due to Advantage of Next-Year Challenger and Its Successors over Present Challenger and Its Successors
0%	$3,416	$2,228	$1,188
20%	2,818	2,083	735
40%	2,406	1,937	469

It is evident that moderate differences in assumed challenger salvage values cause substantial differences in the allowances for future technological progress due to the expected superiority of future challengers.

Example D–1 illustrates a simple application of the two first MAPI methods. It brings out certain differences between the methods that existed even when the challenger was assumed to have zero terminal salvage value.

EXAMPLE D–1. A REPLACEMENT STUDY ILLUSTRATING TWO MAPI TECHNIQUES

Facts of the Case. The first cost of a proposed new cutter grinder is $6,124. The present salvage value of the existing 12-year-old cutter grinder is $400; this is expected to decline to $200 next year. Because the challenger can grind to closer tolerances, it is expected to increase next-year revenues by $500. Expected savings in next-year operating disbursements are $2,255 in direct labor, $565 in fringe benefits, and $150 in maintenance. Next-year insurance will be $60 higher with the challenger.

The following calculations illustrate the types of analysis explained in *Dynamic Equipment Policy* and *MAPI Replacement Manual*. The assumed interest rate i (in effect, the before-tax minimum attractive rate of return) is 15%. The challenger is assumed to have zero terminal salvage value. For the analysis using the methods of *MAPI Replacement Manual*, we shall assume a challenger service life of 15 years.

Defender's Adverse Minimum. This is the sum of the defender's next-year operating inferiority and its next-year capital costs. The calculation of operating inferiority may be tabulated as follows.

	Next-Year Operating Advantage	
	Defender	*Challenger*
Increased receipts due to quality improvement		$ 500
Direct labor costs		2,255
Fringe benefits		565
Maintenance		150
Insurance	$60	
	$60	$3,470

Net challenger advantage (defender inferiority) = $3,470 − $60 = $3,410

The next-year capital costs for the defender are interest on present salvage value plus decline in salvage value. This sum is $400(0.15) + ($400 − $200) = $60 + $200 = $260.

The defender's adverse minimum is $3,410 + $260 = $3,670.

Challenger's Adverse Minimum Based on Estimated Challenger Gradient. To find the past gradient, we divide the defender's operating inferiority, $3,410, by its age, 12 years, and secure a figure of $282. If we assume that this gradient will continue in the future, we can use it in the approximate zero-salvage formula from *Dynamic Equipment Policy*, as follows:

$$U_{\min} = \sqrt{2cG} + \frac{ic - G}{2}$$

$$= \sqrt{2(\$6,124)(\$282)} + \frac{0.15(\$6,124) - \$282}{2}$$

$$= \$1,858 + \$318 = \$2,176$$

This $2,176 should be compared with $3,670, the defender's adverse minimum. The comparison favors the challenger by $1,494. The $1,494 should be interpreted as a one-year difference favoring immediate replacement in comparison with replacement one year hence.

In this analysis assuming zero salvage value, the implied challenger life is the adverse minimum, $2,176, divided by the gradient, $282; this is between 7 and 8 years.

Challenger's Adverse Minimum Based on Estimated Service Life and Salvage Value. As we are assuming zero salvage value, we may use the no-salvage version of the formula from *MAPI Replacement Manual*, as follows:

$$U_{\min} = \frac{cni^2}{in + \dfrac{1}{(1 + i)^n} - 1}$$

$$= \frac{(\$6,124)(15)(0.15)^2}{0.15(15) + 0.1229 - 1} = \$1,505$$

A comparison of this $1,505 with the $3,670 defender's adverse minimum favors the challenger by $2,165.

In this analysis assuming zero salvage value, the implied gradient is the adverse minimum, $1,505, divided by the life, 15 years; this is $100.

Source of Differences in Zero-Salvage Case. The defender's adverse minimum is the same whether an analyst uses the methods of *Dynamic Equipment Policy* or *MAPI Replacement Manual*. The difference between the values of $2,176 and $1,505 for challenger's adverse minimum with the two methods is really caused by a difference in the estimated inferiority gradient of the challenger. This gradient was explicitly assumed to be $282 on the basis of past experience in one method. In the other method, the estimate of a 15-year life implied a gradient of $100. The higher estimated gradient of $282 causes higher capital recovery costs because it leads to a shorter estimated challenger service life. It also causes a greater allowance for the expected long-run superiority of the next-year challenger and its successors to the present challenger and its successors.

Some Changes in the Later MAPI Models. For the sake of brevity in the following discussion, we shall refer to the model used in *Business Investment Policy* as the 1958 model and the one used in *Business Investment Management* as the 1967 model.

Both models broadened the problem to an evaluation of *any* proposed investments in plant and equipment. Nevertheless, many of the features of the earlier models were maintained. Anyone who wishes to understand the later models should first study *Dynamic Equipment Policy,* which is the only one of the four volumes that contains a step-by-step exposition of underlying theory.

The later models were like the earlier ones in always considering alternatives in pairs. Where there was no asset that might be replaced, the defender was, in effect, a continuation of a present condition. (Some of the specialized terminology introduced in the earlier volumes was abandoned in the 1958 and 1967 books. But even though the words *challenger, defender,* and *gradient* are not used in the two later volumes, the useful concepts described by these words continue to be employed.)

Just as in the earlier books, a formal allowance was made for the prospect that future challengers will be superior to present ones. And this prospect of superiority of future challengers was, in effect, converted to a single equivalent monetary amount to permit a next-year comparison between the alternatives of (a) selecting the present challenger at once, and (b) continuing with the defender for one more year and then acquiring the next-year challenger. The 1958 and 1967 models were like the 1950 model of *MAPI Replacement Manual* in basing their assumptions regarding the superiority of future challengers on the estimated life and salvage value of the present one. The 1950, 1958, and 1967 models were alike in making the conclusions of a study quite sensitive to the estimated salvage percentage of a challenger.

However, the 1958 and 1967 MAPI methods had a number of points of difference from the earlier ones. Some important differences were:

1. The previous models had involved comparisons before income taxes; the 1958 and 1967 techniques involved after-tax comparisons.

2. Whereas the previous models had given a next-year difference in adverse minimum (in effect, in annual cost) between defender and chal-

lenger, the 1958 and 1967 models gave a next-year rate of return on the extra investment needed to acquire the challenger. In the 1958 volume, this rate of return was called the "MAPI urgency rating."

3. Certain aspects of the mathematical models assumed in the earlier methods were illustrated here in Figure D–1. In the 1958 and 1967 models, just as in the earlier ones, technological progress was assumed to take place by a constant amount each year. This assumption about improvement in technology was indicated in Figure D–1 by the straight line AJDLFNHP.

In the earlier methods the gradual increase of operation and maintenance costs (and/or decrease of revenues) with the age of an asset was also assumed to follow a uniform gradient. This increase was shown in Figure D–1 by the parallel straight lines ABC, JK, DE, LM, FG, and NO. In *Business Investment Policy*, such a uniform increase is described as the "standard" projection pattern. But other projection patterns also were made available in the 1958 volume; it was possible to assume that annual disbursements increase either at a decreasing rate or an increasing rate.[3]

The 1967 MAPI model reverted to the single assumption of a uniform gradient for operation and maintenance costs. Presumably the other optional projection patterns had not been used to any great extent by the companies that adopted the 1958 MAPI methods.

4. The most complicated aspects of the 1958 and 1967 models came from the introduction of income taxes. The earlier models had discounted the infinite chain of estimated differences in cash flow between the present challenger and its successors and the next-year challenger and its successors. In making a similar calculation that reflected income taxes, it became necessary, in effect, to discount an infinite chain of differences in cash flow for income taxes. The 1967 volume supplied the analyst with charts applicable to straight-line, years-digits, and declining-balance depreciation methods. (In 1958, it had been stipulated that a years-digits chart would be used whenever the declining-balance method was to be adopted.) In all cases it was necessary to assume that the challenger life and salvage value adopted for the MAPI evaluation would also be used for income tax purposes. (The reader may recall that we made a similar simplification in our calculation of income tax differences in Chapters 6 through 15.)

[3] An earlier mathematical model assuming that annual disbursements for operation and maintenance increase at a decreasing rate was described in A. A. Alchian's *Economic Replacement Policy*, Publication R-224 (Santa Monica, Calif.: The Rand Corporation, 1952). Our Figure D–1 was suggested by Figure 2.1, p. 8 of the Alchian pamphlet.

In computing the future chain of income tax differences, it was assumed that the tax rate would be 50%, and that 25% of any project would be financed by debt bearing an interest rate of 3%.

5. In the discounting of the infinite chain of cash flow differences in the earlier models, the discount rate had been the stipulated value of i (in effect, the before-tax minimum attractive rate of return). But the 1958 and 1967 volumes dealt with rate-of-return models, not annual-cost models.

In conventional rate-of-return calculations such as those we have illustrated starting with Chapter 8, the purpose of the analysis is to find an unknown value of i applicable to the entire study period; there is no figure for i stipulated in advance to be used in compound interest conversions. But the 1958 and 1967 MAPI models aimed to find a one-year rate of return. Therefore, it was necessary to adopt a value of i to apply to the infinite chain of estimated cash flow differences after date 1. For this purpose it was assumed that there would be 75% of equity capital earning an average after-tax return of 10% and 25% of borrowed capital at an average interest cost of 3%. The weighted average of these gave an i of 8.25% to be used in the discounting. (The reader may recall our comments in Chapter 18 regarding project evaluation on the assumption of a standardized mixture of debt and equity capital.)

The 1958 and 1967 models, which gave as their answer a one-year rate of return, therefore constituted an analysis using two interest rates, namely, the discount rate applied to all cash flow differences after the first year, and the next-year rate of return found at the conclusion of the analysis.

6. Beginning with the first MAPI methods in 1949, all MAPI systems have been geared to a next-year comparison as the desirable one. But all have provided approximate methods for applying the MAPI philosophy to comparison periods of more than one year in cases where a one-year period was not appropriate for the defender. The 1967 book provides a special auxiliary chart to be used in such cases.

Both the 1958 and 1967 volumes are useful reading for business managers and analysts engaged in project evaluation even though it is not planned to use any of the various MAPI systems. Most of the topics discussed by Terborgh are of general application in investment analysis, and his comments are of interest apart from the particular MAPI system that is being explained.

The Issue of How To Consider the Prospect of Future Technological Change in Making Present Replacement Decisions. Although the various MAPI methods have differed from one another, one element that

they have had in common has been the use of a formal monetary figure
—usually implied rather than explicitly stated—to reflect the likelihood
that future challengers will be superior to present ones. In fact, this
formal allowance has been the new element that these mathematical
models have introduced into replacement economy.

In the common case where replacement decisions are made without
the use of a mathematical model of this type, one possibility is to make
the required monetary comparisons with no special allowance for the
prospect that there will be a better challenger in the near future. Then,
whenever deemed relevant, this prospect can be recognized as a nonmonetary element in making the decision. In effect, this prospect is
viewed as part of the irreducible data for decision making.

An alternate possibility is to require challengers in replacement studies to meet more severe criteria than are imposed on other proposals for
new assets. For example, somewhat higher minimum attractive rates of
return might be used in replacement studies than in other studies. More
commonly, this device of using severe criteria takes the form of shortening the estimated service life of the challenger.

An extreme shortening of challenger service life in replacement studies constitutes an irrational obstacle to technological progress. If old
assets are kept in service until new ones will "pay for themselves" in one
or two years, the old assets will generally be kept for much too long a
time. The adverse social consequences to be expected from a widespread
use of extreme short payoff periods were stressed by George Terborgh in
Dynamic Equipment Policy.

On the other hand, *some* shortening of the estimated life of a challenger in its initial or primary service has an effect not unlike the one
obtained from using certain MAPI models. It is roughly true, although
not exactly so, that a comparison using the zero-salvage formula from
MAPI Replacement Manual and a challenger service life of n will give
the same results as a conventional economy study using a challenger
service life of $n/2$ and zero salvage. For example, we computed the
challenger's adverse minimum to be $342 where first cost was $1,000, life
was 8 years, salvage was zero, and interest was 15%. For the same asset
the capital recovery cost is $350 for a 4-year life and zero salvage value.

**Some General Comments on the Use of Complex Mathematical
Models as Aids in Making Economic Decisions.** If the use of a mathematical model is under consideration as a possible basis for decision
making—either on a proposed replacement or on any other matter—certain questions need to be examined. One question is which of the available models seems to be best adapted to the particular circumstances.
(It sometimes happens that although no available model is suitable, a
new one can be devised that is more nearly adequate.) Another ques-

tion is whether or not the formalized assumptions of the best model are close enough to the facts. In general, these questions cannot be answered in a satisfactory way except by someone who understands both the facts and the assumptions underlying the various models. Judgment on these questions is more difficult for complex mathematical models than for simple ones.

It is not a valid objection to a particular model to point out some way in which the model fails to fit the exact circumstances of a case. Assumptions that can be incorporated into mathematical formulas will seldom fit economic facts perfectly. In judging the suitability of a certain model to a particular case, the important matter is to judge whether the *decision* based on the use of the model is likely to be sensitive to the various ways in which the assumptions depart from the facts of the case.

The foregoing comment about the importance of sensitivity may be illustrated with reference to several of the assumptions made in all of the MAPI models. Consider the assumptions (1) that the service period is perpetual, (2) that all future challengers will have the same first costs, salvage values, and lives as the present one and that technological progress will occur at a uniform rate, and (3) that the appropriate comparison is between replacement at once with the present challenger and continuing the defender in service one year more and then replacing it with the next-year challenger.

1. In general, with the interest rates of 8% or more commonly used in replacement studies, the present worth of the assumed distant consequences of present decisions is quite small. If a service is likely to be needed for a fairly long time, no serious error in decision making will be caused by using a model that assumes perpetual service. But such a model clearly is inappropriate whenever it is expected that the service will terminate at a foreseeable date in the near future.

2. It was pointed out in Chapter 17 (following the discussion of Example 17-4) that there sometimes is a reasonable basis for making specific forecasts about the challengers to be expected in the next few years. Different forecasts have different implications regarding the present replacement decision. For example, the expectation that challengers in the near future will have considerably higher first costs than the present challenger is favorable to immediate replacement; the expectation of substantial technological improvement in the near future is favorable to putting off replacement. Where a basis exists for such specific forecasts, better decisions are likely to be made by an analysis incorporating these forecasts than by an analysis using a mathematical model that depends on generalized forecasts about future challengers.

3. The question of selecting the defender remaining life that is most favorable to the defender was discussed in Chapter 17 (following Ex-

ample 17–4). It was pointed out that under certain circumstances this life is one year; under other circumstances it may be considerably longer. In those circumstances where a defender life of more than one year should be used in a replacement study, a next-year analysis may lead to an incorrect decision favorable to the challenger.

In general, it should be emphasized that a prerequisite to the use of *any* mathematical model to guide an economic decision should be a clear understanding of the assumptions of the particular model by the person who makes (or recommends) the decision.

PROBLEMS

The following problems are all based on a single replacement proposal, for which the circumstances have been suggested by an example on pages 136–39 of *Dynamic Equipment Policy*. The purpose of the problems is to help the reader to examine certain aspects of various replacement models by making a series of calculations about a specific case. The facts and estimates regarding the replacement proposal are as follows:

The management of a metalworking plant is considering the replacement of a 19-year old planer. The proposed new planer (challenger) has a first cost of $30,000. The old planer (defender) has a net salvage value of $6,000. It is estimated that this salvage value will decline to $5,000 one year hence. The challenger will save $1,550 a year in direct labor cost and labor extras on the planing operation. Moreover, the greater precision of the challenger reduces the amount of work needed on subsequent operations, with a resulting annual saving of $2,440 in direct labor cost and labor extras. It is estimated the maintenance cost for the challenger next year will be $250 less than the maintenance cost for the defender; however, this saving in maintenance costs will be offset by $250 higher challenger costs for property taxes and insurance.

D–1. Assume that a before-tax comparison is to be made, computing challenger's adverse minimum by the approximate no-salvage formula from *Dynamic Equipment Policy*, $U_{min} = \sqrt{2cG} + \dfrac{ic - G}{2}$. An interest rate (minimum attractive rate of return before income taxes) of 10% is to be used. The future gradient is to be assumed the same as the past gradient.

(a) What is the gradient? (*Ans.* = $210.)
(b) What is the defender's adverse minimum? (*Ans.* = $5,590.)
(c) What is the challenger's adverse minimum? (*Ans.* = $4,945.)
(d) What challenger service life can be derived from the challenger's adverse minimum? (*Ans.* = between 23 and 24 years.)

D–2. Assume that a before-tax comparison is to be made, computing challenger's adverse minimum by the no-salvage formula used in *MAPI Replacement Manual*, $U_{min} = \dfrac{cni^2}{in + (1 + i)^{-n} - 1}$. An interest rate of 10% is to be used. The estimated challenger life is 24 years.

(a) What is the defender's adverse minimum? (*Ans.* = $5,590.)
(b) What is the challenger's adverse minimum? (*Ans.* = $4,795.)
(c) What gradient is implied by the challenger's adverse minimum? (*Ans.* = $200.)

D–3. It is evident that the past gradient has been due entirely to obsolescence. (The lower prospective next-year maintenance costs for the challenger are offset by equal higher prospective next-year costs for property taxes and insurance.) What is the excess of the total $4,795 challenger's adverse minimum in Problem D–2 over the challenger's capital recovery cost? Show that this excess is equal to the present worth one year hence of the advantage gained thereafter by an infinite series of challengers starting a year hence and having 24-year lives, as compared to a similar infinite series starting at once with the present challenger. In this calculation, assume that the superiority of future challengers will correspond to the gradient computed in Problem D–2.

D–4. Solve Problem D–1, using an interest rate (minimum attractive rate of return before income taxes) of 20%.

D–5. Solve Problem D–2, using an interest rate of 20%.

D–6. On the basis of your analysis of Problems D–1 to D–5 and any further analysis that you believe is appropriate, discuss the sensitivity of the choice between challenger and defender to (a) present defender salvage value; (b) estimated decline in defender salvage value during the coming year; and (c) assumed interest rate. Discuss the sensitivity of the choice to assumed gradient where the challenger's adverse minimum is based on estimated gradient, as Problems D–1 and D–4. Discuss the sensitivity of the choice to assumed challenger service life where challenger's adverse minimum is based on service life, as in Problems D–2 and D–5.

D–7. Tabulate the prospective differences in cash flow before taxes between retiring the defender at once and retiring it one year hence in favor of a challenger that will reduce annual operating disbursements $200 below those expected with the present challenger. Assume that the first cost of the new challenger will also be $30,000. Compute figures for each of the next 5 years and indicate the pattern of differences thereafter.

D–8. Assume that the present defender can be kept in service for, say, the next 10 years with substantially the same annual disbursements as at present, but that its salvage value will be zero when finally retired. Compute the year-by-year differences in cash flow for each of the next 10 years. (Assume that differences in challenger and defender maintenance cost will continue to be offset by differences in property taxes.) Compute the period for crude payout before income taxes.

E

Compound Interest Tables

FORMULAS FOR CALCULATING COMPOUND INTEREST FACTORS

Single Payment—Compound Amount Factor

$(F/P, i, n)$

$$(1+i)^n$$

Single Payment—Present Worth Factor

$(P/F, i, n)$

$$\frac{1}{(1+i)^n}$$

Sinking Fund Factor

$(A/F, i, n)$

$$\frac{i}{(1+i)^n - 1}$$

Capital Recovery Factor

$(A/P, i, n)$

$$\frac{i(1+i)^n}{(1+i)^n - 1}$$

Uniform Series—Compound Amount Factor

$(F/A, i, n)$

$$\frac{(1+i)^n - 1}{i}$$

Uniform Series—Present Worth Factor

$(P/A, i, n)$

$$\frac{(1+i)^n - 1}{i(1+i)^n}$$

TABLE E-1

1% Compound Interest Factors

	Single Payment		Uniform Series				
	Compound Amount Factor	Present Worth Factor	Sinking Fund Factor	Capital Recovery Factor	Compound Amount Factor	Present Worth Factor	
n	F/P	P/F	A/F	A/P	F/A	P/A	n
1	1.0100	0.9901	1.000 00	1.010 00	1.000	0.990	1
2	1.0201	0.9803	0.497 51	0.507 51	2.010	1.970	2
3	1.0303	0.9706	0.330 02	0.340 02	3.030	2.941	3
4	1.0406	0.9610	0.246 28	0.256 28	4.060	3.902	4
5	1.0510	0.9515	0.196 04	0.206 04	5.101	4.853	5
6	1.0615	0.9420	0.162 55	0.172 55	6.152	5.795	6
7	1.0721	0.9327	0.138 63	0.148 63	7.214	6.728	7
8	1.0829	0.9235	0.120 69	0.130 69	8.286	7.652	8
9	1.0937	0.9143	0.106 74	0.116 74	9.369	8.566	9
10	1.1046	0.9053	0.095 58	0.105 58	10.462	9.471	10
11	1.1157	0.8963	0.086 45	0.096 45	11.567	10.368	11
12	1.1268	0.8874	0.078 85	0.088 85	12.683	11.255	12
13	1.1381	0.8787	0.072 41	0.082 41	13.809	12.134	13
14	1.1495	0.8700	0.066 90	0.076 90	14.947	13.004	14
15	1.1610	0.8613	0.062 12	0.072 12	16.097	13.865	15
16	1.1726	0.8528	0.057 94	0.067 94	17.258	14.718	16
17	1.1843	0.8444	0.054 26	0.064 26	18.430	15.562	17
18	1.1961	0.8360	0.050 98	0.060 98	19.615	16.398	18
19	1.2081	0.8277	0.048 05	0.058 05	20.811	17.226	19
20	1.2202	0.8195	0.045 42	0.055 42	22.019	18.046	20
21	1.2324	0.8114	0.043 03	0.053 03	23.239	18.857	21
22	1.2447	0.8034	0.040 86	0.050 86	24.472	19.660	22
23	1.2572	0.7954	0.038 89	0.048 89	25.716	20.456	23
24	1.2697	0.7876	0.037 07	0.047 07	26.973	21.243	24
25	1.2824	0.7798	0.035 41	0.045 41	28.243	22.023	25
26	1.2953	0.7720	0.033 87	0.043 87	29.526	22.795	26
27	1.3082	0.7644	0.032 45	0.042 45	30.821	23.560	27
28	1.3213	0.7568	0.031 12	0.041 12	32.129	24.316	28
29	1.3345	0.7493	0.029 90	0.039 90	33.450	25.066	29
30	1.3478	0.7419	0.028 75	0.038 75	34.785	25.808	30
31	1.3613	0.7346	0.027 68	0.037 68	36.133	26.542	31
32	1.3749	0.7273	0.026 67	0.036 67	37.494	27.270	32
33	1.3887	0.7201	0.025 73	0.035 73	38.869	27.990	33
34	1.4026	0.7130	0.024 84	0.034 84	40.258	28.703	34
35	1.4166	0.7059	0.024 00	0.034 00	41.660	29.409	35
40	1.4889	0.6717	0.020 46	0.030 46	48.886	32.835	40
45	1.5648	0.6391	0.017 71	0.027 71	56.481	36.095	45
50	1.6446	0.6080	0.015 51	0.025 51	64.463	39.196	50
55	1.7285	0.5785	0.013 73	0.023 73	72.852	42.147	55
60	1.8167	0.5504	0.012 24	0.022 24	81.670	44.955	60
65	1.9094	0.5237	0.011 00	0.021 00	90.937	47.627	65
70	2.0068	0.4983	0.009 93	0.019 93	100.676	50.169	70
75	2.1091	0.4741	0.009 02	0.019 02	110.913	52.587	75
80	2.2167	0.4511	0.008 22	0.018 22	121.672	54.888	80
85	2.3298	0.4292	0.007 52	0.017 52	132.979	57.078	85
90	2.4486	0.4084	0.006 90	0.016 90	144.863	59.161	90
95	2.5735	0.3886	0.006 36	0.016 36	157.354	61.143	95
100	2.7048	0.3697	0.005 87	0.015 87	170.481	63.029	100

TABLE E-2
1¼% Compound Interest Factors

	Single Payment		Uniform Series				
	Compound Amount Factor	Present Worth Factor	Sinking Fund Factor	Capital Recovery Factor	Compound Amount Factor	Present Worth Factor	
n	F/P	P/F	A/F	A/P	F/A	P/A	n
1	1.0125	0.9877	1.000 00	1.012 50	1.000	0.988	1
2	1.0252	0.9755	0.496 89	0.509 39	2.012	1.963	2
3	1.0380	0.9634	0.329 20	0.341 70	3.038	2.927	3
4	1.0509	0.9515	0.245 36	0.257 86	4.076	3.878	4
5	1.0641	0.9398	0.195 06	0.207 56	5.127	4.818	5
6	1.0774	0.9282	0.161 53	0.174 03	6.191	5.746	6
7	1.0909	0.9167	0.137 59	0.150 09	7.268	6.663	7
8	1.1045	0.9054	0.119 63	0.132 13	8.359	7.568	8
9	1.1183	0.8942	0.105 67	0.118 17	9.463	8.462	9
10	1.1323	0.8832	0.094 50	0.107 00	10.582	9.346	10
11	1.1464	0.8723	0.085 37	0.097 87	11.714	10.218	11
12	1.1608	0.8615	0.077 76	0.090 26	12.860	11.079	12
13	1.1753	0.8509	0.071 32	0.083 82	14.021	11.930	13
14	1.1900	0.8404	0.065 81	0.078 31	15.196	12.771	14
15	1.2048	0.8300	0.061 03	0.073 53	16.386	13.601	15
16	1.2199	0.8197	0.056 85	0.069 35	17.591	14.420	16
17	1.2351	0.8096	0.053 16	0.065 66	18.811	15.230	17
18	1.2506	0.7996	0.049 88	0.062 38	20.046	16.030	18
19	1.2662	0.7898	0.046 96	0.059 46	21.297	16.819	19
20	1.2820	0.7800	0.044 32	0.056 82	22.563	17.599	20
21	1.2981	0.7704	0.041 94	0.054 44	23.845	18.370	21
22	1.3143	0.7609	0.039 77	0.052 27	25.143	19.131	22
23	1.3307	0.7515	0.037 80	0.050 30	26.457	19.882	23
24	1.3474	0.7422	0.035 99	0.048 49	27.788	20.624	24
25	1.3642	0.7330	0.034 32	0.046 82	29.135	21.357	25
26	1.3812	0.7240	0.032 79	0.045 29	30.500	22.081	26
27	1.3985	0.7150	0.031 37	0.043 87	31.881	22.796	27
28	1.4160	0.7062	0.030 05	0.042 55	33.279	23.503	28
29	1.4337	0.6975	0.028 82	0.041 32	34.695	24.200	29
30	1.4516	0.6889	0.027 68	0.040 18	36.129	24.889	30
31	1.4698	0.6804	0.026 61	0.039 11	37.581	25.569	31
32	1.4881	0.6720	0.025 61	0.038 11	39.050	26.241	32
33	1.5067	0.6637	0.024 67	0.037 17	40.539	26.905	33
34	1.5256	0.6555	0.023 78	0.036 28	42.045	27.560	34
35	1.5446	0.6474	0.022 95	0.035 45	43.571	28.208	35
40	1.6436	0.6084	0.019 42	0.031 92	51.490	31.327	40
45	1.7489	0.5718	0.016 69	0.029 19	59.916	34.258	45
50	1.8610	0.5373	0.014 52	0.027 02	68.882	37.013	50
55	1.9803	0.5050	0.012 75	0.025 25	78.422	39.602	55
60	2.1072	0.4746	0.011 29	0.023 79	88.575	42.035	60
65	2.2422	0.4460	0.010 06	0.022 56	99.377	44.321	65
70	2.3859	0.4191	0.009 02	0.021 52	110.872	46.470	70
75	2.5388	0.3939	0.008 12	0.020 62	123.103	48.489	75
80	2.7015	0.3702	0.007 35	0.019 85	136.119	50.387	80
85	2.8746	0.3479	0.006 67	0.019 17	149.968	52.170	85
90	3.0588	0.3269	0.006 07	0.018 57	164.705	53.846	90
95	3.2548	0.3072	0.005 54	0.018 04	180.386	55.421	95
100	3.4634	0.2887	0.005 07	0.017 57	197.072	56.901	100

TABLE E–3
1½% Compound Interest Factors

	Single Payment		Uniform Series				
	Compound Amount Factor	Present Worth Factor	Sinking Fund Factor	Capital Recovery Factor	Compound Amount Factor	Present Worth Factor	
n	F/P	P/F	A/F	A/P	F/A	P/A	n
1	1.0150	0.9852	1.000 00	1.015 00	1.000	0.985	1
2	1.0302	0.9707	0.496 28	0.511 28	2.015	1.956	2
3	1.0457	0.9563	0.328 38	0.343 38	3.045	2.912	3
4	1.0614	0.9422	0.244 44	0.259 44	4.091	3.854	4
5	1.0773	0.9283	0.194 09	0.209 09	5.152	4.783	5
6	1.0934	0.9145	0.160 53	0.175 53	6.230	5.697	6
7	1.1098	0.9010	0.136 56	0.151 56	7.323	6.598	7
8	1.1265	0.8877	0.118 58	0.133 58	8.433	7.486	8
9	1.1434	0.8746	0.104 61	0.119 61	9.559	8.361	9
10	1.1605	0.8617	0.093 43	0.108 43	10.703	9.222	10
11	1.1779	0.8489	0.084 29	0.099 29	11.863	10.071	11
12	1.1956	0.8364	0.076 68	0.091 68	13.041	10.908	12
13	1.2136	0.8240	0.070 24	0.085 24	14.237	11.732	13
14	1.2318	0.8118	0.064 72	0.079 72	15.450	12.543	14
15	1.2502	0.7999	0.059 94	0.074 94	16.682	13.343	15
16	1.2690	0.7880	0.055 77	0.070 77	17.932	14.131	16
17	1.2880	0.7764	0.052 08	0.067 08	19.201	14.908	17
18	1.3073	0.7649	0.048 81	0.063 81	20.489	15.673	18
19	1.3270	0.7536	0.045 88	0.060 88	21.797	16.426	19
20	1.3469	0.7425	0.043 25	0.058 25	23.124	17.169	20
21	1.3671	0.7315	0.040 87	0.055 87	24.471	17.900	21
22	1.3876	0.7207	0.038 70	0.053 70	25.838	18.621	22
23	1.4084	0.7100	0.036 73	0.051 73	27.225	19.331	23
24	1.4300	0.6995	0.034 92	0.049 92	28.634	20.030	24
25	1.4509	0.6892	0.033 26	0.048 26	30.063	20.720	25
26	1.4727	0.6790	0.031 73	0.046 73	31.514	21.399	26
27	1.4948	0.6690	0.030 32	0.045 32	32.987	22.068	27
28	1.5172	0.6591	0.029 00	0.044 00	34.481	22.727	28
29	1.5400	0.6494	0.027 78	0.042 78	35.999	23.376	29
30	1.5631	0.6398	0.026 64	0.041 64	37.539	24.016	30
31	1.5865	0.6303	0.025 57	0.040 57	39.102	24.646	31
32	1.6103	0.6210	0.024 58	0.039 58	40.688	25.267	32
33	1.6345	0.6118	0.023 64	0.038 64	42.299	25.879	33
34	1.6590	0.6028	0.022 76	0.037 76	43.933	26.482	34
35	1.6839	0.5939	0.021 93	0.036 93	45.592	27.076	35
40	1.8140	0.5513	0.018 43	0.033 43	54.268	29.916	40
45	1.9542	0.5117	0.015 72	0.030 72	63.614	32.552	45
50	2.1052	0.4750	0.013 57	0.028 57	73.683	35.000	50
55	2.2679	0.4409	0.011 83	0.026 83	84.530	37.271	55
60	2.4432	0.4093	0.010 39	0.025 39	96.215	39.380	60
65	2.6320	0.3799	0.009 19	0.024 19	108.803	41.338	65
70	2.8355	0.3527	0.008 17	0.023 17	122.364	43.155	70
75	3.0546	0.3274	0.007 30	0.022 30	136.973	44.842	75
80	3.2907	0.3039	0.006 55	0.021 55	152.711	46.407	80
85	3.5450	0.2821	0.005 89	0.020 89	169.665	47.861	85
90	3.8189	0.2619	0.005 32	0.020 32	187.930	49.210	90
95	4.1141	0.2431	0.004 82	0.019 82	207.606	50.462	95
100	4.4320	0.2256	0.004 37	0.019 37	228.803	51.625	100

TABLE E–4

1¾% Compound Interest Factors

	Single Payment		Uniform Series				
	Compound Amount Factor F/P	Present Worth Factor P/F	Sinking Fund Factor A/F	Capital Recovery Factor A/P	Compound Amount Factor F/A	Present Worth Factor P/A	
n							n
1	1.0175	0.9828	1.000 00	1.017 50	1.000	0.983	1
2	1.0353	0.9659	0.495 66	0.513 16	2.018	1.949	2
3	1.0534	0.9493	0.327 57	0.345 07	3.053	2.898	3
4	1.0719	0.9330	0.243 53	0.261 03	4.106	3.831	4
5	1.0906	0.9169	0.193 12	0.210 62	5.178	4.748	5
6	1.1097	0.9011	0.159 52	0.177 02	6.269	5.649	6
7	1.1291	0.8856	0.135 53	0.153 03	7.378	6.535	7
8	1.1489	0.8704	0.117 54	0.135 04	8.508	7.405	8
9	1.1690	0.8554	0.103 56	0.121 06	9.656	8.260	9
10	1.1894	0.8407	0.092 38	0.109 88	10.825	9.101	10
11	1.2103	0.8263	0.083 23	0.100 73	12.015	9.927	11
12	1.2314	0.8121	0.075 61	0.093 11	13.225	10.740	12
13	1.2530	0.7981	0.069 17	0.086 67	14.457	11.538	13
14	1.2749	0.7844	0.063 66	0.081 16	15.710	12.322	14
15	1.2972	0.7709	0.058 88	0.076 38	16.984	13.093	15
16	1.3199	0.7576	0.054 70	0.072 20	18.282	13.850	16
17	1.3430	0.7446	0.051 02	0.068 52	19.602	14.595	17
18	1.3665	0.7318	0.047 74	0.065 24	20.945	15.327	18
19	1.3904	0.7192	0.044 82	0.062 32	22.311	16.046	19
20	1.4148	0.7068	0.042 19	0.059 69	23.702	16.753	20
21	1.4395	0.6947	0.039 81	0.057 31	25.116	17.448	21
22	1.4647	0.6827	0.037 66	0.055 16	26.556	18.130	22
23	1.4904	0.6710	0.035 69	0.053 19	28.021	18.801	23
24	1.5164	0.6594	0.033 89	0.051 39	29.511	19.461	24
25	1.5430	0.6481	0.032 23	0.049 73	31.027	20.109	25
26	1.5700	0.6369	0.030 70	0.048 20	32.570	20.746	26
27	1.5975	0.6260	0.029 29	0.046 79	34.140	21.372	27
28	1.6254	0.6152	0.027 98	0.045 48	35.738	21.987	28
29	1.6539	0.6046	0.026 76	0.044 26	37.363	22.592	29
30	1.6828	0.5942	0.025 63	0.043 13	39.017	23.186	30
31	1.7122	0.5840	0.024 57	0.042 07	40.700	23.770	31
32	1.7422	0.5740	0.023 58	0.041 08	42.412	24.344	32
33	1.7727	0.5641	0.022 65	0.040 15	44.154	24.908	33
34	1.8037	0.5544	0.021 77	0.039 27	45.927	25.462	34
35	1.8353	0.5449	0.020 95	0.038 45	47.731	26.007	35
40	2.0016	0.4996	0.017 47	0.034 97	57.234	28.594	40
45	2.1830	0.4581	0.014 79	0.032 29	67.599	30.966	45
50	2.3808	0.4200	0.012 67	0.030 17	78.902	33.141	50
55	2.5965	0.3851	0.010 96	0.028 46	91.230	35.135	55
60	2.8318	0.3531	0.009 55	0.027 05	104.675	36.964	60
65	3.0884	0.3238	0.008 38	0.025 88	119.339	38.641	65
70	3.3683	0.2969	0.007 39	0.024 89	135.331	40.178	70
75	3.6735	0.2722	0.006 55	0.024 05	152.772	41.587	75
80	4.0064	0.2496	0.005 82	0.023 32	171.794	42.880	80
85	4.3694	0.2289	0.005 19	0.022 69	192.539	44.065	85
90	4.7654	0.2098	0.004 65	0.022 15	215.165	45.152	90
95	5.1972	0.1924	0.004 17	0.021 67	239.840	46.148	95
100	5.6682	0.1764	0.003 75	0.021 25	266.752	47.061	100

TABLE E–5

2% Compound Interest Factors

	Single Payment		Uniform Series				
	Compound Amount Factor	Present Worth Factor	Sinking Fund Factor	Capital Recovery Factor	Compound Amount Factor	Present Worth Factor	
n	*F/P*	*P/F*	*A/F*	*A/P*	*F/A*	*P/A*	*n*
1	1.0200	0.9804	1.000 00	1.020 00	1.000	0.980	1
2	1.0404	0.9612	0.495 05	0.515 05	2.020	1.942	2
3	1.0612	0.9423	0.326 75	0.346 75	3.060	2.884	3
4	1.0824	0.9238	0.242 62	0.262 62	4.122	3.808	4
5	1.1041	0.9057	0.192 16	0.212 16	5.204	4.713	5
6	1.1262	0.8880	0.158 53	0.178 53	6.308	5.601	6
7	1.1487	0.8706	0.134 51	0.154 51	7.434	6.472	7
8	1.1717	0.8535	0.116 51	0.136 51	8.583	7.325	8
9	1.1951	0.8368	0.102 52	0.122 52	9.755	8.162	9
10	1.2190	0.8203	0.091 33	0.111 33	10.950	8.983	10
11	1.2434	0.8043	0.082 18	0.102 18	12.169	9.787	11
12	1.2682	0.7885	0.074 56	0.094 56	13.412	10.575	12
13	1.2936	0.7730	0.068 12	0.088 12	14.680	11.348	13
14	1.3195	0.7579	0.062 60	0.082 60	15.974	12.106	14
15	1.3459	0.7430	0.057 83	0.077 83	17.293	12.849	15
16	1.3728	0.7284	0.053 65	0.073 65	18.639	13.578	16
17	1.4002	0.7142	0.049 97	0.069 97	20.012	14.292	17
18	1.4282	0.7002	0.046 70	0.066 70	21.412	14.992	18
19	1.4568	0.6864	0.043 78	0.063 78	22.841	15.678	19
20	1.4859	0.6730	0.041 16	0.061 16	24.297	16.351	20
21	1.5157	0.6598	0.038 78	0.058 78	25.783	17.011	21
22	1.5460	0.6468	0.036 63	0.056 63	27.299	17.658	22
23	1.5769	0.6342	0.034 67	0.054 67	28.845	18.292	23
24	1.6084	0.6217	0.032 87	0.052 87	30.422	18.914	24
25	1.6406	0.6095	0.031 22	0.051 22	32.030	19.523	25
26	1.6734	0.5976	0.029 70	0.049 70	33.671	20.121	26
27	1.7069	0.5859	0.028 29	0.048 29	35.344	20.707	27
28	1.7410	0.5744	0.026 99	0.046 99	37.051	21.281	28
29	1.7758	0.5631	0.025 78	0.045 78	38.792	21.844	29
30	1.8114	0.5521	0.024 65	0.044 65	40.568	22.396	30
31	1.8476	0.5412	0.023 60	0.043 60	42.379	22.938	31
32	1.8845	0.5306	0.022 61	0.042 61	44.227	23.468	32
33	1.9222	0.5202	0.021 69	0.041 69	46.112	23.989	33
34	1.9607	0.5100	0.020 82	0.040 82	48.034	24.499	34
35	1.9999	0.5000	0.020 00	0.040 00	49.994	24.999	35
40	2.2080	0.4529	0.016 56	0.036 56	60.402	27.355	40
45	2.4379	0.4102	0.013 91	0.033 91	71.893	29.490	45
50	2.6916	0.3715	0.011 82	0.031 82	84.579	31.424	50
55	2.9717	0.3365	0.010 14	0.030 14	98.587	33.175	55
60	3.2810	0.3048	0.008 77	0.028 77	114.052	34.761	60
65	3.6225	0.2761	0.007 63	0.027 63	131.126	36.197	65
70	3.9996	0.2500	0.006 67	0.026 67	149.978	37.499	70
75	4.4158	0.2265	0.005 86	0.025 86	170.792	38.677	75
80	4.8754	0.2051	0.005 16	0.025 16	193.772	39.745	80
85	5.3829	0.1858	0.004 56	0.024 56	219.144	40.711	85
90	5.9431	0.1683	0.004 05	0.024 05	247.157	41.587	90
95	6.5617	0.1524	0.003 60	0.023 60	278.085	42.380	95
100	7.2446	0.1380	0.003 20	0.023 20	312.232	43.098	100

TABLE E–6

2½% Compound Interest Factors

	Single Payment		Uniform Series				
	Compound Amount Factor	Present Worth Factor	Sinking Fund Factor	Capital Recovery Factor	Compound Amount Factor	Present Worth Factor	
n	F/P	P/F	A/F	A/P	F/A	P/A	n
1	1.0250	0.9756	1.000 00	1.025 00	1.000	0.976	1
2	1.0506	0.9518	0.493 83	0.518 83	2.025	1.927	2
3	1.0769	0.9286	0.325 14	0.350 14	3.076	2.856	3
4	1.1038	0.9060	0.240 82	0.265 82	4.153	3.762	4
5	1.1314	0.8839	0.190 25	0.215 25	5.256	4.646	5
6	1.1597	0.8623	0.156 55	0.181 55	6.388	5.508	6
7	1.1887	0.8413	0.132 50	0.157 50	7.547	6.349	7
8	1.2184	0.8207	0.114 47	0.139 47	8.736	7.170	8
9	1.2489	0.8007	0.100 46	0.125 46	9.955	7.971	9
10	1.2801	0.7812	0.089 26	0.114 26	11.203	8.752	10
11	1.3121	0.7621	0.080 11	0.105 11	12.483	9.514	11
12	1.3449	0.7436	0.072 49	0.097 49	13.796	10.258	12
13	1.3785	0.7254	0.066 05	0.091 05	15.140	10.983	13
14	1.4130	0.7077	0.060 54	0.085 54	16.519	11.691	14
15	1.4483	0.6905	0.055 77	0.080 77	17.932	12.381	15
16	1.4845	0.6736	0.051 60	0.076 60	19.380	13.055	16
17	1.5216	0.6572	0.047 93	0.072 93	20.865	13.712	17
18	1.5597	0.6412	0.044 67	0.069 67	22.386	14.353	18
19	1.5987	0.6255	0.041 76	0.066 76	23.946	14.979	19
20	1.6386	0.6103	0.039 15	0.064 15	25.545	15.589	20
21	1.6796	0.5954	0.036 79	0.061 79	27.183	16.185	21
22	1.7216	0.5809	0.034 65	0.059 65	28.863	16.765	22
23	1.7646	0.5667	0.032 70	0.057 70	30.584	17.332	23
24	1.8087	0.5529	0.030 91	0.055 91	32.349	17.885	24
25	1.8539	0.5394	0.029 28	0.054 28	34.158	18.424	25
26	1.9003	0.5262	0.027 77	0.052 77	36.012	18.951	26
27	1.9478	0.5134	0.026 38	0.051 38	37.912	19.464	27
28	1.9965	0.5009	0.025 09	0.050 09	39.860	19.965	28
29	2.0464	0.4887	0.023 89	0.048 89	41.856	20.454	29
30	2.0976	0.4767	0.022 78	0.047 78	43.903	20.930	30
31	2.1500	0.4651	0.021 74	0.046 74	46.000	21.395	31
32	2.2038	0.4538	0.020 77	0.045 77	48.150	21.849	32
33	2.2589	0.4427	0.019 86	0.044 86	50.354	22.292	33
34	2.3153	0.4319	0.019 01	0.044 01	52.613	22.724	34
35	2.3732	0.4214	0.018 21	0.043 21	54.928	23.145	35
40	2.6851	0.3724	0.014 84	0.039 84	67.403	25.103	40
45	3.0379	0.3292	0.012 27	0.037 27	81.516	26.833	45
50	3.4371	0.2909	0.010 26	0.035 26	97.484	28.362	50
55	3.8888	0.2572	0.008 65	0.033 65	115.551	29.714	55
60	4.3998	0.2273	0.007 35	0.032 35	135.992	30.909	60
65	4.9780	0.2009	0.006 28	0.031 28	159.118	31.965	65
70	5.6321	0.1776	0.005 40	0.030 40	185.284	32.898	70
75	6.3722	0.1569	0.004 65	0.029 65	214.888	33.723	75
80	7.2100	0.1387	0.004 03	0.029 03	248.383	34.452	80
85	8.1570	0.1226	0.003 49	0.028 49	286.279	35.096	85
90	9.2289	0.1084	0.003 04	0.028 04	329.154	35.666	90
95	10.4416	0.0958	0.002 65	0.027 65	377.664	36.169	95
100	11.8137	0.0846	0.002 31	0.027 31	432.549	36.614	100

TABLE E–7
3% Compound Interest Factors

	Single Payment		Uniform Series				
	Compound Amount Factor	Present Worth Factor	Sinking Fund Factor	Capital Recovery Factor	Compound Amount Factor	Present Worth Factor	
n	F/P	P/F	A/F	A/P	F/A	P/A	n
1	1.0300	0.9709	1.000 00	1.030 00	1.000	0.971	1
2	1.0609	0.9426	0.492 61	0.522 61	2.030	1.913	2
3	1.0927	0.9151	0.323 53	0.353 53	3.091	2.829	3
4	1.1255	0.8885	0.239 03	0.269 03	4.184	3.717	4
5	1.1593	0.8626	0.188 35	0.218 35	5.309	4.580	5
6	1.1941	0.8375	0.154 60	0.184 60	6.468	5.417	6
7	1.2299	0.8131	0.130 51	0.160 51	7.662	6.230	7
8	1.2668	0.7894	0.112 46	0.142 46	8.892	7.020	8
9	1.3048	0.7664	0.098 43	0.128 43	10.159	7.786	9
10	1.3439	0.7441	0.087 23	0.117 23	11.464	8.530	10
11	1.3842	0.7224	0.078 08	0.108 08	12.808	9.253	11
12	1.4258	0.7014	0.070 46	0.100 46	14.192	9.954	12
13	1.4685	0.6810	0.064 03	0.094 03	15.618	10.635	13
14	1.5126	0.6611	0.058 53	0.088 53	17.086	11.296	14
15	1.5580	0.6419	0.053 77	0.083 77	18.599	11.938	15
16	1.6047	0.6232	0.049 61	0.079 61	20.157	12.561	16
17	1.6528	0.6050	0.045 95	0.075 95	21.762	13.166	17
18	1.7024	0.5874	0.042 71	0.072 71	23.414	13.754	18
19	1.7535	0.5703	0.039 81	0.069 81	25.117	14.324	19
20	1.8061	0.5537	0.037 22	0.067 22	26.870	14.877	20
21	1.8603	0.5375	0.034 87	0.064 87	28.676	15.415	21
22	1.9161	0.5219	0.032 75	0.062 75	30.537	15.937	22
23	1.9736	0.5067	0.030 81	0.060 81	32.453	16.444	23
24	2.0328	0.4919	0.029 05	0.059 05	34.426	16.936	24
25	2.0938	0.4776	0.027 43	0.057 43	36.459	17.413	25
26	2.1566	0.4637	0.025 94	0.055 94	38.553	17.877	26
27	2.2213	0.4502	0.024 56	0.054 56	40.710	18.327	27
28	2.2879	0.4371	0.023 29	0.053 29	42.931	18.764	28
29	2.3566	0.4243	0.022 11	0.052 11	45.219	19.188	29
30	2.4273	0.4120	0.021 02	0.051 02	47.575	19.600	30
31	2.5001	0.4000	0.020 00	0.050 00	50.003	20.000	31
32	2.5751	0.3883	0.019 05	0.049 05	52.503	20.389	32
33	2.6523	0.3770	0.018 16	0.048 16	55.078	20.766	33
34	2.7319	0.3660	0.017 32	0.047 32	57.730	21.132	34
35	2.8139	0.3554	0.016 54	0.046 54	60.462	21.487	35
40	3.2620	0.3066	0.013 26	0.043 26	75.401	23.115	40
45	3.7816	0.2644	0.010 79	0.040 79	92.720	24.519	45
50	4.3839	0.2281	0.008 87	0.038 87	112.797	25.730	50
55	5.0821	0.1968	0.007 35	0.037 35	136.072	26.774	55
60	5.8916	0.1697	0.006 13	0.036 13	163.053	27.676	60
65	6.8300	0.1464	0.005 15	0.035 15	194.333	28.453	65
70	7.9178	0.1263	0.004 34	0.034 34	230.594	29.123	70
75	9.1789	0.1089	0.003 67	0.033 67	272.631	29.702	75
80	10.6409	0.0940	0.003 11	0.033 11	321.363	30.201	80
85	12.3357	0.0811	0.002 65	0.032 65	377.857	30.631	85
90	14.3005	0.0699	0.002 26	0.032 26	443.349	31.002	90
95	16.5782	0.0603	0.001 93	0.031 93	519.272	31.323	95
100	19.2186	0.0520	0.001 65	0.031 65	607.288	31.599	100

TABLE E–8

3½% Compound Interest Factors

	Single Payment		Uniform Series				
	Compound Amount Factor F/P	Present Worth Factor P/F	Sinking Fund Factor A/F	Capital Recovery Factor A/P	Compound Amount Factor F/A	Present Worth Factor P/A	
n							n
1	1.0350	0.9662	1.000 00	1.035 00	1.000	0.966	1
2	1.0712	0.9335	0.491 40	0.526 40	2.035	1.900	2
3	1.1087	0.9019	0.321 93	0.356 93	3.106	2.802	3
4	1.1475	0.8714	0.237 25	0.272 25	4.215	3.673	4
5	1.1877	0.8420	0.186 48	0.221 48	5.362	4.515	5
6	1.2293	0.8135	0.152 67	0.187 67	6.550	5.329	6
7	1.2723	0.7860	0.128 54	0.163 54	7.779	6.115	7
8	1.3168	0.7594	0.110 48	0.145 48	9.052	6.874	8
9	1.3629	0.7337	0.096 45	0.131 45	10.368	7.608	9
10	1.4106	0.7089	0.085 24	0.120 24	11.731	8.317	10
11	1.4600	0.6849	0.076 09	0.111 09	13.142	9.002	11
12	1.5111	0.6618	0.068 48	0.103 48	14.602	9.663	12
13	1.5640	0.6394	0.062 06	0.097 06	16.113	10.303	13
14	1.6187	0.6178	0.056 57	0.091 57	17.677	10.921	14
15	1.6753	0.5969	0.051 83	0.086 83	19.296	11.517	15
16	1.7340	0.5767	0.047 68	0.082 68	20.971	12.094	16
17	1.7947	0.5572	0.044 04	0.079 04	22.705	12.651	17
18	1.8575	0.5384	0.040 82	0.075 82	24.500	13.190	18
19	1.9225	0.5202	0.037 94	0.072 94	26.357	13.710	19
20	1.9898	0.5026	0.035 36	0.070 36	28.280	14.212	20
21	2.0594	0.4856	0.033 04	0.068 04	30.269	14.698	21
22	2.1315	0.4692	0.030 93	0.065 93	32.329	15.167	22
23	2.2061	0.4533	0.029 02	0.064 02	34.460	15.620	23
24	2.2833	0.4380	0.027 27	0.062 27	36.667	16.058	24
25	2.3632	0.4231	0.025 67	0.060 67	38.950	16.482	25
26	2.4460	0.4088	0.024 21	0.059 21	41.313	16.890	26
27	2.5316	0.3950	0.022 85	0.057 85	43.759	17.285	27
28	2.6202	0.3817	0.021 60	0.056 60	46.291	17.667	28
29	2.7119	0.3687	0.020 45	0.055 45	48.911	18.036	29
30	2.8068	0.3563	0.019 37	0.054 37	51.623	18.392	30
31	2.9050	0.3442	0.018 37	0.053 37	54.429	18.736	31
32	3.0067	0.3326	0.017 44	0.052 44	57.335	19.069	32
33	3.1119	0.3213	0.016 57	0.051 57	60.341	19.390	33
34	3.2209	0.3105	0.015 76	0.050 76	63.453	19.701	34
35	3.3336	0.3000	0.015 00	0.050 00	66.674	20.001	35
40	3.9593	0.2526	0.011 83	0.046 83	84.550	21.355	40
45	4.7024	0.2127	0.009 45	0.044 45	105.782	22.495	45
50	5.5849	0.1791	0.007 63	0.042 63	130.998	23.456	50
55	6.6331	0.1508	0.006 21	0.041 21	160.947	24.264	55
60	7.8781	0.1269	0.005 09	0.040 09	196.517	24.945	60
65	9.3567	0.1069	0.004 19	0.039 19	238.763	25.518	65
70	11.1128	0.0900	0.003 46	0.038 46	288.938	26.000	70
75	13.1986	0.0758	0.002 87	0.037 87	348.530	26.407	75
80	15.6757	0.0638	0.002 38	0.037 38	419.307	26.749	80
85	18.6179	0.0537	0.001 99	0.036 99	503.367	27.037	85
90	22.1122	0.0452	0.001 66	0.036 66	603.205	27.279	90
95	26.2623	0.0381	0.001 39	0.036 39	721.781	27.484	95
100	31.1914	0.0321	0.001 16	0.036 16	862.612	27.655	100

TABLE E–9

4% Compound Interest Factors

	Single Payment		Uniform Series				
n	Compound Amount Factor F/P	Present Worth Factor P/F	Sinking Fund Factor A/F	Capital Recovery Factor A/P	Compound Amount Factor F/A	Present Worth Factor P/A	n
1	1.0400	0.9615	1.000 00	1.040 00	1.000	0.962	1
2	1.0816	0.9246	0.490 20	0.530 20	2.040	1.886	2
3	1.1249	0.8890	0.320 35	0.360 35	3.122	2.775	3
4	1.1699	0.8548	0.235 49	0.275 49	4.246	3.630	4
5	1.2167	0.8219	0.184 63	0.224 63	5.416	4.452	5
6	1.2653	0.7903	0.150 76	0.190 76	6.633	5.242	6
7	1.3159	0.7599	0.126 61	0.166 61	7.898	6.002	7
8	1.3686	0.7307	0.108 53	0.148 53	9.214	6.733	8
9	1.4233	0.7026	0.094 49	0.134 49	10.583	7.435	9
10	1.4802	0.6756	0.083 29	0.123 29	12.006	8.111	10
11	1.5395	0.6496	0.074 15	0.114 15	13.486	8.760	11
12	1.6010	0.6246	0.066 55	0.106 55	15.026	9.385	12
13	1.6651	0.6006	0.060 14	0.100 14	16.627	9.986	13
14	1.7317	0.5775	0.054 67	0.094 67	18.292	10.563	14
15	1.8009	0.5553	0.049 94	0.089 94	20.024	11.118	15
16	1.8730	0.5339	0.045 82	0.085 82	21.825	11.652	16
17	1.9479	0.5134	0.042 20	0.082 20	23.698	12.166	17
18	2.0258	0.4936	0.038 99	0.078 99	25.645	12.659	18
19	2.1068	0.4746	0.036 14	0.076 14	27.671	13.134	19
20	2.1911	0.4564	0.033 58	0.073 58	29.778	13.590	20
21	2.2788	0.4388	0.031 28	0.071 28	31.969	14.029	21
22	2.3699	0.4220	0.029 20	0.069 20	34.248	14.451	22
23	2.4647	0.4057	0.027 31	0.067 31	36.618	14.857	23
24	2.5633	0.3901	0.025 59	0.065 59	39.083	15.247	24
25	2.6658	0.3751	0.024 01	0.064 01	41.646	15.622	25
26	2.7725	0.3607	0.022 57	0.062 57	44.312	15.983	26
27	2.8834	0.3468	0.021 24	0.061 24	47.084	16.330	27
28	2.9987	0.3335	0.020 01	0.060 01	49.968	16.663	28
29	3.1187	0.3207	0.018 88	0.058 88	52.966	16.984	29
30	3.2434	0.3083	0.017 83	0.057 83	56.085	17.292	30
31	3.3731	0.2965	0.016 86	0.056 86	59.328	17.588	31
32	3.5081	0.2851	0.015 95	0.055 95	62.701	17.874	32
33	3.6484	0.2741	0.015 10	0.055 10	66.210	18.148	33
34	3.7943	0.2636	0.014 31	0.054 31	69.858	18.411	34
35	3.9461	0.2534	0.013 58	0.053 58	73.652	18.665	35
40	4.8010	0.2083	0.010 52	0.050 52	95.026	19.793	40
45	5.8412	0.1712	0.008 26	0.048 26	121.029	20.720	45
50	7.1067	0.1407	0.006 55	0.046 55	152.667	21.482	50
55	8.6464	0.1157	0.005 23	0.045 23	191.159	22.109	55
60	10.5196	0.0951	0.004 20	0.044 20	237.991	22.623	60
65	12.7987	0.0781	0.003 39	0.043 39	294.968	23.047	65
70	15.5716	0.0642	0.002 75	0.042 75	364.290	23.395	70
75	18.9453	0.0528	0.002 23	0.042 23	448.631	23.680	75
80	23.0500	0.0434	0.001 81	0.041 81	551.245	23.915	80
85	28.0436	0.0357	0.001 48	0.041 48	676.090	24.109	85
90	34.1193	0.0293	0.001 21	0.041 21	827.983	24.267	90
95	41.5114	0.0241	0.000 99	0.040 99	1 012.785	24.398	95
100	50.5049	0.0198	0.000 81	0.040 81	1 237.624	24.505	100

TABLE E-10

4½% Compound Interest Factors

	Single Payment		Uniform Series				
	Compound Amount Factor F/P	Present Worth Factor P/F	Sinking Fund Factor A/F	Capital Recovery Factor A/P	Compound Amount Factor F/A	Present Worth Factor P/A	
n							*n*
1	1.0450	0.9569	1.000 00	1.045 00	1.000	0.957	1
2	1.0920	0.9157	0.489 00	0.534 00	2.045	1.873	2
3	1.1412	0.8763	0.318 77	0.363 77	3.137	2.749	3
4	1.1925	0.8386	0.233 74	0.278 74	4.278	3.588	4
5	1.2462	0.8025	0.182 79	0.227 79	5.471	4.390	5
6	1.3023	0.7679	0.148 88	0.193 88	6.717	5.158	6
7	1.3609	0.7348	0.124 70	0.169 70	8.019	5.893	7
8	1.4221	0.7032	0.106 61	0.151 61	9.380	6.596	8
9	1.4861	0.6729	0.092 57	0.137 57	10.802	7.269	9
10	1.5530	0.6439	0.081 38	0.126 38	12.288	7.913	10
11	1.6229	0.6162	0.072 25	0.117 25	13.841	8.529	11
12	1.6959	0.5897	0.064 67	0.109 67	15.464	9.119	12
13	1.7722	0.5643	0.058 28	0.103 28	17.160	9.683	13
14	1.8519	0.5400	0.052 82	0.097 82	18.932	10.223	14
15	1.9353	0.5167	0.048 11	0.093 11	20.784	10.740	15
16	2.0224	0.4945	0.044 02	0.089 02	22.719	11.234	16
17	2.1134	0.4732	0.040 42	0.085 42	24.742	11.707	17
18	2.2085	0.4528	0.037 24	0.082 24	26.855	12.160	18
19	2.3079	0.4333	0.034 41	0.079 41	29.064	12.593	19
20	2.4117	0.4146	0.031 88	0.076 88	31.371	13.008	20
21	2.5202	0.3968	0.029 60	0.074 60	33.783	13.405	21
22	2.6337	0.3797	0.027 55	0.072 55	36.303	13.784	22
23	2.7522	0.3634	0.025 68	0.070 68	38.937	14.148	23
24	2.8760	0.3477	0.023 99	0.068 99	41.689	14.495	24
25	3.0054	0.3327	0.022 44	0.067 44	44.565	14.828	25
26	3.1407	0.3184	0.021 02	0.066 02	47.571	15.147	26
27	3.2820	0.3047	0.019 72	0.064 72	50.711	15.451	27
28	3.4397	0.2916	0.018 52	0.063 52	53.993	15.743	28
29	3.5840	0.2790	0.017 41	0.062 41	57.423	16.022	29
30	3.7453	0.2670	0.016 39	0.061 39	61.007	16.289	30
31	3.9139	0.2555	0.015 44	0.060 44	64.752	16.544	31
32	4.0900	0.2445	0.014 56	0.059 56	68.666	16.789	32
33	4.2740	0.2340	0.013 74	0.058 74	72.756	17.023	33
34	4.4664	0.2239	0.012 98	0.057 98	77.030	17.247	34
35	4.6673	0.2143	0.012 27	0.057 27	81.497	17.461	35
40	5.8164	0.1719	0.009 34	0.054 34	107.030	18.402	40
45	7.2482	0.1380	0.007 20	0.052 20	138.850	19.156	45
50	9.0326	0.1107	0.005 60	0.050 60	178.503	19.762	50
55	11.2563	0.0888	0.004 39	0.049 39	227.918	20.248	55
60	14.0274	0.0713	0.003 45	0.048 45	289.498	20.638	60
65	17.4807	0.0572	0.002 73	0.047 73	366.238	20.951	65
70	21.7841	0.0459	0.002 17	0.047 17	461.870	21.202	70
75	27.1470	0.0368	0.001 72	0.046 72	581.044	21.404	75
80	33.8301	0.0296	0.001 37	0.046 37	729.558	21.565	80
85	42.1585	0.0237	0.001 09	0.046 09	914.632	21.695	85
90	52.5371	0.0190	0.000 87	0.045 87	1 145.269	21.799	90
95	65.4708	0.0153	0.000 70	0.045 70	1 432.684	21.883	95
100	81.5885	0.0123	0.000 56	0.045 56	1 790.856	21.950	100

TABLE E–11

5% Compound Interest Factors

	Single Payment		Uniform Series				
	Compound Amount Factor	Present Worth Factor	Sinking Fund Factor	Capital Recovery Factor	Compound Amount Factor	Present Worth Factor	
n	F/P	P/F	A/F	A/P	F/A	P/A	n
1	1.0500	0.9524	1.000 00	1.050 00	1.000	0.952	1
2	1.1025	0.9070	0.487 80	0.537 80	2.050	1.859	2
3	1.1576	0.8638	0.317 21	0.367 21	3.153	2.723	3
4	1.2155	0.8227	0.232 01	0.282 01	4.310	3.546	4
5	1.2763	0.7835	0.180 97	0.230 97	5.526	4.329	5
6	1.3401	0.7462	0.147 02	0.197 02	6.802	5.076	6
7	1.4071	0.7107	0.122 82	0.172 82	8.142	5.786	7
8	1.4775	0.6768	0.104 72	0.154 72	9.549	6.463	8
9	1.5513	0.6446	0.090 69	0.140 69	11.027	7.108	9
10	1.6289	0.6139	0.079 50	0.129 50	12.578	7.722	10
11	1.7103	0.5847	0.070 39	0.120 39	14.207	8.306	11
12	1.7959	0.5568	0.062 83	0.112 83	15.917	8.863	12
13	1.8856	0.5303	0.056 46	0.106 46	17.713	9.394	13
14	1.9800	0.5051	0.051 02	0.101 02	19.599	9.899	14
15	2.0789	0.4810	0.046 34	0.096 34	21.579	10.380	15
16	2.1829	0.4581	0.042 27	0.092 27	23.657	10.838	16
17	2.2920	0.4363	0.038 70	0.088 70	25.840	11.274	17
18	2.4066	0.4155	0.035 55	0.085 55	28.132	11.690	18
19	2.5270	0.3957	0.032 75	0.082 75	30.539	12.085	19
20	2.6533	0.3769	0.030 24	0.080 24	33.066	12.462	20
21	2.7860	0.3589	0.028 00	0.078 00	35.719	12.821	21
22	2.9253	0.3418	0.025 97	0.075 97	38.505	13.163	22
23	3.0715	0.3256	0.024 14	0.074 14	41.430	13.489	23
24	3.2251	0.3101	0.022 47	0.072 47	44.502	13.799	24
25	3.3864	0.2953	0.020 95	0.070 95	47.727	14.094	25
26	3.5557	0.2812	0.019 56	0.069 56	51.113	14.375	26
27	3.7335	0.2678	0.018 29	0.068 29	54.669	14.643	27
28	3.9201	0.2551	0.017 12	0.067 12	58.403	14.898	28
29	4.1161	0.2429	0.016 05	0.066 05	62.323	15.141	29
30	4.3219	0.2314	0.015 05	0.065 05	66.439	15.372	30
31	4.5380	0.2204	0.014 13	0.064 13	70.761	15.593	31
32	4.7649	0.2099	0.013 28	0.063 28	75.299	15.803	32
33	5.0032	0.1999	0.012 49	0.062 49	80.064	16.003	33
34	5.2533	0.1904	0.011 76	0.061 76	85.067	16.193	34
35	5.5160	0.1813	0.011 07	0.061 07	90.320	16.374	35
40	7.0400	0.1420	0.008 28	0.058 28	120.800	17.159	40
45	8.9850	0.1113	0.006 26	0.056 26	159.700	17.774	45
50	11.4674	0.0872	0.004 78	0.054 78	209.348	18.256	50
55	14.6356	0.0683	0.003 67	0.053 67	272.713	18.633	55
60	18.6792	0.0535	0.002 83	0.052 83	353.584	18.929	60
65	23.8399	0.0419	0.002 19	0.052 19	456.798	19.161	65
70	30.4264	0.0329	0.001 70	0.051 70	588.529	19.343	70
75	38.8327	0.0258	0.001 32	0.051 32	756.654	19.485	75
80	49.5614	0.0202	0.001 03	0.051 03	971.229	19.596	80
85	63.2544	0.0158	0.000 80	0.050 80	1 245.087	19.684	85
90	80.7304	0.0124	0.000 63	0.050 63	1 594.607	19.752	90
95	103.0357	0.0097	0.000 49	0.050 49	2 040.694	19.806	95
100	131.5013	0.0076	0.000 38	0.050 38	2 610.025	19.848	100

TABLE E–12

5½% Compound Interest Factors

	Single Payment		Uniform Series				
	Compound Amount Factor F/P	Present Worth Factor P/F	Sinking Fund Factor A/F	Capital Recovery Factor A/P	Compound Amount Factor F/A	Present Worth Factor P/A	
n							n
1	1.0550	0.9479	1.000 00	1.055 00	1.000	0.948	1
2	1.1130	0.8985	0.486 62	0.541 62	2.055	1.846	2
3	1.1742	0.8516	0.315 65	0.370 65	3.168	2.698	3
4	1.2388	0.8072	0.230 29	0.285 29	4.342	3.505	4
5	1.3070	0.7651	0.179 18	0.234 18	5.581	4.270	5
6	1.3788	0.7252	0.145 18	0.200 18	6.888	4.996	6
7	1.4547	0.6874	0.120 96	0.175 96	8.267	5.683	7
8	1.5347	0.6516	0.102 86	0.157 86	9.722	6.335	8
9	1.6191	0.6176	0.088 84	0.143 84	11.256	6.952	9
10	1.7081	0.5854	0.077 67	0.132 67	12.875	7.538	10
11	1.8021	0.5549	0.068 57	0.123 57	14.583	8.093	11
12	1.9012	0.5260	0.061 03	0.116 03	16.386	8.619	12
13	2.0058	0.4986	0.054 68	0.109 68	18.287	9.117	13
14	2.1161	0.4726	0.049 28	0.104 28	20.293	9.590	14
15	2.2325	0.4479	0.044 63	0.099 63	22.409	10.038	15
16	2.3553	0.4246	0.040 58	0.095 58	24.641	10.462	16
17	2.4848	0.4024	0.037 04	0.092 04	26.996	10.865	17
18	2.6215	0.3815	0.033 92	0.088 92	29.481	11.246	18
19	2.7656	0.3616	0.031 15	0.086 15	32.103	11.608	19
20	2.9178	0.3427	0.028 68	0.083 68	34.868	11.950	20
21	3.0782	0.3249	0.026 46	0.081 46	37.786	12.275	21
22	3.2475	0.3079	0.024 47	0.079 47	40.864	12.583	22
23	3.4262	0.2919	0.022 67	0.077 67	44.112	12.875	23
24	3.6146	0.2767	0.021 04	0.076 04	47.538	13.152	24
25	3.8134	0.2622	0.019 55	0.074 55	51.153	13.414	25
26	4.0231	0.2486	0.018 19	0.073 19	54.966	13.662	26
27	4.2444	0.2356	0.016 95	0.071 95	58.989	13.898	27
28	4.4778	0.2233	0.015 81	0.070 81	63.234	14.121	28
29	4.7241	0.2117	0.014 77	0.069 77	67.711	14.333	29
30	4.9840	0.2006	0.013 81	0.068 81	72.435	14.534	30
31	5.2581	0.1902	0.012 92	0.067 92	77.419	14.724	31
32	5.5473	0.1803	0.012 10	0.067 10	82.677	14.904	32
33	5.8524	0.1709	0.011 33	0.066 33	88.225	15.075	33
34	6.1742	0.1620	0.010 63	0.065 63	94.077	15.237	34
35	6.5138	0.1535	0.009 97	0.064 97	100.251	15.391	35
40	8.5133	0.1175	0.007 32	0.062 32	136.606	16.046	40
45	11.1266	0.0899	0.005 43	0.060 43	184.119	16.548	45
50	14.5420	0.0688	0.004 06	0.059 06	246.217	16.932	50
55	19.0058	0.0526	0.003 05	0.058 05	327.377	17.225	55
60	24.8398	0.0403	0.002 31	0.057 31	433.450	17.450	60
65	32.4646	0.0308	0.001 75	0.056 75	572.083	17.622	65
70	42.4299	0.0236	0.001 33	0.056 33	753.271	17.753	70
75	55.4542	0.0180	0.001 01	0.056 01	990.076	17.854	75
80	72.4764	0.0138	0.000 77	0.055 77	1 299.571	17.931	80
85	94.7238	0.0106	0.000 59	0.055 59	1 704.069	17.990	85
90	123.8002	0.0081	0.000 45	0.055 45	2 232.731	18.035	90
95	161.8019	0.0062	0.000 34	0.055 34	2 923.671	18.069	95
100	211.4686	0.0047	0.000 26	0.055 26	3 826.702	18.096	100

TABLE E–13

6% Compound Interest Factors

	Single Payment		Uniform Series				
	Compound Amount Factor	Present Worth Factor	Sinking Fund Factor	Capital Recovery Factor	Compound Amount Factor	Present Worth Factor	
n	F/P	P/F	A/F	A/P	F/A	P/A	n
1	1.0600	0.9434	1.000 00	1.060 00	1.000	0.943	1
2	1.1236	0.8900	0.485 44	0.545 44	2.060	1.833	2
3	1.1910	0.8396	0.314 11	0.374 11	3.184	2.673	3
4	1.2625	0.7921	0.228 59	0.288 59	4.375	3.465	4
5	1.3382	0.7473	0.177 40	0.237 40	5.637	4.212	5
6	1.4185	0.7050	0.143 36	0.203 36	6.975	4.917	6
7	1.5036	0.6651	0.119 14	0.179 14	8.394	5.582	7
8	1.5938	0.6274	0.101 04	0.161 04	9.897	6.210	8
9	1.6895	0.5919	0.087 02	0.147 02	11.491	6.802	9
10	1.7908	0.5584	0.075 87	0.135 87	13.181	7.360	10
11	1.8983	0.5268	0.066 79	0.126 79	14.972	7.887	11
12	2.0122	0.4970	0.059 28	0.119 28	16.870	8.384	12
13	2.1329	0.4688	0.052 96	0.112 96	18.882	8.853	13
14	2.2609	0.4423	0.047 58	0.107 58	21.015	9.295	14
15	2.3966	0.4173	0.042 96	0.102 96	23.276	9.712	15
16	2.5404	0.3936	0.038 95	0.098 95	25.673	10.106	16
17	2.6928	0.3714	0.035 44	0.095 44	28.213	10.477	17
18	2.8543	0.3503	0.032 36	0.092 36	30.906	10.828	18
19	3.0256	0.3305	0.029 62	0.089 62	33.760	11.158	19
20	3.2071	0.3118	0.027 18	0.087 18	36.786	11.470	20
21	3.3996	0.2942	0.025 00	0.085 00	39.993	11.764	21
22	3.6035	0.2775	0.023 05	0.083 05	43.392	12.042	22
23	3.8197	0.2618	0.021 28	0.081 28	46.996	12.303	23
24	4.0489	0.2470	0.019 68	0.079 68	50.816	12.550	24
25	4.2919	0.2330	0.018 23	0.078 23	54.865	12.783	25
26	4.5494	0.2198	0.016 90	0.076 90	59.156	13.003	26
27	4.8223	0.2074	0.015 70	0.075 70	63.706	13.211	27
28	5.1117	0.1956	0.014 59	0.074 59	68.528	13.406	28
29	5.4184	0.1846	0.013 58	0.073 58	73.640	13.591	29
30	5.7435	0.1741	0.012 65	0.072 65	79.058	13.765	30
31	6.0881	0.1643	0.011 79	0.071 79	84.802	13.929	31
32	6.4534	0.1550	0.011 00	0.071 00	90.890	14.084	32
33	6.8406	0.1462	0.010 27	0.070 27	97.343	14.230	33
34	7.2510	0.1379	0.009 60	0.069 60	104.184	14.368	34
35	7.6861	0.1301	0.008 97	0.068 97	111.435	14.498	35
40	10.2857	0.0972	0.006 46	0.066 46	154.762	15.046	40
45	13.7646	0.0727	0.004 70	0.064 70	212.744	15.456	45
50	18.4202	0.0543	0.003 44	0.063 44	290.336	15.762	50
55	24.6503	0.0406	0.002 54	0.062 54	394.172	15.991	55
60	32.9877	0.0303	0.001 88	0.061 88	533.128	16.161	60
65	44.1450	0.0227	0.001 39	0.061 39	719.083	16.289	65
70	59.0759	0.0169	0.001 03	0.061 03	967.932	16.385	70
75	79.0569	0.0126	0.000 77	0.060 77	1 300.949	16.456	75
80	105.7960	0.0095	0.000 57	0.060 57	1 746.600	16.509	80
85	141.5789	0.0071	0.000 43	0.060 43	2 342.982	16.549	85
90	189.4645	0.0053	0.000 32	0.060 32	3 141.075	16.579	90
95	253.5463	0.0039	0.000 24	0.060 24	4 209.104	16.601	95
100	339.3021	0.0029	0.000 18	0.060 18	5 638.368	16.618	100

TABLE E-14

7% Compound Interest Factors

	Single Payment		Uniform Series				
	Compound Amount Factor	Present Worth Factor	Sinking Fund Factor	Capital Recovery Factor	Compound Amount Factor	Present Worth Factor	
n	F/P	P/F	A/F	A/P	F/A	P/A	n
1	1.0700	0.9346	1.000 00	1.070 00	1.000	0.935	1
2	1.1449	0.8734	0.483 09	0.553 09	2.070	1.808	2
3	1.2250	0.8163	0.311 05	0.381 05	3.215	2.624	3
4	1.3108	0.7629	0.225 23	0.295 23	4.440	3.387	4
5	1.4026	0.7130	0.173 89	0.243 89	5.751	4.100	5
6	1.5007	0.6663	0.139 80	0.209 80	7.153	4.767	6
7	1.6058	0.6227	0.115 55	0.185 55	8.654	5.389	7
8	1.7182	0.5820	0.097 47	0.167 47	10.260	5.971	8
9	1.8385	0.5439	0.083 49	0.153 49	11.978	6.515	9
10	1.9672	0.5083	0.072 38	0.142 38	13.816	7.024	10
11	2.1049	0.4751	0.063 36	0.133 36	15.784	7.499	11
12	2.2522	0.4440	0.055 90	0.125 90	17.888	7.943	12
13	2.4098	0.4150	0.049 65	0.119 65	20.141	8.358	13
14	2.5785	0.3878	0.044 34	0.114 34	22.550	8.745	14
15	2.7590	0.3624	0.039 79	0.109 79	25.129	9.108	15
16	2.9522	0.3387	0.035 86	0.105 86	27.888	9.447	16
17	3.1588	0.3166	0.032 43	0.102 43	30.840	9.763	17
18	3.3799	0.2959	0.029 41	0.099 41	33.999	10.059	18
19	3.6165	0.2765	0.026 75	0.096 75	37.379	10.336	19
20	3.8697	0.2584	0.024 39	0.094 39	40.995	10.594	20
21	4.1406	0.2415	0.022 29	0.092 29	44.865	10.836	21
22	4.4304	0.2257	0.020 41	0.090 41	49.006	11.061	22
23	4.7405	0.2109	0.018 71	0.088 71	53.436	11.272	23
24	5.0724	0.1971	0.017 19	0.087 19	58.177	11.469	24
25	5.4274	0.1842	0.015 81	0.085 81	63.249	11.654	25
26	5.8074	0.1722	0.014 56	0.084 56	68.676	11.826	26
27	6.2139	0.1609	0.013 43	0.083 43	74.484	11.987	27
28	6.6488	0.1504	0.012 39	0.082 39	80.698	12.137	28
29	7.1143	0.1406	0.011 45	0.081 45	87.347	12.278	29
30	7.6123	0.1314	0.010 59	0.080 59	94.461	12.409	30
31	8.1451	0.1228	0.009 80	0.079 80	102.073	12.532	31
32	8.7153	0.1147	0.009 07	0.079 07	110.218	12.647	32
33	9.3253	0.1072	0.008 41	0.078 41	118.933	12.754	33
34	9.9781	0.1002	0.007 80	0.077 80	128.259	12.854	34
35	10.6766	0.0937	0.007 23	0.077 23	138.237	12.948	35
40	14.9745	0.0668	0.005 01	0.075 01	199.635	13.332	40
45	21.0025	0.0476	0.003 50	0.073 50	285.749	13.606	45
50	29.4570	0.0339	0.002 46	0.072 46	406.529	13.801	50
55	41.3150	0.0242	0.001 74	0.071 74	575.929	13.940	55
60	57.9464	0.0173	0.001 23	0.071 23	813.520	14.039	60
65	81.2729	0.0123	0.000 87	0.070 87	1 146.755	14.110	65
70	113.9894	0.0088	0.000 62	0.070 62	1 614.134	14.160	70
75	159.8760	0.0063	0.000 44	0.070 44	2 269.657	14.196	75
80	224.2344	0.0045	0.000 31	0.070 31	3 189.063	14.222	80
85	314.5003	0.0032	0.000 22	0.070 22	4 478.576	14.240	85
90	441.1030	0.0023	0.000 16	0.070 16	6 287.185	14.253	90
95	618.6697	0.0016	0.000 11	0.070 11	8 823.854	14.263	95
100	867.7163	0.0012	0.000 08	0.070 08	12 381.662	14.269	100

TABLE E–15

8% Compound Interest Factors

	Single Payment		Uniform Series				
	Compound Amount Factor	Present Worth Factor	Sinking Fund Factor	Capital Recovery Factor	Compound Amount Factor	Present Worth Factor	
n	F/P	P/F	A/F	A/P	F/A	P/A	n
1	1.0800	0.9259	1.000 00	1.080 00	1.000	0.926	1
2	1.1664	0.8573	0.480 77	0.560 77	2.080	1.783	2
3	1.2597	0.7938	0.308 03	0.388 03	3.246	2.577	3
4	1.3605	0.7350	0.221 92	0.301 92	4.506	3.312	4
5	1.4693	0.6806	0.170 46	0.250 46	5.867	3.993	5
6	1.5869	0.6302	0.136 32	0.216 32	7.336	4.623	6
7	1.7138	0.5835	0.112 07	0.192 07	8.923	5.206	7
8	1.8509	0.5403	0.094 01	0.174 01	10.637	5.747	8
9	1.9990	0.5002	0.080 08	0.160 08	12.488	6.247	9
10	2.1589	0.4632	0.069 03	0.149 03	14.487	6.710	10
11	2.3316	0.4289	0.060 08	0.140 08	16.645	7.139	11
12	2.5182	0.3971	0.052 70	0.132 70	18.977	7.536	12
13	2.7196	0.3677	0.046 52	0.126 52	21.495	7.904	13
14	2.9372	0.3405	0.041 30	0.121 30	24.215	8.244	14
15	3.1722	0.3152	0.036 83	0.116 83	27.152	8.559	15
16	3.4259	0.2919	0.032 98	0.112 98	30.324	8.851	16
17	3.7000	0.2703	0.029 63	0.109 63	33.750	9.122	17
18	3.9960	0.2502	0.026 70	0.106 70	37.450	9.372	18
19	4.3157	0.2317	0.024 13	0.104 13	41.446	9.604	19
20	4.6610	0.2145	0.021 85	0.101 85	45.762	9.818	20
21	5.0338	0.1987	0.019 83	0.099 83	50.423	10.017	21
22	5.4365	0.1839	0.018 03	0.098 03	55.457	10.201	22
23	5.8715	0.1703	0.016 42	0.096 42	60.893	10.371	23
24	6.3412	0.1577	0.014 98	0.094 98	66.765	10.529	24
25	6.8485	0.1460	0.013 68	0.093 68	73.106	10.675	25
26	7.3964	0.1352	0.012 51	0.092 51	79.954	10.810	26
27	7.9881	0.1252	0.011 45	0.091 45	87.351	10.935	27
28	8.6271	0.1159	0.010 49	0.090 49	95.339	11.051	28
29	9.3173	0.1073	0.009 62	0.089 62	103.966	11.158	29
30	10.0627	0.0994	0.008 83	0.088 83	113.283	11.258	30
31	10.8677	0.0920	0.008 11	0.088 11	123.346	11.350	31
32	11.7371	0.0852	0.007 45	0.087 45	134.214	11.435	32
33	12.6760	0.0789	0.006 85	0.086 85	145.951	11.514	33
34	13.6901	0.0730	0.006 30	0.086 30	158.627	11.587	34
35	14.7853	0.0676	0.005 80	0.085 80	172.317	11.655	35
40	21.7245	0.0460	0.003 86	0.083 86	259.057	11.925	40
45	31.9204	0.0313	0.002 59	0.082 59	386.506	12.108	45
50	46.9016	0.0213	0.001 74	0.081 74	573.770	12.233	50
55	68.9139	0.0145	0.001 18	0.081 18	848.923	12.319	55
60	101.2571	0.0099	0.000 80	0.080 80	1 253.213	12.377	60
65	148.7798	0.0067	0.000 54	0.080 54	1 847.248	12.416	65
70	218.6064	0.0046	0.000 37	0.080 37	2 720.080	12.443	70
75	321.2045	0.0031	0.000 25	0.080 25	4 002.557	12.461	75
80	471.9548	0.0021	0.000 17	0.080 17	5 886.935	12.474	80
85	693.4565	0.0014	0.000 12	0.080 12	8 655.706	12.482	85
90	1 018.9151	0.0010	0.000 08	0.080 08	12 723.939	12.488	90
95	1 497.1205	0.0007	0.000 05	0.080 05	18 701.507	12.492	95
100	2 199.7613	0.0005	0.000 04	0.080 04	27 484.516	12.494	100

TABLE E–16

10% Compound Interest Factors

	Single Payment		Uniform Series				
	Compound Amount Factor	Present Worth Factor	Sinking Fund Factor	Capital Recovery Factor	Compound Amount Factor	Present Worth Factor	
n	F/P	P/F	A/F	A/P	F/A	P/A	n
1	1.1000	0.9091	1.000 00	1.100 00	1.000	0.909	1
2	1.2100	0.8264	0.476 19	0.576 19	2.100	1.736	2
3	1.3310	0.7513	0.302 11	0.402 11	3.310	2.487	3
4	1.4641	0.6830	0.215 47	0.315 47	4.641	3.170	4
5	1.6105	0.6209	0.163 80	0.263 80	6.105	3.791	5
6	1.7716	0.5645	0.129 61	0.229 61	7.716	4.355	6
7	1.9487	0.5132	0.105 41	0.205 41	9.487	4.868	7
8	2.1436	0.4665	0.087 44	0.187 44	11.436	5.335	8
9	2.3579	0.4241	0.073 64	0.173 64	13.579	5.759	9
10	2.5937	0.3855	0.062 75	0.162 75	15.937	6.144	10
11	2.8531	0.3505	0.053 96	0.153 96	18.531	6.495	11
12	3.1384	0.3186	0.046 76	0.146 76	21.384	6.814	12
13	3.4523	0.2897	0.040 78	0.140 78	24.523	7.103	13
14	3.7975	0.2633	0.035 75	0.135 75	27.975	7.367	14
15	4.1772	0.2394	0.031 47	0.131 47	31.772	7.606	15
16	4.5950	0.2176	0.027 82	0.127 82	35.950	7.824	16
17	5.0545	0.1978	0.024 66	0.124 66	40.545	8.022	17
18	5.5599	0.1799	0.021 93	0.121 93	45.599	8.201	18
19	6.1159	0.1635	0.019 55	0.119 55	51.159	8.365	19
20	6.7275	0.1486	0.017 46	0.117 46	57.275	8.514	20
21	7.4002	0.1351	0.015 62	0.115 62	64.002	8.649	21
22	8.1403	0.1228	0.014 01	0.114 01	71.403	8.772	22
23	8.9543	0.1117	0.012 57	0.112 57	79.543	8.883	23
24	9.8497	0.1015	0.011 30	0.111 30	88.497	8.985	24
25	10.8347	0.0923	0.010 17	0.110 17	98.347	9.077	25
26	11.9182	0.0839	0.009 16	0.109 16	109.182	9.161	26
27	13.1100	0.0763	0.008 26	0.108 26	121.100	9.237	27
28	14.4210	0.0693	0.007 45	0.107 45	134.210	9.307	28
29	15.8631	0.0630	0.006 73	0.106 73	148.631	9.370	29
30	17.4494	0.0573	0.006 08	0.106 08	164.494	9.427	30
31	19.1943	0.0521	0.005 50	0.105 50	181.943	9.479	31
32	21.1138	0.0474	0.004 97	0.104 97	201.138	9.526	32
33	23.2252	0.0431	0.004 50	0.104 50	222.252	9.569	33
34	25.5477	0.0391	0.004 07	0.104 07	245.477	9.609	34
35	28.1024	0.0356	0.003 69	0.103 69	271.024	9.644	35
40	45.2593	0.0221	0.002 26	0.102 26	442.593	9.779	40
45	72.8905	0.0137	0.001 39	0.101 39	718.905	9.863	45
50	117.3909	0.0085	0.000 86	0.100 86	1 163.909	9.915	50
55	189.0591	0.0053	0.000 53	0.100 53	1 880.591	9.947	55
60	304.4816	0.0033	0.000 33	0.100 33	3 034.816	9.967	60
65	490.3707	0.0020	0.000 20	0.100 20	4 893.707	9.980	65
70	789.7470	0.0013	0.000 13	0.100 13	7 887.470	9.987	70
75	1 271.8952	0.0008	0.000 08	0.100 08	12 708.954	9.992	75
80	2 048.4002	0.0005	0.000 05	0.100 05	20 474.002	9.995	80
85	3 298.9690	0.0003	0.000 03	0.100 03	32 979.690	9.997	85
90	5 313.0226	0.0002	0.000 02	0.100 02	53 120.226	9.998	90
95	8 556.6760	0.0001	0.000 01	0.100 01	85 556.760	9.999	95
100	13 780.6123	0.0001	0.000 01	0.100 01	137 796.123	9.999	100

TABLE E-17
12% Compound Interest Factors

	Single Payment		Uniform Series				
	Compound Amount Factor	Present Worth Factor	Sinking Fund Factor	Capital Recovery Factor	Compound Amount Factor	Present Worth Factor	
n	F/P	P/F	A/F	A/P	F/A	P/A	n
1	1.1200	0.8929	1.000 00	1.120 00	1.000	0.893	1
2	1.2544	0.7972	0.471 70	0.591 70	2.120	1.690	2
3	1.4049	0.7118	0.296 35	0.416 35	3.374	2.402	3
4	1.5735	0.6355	0.209 23	0.329 23	4.779	3.037	4
5	1.7623	0.5674	0.157 41	0.277 41	6.353	3.605	5
6	1.9738	0.5066	0.123 23	0.243 23	8.115	4.111	6
7	2.2107	0.4523	0.099 12	0.219 12	10.089	4.564	7
8	2.4760	0.4039	0.081 30	0.201 30	12.300	4.968	8
9	2.7731	0.3606	0.067 68	0.187 68	14.776	5.328	9
10	3.1058	0.3220	0.056 98	0.176 98	17.549	5.650	10
11	3.4785	0.2875	0.048 42	0.168 42	20.655	5.938	11
12	3.8960	0.2567	0.041 44	0.161 44	24.133	6.194	12
13	4.3635	0.2292	0.035 68	0.155 68	28.029	6.424	13
14	4.8871	0.2046	0.030 87	0.150 87	32.393	6.628	14
15	5.4736	0.1827	0.026 82	0.146 82	37.280	6.811	15
16	6.1304	0.1631	0.023 39	0.143 39	42.753	6.974	16
17	6.8660	0.1456	0.020 46	0.140 46	48.884	7.120	17
18	7.6900	0.1300	0.017 94	0.137 94	55.750	7.250	18
19	8.6128	0.1161	0.015 76	0.135 76	63.440	7.366	19
20	9.6463	0.1037	0.013 88	0.133 88	72.052	7.469	20
21	10.8038	0.0926	0.012 24	0.132 24	81.699	7.562	21
22	12.1003	0.0826	0.010 81	0.130 81	92.503	7.645	22
23	13.5523	0.0738	0.009 56	0.129 56	104.603	7.718	23
24	15.1786	0.0659	0.008 46	0.128 46	118.155	7.784	24
25	17.0001	0.0588	0.007 50	0.127 50	133.334	7.843	25
26	19.0401	0.0525	0.006 65	0.126 65	150.334	7.896	26
27	21.3249	0.0469	0.005 90	0.125 90	169.374	7.943	27
28	23.8839	0.0419	0.005 24	0.125 24	190.699	7.984	28
29	26.7499	0.0374	0.004 66	0.124 66	214.583	8.022	29
30	29.9599	0.0334	0.004 14	0.124 14	241.333	8.055	30
31	33.5551	0.0298	0.003 69	0.123 69	271.292	8.085	31
32	37.5817	0.0266	0.003 28	0.123 28	304.847	8.112	32
33	42.0915	0.0238	0.002 92	0.122 92	342.429	8.135	33
34	47.1425	0.0212	0.002 60	0.122 60	384.520	8.157	34
35	52.7996	0.0189	0.002 32	0.122 32	431.663	8.176	35
40	93.0510	0.0107	0.001 30	0.121 30	767.091	8.244	40
45	163.9876	0.0061	0.000 74	0.120 74	1 358.230	8.283	45
50	289.0022	0.0035	0.000 42	0.120 42	2 400.018	8.305	50
∞				0.120 00		8.333	∞

TABLE E–18

15% Compound Interest Factors

	Single Payment		Uniform Series				
	Compound Amount Factor	Present Worth Factor	Sinking Fund Factor	Capital Recovery Factor	Compound Amount Factor	Present Worth Factor	
n	F/P	P/F	A/F	A/P	F/A	P/A	n
1	1.1500	0.8696	1.000 00	1.150 00	1.000	0.870	1
2	1.3225	0.7561	0.465 12	0.615 12	2.150	1.626	2
3	1.5209	0.6575	0.287 98	0.437 98	3.472	2.283	3
4	1.7490	0.5718	0.200 26	0.350 27	4.993	2.855	4
5	2.0114	0.4972	0.148 32	0.298 32	6.742	3.352	5
6	2.3131	0.4323	0.114 24	0.264 24	8.754	3.784	6
7	2.6600	0.3759	0.090 36	0.240 36	11.067	4.160	7
8	3.0590	0.3269	0.072 85	0.222 85	13.727	4.487	8
9	3.5179	0.2843	0.059 57	0.209 57	16.786	4.772	9
10	4.0456	0.2472	0.049 25	0.199 25	20.304	5.019	10
11	4.6524	0.2149	0.041 07	0.191 07	24.349	5.234	11
12	5.3503	0.1869	0.034 48	0.184 48	29.002	5.421	12
13	6.1528	0.1625	0.029 11	0.179 11	34.352	5.583	13
14	7.0757	0.1413	0.024 69	0.174 69	40.505	5.724	14
15	8.1371	0.1229	0.021 02	0.171 02	47.580	5.847	15
16	9.3576	0.1069	0.017 95	0.167 95	55.717	5.954	16
17	10.7613	0.0929	0.015 37	0.165 37	65.075	6.047	17
18	12.3755	0.0808	0.013 19	0.163 19	75.836	6.128	18
19	14.2318	0.0703	0.011 34	0.161 34	88.212	6.198	19
20	16.3665	0.0611	0.009 76	0.159 76	102.444	6.259	20
21	18.8215	0.0531	0.008 42	0.158 42	118.810	6.312	21
22	21.6447	0.0462	0.007 27	0.157 27	137.632	6.359	22
23	24.8915	0.0402	0.006 28	0.156 28	159.276	6.399	23
24	28.6252	0.0349	0.005 43	0.155 43	184.168	6.434	24
25	32.9190	0.0304	0.004 70	0.154 70	212.793	6.464	25
26	37.8568	0.0264	0.004 07	0.154 07	245.712	6.491	26
27	43.5353	0.0230	0.003 53	0.153 53	283.569	6.514	27
28	50.0656	0.0200	0.003 06	0.153 06	327.104	6.534	28
29	57.5755	0.0174	0.002 65	0.152 65	377.170	6.551	29
30	66.2118	0.0151	0.002 30	0.152 30	434.745	6.566	30
31	76.1435	0.0131	0.002 00	0.152 00	500.957	6.579	31
32	87.5651	0.0114	0.001 73	0.151 73	577.100	6.591	32
33	100.6998	0.0099	0.001 50	0.151 50	664.666	6.600	33
34	115.8048	0.0086	0.001 31	0.151 31	765.365	6.609	34
35	133.1755	0.0075	0.001 13	0.151 13	881.170	6.617	35
40	267.8635	0.0037	0.000 56	0.150 56	1 779.090	6.642	40
45	538.7693	0.0019	0.000 28	0.150 28	3 585.128	6.654	45
50	1 083.6574	0.0009	0.000 14	0.150 14	7 217.716	6.661	50
∞				0.150 00		6.667	∞

TABLE E–19

20% Compound Interest Factors

	Single Payment		Uniform Series				
	Compound Amount Factor	Present Worth Factor	Sinking Fund Factor	Capital Recovery Factor	Compound Amount Factor	Present Worth Factor	
n	*F/P*	*P/F*	*A/F*	*A/P*	*F/A*	*P/A*	*n*
1	1.2000	0.8333	1.000 00	1.200 00	1.000	0.833	1
2	1.4400	0.6944	0.454 55	0.654 55	2.200	1.528	2
3	1.7280	0.5787	0.274 73	0.474 73	3.640	2.106	3
4	2.0736	0.4823	0.186 29	0.386 29	5.368	2.589	4
5	2.4883	0.4019	0.134 38	0.334 38	7.442	2.991	5
6	2.9860	0.3349	0.100 71	0.300 71	9.930	3.326	6
7	3.5832	0.2791	0.077 42	0.277 42	12.916	3.605	7
8	4.2998	0.2326	0.060 61	0.260 61	16.499	3.837	8
9	5.1598	0.1938	0.048 08	0.248 08	20.799	4.031	9
10	6.1917	0.1615	0.038 52	0.238 52	25.959	4.192	10
11	7.4301	0.1346	0.031 10	0.231 10	32.150	4.327	11
12	8.9161	0.1122	0.025 26	0.225 26	39.581	4.439	12
13	10.6993	0.0935	0.020 62	0.220 62	48.497	4.533	13
14	12.8392	0.0779	0.016 89	0.216 89	59.196	4.611	14
15	15.4070	0.0649	0.013 88	0.213 88	72.035	4.675	15
16	18.4884	0.0541	0.011 44	0.211 44	87.442	4.730	16
17	22.1861	0.0451	0.009 44	0.209 44	105.931	4.775	17
18	26.6233	0.0376	0.007 81	0.207 81	128.117	4.812	18
19	31.9480	0.0313	0.006 46	0.206 46	154.740	4.844	19
20	38.3376	0.0261	0.005 36	0.205 36	186.688	4.870	20
21	46.0051	0.0217	0.004 44	0.204 44	225.026	4.891	21
22	55.2061	0.0181	0.003 69	0.203 69	271.031	4.909	22
23	66.2474	0.0151	0.003 07	0.203 07	326.237	4.925	23
24	79.4968	0.0126	0.002 55	0.202 55	392.484	4.937	24
25	95.3962	0.0105	0.002 12	0.202 12	471.981	4.948	25
26	114.4755	0.0087	0.001 76	0.201 76	567.377	4.956	26
27	137.3706	0.0073	0.001 47	0.201 47	681.853	4.964	27
28	164.8447	0.0061	0.001 22	0.201 22	819.223	4.970	28
29	197.8136	0.0051	0.001 02	0.201 02	984.068	4.975	29
30	237.3763	0.0042	0.000 85	0.200 85	1 181.882	4.979	30
31	284.8516	0.0035	0.000 70	0.200 70	1 419.258	4.982	31
32	341.8219	0.0029	0.000 59	0.200 59	1 704.109	4.985	32
33	410.1863	0.0024	0.000 49	0.200 49	2 045.931	4.988	33
34	492.2235	0.0020	0.000 41	0.200 41	2 456.118	4.990	34
35	590.6682	0.0017	0.000 34	0.200 34	2 948.341	4.992	35
40	1 469.7716	0.0007	0.000 14	0.200 14	7 343.858	4.997	40
45	3 657.2620	0.0003	0.000 05	0.200 05	18 281.310	4.999	45
50	9 100.4382	0.0001	0.000 02	0.200 02	45 497.191	4.999	50
∞				0.200 00		5.000	∞

TABLE E–20

25% Compound Interest Factors

	Single Payment		Uniform Series				
n	Compound Amount Factor F/P	Present Worth Factor P/F	Sinking Fund Factor A/F	Capital Recovery Factor A/P	Compound Amount Factor F/A	Present Worth Factor P/A	n
1	1.2500	0.8000	1.000 00	1.250 00	1.000	0.800	1
2	1.5625	0.6400	0.444 44	0.694 44	2.250	1.440	2
3	1.9531	0.5120	0.262 30	0.512 30	3.813	1.952	3
4	2.4414	0.4096	0.173 44	0.423 44	5.766	2.362	4
5	3.0518	0.3277	0.121 85	0.371 85	8.207	2.689	5
6	3.8147	0.2621	0.088 82	0.338 82	11.259	2.951	6
7	4.7684	0.2097	0.066 34	0.316 34	15.073	3.161	7
8	5.9605	0.1678	0.050 40	0.300 40	19.842	3.329	8
9	7.4506	0.1342	0.038 76	0.288 76	25.802	3.463	9
10	9.3132	0.1074	0.030 07	0.280 07	33.253	3.571	10
11	11.6415	0.0859	0.023 49	0.273 49	42.566	3.656	11
12	14.5519	0.0687	0.018 45	0.268 45	54.208	3.725	12
13	18.1899	0.0550	0.014 54	0.264 54	68.760	3.780	13
14	22.7374	0.0440	0.011 50	0.261 50	86.949	3.824	14
15	28.4217	0.0352	0.009 12	0.259 12	109.687	3.859	15
16	35.5271	0.0281	0.007 24	0.257 24	138.109	3.887	16
17	44.4089	0.0225	0.005 76	0.255 76	173.636	3.910	17
18	55.5112	0.0180	0.004 59	0.254 59	218.045	3.928	18
19	69.3889	0.0144	0.003 66	0.253 66	273.556	3.942	19
20	86.7362	0.0115	0.002 92	0.252 92	342.945	3.954	20
21	108.4202	0.0092	0.002 33	0.252 33	429.681	3.963	21
22	135.5253	0.0074	0.001 86	0.251 86	538.101	3.970	22
23	169.4066	0.0059	0.001 48	0.251 48	673.626	3.976	23
24	211.7582	0.0047	0.001 19	0.251 19	843.033	3.981	24
25	264.6978	0.0038	0.000 95	0.250 95	1 054.791	3.985	25
26	330.8722	0.0030	0.000 76	0.250 76	1 319.489	3.988	26
27	413.5903	0.0024	0.000 61	0.250 61	1 650.361	3.990	27
28	516.9879	0.0019	0.000 48	0.250 48	2 063.952	3.992	28
29	646.2349	0.0015	0.000 39	0.250 39	2 580.939	3.994	29
30	807.7936	0.0012	0.000 31	0.250 31	3 227.174	3.995	30
31	1 009.7420	0.0010	0.000 25	0.250 25	4 034.968	3.996	31
32	1 262.1774	0.0008	0.000 20	0.250 20	5 044.710	3.997	32
33	1 577.7218	0.0006	0.000 16	0.250 16	6 306.887	3.997	33
34	1 972.1523	0.0005	0.000 13	0.250 13	7 884.609	3.998	34
35	2 465.1903	0.0004	0.000 10	0.250 10	9 856.761	3.998	35
40	7 523.1638	0.0001	0.000 03	0.250 03	30 088.655	3.999	40
45	22 958.8740	0.0001	0.000 01	0.250 01	91 831.496	4.000	45
50	70 064.9232	0.0000	0.000 00	0.250 00	280 255.693	4.000	50
∞				0.250 00		4.000	∞

TABLE E-21
30% Compound Interest Factors

	Single Payment		Uniform Series				
	Compound Amount Factor	Present Worth Factor	Sinking Fund Factor	Capital Recovery Factor	Compound Amount Factor	Present Worth Factor	
n	F/P	P/F	A/F	A/P	F/A	P/A	n
1	1.3000	0.7692	1.000 00	1.300 00	1.000	0.769	1
2	1.6900	0.5917	0.434 78	0.734 78	2.300	1.361	2
3	2.1970	0.4552	0.250 63	0.550 63	3.990	1.816	3
4	2.8561	0.3501	0.161 63	0.461 63	6.187	2.166	4
5	3.7129	0.2693	0.110 58	0.410 58	9.043	2.436	5
6	4.8268	0.2072	0.078 39	0.378 39	12.756	2.643	6
7	6.2749	0.1594	0.056 87	0.356 87	17.583	2.802	7
8	8.1573	0.1226	0.041 92	0.341 92	23.858	2.925	8
9	10.6045	0.0943	0.031 24	0.331 24	32.015	3.019	9
10	13.7858	0.0725	0.023 46	0.323 46	42.619	3.092	10
11	17.9216	0.0558	0.017 73	0.317 73	56.405	3.147	11
12	23.2981	0.0429	0.013 45	0.313 45	74.327	3.190	12
13	30.2875	0.0330	0.010 24	0.310 24	97.625	3.223	13
14	39.3738	0.0254	0.007 82	0.307 82	127.913	3.249	14
15	51.1859	0.0195	0.005 98	0.305 98	167.286	3.268	15
16	66.5417	0.0150	0.004 58	0.304 58	218.472	3.283	16
17	86.5042	0.0116	0.003 51	0.303 51	285.014	3.295	17
18	112.4554	0.0089	0.002 69	0.302 69	371.518	3.304	18
19	146.1920	0.0068	0.002 07	0.302 07	483.973	3.311	19
20	190.0496	0.0053	0.001 59	0.301 59	630.165	3.316	20
21	247.0645	0.0040	0.001 22	0.301 22	820.215	3.320	21
22	321.1839	0.0031	0.000 94	0.300 94	1 067.280	3.323	22
23	417.5391	0.0024	0.000 72	0.300 72	1 388.464	3.325	23
24	542.8008	0.0018	0.000 55	0.300 55	1 806.003	3.327	24
25	705.6410	0.0014	0.000 43	0.300 43	2 348.803	3.329	25
26	917.3333	0.0011	0.000 33	0.300 33	3 054.444	3.330	26
27	1 192.5333	0.0008	0.000 25	0.300 25	3 971.778	3.331	27
28	1 550.2933	0.0006	0.000 19	0.300 19	5 164.311	3.331	28
29	2 015.3813	0.0005	0.000 15	0.300 15	6 714.604	3.332	29
30	2 619.9956	0.0004	0.000 11	0.300 11	8 729.985	3.332	30
31	3 405.9943	0.0003	0.000 09	0.300 09	11 349.981	3.332	31
32	4 427.7926	0.0002	0.000 07	0.300 07	14 755.975	3.333	32
33	5 756.1304	0.0002	0.000 05	0.300 05	19 183.768	3.333	33
34	7 482.9696	0.0001	0.000 04	0.300 04	24 939.899	3.333	34
35	9 727.8604	0.0001	0.000 03	0.300 03	32 422.868	3.333	35
∞				0.300 00		3.333	∞

TABLE E–22
35% Compound Interest Factors

	Single Payment		Uniform Series				
n	Compound Amount Factor F/P	Present Worth Factor P/F	Sinking Fund Factor A/F	Capital Recovery Factor A/P	Compound Amount Factor F/A	Present Worth Factor P/A	n
1	1.3500	0.7407	1.000 00	1.350 00	1.000	0.741	1
2	1.8225	0.5487	0.425 53	0.775 53	2.350	1.289	2
3	2.4604	0.4064	0.239 66	0.589 66	4.172	1.696	3
4	3.3215	0.3011	0.150 76	0.500 76	6.633	1.997	4
5	4.4840	0.2230	0.100 46	0.450 46	9.954	2.220	5
6	6.0534	0.1652	0.069 26	0.419 26	14.438	2.385	6
7	8.1722	0.1224	0.048 80	0.398 80	20.492	2.507	7
8	11.0324	0.0906	0.034 89	0.384 89	28.664	2.598	8
9	14.8937	0.0671	0.025 19	0.375 19	39.696	2.665	9
10	20.1066	0.0497	0.018 32	0.368 32	54.590	2.715	10
11	27.1439	0.0368	0.013 39	0.363 39	74.697	2.752	11
12	36.6442	0.0273	0.009 82	0.359 82	101.841	2.779	12
13	49.4697	0.0202	0.007 22	0.357 22	138.485	2.799	13
14	66.7841	0.0150	0.005 32	0.355 32	187.954	2.814	14
15	90.1585	0.0111	0.003 93	0.353 93	254.738	2.825	15
16	121.7139	0.0082	0.002 90	0.352 90	344.897	2.834	16
17	164.3138	0.0061	0.002 14	0.352 14	466.611	2.840	17
18	221.8236	0.0045	0.001 59	0.351 58	630.925	2.844	18
19	299.4619	0.0033	0.001 17	0.351 17	852.748	2.848	19
20	404.2736	0.0025	0.000 87	0.350 87	1 152.210	2.850	20
21	545.7693	0.0018	0.000 64	0.350 64	1 556.484	2.852	21
22	736.7886	0.0014	0.000 48	0.350 48	2 102.253	2.853	22
23	994.6646	0.0010	0.000 35	0.350 35	2 839.042	2.854	23
24	1 342.7973	0.0007	0.000 26	0.350 26	3 833.706	2.855	24
25	1 812.7763	0.0006	0.000 19	0.350 19	5 176.504	2.856	25
26	2 447.2480	0.0004	0.000 14	0.350 14	6 989.280	2.856	26
27	3 303.7848	0.0003	0.000 11	0.350 11	9 436.528	2.856	27
28	4 460.1095	0.0002	0.000 08	0.350 08	12 740.313	2.857	28
29	6 021.1478	0.0002	0.000 06	0.350 06	17 200.422	2.857	29
30	8 128.5495	0.0001	0.000 04	0.350 04	23 221.570	2.857	30
31	10 973.5418	0.0001	0.000 03	0.350 03	31 350.120	2.857	31
32	14 814.2815	0.0001	0.000 02	0.350 02	42 323.661	2.857	32
33	19 999.2800	0.0001	0.000 02	0.350 02	57 137.943	2.857	33
34	26 999.0280	0.0000	0.000 01	0.350 01	77 137.223	2.857	34
35	36 448.6878	. . . . . .	0.000 01	0.350 01	104 136.251	2.857	35
∞				0.350 00		2.857	∞

TABLE E-23

40% Compound Interest Factors

	Single Payment		Uniform Series				
	Compound Amount Factor	Present Worth Factor	Sinking Fund Factor	Capital Recovery Factor	Compound Amount Factor	Present Worth Factor	
n	F/P	P/F	A/F	A/P	F/A	P/A	n
1	1.4000	0.7143	1.000 00	1.400 00	1.000	0.714	1
2	1.9600	0.5102	0.416 67	0.816 67	2.400	1.224	2
3	2.7440	0.3644	0.229 36	0.629 36	4.360	1.589	3
4	3.8416	0.2603	0.140 77	0.540 77	7.104	1.849	4
5	5.3782	0.1859	0.091 36	0.491 36	10.946	2.035	5
6	7.5295	0.1328	0.061 26	0.461 26	16.324	2.168	6
7	10.5414	0.0949	0.041 92	0.441 92	23.853	2.263	7
8	14.7579	0.0678	0.029 07	0.429 07	34.395	2.331	8
9	20.6610	0.0484	0.020 34	0.420 34	49.153	2.379	9
10	28.9255	0.0346	0.014 32	0.414 32	69.814	2.414	10
11	40.4957	0.0247	0.010 13	0.410 13	98.739	2.438	11
12	56.6939	0.0176	0.007 18	0.407 18	139.235	2.456	12
13	79.3715	0.0126	0.005 10	0.405 10	195.929	2.469	13
14	111.1201	0.0090	0.003 63	0.403 63	275.300	2.478	14
15	155.5681	0.0064	0.002 59	0.402 59	386.420	2.484	15
16	217.7953	0.0046	0.001 85	0.401 85	541.988	2.489	16
17	304.9135	0.0033	0.001 32	0.401 32	759.784	2.492	17
18	426.8789	0.0023	0.000 94	0.400 94	1 064.697	2.494	18
19	597.6304	0.0017	0.000 67	0.400 67	1 491.576	2.496	19
20	836.6826	0.0012	0.000 48	0.400 48	2 089.206	2.497	20
21	1 171.3554	0.0009	0.000 34	0.400 34	2 925.889	2.498	21
22	1 639.8976	0.0006	0.000 24	0.400 24	4 097.245	2.498	22
23	2 295.8569	0.0004	0.000 17	0.400 17	5 737.142	2.499	23
24	3 214.1997	0.0003	0.000 12	0.400 12	8 032.999	2.499	24
25	4 499.8796	0.0002	0.000 09	0.400 09	11 247.199	2.499	25
26	6 299.8314	0.0002	0.000 06	0.400 06	15 747.079	2.500	26
27	8 819.7640	0.0001	0.000 05	0.400 05	22 046.910	2.500	27
28	12 347.6696	0.0001	0.000 03	0.400 03	30 866.674	2.500	28
29	17 286.7374	0.0001	0.000 02	0.400 02	43 214.343	2.500	29
30	24 201.4324	0.0000	0.000 01	0.400 02	60 501.081	2.500	30
31	33 882.0053	......	0.000 01	0.400 01	84 702.513	2.500	31
32	47 434.8074	......	0.000 01	0.400 01	118 584.519	2.500	32
33	66 408.7304	......	0.000 01	0.400 01	166 019.326	2.500	33
34	92 972.2225	......	0.000 00	0.400 00	232 428.056	2.500	34
35	130 161.1116	......	......	0.400 00	325 400.279	2.500	35
∞				0.400 00		2.500	∞

TABLE E–24

45% Compound Interest Factors

	Single Payment		Uniform Series				
	Compound Amount Factor	Present Worth Factor	Sinking Fund Factor	Capital Recovery Factor	Compound Amount Factor	Present Worth Factor	
n	F/P	P/F	A/F	A/P	F/A	P/A	n
1	1.4500	0.6897	1.000 00	1.450 00	1.000	0.690	1
2	2.1025	0.4756	0.408 16	0.858 16	2.450	1.165	2
3	3.0486	0.3280	0.219 66	0.669 66	4.552	1.493	3
4	4.4205	0.2262	0.131 56	0.581 56	7.601	1.720	4
5	6.4097	0.1560	0.083 18	0.533 18	12.022	1.876	5
6	9.2941	0.1076	0.054 26	0.504 26	18.431	1.983	6
7	13.4765	0.0742	0.036 07	0.486 07	27.725	2.057	7
8	19.5409	0.0512	0.024 27	0.474 27	41.202	2.109	8
9	28.3343	0.0353	0.016 46	0.466 46	60.743	2.144	9
10	41.0847	0.0243	0.011 23	0.461 23	89.077	2.168	10
11	59.5728	0.0168	0.007 68	0.457 68	130.162	2.185	11
12	86.3806	0.0116	0.005 27	0.455 27	189.735	2.196	12
13	125.2518	0.0080	0.003 62	0.453 62	276.115	2.204	13
14	181.6151	0.0055	0.002 49	0.452 49	401.367	2.210	14
15	263.3419	0.0038	0.001 72	0.451 72	582.982	2.214	15
16	381.8458	0.0026	0.001 18	0.451 18	846.324	2.216	16
17	553.6764	0.0018	0.000 81	0.450 81	1 228.170	2.218	17
18	802.8308	0.0012	0.000 56	0.450 56	1 781.846	2.219	18
19	1 164.1047	0.0009	0.000 39	0.450 39	2 584.677	2.220	19
20	1 687.9518	0.0006	0.000 27	0.450 27	3 748.782	2.221	20
21	2 447.5301	0.0004	0.000 18	0.450 18	5 436.734	2.221	21
22	3 548.9187	0.0003	0.000 13	0.450 13	7 884.264	2.222	22
23	5 145.9321	0.0002	0.000 09	0.450 09	11 433.182	2.222	23
24	7 461.6015	0.0001	0.000 06	0.450 06	16 579.115	2.222	24
25	10 819.3222	0.0001	0.000 04	0.450 04	24 040.716	2.222	25
26	15 688.0173	0.0001	0.000 03	0.450 03	34 860.038	2.222	26
27	22 747.6250	0.0000	0.000 02	0.450 02	50 548.056	2.222	27
28	32 984.0563	. . . . . .	0.000 01	0.450 01	73 295.681	2.222	28
29	47 826.8816	. . . . . .	0.000 01	0.450 01	106 279.737	2.222	29
30	69 348.9783	. . . . . .	0.000 01	0.450 01	154 106.618	2.222	30
∞				0.450 00		2.222	∞

TABLE E–25

50% Compound Interest Factors

	Single Payment		Uniform Series				
	Compound Amount Factor	Present Worth Factor	Sinking Fund Factor	Capital Recovery Factor	Compound Amount Factor	Present Worth Factor	
n	F/P	P/F	A/F	A/P	F/A	P/A	n
1	1.5000	0.6667	1.000 00	1.500 00	1.000	0.667	1
2	2.2500	0.4444	0.400 00	0.900 00	2.500	1.111	2
3	3.3750	0.2963	0.210 53	0.710 53	4.750	1.407	3
4	5.0625	0.1975	0.123 08	0.623 08	8.125	1.605	4
5	7.5938	0.1317	0.075 83	0.575 83	13.188	1.737	5
6	11.3906	0.0878	0.048 12	0.548 12	20.781	1.824	6
7	17.0859	0.0585	0.031 08	0.531 08	32.172	1.883	7
8	25.6289	0.0390	0.020 30	0.520 30	49.258	1.922	8
9	38.4434	0.0260	0.013 35	0.513 35	74.887	1.948	9
10	57.6650	0.0173	0.008 82	0.508 82	113.330	1.965	10
11	86.4976	0.0116	0.005 85	0.505 85	170.995	1.977	11
12	129.7463	0.0077	0.003 88	0.503 88	257.493	1.985	12
13	194.6195	0.0051	0.002 58	0.502 58	387.239	1.990	13
14	291.9293	0.0034	0.001 72	0.501 72	581.859	1.993	14
15	437.8939	0.0023	0.001 14	0.501 14	873.788	1.995	15
16	656.8408	0.0015	0.000 76	0.500 76	1 311.682	1.997	16
17	985.2613	0.0010	0.000 51	0.500 51	1 968.523	1.998	17
18	1 477.8919	0.0007	0.000 34	0.500 34	2 953.784	1.999	18
19	2 216.8378	0.0005	0.000 23	0.500 23	4 431.676	1.999	19
20	3 325.2567	0.0003	0.000 15	0.500 15	6 648.513	1.999	20
21	4 987.8851	0.0002	0.000 10	0.500 10	9 973.770	2.000	21
22	7 481.8276	0.0001	0.000 07	0.500 07	14 961.655	2.000	22
23	11 222.7415	0.0001	0.000 04	0.500 04	22 443.483	2.000	23
24	16 834.1122	0.0001	0.000 03	0.500 03	33 666.224	2.000	24
25	25 251.1683	0.0000	0.000 02	0.500 02	50 500.337	2.000	25
∞				0.500 00		2.000	∞

TABLE E–26

Factors To Convert a Gradient Series to an Equivalent Uniform Annual Series

This table contains multipliers for a gradient G to convert the n-year end-of-year series 0, G, 2G, ... (n − 1)G to an equivalent uniform annual series for n years.

n	1%	2%	3%	4%	5%	6%	7%	8%	10%	n
2	0.50	0.50	0.49	0.49	0.49	0.49	0.48	0.48	0.48	2
3	0.99	0.99	0.98	0.97	0.97	0.96	0.95	0.95	0.94	3
4	1.49	1.48	1.46	1.45	1.44	1.43	1.42	1.40	1.38	4
5	1.98	1.96	1.94	1.92	1.90	1.88	1.86	1.85	1.81	5
6	2.47	2.44	2.41	2.39	2.36	2.33	2.30	2.28	2.22	6
7	2.96	2.92	2.88	2.84	2.81	2.77	2.73	2.69	2.62	7
8	3.45	3.40	3.34	3.29	3.24	3.20	3.15	3.10	3.00	8
9	3.93	3.87	3.80	3.74	3.68	3.61	3.55	3.49	3.37	9
10	4.42	4.34	4.26	4.18	4.10	4.02	3.95	3.87	3.73	10
11	4.90	4.80	4.70	4.61	4.51	4.42	4.33	4.24	4.06	11
12	5.38	5.26	5.15	5.03	4.92	4.81	4.70	4.60	4.39	12
13	5.86	5.72	5.59	5.45	5.32	5.19	5.06	4.94	4.70	13
14	6.34	6.18	6.02	5.87	5.71	5.56	5.42	5.27	5.00	14
15	6.81	6.63	6.45	6.27	6.10	5.93	5.76	5.59	5.28	15
16	7.29	7.08	6.87	6.67	6.47	6.28	6.09	5.90	5.55	16
17	7.76	7.52	7.29	7.07	6.84	6.62	6.41	6.20	5.81	17
18	8.23	7.97	7.71	7.45	7.20	6.96	6.72	6.49	6.05	18
19	8.70	8.41	8.12	7.83	7.56	7.29	7.02	6.77	6.29	19
20	9.17	8.84	8.52	8.21	7.90	7.61	7.32	7.04	6.51	20
21	9.63	9.28	8.92	8.58	8.24	7.92	7.60	7.29	6.72	21
22	10.10	9.70	9.32	8.94	8.57	8.22	7.87	7.54	6.92	22
23	10.56	10.13	9.71	9.30	8.90	8.51	8.14	7.78	7.11	23
24	11.02	10.55	10.10	9.65	9.21	8.80	8.39	8.01	7.29	24
25	11.48	10.97	10.48	9.99	9.52	9.07	8.64	8.23	7.46	25
26	11.94	11.39	10.85	10.33	9.83	9.34	8.88	8.44	7.62	26
27	12.39	11.80	11.23	10.66	10.12	9.60	9.11	8.64	7.77	27
28	12.85	12.21	11.59	10.99	10.41	9.86	9.33	8.83	7.91	28
29	13.30	12.62	11.96	11.31	10.69	10.10	9.54	9.01	8.05	29
30	13.75	13.02	12.31	11.63	10.97	10.34	9.75	9.19	8.18	30
31	14.20	13.42	12.67	11.94	11.24	10.57	9.95	9.36	8.30	31
32	14.65	13.82	13.02	12.24	11.50	10.80	10.14	9.52	8.41	32
33	15.10	14.22	13.36	12.54	11.76	11.02	10.32	9.67	8.52	33
34	15.54	14.61	13.70	12.83	12.01	11.23	10.50	9.82	8.61	34
35	15.98	15.00	14.04	13.12	12.25	11.43	10.67	9.96	8.71	35
40	18.18	16.89	15.65	14.48	13.38	12.36	11.42	10.57	9.10	40
45	20.33	18.70	17.16	15.70	14.36	13.14	12.04	11.04	9.37	45
50	22.44	20.44	18.56	16.81	15.22	13.80	12.53	11.41	9.57	50
60	26.53	23.70	21.07	18.70	16.61	14.79	13.23	11.90	9.80	60
70	30.47	26.66	23.21	20.20	17.62	15.46	13.67	12.18	9.91	70
80	34.25	29.36	25.04	21.37	18.35	15.90	13.93	12.33	9.96	80
90	37.87	31.79	26.57	22.28	18.87	16.19	14.08	12.41	9.98	90
100	41.34	33.99	27.84	22.98	19.23	16.37	14.17	12.45	9.99	100

TABLE E–26—*Continued*

Factors To Convert a Gradient Series to an Equivalent Uniform Annual Series

This table contains multipliers for a gradient G to convert the n-year end-of-year series 0, G, 2G, ... (n — 1)G to an equivalent uniform annual series for n years.

n	12%	15%	20%	25%	30%	35%	40%	45%	50%	n
2	0.47	0.47	0.45	0.44	0.43	0.43	0.42	0.41	0.40	2
3	0.92	0.91	0.88	0.85	0.83	0.80	0.78	0.76	0.74	3
4	1.36	1.33	1.27	1.22	1.18	1.13	1.09	1.05	1.02	4
5	1.77	1.72	1.64	1.56	1.49	1.42	1.36	1.30	1.24	5
6	2.17	2.10	1.98	1.87	1.77	1.67	1.58	1.50	1.42	6
7	2.55	2.45	2.29	2.14	2.01	1.88	1.77	1.66	1.56	7
8	2.91	2.78	2.58	2.39	2.22	2.06	1.92	1.79	1.68	8
9	3.26	3.09	2.84	2.60	2.40	2.21	2.04	1.89	1.76	9
10	3.58	3.38	3.07	2.80	2.55	2.33	2.14	1.97	1.82	10
11	3.90	3.65	3.29	2.97	2.68	2.44	2.22	2.03	1.87	11
12	4.19	3.91	3.48	3.11	2.80	2.52	2.28	2.08	1.91	12
13	4.47	4.14	3.66	3.24	2.89	2.59	2.33	2.12	1.93	13
14	4.73	4.36	3.82	3.36	2.97	2.64	2.37	2.14	1.95	14
15	4.98	4.56	3.96	3.45	3.03	2.69	2.40	2.17	1.97	15
16	5.21	4.75	4.09	3.54	3.09	2.72	2.43	2.18	1.98	16
17	5.44	4.93	4.20	3.61	3.13	2.75	2.44	2.19	1.98	17
18	5.64	5.08	4.30	3.67	3.17	2.78	2.46	2.20	1.99	18
19	5.84	5.23	4.39	3.72	3.20	2.79	2.47	2.21	1.99	19
20	6.02	5.37	4.46	3.77	3.23	2.81	2.48	2.21	1.99	20
21	6.19	5.49	4.53	3.80	3.25	2.82	2.48	2.21	2.00	21
22	6.35	5.60	4.59	3.84	3.26	2.83	2.49	2.22	2.00	22
23	6.50	5.70	4.65	3.86	3.28	2.83	2.49	2.22	2.00	23
24	6.64	5.80	4.69	3.89	3.29	2.84	2.49	2.22	2.00	24
25	6.77	5.88	4.74	3.91	3.30	2.84	2.49	2.22	2.00	25
26	6.89	5.96	4.77	3.92	3.30	2.85	2.50	2.22	2.00	26
27	7.00	6.03	4.80	3.94	3.31	2.85	2.50	2.22	2.00	27
28	7.11	6.10	4.83	3.95	3.32	2.85	2.50	2.22	2.00	28
29	7.21	6.15	4.85	3.96	3.32	2.85	2.50	2.22	2.00	29
30	7.30	6.21	4.87	3.96	3.32	2.85	2.50	2.22	2.00	30
31	7.38	6.25	4.89	3.97	3.32	2.85	2.50	2.22	2.00	31
32	7.46	6.30	4.91	3.97	3.33	2.85	2.50	2.22	2.00	32
33	7.53	6.34	4.92	3.98	3.33	2.86	2.50	2.22	2.00	33
34	7.60	6.37	4.93	3.98	3.33	2.86	2.50	2.22	2.00	34
35	7.66	6.40	4.94	3.99	3.33	2.86	2.50	2.22	2.00	35
40	7.90	6.52	4.97	4.00	3.33	2.86	2.50	2.22	2.00	40
45	8.06	6.58	4.99	4.00	3.33	2.86	2.50	2.22	2.00	45
50	8.16	6.62	4.99	4.00	3.33	2.86	2.50	2.22	2.00	50
60	8.27	6.65	5.00	4.00	3.33	2.86	2.50	2.22	2.00	60
70	8.31	6.66	5.00	4.00	3.33	2.86	2.50	2.22	2.00	70
80	8.32	6.67	5.00	4.00	3.33	2.86	2.50	2.22	2.00	80
90	8.33	6.67	5.00	4.00	3.33	2.86	2.50	2.22	2.00	90
100	8.33	6.67	5.00	4.00	3.33	2.86	2.50	2.22	2.00	100

TABLE E–27

Factors To Compute the Present Worth of a Gradient Series —Interest Rates from 1% to 50%

This table contains multipliers for a gradient G to find the present worth of the n-year end-of-year series 0, G, 2G, ... (n − 1)G.

n	1%	2%	3%	4%	5%	6%	n
1	0.0000	0.0000	0.0000	0.0000	0.0000	0.0000	1
2	0.9803	0.9612	0.9426	0.9246	0.9070	0.8900	2
3	2.9215	2.8458	2.7729	2.7025	2.6347	2.5692	3
4	5.8044	5.6173	5.4383	5.2670	5.1028	4.9455	4
5	9.6103	9.2403	8.8888	8.5547	8.2369	7.9345	5
6	14.3205	13.6801	13.0762	12.5062	11.9680	11.4594	6
7	19.9168	18.9035	17.9547	17.0657	16.2321	15.4497	7
8	26.3812	24.8779	23.4806	22.1806	20.9700	19.8416	8
9	33.6959	31.5720	29.6119	27.8013	26.1268	24.5768	9
10	41.8435	38.9551	36.3088	33.8814	31.6520	29.6023	10
11	50.8067	46.9977	43.5330	40.3772	37.4988	34.8702	11
12	60.5687	55.6712	51.2482	47.2477	43.6241	40.3369	12
13	71.1126	64.9475	59.4196	54.4546	49.9879	45.9629	13
14	82.4221	74.7999	68.0141	61.9618	56.5538	51.7128	14
15	94.4810	85.2021	77.0002	69.7355	63.2880	57.5546	15
16	107.2734	96.1288	86.3477	77.7441	70.1597	63.4592	16
17	120.7834	107.5554	96.0280	85.9581	77.1405	69.4011	17
18	134.9957	119.4581	106.0137	94.3498	84.2043	75.3569	18
19	149.8950	131.8139	116.2788	102.8933	91.3275	81.3062	19
20	165.4664	144.6003	126.7987	111.5647	98.4884	87.2304	20
21	181.6950	157.7959	137.5496	120.3414	105.6673	93.1136	21
22	198.5663	171.3795	148.5094	129.2024	112.8461	98.9412	22
23	216.0660	185.3309	159.6566	138.1284	120.0087	104.7007	23
24	234.1800	199.6305	170.9711	147.1012	127.1402	110.3812	24
25	252.8945	214.2592	182.4336	156.1040	134.2275	115.9732	25
30	355.0021	291.7164	241.3613	201.0618	168.6226	142.3588	30
35	470.1583	374.8826	301.6267	244.8768	200.5807	165.7427	35
40	596.8561	461.9931	361.7500	286.5303	229.5452	185.9568	40
45	733.7038	551.5652	420.6325	325.4028	255.3146	203.1097	45
50	879.4177	642.3606	477.4804	361.1639	277.9148	217.4574	50

n	7%	8%	10%	12%	15%	20%	n
1	0.0000	0.0000	0.0000	0.0000	0.0000	0.0000	1
2	0.8734	0.8573	0.8264	0.7972	0.7561	0.6944	2
3	2.5060	2.4450	2.3291	2.2208	2.0712	1.8519	3
4	4.7947	4.6501	4.3781	4.1273	3.7864	3.2986	4
5	7.6467	7.3724	6.8618	6.3970	5.7751	4.9061	5
6	10.9784	10.5233	9.6842	8.9302	7.9368	6.5806	6
7	14.7149	14.0242	12.7631	11.6443	10.1924	8.2551	7
8	18.7889	17.8061	16.0287	14.4715	12.4807	9.8831	8
9	23.1404	21.8081	19.4215	17.3563	14.7548	11.4335	9
10	27.7156	25.9768	22.8913	20.2541	16.9795	12.8871	10
11	32.4665	30.2657	26.3963	23.1289	19.1289	14.2330	11
12	37.3506	34.6339	29.9012	25.9523	21.1849	15.4667	12
13	42.3302	39.0463	33.3772	28.7024	23.1352	16.5883	13
14	47.3718	43.4723	36.8005	31.3624	24.9725	17.6008	14
15	52.4461	47.8857	40.1520	33.9202	26.6930	18.5095	15

622

Factors To Compute the Present Worth of a Gradient Series
—Interest Rates from 1% to 50%

This table contains multipliers for a gradient G to find the present worth of the n-year end-of-year series 0, G, 2G, ... (n — 1)G.

n	7%	8%	10%	12%	15%	20%	n
16	57.5271	52.2640	43.4164	36.3670	28.2960	19.3208	16
17	62.5923	56.5883	46.5820	38.6973	29.7828	20.0419	17
18	67.6220	60.8426	49.6396	40.9080	31.1565	20.6805	18
19	72.5991	65.0134	52.5827	42.9979	32.4213	21.2439	19
20	77.5091	69.0898	55.4069	44.9676	33.5822	21.7395	20
21	82.3393	73.0629	58.1095	46.8188	34.6448	22.1742	21
22	87.0793	76.9257	60.6893	48.5543	35.6150	22.5546	22
23	91.7201	80.6726	63.1462	50.1776	36.4988	22.8867	23
24	96.2545	84.2997	65.4813	51.6929	37.3023	23.1760	24
25	100.6765	87.8041	67.6964	53.1047	38.0314	23.4276	25
30	120.9718	103.4558	77.0766	58.7821	40.7526	24.2628	30
35	138.1353	116.0920	83.9872	62.6052	42.3587	24.6614	35
40	152.2928	126.0422	88.9526	65.1159	43.2830	24.8469	40
45	163.7559	133.7331	92.4545	66.7343	43.8051	24.9316	45
50	172.9051	139.5928	94.8889	67.7625	44.0958	24.9698	50

n	25%	30%	35%	40%	45%	50%	n
1	0.0000	0.0000	0.0000	0.0000	0.0000	0.0000	1
2	0.6400	0.5917	0.5487	0.5102	0.4756	0.4444	2
3	1.6640	1.5020	1.3616	1.2391	1.1317	1.0370	3
4	2.8928	2.5524	2.2648	2.0200	1.8103	1.6296	4
5	4.2035	3.6297	3.1568	2.7637	2.4344	2.1564	5
6	5.5142	4.6656	3.9828	3.4278	2.9723	2.5953	6
7	6.7725	5.6218	4.7170	3.9970	3.4176	2.9465	7
8	7.9469	6.4800	5.3515	4.4713	3.7758	3.2196	8
9	9.0207	7.2344	5.8887	4.8585	4.0581	3.4277	9
10	9.9870	7.8872	6.3363	5.1696	4.2772	3.5838	10
11	10.8460	8.4452	6.7047	5.4166	4.4450	3.6994	11
12	11.6020	8.9173	7.0049	5.6106	4.5724	3.7842	12
13	12.2617	9.3135	7.2474	5.7618	4.6682	3.8459	13
14	12.8334	9.6437	7.4421	5.8788	4.7398	3.8904	14
15	13.3260	9.9172	7.5974	5.9688	4.7929	3.9224	15
16	13.7482	10.1426	7.7206	6.0376	4.8322	3.9452	16
17	14.1085	10.3276	7.8180	6.0901	4.8611	3.9614	17
18	14.4147	10.4788	7.8946	6.1299	4.8823	3.9729	18
19	14.6741	10.6019	7.9547	6.1601	4.8978	3.9811	19
20	14.8932	10.7019	8.0017	6.1828	4.9090	3.9868	20
21	15.0777	10.7828	8.0384	6.1998	4.9172	3.9908	21
22	15.2326	10.8482	8.0669	6.2127	4.9231	3.9936	22
23	15.3625	10.9009	8.0890	6.2222	4.9274	3.9955	23
24	15.4711	10.9433	8.1061	6.2294	4.9305	3.9969	24
25	15.5618	10.9773	8.1194	6.2347	4.9327	3.9979	25
30	15.8316	11.0687	8.1517	6.2466	4.9372	3.9997	30
35	15.9367	11.0980	8.1603	6.2493	4.9381		35
40	15.9766	11.1071	8.1625	6.2498			40
45	15.9915	11.1099	8.1631				45
50	15.9969	11.1108					50

TABLE E–28

Present Worth at Zero Date of $1 Flowing Uniformly Throughout One-Year Periods

This table assumes continuous compounding of interest at various stated effective rates per annum.

Period	1%	2%	3%	4%	5%	6%	7%	8%	10%
0 to 1	0.9950	0.9902	0.9854	0.9806	0.9760	0.9714	0.9669	0.9625	0.9538
1 to 2	0.9852	0.9707	0.9567	0.9429	0.9295	0.9164	0.9037	0.8912	0.8671
2 to 3	0.9754	0.9517	0.9288	0.9067	0.8853	0.8646	0.8445	0.8252	0.7883
3 to 4	0.9658	0.9331	0.9017	0.8718	0.8431	0.8156	0.7893	0.7641	0.7166
4 to 5	0.9562	0.9148	0.8755	0.8383	0.8030	0.7695	0.7377	0.7075	0.6515
5 to 6	0.9467	0.8968	0.8500	0.8060	0.7647	0.7259	0.6894	0.6551	0.5922
6 to 7	0.9374	0.8792	0.8252	0.7750	0.7283	0.6848	0.6443	0.6065	0.5384
7 to 8	0.9281	0.8620	0.8012	0.7452	0.6936	0.6461	0.6021	0.5616	0.4895
8 to 9	0.9189	0.8451	0.7779	0.7165	0.6606	0.6095	0.5628	0.5200	0.4450
9 to 10	0.9098	0.8285	0.7552	0.6890	0.6291	0.5750	0.5259	0.4815	0.4045
10 to 11	0.9008	0.8123	0.7332	0.6625	0.5992	0.5424	0.4915	0.4458	0.3677
11 to 12	0.8919	0.7964	0.7118	0.6370	0.5706	0.5117	0.4594	0.4128	0.3343
12 to 13	0.8830	0.7807	0.6911	0.6125	0.5435	0.4828	0.4293	0.3822	0.3039
13 to 14	0.8743	0.7654	0.6710	0.5889	0.5176	0.4554	0.4012	0.3539	0.2763
14 to 15	0.8656	0.7504	0.6514	0.5663	0.4929	0.4297	0.3750	0.3277	0.2512
15 to 16	0.8571	0.7357	0.6325	0.5445	0.4695	0.4053	0.3505	0.3034	0.2283
16 to 17	0.8486	0.7213	0.6140	0.5236	0.4471	0.3824	0.3275	0.2809	0.2076
17 to 18	0.8402	0.7071	0.5962	0.5034	0.4258	0.3608	0.3061	0.2601	0.1887
18 to 19	0.8319	0.6933	0.5788	0.4841	0.4055	0.3403	0.2861	0.2409	0.1716
19 to 20	0.8236	0.6797	0.5619	0.4655	0.3862	0.3211	0.2674	0.2230	0.1560
20 to 21	0.8155	0.6664	0.5456	0.4476	0.3678	0.3029	0.2499	0.2065	0.1418
21 to 22	0.8074	0.6533	0.5297	0.4303	0.3503	0.2857	0.2335	0.1912	0.1289
22 to 23	0.7994	0.6405	0.5143	0.4138	0.3336	0.2696	0.2182	0.1770	0.1172
23 to 24	0.7915	0.6279	0.4993	0.3979	0.3178	0.2543	0.2040	0.1639	0.1065
24 to 25	0.7837	0.6156	0.4847	0.3826	0.3026	0.2399	0.1906	0.1518	0.0968
25 to 26	0.7759	0.6035	0.4706	0.3679	0.2882	0.2263	0.1782	0.1405	0.0880
26 to 27	0.7682	0.5917	0.4569	0.3537	0.2745	0.2135	0.1665	0.1301	0.0800
27 to 28	0.7606	0.5801	0.4436	0.3401	0.2614	0.2014	0.1556	0.1205	0.0728
28 to 29	0.7531	0.5687	0.4307	0.3270	0.2490	0.1900	0.1454	0.1116	0.0661
29 to 30	0.7456	0.5576	0.4181	0.3144	0.2371	0.1793	0.1359	0.1033	0.0601
30 to 31	0.7382	0.5466	0.4060	0.3024	0.2258	0.1691	0.1270	0.0956	0.0547
31 to 32	0.7309	0.5359	0.3941	0.2907	0.2151	0.1596	0.1187	0.0886	0.0497
32 to 33	0.7237	0.5254	0.3827	0.2795	0.2048	0.1505	0.1109	0.0820	0.0452
33 to 34	0.7165	0.5151	0.3715	0.2688	0.1951	0.1420	0.1037	0.0759	0.0411
34 to 35	0.7094	0.5050	0.3607	0.2585	0.1858	0.1340	0.0969	0.0703	0.0373
35 to 36	0.7024	0.4951	0.3502	0.2485	0.1769	0.1264	0.0906	0.0651	0.0339
36 to 37	0.6955	0.4854	0.3400	0.2390	0.1685	0.1192	0.0846	0.0603	0.0309
37 to 38	0.6886	0.4759	0.3301	0.2298	0.1605	0.1125	0.0791	0.0558	0.0281
38 to 39	0.6818	0.4666	0.3205	0.2209	0.1528	0.1061	0.0739	0.0517	0.0255
39 to 40	0.6750	0.4574	0.3111	0.2124	0.1456	0.1001	0.0691	0.0478	0.0232
40 to 41	0.6683	0.4484	0.3021	0.2043	0.1386	0.0944	0.0646	0.0443	0.0211
41 to 42	0.6617	0.4396	0.2933	0.1964	0.1320	0.0891	0.0603	0.0410	0.0192
42 to 43	0.6552	0.4310	0.2847	0.1888	0.1257	0.0841	0.0564	0.0380	0.0174
43 to 44	0.6487	0.4226	0.2764	0.1816	0.1198	0.0793	0.0527	0.0352	0.0158
44 to 45	0.6422	0.4143	0.2684	0.1746	0.1141	0.0748	0.0493	0.0326	0.0144
45 to 46	0.6359	0.4062	0.2606	0.1679	0.1086	0.0706	0.0460	0.0302	0.0131
46 to 47	0.6296	0.3982	0.2530	0.1614	0.1035	0.0666	0.0430	0.0279	0.0119
47 to 48	0.6234	0.3904	0.2456	0.1552	0.0985	0.0628	0.0402	0.0259	0.0108
48 to 49	0.6172	0.3827	0.2385	0.1492	0.0938	0.0593	0.0376	0.0239	0.0098
49 to 50	0.6111	0.3752	0.2315	0.1435	0.0894	0.0559	0.0351	0.0222	0.0089

Present Worth at Zero Date of $1 Flowing Uniformly Throughout One-Year Periods

This table assumes continuous compounding of interest at various stated effective rates per annum.

Period	12%	15%	20%	25%	30%	35%	40%	45%	50%
0 to 1	0.9454	0.9333	0.9141	0.8963	0.8796	0.8639	0.8491	0.8352	0.8221
1 to 2	0.8441	0.8115	0.7618	0.7170	0.6766	0.6399	0.6065	0.5760	0.5481
2 to 3	0.7537	0.7057	0.6348	0.5736	0.5205	0.4740	0.4332	0.3973	0.3654
3 to 4	0.6729	0.6136	0.5290	0.4589	0.4004	0.3511	0.3095	0.2740	0.2436
4 to 5	0.6008	0.5336	0.4408	0.3671	0.3080	0.2601	0.2210	0.1889	0.1624
5 to 6	0.5365	0.4640	0.3674	0.2937	0.2369	0.1927	0.1579	0.1303	0.1083
6 to 7	0.4790	0.4035	0.3061	0.2350	0.1822	0.1427	0.1128	0.0899	0.0722
7 to 8	0.4277	0.3508	0.2551	0.1880	0.1402	0.1057	0.0806	0.0620	0.0481
8 to 9	0.3818	0.3051	0.2126	0.1504	0.1078	0.0783	0.0575	0.0427	0.0321
9 to 10	0.3409	0.2653	0.1772	0.1203	0.0829	0.0580	0.0411	0.0295	0.0214
10 to 11	0.3044	0.2307	0.1476	0.0962	0.0638	0.0430	0.0294	0.0203	0.0143
11 to 12	0.2718	0.2006	0.1230	0.0770	0.0491	0.0318	0.0210	0.0140	0.0095
12 to 13	0.2427	0.1744	0.1025	0.0616	0.0378	0.0236	0.0150	0.0097	0.0063
13 to 14	0.2167	0.1517	0.0854	0.0493	0.0290	0.0175	0.0107	0.0067	0.0042
14 to 15	0.1935	0.1319	0.0712	0.0394	0.0223	0.0129	0.0076	0.0046	0.0028
15 to 16	0.1727	0.1147	0.0593	0.0315	0.0172	0.0096	0.0055	0.0032	0.0019
16 to 17	0.1542	0.0997	0.0494	0.0252	0.0132	0.0071	0.0039	0.0022	0.0013
17 to 18	0.1377	0.0867	0.0412	0.0202	0.0102	0.0053	0.0028	0.0015	0.0008
18 to 19	0.1229	0.0754	0.0343	0.0161	0.0078	0.0039	0.0020	0.0010	0.0006
19 to 20	0.1098	0.0656	0.0286	0.0129	0.0060	0.0029	0.0014	0.0007	0.0004
20 to 21	0.0980	0.0570	0.0238	0.0103	0.0046	0.0021	0.0010	0.0005	0.0002
21 to 22	0.0875	0.0496	0.0199	0.0083	0.0036	0.0016	0.0007	0.0003	0.0002
22 to 23	0.0781	0.0431	0.0166	0.0066	0.0027	0.0012	0.0005	0.0002	0.0001
23 to 24	0.0698	0.0375	0.0138	0.0053	0.0021	0.0009	0.0004	0.0002	0.0001
24 to 25	0.0623	0.0326	0.0115	0.0042	0.0016	0.0006	0.0003	0.0001	
25 to 26	0.0556	0.0284	0.0096	0.0034	0.0012	0.0005	0.0002	0.0001	
26 to 27	0.0497	0.0247	0.0080	0.0027	0.0010	0.0004	0.0001	0.0001	
27 to 28	0.0443	0.0214	0.0067	0.0022	0.0007	0.0003	0.0001		
28 to 29	0.0396	0.0186	0.0055	0.0017	0.0006	0.0002	0.0001		
29 to 30	0.0353	0.0162	0.0046	0.0014	0.0004	0.0001			
30 to 31	0.0316	0.0141	0.0039	0.0011	0.0003	0.0001			
31 to 32	0.0282	0.0123	0.0032	0.0009	0.0003	0.0001			
32 to 33	0.0252	0.0107	0.0027	0.0007	0.0002	0.0001			
33 to 34	0.0225	0.0093	0.0022	0.0006	0.0002				
34 to 35	0.0201	0.0081	0.0019	0.0005	0.0001				
35 to 36	0.0179	0.0070	0.0015	0.0004	0.0001				
36 to 37	0.0160	0.0061	0.0013	0.0003	0.0001				
37 to 38	0.0143	0.0053	0.0011	0.0002	0.0001				
38 to 39	0.0127	0.0046	0.0009	0.0002					
39 to 40	0.0114	0.0040	0.0007	0.0001					
40 to 41	0.0102	0.0035	0.0006	0.0001					
41 to 42	0.0091	0.0030	0.0005	0.0001					
42 to 43	0.0081	0.0026	0.0004	0.0001					
43 to 44	0.0072	0.0023	0.0004	0.0001					
44 to 45	0.0065	0.0020	0.0003						
45 to 46	0.0058	0.0017	0.0002						
46 to 47	0.0051	0.0015	0.0002						
47 to 48	0.0046	0.0013	0.0002						
48 to 49	0.0041	0.0011	0.0001						
49 to 50	0.0037	0.0010	0.0001						

TABLE E–29

Present Worth at Zero Date of $1 Per Year Flowing Uniformly Throughout Stated Periods Starting at Zero Date

This table assumes continuous compounding of interest at various stated effective rates per annum.

Period	1%	2%	3%	4%	5%	6%	7%	8%	10%
0 to 1	0.995	0.990	0.985	0.981	0.976	0.971	0.967	0.962	0.954
0 to 2	1.980	1.961	1.942	1.924	1.906	1.888	1.871	1.854	1.821
0 to 3	2.956	2.913	2.871	2.830	2.791	2.752	2.715	2.679	2.609
0 to 4	3.921	3.846	3.773	3.702	3.634	3.568	3.504	3.443	3.326
0 to 5	4.878	4.760	4.648	4.540	4.437	4.338	4.242	4.150	3.977
0 to 6	5.824	5.657	5.498	5.346	5.202	5.063	4.931	4.805	4.570
0 to 7	6.762	6.536	6.323	6.121	5.930	5.748	5.576	5.412	5.108
0 to 8	7.690	7.398	7.124	6.867	6.623	6.394	6.178	5.974	5.597
0 to 9	8.609	8.244	7.902	7.583	7.284	7.004	6.741	6.494	6.042
0 to 10	9.519	9.072	8.658	8.272	7.913	7.579	7.267	6.975	6.447
0 to 11	10.419	9.884	9.391	8.935	8.512	8.121	7.758	7.421	6.815
0 to 12	11.311	10.681	10.103	9.572	9.083	8.633	8.218	7.834	7.149
0 to 13	12.194	11.461	10.794	10.184	9.627	9.116	8.647	8.216	7.453
0 to 14	13.069	12.227	11.465	10.773	10.144	9.571	9.048	8.570	7.729
0 to 15	13.934	12.977	12.116	11.339	10.637	10.001	9.423	8.897	7.980
0 to 16	14.791	13.713	12.749	11.884	11.107	10.406	9.774	9.201	8.209
0 to 17	15.640	14.434	13.363	12.407	11.554	10.789	10.101	9.482	8.416
0 to 18	16.480	15.141	13.959	12.911	11.979	11.149	10.407	9.742	8.605
0 to 19	17.312	15.835	14.538	13.395	12.385	11.490	10.693	9.983	8.777
0 to 20	18.136	16.514	15.100	13.860	12.771	11.811	10.961	10.206	8.932
0 to 21	18.951	17.181	15.645	14.308	13.139	12.114	11.210	10.412	9.074
0 to 22	19.759	17.834	16.175	14.738	13.489	12.399	11.444	10.604	9.203
0 to 23	20.558	18.475	16.689	15.152	13.823	12.669	11.662	10.781	9.320
0 to 24	21.349	19.102	17.188	15.550	14.141	12.923	11.866	10.945	9.427
0 to 25	22.133	19.718	17.673	15.932	14.443	13.163	12.057	11.096	9.524
0 to 26	22.909	20.322	18.144	16.300	14.732	13.389	12.235	11.237	9.612
0 to 27	23.677	20.913	18.601	16.654	15.006	13.603	12.402	11.367	9.692
0 to 28	24.438	21.493	19.044	16.994	15.268	13.804	12.557	11.487	9.765
0 to 29	25.191	22.062	19.475	17.321	15.517	13.994	12.703	11.599	9.831
0 to 30	25.937	22.620	19.893	17.636	15.754	14.174	12.838	11.702	9.891
0 to 31	26.675	23.166	20.299	17.938	15.979	14.343	12.965	11.798	9.945
0 to 32	27.406	23.702	20.693	18.229	16.195	14.502	13.084	11.887	9.995
0 to 33	28.129	24.228	21.076	18.508	16.399	14.653	13.195	11.969	10.040
0 to 34	28.846	24.743	21.447	18.777	16.594	14.795	13.299	12.044	10.081
0 to 35	29.555	25.248	21.808	19.035	16.780	14.929	13.396	12.115	10.119
0 to 40	32.999	27.628	23.460	20.186	17.585	15.493	13.793	12.395	10.260
0 to 45	36.275	29.784	24.885	21.132	18.215	15.915	14.076	12.587	10.348
0 to 50	39.392	31.737	26.114	21.909	18.709	16.230	14.278	12.717	10.403
0 to 55	42.358	33.505	27.174	22.548	19.096	16.466	14.422	12.805	10.437
0 to 60	45.179	35.107	28.089	23.073	19.399	16.642	14.525	12.865	10.458
0 to 65	47.864	36.558	28.878	23.505	19.636	16.773	14.598	12.906	10.471
0 to 70	50.419	37.872	29.558	23.859	19.822	16.871	14.650	12.934	10.479
0 to 75	52.850	39.063	30.145	24.151	19.968	16.945	14.688	12.953	10.484
0 to 80	55.162	40.141	30.652	24.391	20.082	17.000	14.714	12.966	10.487
0 to 85	57.363	41.117	31.088	24.588	20.172	17.041	14.733	12.975	10.489
0 to 90	59.456	42.001	31.465	24.749	20.242	17.071	14.747	12.981	10.490
0 to 95	61.448	42.802	31.790	24.883	20.297	17.094	14.756	12.985	10.491
0 to 100	63.344	43.528	32.071	24.992	20.340	17.111	14.763	12.988	10.491

Present Worth at Zero Date of $1 Per Year Flowing Uniformly Throughout Stated Periods Starting at Zero Date

This table assumes continuous compounding of interest at various stated effective rates per annum.

Period	12%	15%	20%	25%	30%	35%	40%	45%	50%
0 to 1	0.945	0.933	0.914	0.896	0.880	0.864	0.849	0.835	0.822
0 to 2	1.790	1.745	1.676	1.613	1.556	1.504	1.456	1.411	1.370
0 to 3	2.543	2.450	2.311	2.187	2.077	1.978	1.889	1.809	1.736
0 to 4	3.216	3.064	2.840	2.646	2.477	2.329	2.198	2.083	1.979
0 to 5	3.817	3.598	3.281	3.013	2.785	2.589	2.419	2.271	2.142
0 to 6	4.353	4.062	3.648	3.307	3.022	2.782	2.577	2.402	2.250
0 to 7	4.832	4.465	3.954	3.542	3.204	2.924	2.690	2.492	2.322
0 to 8	5.260	4.816	4.209	3.730	3.344	3.030	2.771	2.554	2.370
0 to 9	5.642	5.121	4.422	3.880	3.452	3.108	2.828	2.596	2.402
0 to 10	5.983	5.386	4.599	4.000	3.535	3.166	2.869	2.626	4.424
0 to 11	6.287	5.617	4.747	4.096	3.599	3.209	2.899	2.646	2.438
0 to 12	6.559	5.818	4.870	4.173	3.648	3.241	2.920	2.660	2.447
0 to 13	6.802	5.992	4.972	4.235	3.686	3.265	2.935	2.670	2.454
0 to 14	7.018	6.144	5.058	4.284	3.715	3.282	2.945	2.677	2.458
0 to 15	7.212	6.276	5.129	4.324	3.737	3.295	2.953	2.681	2.461
0 to 16	7.385	6.390	5.188	4.355	3.754	3.305	2.958	2.684	2.463
0 to 17	7.539	6.490	5.238	4.381	3.767	3.312	2.962	2.686	2.464
0 to 18	7.676	6.577	5.279	4.401	3.778	3.317	2.965	2.688	2.465
0 to 19	7.799	6.652	5.313	4.417	3.785	3.321	2.967	2.689	2.465
0 to 20	7.909	6.718	5.342	4.430	3.791	3.324	2.968	2.690	2.466
0 to 21	8.007	6.775	5.366	4.440	3.796	3.326	2.969	2.690	2.466
0 to 22	8.095	6.824	5.385	4.448	3.800	3.328	2.970	2.691	2.466
0 to 23	8.173	6.868	5.402	4.455	3.802	3.329	2.971	2.691	2.466
0 to 24	8.243	6.905	5.416	4.460	3.804	3.330	2.971	2.691	2.466
0 to 25	8.305	6.938	5.427	4.465	3.806	3.330	2.971	2.691	2.466
0 to 26	8.360	6.966	5.437	4.468	3.807	3.331	2.972	2.691	2.466
0 to 27	8.410	6.991	5.445	4.471	3.808	3.331	2.972	2.691	2.466
0 to 28	8.454	7.012	5.452	4.473	3.809	3.331	2.972	2.691	2.466
0 to 29	8.494	7.031	5.457	4.474	3.810	3.332	2.972	2.691	2.466
0 to 30	8.529	7.047	5.462	4.476	3.810	3.332	2.972	2.691	2.466
0 to 31	8.561	7.061	5.466	4.477	3.810	3.332	2.972	2.691	2.466
0 to 32	8.589	7.073	5.469	4.478	3.811	3.332	2.972	2.691	2.466
0 to 33	8.614	7.084	5.471	4.479	3.811	3.332	2.972	2.691	2.466
0 to 34	8.637	7.093	5.474	4.479	3.811	3.332	2.972	2.691	2.466
0 to 35	8.657	7.101	5.476	4.480	3.811	3.332	2.972	2.691	2.466
0 to 40	8.729	7.128	5.481	4.481	3.811	3.332	2.972	2.691	2.466
0 to 45	8.770	7.142	5.483	4.481	3.811	3.332	2.972	2.691	2.466
0 to 50	8.793	7.148	5.484	4.481	3.811	3.332	2.972	2.691	2.466
0 to 55	8.807	7.152	5.485	4.481	3.811	3.332	2.972	2.691	2.466
0 to 60	8.814	7.153	5.485	4.481	3.811	3.332	2.972	2.691	2.466
0 to 65	8.818	7.154	5.485	4.481	3.811	3.332	2.972	2.691	2.466
0 to 70	8.821	7.155	5.485	4.481	3.811	3.332	2.972	2.691	2.466
0 to 75	8.822	7.155	4.485	4.481	3.811	3.332	2.972	2.691	2.466
0 to 80	8.823	7.155	5.485	4.481	3.811	3.332	2.972	2.691	2.466
0 to 85	8.823	7.155	5.485	4.481	3.811	3.332	2.972	2.691	2.466
0 to 90	8.824	7.155	5.485	4.481	3.811	3.332	2.972	2.691	2.466
0 to 95	8.824	7.155	5.485	4.481	3.811	3.332	2.972	2.691	2.466
0 to 100	8.824	7.155	5.485	4.481	3.811	3.332	2.972	2.691	2.466

F

Selected References

AASHO. *Road User Benefit Analysis for Highway Improvements.* Washington, D.C.: American Association of State Highway Officials, 1960. Among highway engineers, this is called the "Red Book."

ALTOUNEY, E. G. *The Role of Uncertainties in the Economic Evaluation of Water-Resources Projects, Report EEP–7.* Stanford, Calif.: Program in Engineering-Economic Planning, Stanford University, 1963.

ANTHONY, R. N. *Management Accounting,* 3d ed. Homewood, Ill.: Richard D. Irwin, Inc., 1964.

APPLE, J. M. *Plant Layout and Materials Handling,* 2d ed. New York: The Ronald Press Co., 1963.

A.T.&T. Co., ENGINEERING DEPARTMENT. *Engineering Economy,* 2d ed. New York: American Telephone and Telegraph Co., 1963.

BABISH, N. N. *Economic Analysis for Engineering and Managerial Decision Making.* New York: McGraw-Hill Book Co., Inc., 1962.

BAUMOL, W. J. *Economic Theory and Operations Analysis,* 2d ed. Englewood Cliffs, N.J.: Prentice-Hall, Inc., 1965.

BIERMAN, H., and SMIDT, S. *The Capital Budgeting Decision,* 2d ed. New York: The Macmillan Co., 1966.

BONBRIGHT, J. C. *Principles of Public Utility Rates.* New York: Columbia University Press, 1961.

———. *Valuation of Property.* New York: McGraw-Hill Book Co., Inc., 1937.

BULLINGER, C. E. *Engineering Economy,* 3d ed. New York: McGraw-Hill Book Co., Inc., 1958.

CARSON, G. B., ed. *Production Handbook,* 2d ed. New York: The Ronald Press Co., 1958.

CLARK, J. M. *Studies in the Economics of Overhead Costs.* Chicago: University of Chicago Press, 1923.

COUGHLAN, J. D., and STRAND, W. K. *Depreciation: Accounting, Taxes, and Business Decisions.* New York: The Ronald Press Co., 1969.

DEAN, JOEL. *Capital Budgeting.* New York: Columbia University Press, 1951.

———. *Managerial Economics.* Englewood Cliffs, N.J.: Prentice-Hall, Inc., 1951.

———. *Sec. 2, Managerial Economics* in *Handbook of Industrial Engineering and Management,* 2d ed., (W. G. Ireson and E. L. Grant, eds.). Englewood Cliffs, N.J.: Prentice-Hall, Inc., 1970.

DE GARMO, E. P. *Engineering Economy,* 4th ed. New York: The Macmillan Co., 1967.

DIVISION OF WATER RESOURCES DEVELOPMENT, ECONOMIC COMMISSION FOR ASIA AND THE FAR EAST. *Manual of Standards and Criteria for Planning Water Resource Projects,* Water Resources Series No. 26, United Nations Publication Sales Number: 64. II, F. 12. New York: United Nations, 1964.

Engineering Economist, The. A quarterly journal published by the Engineering Economy Division of the American Society for Engineering Education. Published at Stevens Institute of Technology, Hoboken, N.J.; first issue was in 1955.

ENGINEERING NEWS-RECORD. *Construction Costs.* Published annually; secure the most recent issue.

ENGLISH, J. M., ed. *Cost Effectiveness: Economic Evaluation of Engineered Systems.* New York: John Wiley & Sons, Inc., 1968.

———, ed. *Workshop on Economics in Engineering Systems.* Los Angeles: Department of Engineering Reports Group, University of California, Los Angeles, Calif., 1968.

FABRYCKY, W. J., and TORGERSON, P. E. *Operations Economy: Industrial Applications of Operations Research.* Englewood Cliffs, N.J.: Prentice-Hall, Inc., 1966.

FINCH, J. K. *An Introduction to the Economics of Civil Engineering.* New York: Columbia University Press, 1942.

FISH, J. C. L. *Engineering Economics,* 2d ed. New York: McGraw-Hill Book Co., Inc., 1923. The first edition of this book, published in 1915, was the first general textbook on what later came to be called engineering economy.

FLEISCHER, G. A. *Capital Allocation Theory.* New York: Appleton-Century-Crofts, Inc., 1969.

———. *The Economic Utilization of Commercial Vehicle Time Saved as the Result of Highway Improvement, Report EEP–3.* Stanford, Calif.: Program in Engineering-Economic Planning, Stanford University, 1962.

GOETZ, B. E. *Management Planning and Control.* New York: McGraw-Hill Book Co., Inc., 1949.

———. *Quantitative Methods: A Survey and Guide for Managers.* New York: McGraw-Hill Book Co., Inc., 1965.

GRANT, E. L. *Statistical Quality Control,* 3d ed. New York: McGraw-Hill Book Co., Inc., 1964.

GRANT, E. L., and BELL, L. F. *Basic Accounting and Cost Accounting,* 2d ed. New York: McGraw-Hill Book Co., Inc., 1964.

GRANT, E. L., and NORTON, P. T., JR. *Depreciation,* rev. printing. New York: The Ronald Press Co., 1955.

HAPPEL, JOHN. *Chemical Process Economics.* New York: John Wiley & Sons, Inc., 1958.

HARVARD BUSINESS REVIEW. *Capital Investment, Part I,* a volume of reprints of 15 articles, 1954–64. Cambridge, Mass.: Harvard Business Review.

———. *Capital Investment, Part II,* a volume of reprints of 14 articles, 1965–68. Cambridge, Mass.: Harvard Business Review.

HILLIER, F. S., and LIEBERMAN, G. J. *Introduction to Operations Research.* San Francisco: Holden-Day, Inc., 1967.

HIRSHLEIFER, J., DEHAVEN, J. C., and MILLIMAN, J. W. *Water Supply: Economics, Technology, and Policy.* Chicago: University of Chicago Press, 1960.

IRESON, W. G. *Factory Planning and Plant Layout.* Englewood Cliffs, N.J.: Prentice-Hall, Inc., 1952.

JAMES, L. D. *A Time-Dependent Planning Process for Combining Structural Measures, Land Use, and Flood Proofing to Minimize the Economic Cost of Floods, Report EEP–12.* Stanford, Calif.: Program in Engineering-Economic Planning, Stanford University, 1964.

JEYNES, P. H. *Profitability and Economic Choice.* Ames, Iowa: Iowa State University Press, 1968.

KRUTILLA, J. V., and ECKSTEIN, OTTO. *Multiple Purpose Development Studies in Applied Economic Analysis.* Baltimore: Johns Hopkins Press, 1958.

KURTZ, MAX. *Engineering Economics for Professional Engineers' Examinations.* New York: McGraw-Hill Book Co., Inc., 1959.

LEAVENWORTH, R. S. *Engineering-Economic Aspects of the Decision-Making Process in Municipal Electric Utilities, Report EEP–10.* Stanford, Calif.: Program in Engineering-Economic Planning, Stanford University, 1964.

LEE, R. R. *Local Government Public Works Decision Making, Report EEP–9.* Stanford, Calif.: Program in Engineering-Economic Planning, Stanford University, 1964.

LEE, R. R., FLEISCHER, G. A., and ROGGEVEEN, V. J. *A Selected Bibliography on Engineering-Economic Planning,* three parts. Stanford, Calif.: Program in Engineering-Economic Planning, Stanford University, 1961.

LESSER, ARTHUR, JR., ed. Summer Symposium Papers of the Engineering Economy Division, American Society for Engineering Education: *Planning and Justifying Capital Expenditures,* 1959; *Applications of Economic Evaluation in Industry,* 1962; *Decision-Making Criteria for Capital Expenditures,* 1965; *Economic Analysis of Complex Problems,* 1968. Hoboken, N.J.: The Engineering Economist, Stevens Institute of Technology.

LINSLEY, R. K., and FRANZINI, J. B. *Water-Resources Engineering,* 2d ed. New York: McGraw-Hill Book Co., Inc., 1963.

LÜDER, KLAUS. *Investitionskontrolle.* Wiesbaden, Germany: Betriebswirtschaftlicher Verlag Dr. Th. Gabler, 1969.

MACHINERY AND ALLIED PRODUCTS INSTITUTE. *MAPI Replacement Manual.* Washington, D.C.: Machinery and Allied Products Institute, 1950.

MARGOLIS, J., MOE, T., PHILIP, P., and VINCENT, P. *Annotated Bibliography: External Economic Effects with Special Reference to Water Resources Projects, Report EEP–18.* Stanford, Calif.: Program in Engineering-Economic Planning, Stanford University, 1965.

MARSTON, A., WINFREY, R., and HEMPSTEAD, J. C. *Engineering Valuation and Depreciation.* Ames, Iowa: Iowa State University Press, 1953.

MAYNARD, H. B., ed. *Industrial Engineering Handbook.* New York: McGraw-Hill Book Co., Inc., 1956.

McKEAN, R. N. *Efficiency in Government Through Systems Analysis.* New York: John Wiley & Sons, Inc., 1958.

MORRIS, W. T. *The Analysis of Managerial Decisions.* Homewood, Ill.: Richard D. Irwin, Inc., 1964.

NEWNAN, D. G. *An Economic Analysis of Railway Grade Crossings on the California State Highway System, Report EEP–16.* Stanford, Calif.: Program in Engineering-Economic Planning, Stanford University, 1965.

NORTON, P. T., JR. *Economic Lot Sizes in Manufacturing.* Virginia Polytechnic Institute Bulletin No. 31, Blacksburg, Va., 1934.

———. Sec. 3, *Engineering Economy* in *Handbook of Industrial Engineering and Management,* 2d ed. (W. G. Ireson and E. L. Grant, eds.). Englewood Cliffs, N.J.: Prentice-Hall, Inc., 1970.

———. *The Selection and Replacement of Manufacturing Equipment.* Virginia Polytechnic Institute Bulletin No. 32, Blacksburg, Va., 1934.

NOVICK, DAVID, ed. *Program Budgeting: Program Analysis and the Federal Budget.* Cambridge, Mass.: Harvard University Press, 1965.

ODIER, LIONEL. *The Economic Benefits of Road Construction and Improvements,* trans. Noel Lindsay from *Les Intérêts Économiques des Travaux Routiers.* Paris: Publications ESTOUP, 1963.

OGLESBY, C. H., ed. *Application of the Principles of Engineering Economy to Highway Improvements, Report EEP–8.* Stanford, Calif.: Program in Engineering-Economic Planning, Stanford University, 1964.

OGLESBY, C. H., and ALTENHOFEN, M. J. *The Economics of Design Standards for Low-Volume Rural Roads, Report EEP–26.* Stanford, Calif.: Program in Engineering-Economic Planning, Stanford University, 1967.

OGLESBY, C. H., and HEWES, L. I. *Highway Engineering,* 2d ed. New York: John Wiley & Sons, Inc., 1963.

OSTERGREN, C. N. *Inflation and Its Impact on Taxes, Depreciation, and the United States Economy, Report EEP–14.* Stanford, Calif.: Program in Engineering-Economic Planning, Stanford University, 1965.

PETERS, M. S., and TIMMERHAUS, K. D. *Plant Design and Economics for Chemical Engineers,* 2d ed. New York: McGraw-Hill Book Co., Inc., 1968.

REUL, R. I. *Sec. 4, Capital Budgeting* in *Handbook of Industrial Engineering and Management,* 2d ed. (W. G. Ireson and E. L. Grant, eds.). Englewood Cliffs, N.J.: Prentice-Hall, Inc., 1970.

RICHMOND, S. B. *Operations Research for Management Decisions.* New York: The Ronald Press Co., 1968.

RIGGS, J. L. *Economic Decision Models for Engineers and Managers.* New York: McGraw-Hill Book Co., Inc., 1968.

RITTER, L. J., JR., and PAQUETTE, R. J. *Highway Engineering,* 3d ed. New York: The Ronald Press Co., 1967.

ROSENTHAL, S. A. *Engineering Economics and Practice.* New York: The Macmillan Co., 1964.

SCHNEIDER, ERICH. *Wirtschaftlichkeits-rechnung.* Tübingen, Germany: J. C. B. Mohr (Paul Siebeck), 1957.

SCHWEYER, H. E. *Analytic Models for Managerial and Engineering Economics.* New York: D. Van Nostrand Reinhold Publishing Co., 1964.

———. *Process Engineering Economics.* New York: McGraw-Hill Book Co., Inc., 1955.

SHANER, W. W. *Economic Evaluation of Investments in Agricultural Penetration Roads in Developing Countries: A Case Study of the Tingo Maria-Tocache Project in Peru, Report EEP–22.* Stanford, Calif.: Program in Engineering-Economic Planning, Stanford University, 1966.

SMITH, G. W. *Engineering Economy: The Analysis of Capital Expenditures.* Ames, Iowa: The Iowa State University Press, 1968.

SMITH, S. C., and CASTLE, E. *Economics and Public Policy in Water Resource Development.* Ames, Iowa: Iowa State University Press, 1964.

SOLOMON, EZRA. *The Theory of Financial Management.* New York: Columbia University Press, 1963.

———, ed. *The Management of Corporate Capital.* New York: The Macmillan Co., 1959.

SOLOMONS, DAVID, ed. *Studies in Cost Analysis,* 2d ed. London: Sweet & Maxwell Limited, 1968.

SPENCER, J. W. *Planning and Programming Local Road Improvements: An Approach Based on Economic Consequences, Report EEP–23.* Stanford, Calif.: Program in Engineering-Economic Planning, Stanford University, 1967.

STEINER, H. M. *Criteria for Planning Rural Roads in a Developing Country: the Case of Mexico, Report EEP–17.* Stanford, Calif.: Program in Engineering-Economic Planning, Stanford University, 1965.

SUBCOMMITTEE ON EVALUATION STANDARDS OF INTER-AGENCY COMMITTEE ON WATER RESOURCES. *Proposed Practices for Economic Analysis of River Basin Projects.* Washington, D. C.: Government Printing Office, 1958. In many writings on the economics of public works, this useful pamphlet is referred to as the "Green Book."

SWALM, R. O. *Capital Expenditure Analysis—A Bibliography.* Syracuse, N.Y.: R. O. Swalm, Syracuse University, 1967. This comprehensive bibliography also was published in *The Engineering Economist,* Vol. 13, No. 2 (Winter, 1968), pp. 105–129.

TAYLOR, G. A. *Managerial and Engineering Economy.* New York: D. Van Nostrand Reinhold Co., 1964.

TERBORGH, GEORGE. *Business Investment Management.* Washington, D.C.: Machinery and Allied Products Institute, 1967.

———. *Business Investment Policy.* Washington, D.C.: Machinery and Allied Products Institute, 1958.

———. *Dynamic Equipment Policy.* Washington, D.C.: Machinery and Allied Products Institute, 1949.

———. *Realistic Depreciation Policy.* Washington, D.C.: Machinery and Allied Products Institute, 1954.

THUESEN, H. G., and FABRYCKY, W. J. *Engineering Economy,* 3d ed. Englewood Cliffs, N.J.: Prentice-Hall, Inc., 1964.

TYLER, C., and WINTER, C. H., JR. *Chemical Engineering Economics,* 4th ed. New York: McGraw-Hill Book Co., Inc., 1959.

WAGNER, H. M. *Introduction to Operations Research.* New York: McGraw-Hill Book Co., Inc., 1969.

WEINGARTNER, H. M. *Mathematical Programming and the Analysis of Capital Budgeting Problems.* Englewood Cliffs, N.J.: Prentice-Hall, Inc., 1963.

WELLINGTON, A. M. *The Economic Theory of Railway Location,* 2d ed. New York: John Wiley & Sons, Inc., 1887.

WINFREY, ROBLEY. *Economic Analysis for Highways.* Scranton, Pa.: International Textbook Co., 1969.

———. *Statistical Analysis of Industrial Property Retirements, Bulletin 125.* Ames, Iowa: Iowa State University Engineering Experiment Station, 1935.

ZANOBETTI, DINO. *Economia dell'Ingegneria.* Bologna, Italy: Casa Editrice Prof. Riccardo Pàtron, 1966.

Index